# SCHOOLS FOR SPECIAL NEEDS 2014

# NINETEENTH EDITION

# SCHOOLS FOR SPECIAL NEEDS 2014

**The complete guide to special needs education in the United Kingdom**

Gabbitas Education
CONSULTANTS SINCE 1873

The global experts in British independent education

KoganPage

LONDON  PHILADELPHIA  NEW DELHI

First published in 1995
This nineteenth edition published in 2014

2nd Floor, 45 Gee Street
London EC1V 3RS
United Kingdom
www.koganpage.com

1518 Walnut Street, Suite 1100
Philadelphia PA 19102
USA

4737/23 Ansari Road
Daryaganj
New Delhi 110002
India

© Gabbitas and Kogan Page, 2014

ISBN      978 0 7494 7039 5
E-ISBN   978 0 7494 7040 1

**British Library Cataloguing in Publication Data**

A CIP record for this book is available from the British Library

Typeset by Graphicraft Limited, Hong Kong
Print production managed by Jellyfish
Printed and bound in Great Britain by Ashford Colour Press Ltd, Gosport

# Contents

# SPECIAL NEEDS – GUIDANCE FOR PARENTS

**1.1**

# Introduction

## Gabbitas Educational Consultants

Choosing the right school for your child is one of the most important decisions you will ever make. For parents of children with special needs, finding the right school may well involve various stages of assessment and the views of the child's teachers, the Local Authority and a range of education and health professionals.

*Schools for Special Needs* is designed specifically for parents, offering step-by-step guidance on all aspects of finding the right provision for a child with special educational needs. It also offers a valuable resource for teachers and other education professionals. As well as information on legal and practical issues, the Guide includes details of special schools throughout the UK together with information on special needs provision at mainstream independent schools.

## Part 1

Part 1 offers extensive guidance written by experts on the many aspects of assessment, statementing and provision, as well as on choice of schools, admissions procedures, special arrangements for examinations, education planning at 16+, social security benefits for children and carers, and advice for parents overseas.

## Part 2

Part 2 gives information about special schools, including a comprehensive directory of independent and non-maintained special schools, plus details of colleges and other establishments providing training and support services for students aged 16+. This is followed by more detailed listings contributed by schools and an index of schools under specific types of provision.

## Part 3

Part 3 includes a complete directory of maintained special schools in each UK education authority.

## Part 4

Part 4 contains a directory of special provision available at mainstream independent schools plus listings contributed by individual schools and an index of schools under specific types of provision.

Each entry includes contact details and basic information about school type and pupil age ranges. Information about special needs provision is divided into three categories: Learning Difficulties; Behavioural, Emotional and Social Disorders; and Physical Impairment and Medical Conditions. Within each category schools are asked to indicate the type of provision available. This may vary widely from one school to another. Some schools offer extensive specialist support in specific areas, most commonly learning difficulties, while others may have more limited resources. Schools are also asked to indicate in each category whether they currently have pupils who have been diagnosed with certain types of learning difficulty or disability.

## Part 5

Part 5 offers suggestions for further reading, an extensive list of useful addresses and associations and details of schools registered under CReSTeD (Council for the Registration of Schools Teaching Dyslexic Pupils).

We are indebted to all those who have helped in the preparation of this Guide, as advisers and authors. A special mention goes to the Heads and Principals who have contributed information about their schools, colleges and support services; without which publication would not have been possible.

### *Acknowledgements*

We should particularly like to acknowledge with thanks the support provided by the following:

AFASIC

Association for Spina Bifida and Hydrocephalus (ASBAH)

Dr Steve Chinn, maths learning difficulties consultant

CReSTeD (Council for the Registration of Schools Teaching Dyslexic Pupils)

Cystic Fibrosis Trust

Priya Dhingra, BA, MA, Cert Ed, MSc, C. Psychol

Disability Alliance

Down's Syndrome Association

Dyslexia Action

The Dyspraxia Foundation

Tracey Eldridge-Hinmers, Associate Veale Wasbrough Vizards

Epilepsy Action

John Friel, Barrister-at-Law, Gray's Inn, Member of the Dyslexia Council, Former Chair of the Advisory Centre for Education Council, Chair of the Special Needs Group of the Educational Law Society

Professor Philip Garner (SEN & Inclusion)

Joint Council for Qualifications

Dr Richard Lansdown, Chartered Psychologist

Liz Malcolm, Chartered Educational Psychologist PSI (UK) Ltd

Muscular Dystrophy Campaign

National Association for Gifted Children

The National Autistic Society Royal Association for Disability and Rehabilitation

Royal National Institute for the Blind (RNIB)

SCOPE Skill (National Bureau for Students with Disabilities)

David Urani, Chartered Educational Psychologist

## Gabbitas Educational Consultants

Established for over 130 years, Gabbitas is uniquely placed to offer parents a wealth of professional expertise, an understanding of their concerns and a personal knowledge of independent schools throughout the UK. Each year Gabbitas helps thousands of parents and students in the UK and abroad seeking guidance at all stages of education. Our expertise covers:

- choice of independent preparatory and senior boarding and day schools;
- choice of independent sixth form or further education colleges;
- educational assessment services;
- sixth form options – A levels, International Baccalaureate, Pre-U, vocational courses;
- university and degree choices and UCAS applications;

- careers assessment and guidance. Gabbitas also advises on specialist areas such as transferring into the British education system from overseas, and guardianship for international students attending boarding schools in the UK.

In this Guide we aim to provide a comprehensive and practical source of advice based on our knowledge and experience – a complete reference source to help you through all stages of your search for the right school for your child.

*Gabbitas Educational Consultants*
*November 2013*

# Sources of Help for Parents

Liz Malcolm, Chartered Educational Psychologist

There are many sources of help for parents who are concerned about their child's learning, physical or emotional development. However, it can be a confusing and anxious time. Knowing who to turn to or who may be best able to support your child is not always easy. Initially, focus is on accurate, professional assessment of special needs. Once needs are identified, many different professionals may be called upon to address them. This brief introduction describes some of the organizations and professional groups that can be involved and provides information on other sources of help.

## Emotionally focused support

### Special Needs Coordinators (SENCo)

Schools vary in their levels of provision when identifying, assessing and providing support strategies for children who may be having difficulties with learning and/or behaviour. Most, however, have a nominated special educational needs coordinator (SENCo) trained in special needs support. The SENCo is often approached to address initial concerns and has a number of other responsibilities including:

- working with, advising and contributing to the training of other teachers;
- the teaching of, and maintaining of records for, children with special educational needs (SEN);
- keeping in touch with the parents of children with SEN;
- working with other agencies, including the educational psychology service, medical and social services and voluntary bodies.

Where additional advice or involvement is required an educational psychologist may be called upon.

### Educational Psychologists

Educational Psychologists (EPs), whether in independent practice or employed by local authorities, are concerned with children's learning and emotional development. They work closely with schools, teachers and parents, to carry out a wide range of tasks with the aim of enhancing children's learning. The service offered includes assessment, support and advice to enable teachers to more effectively help children. An awareness of the range of social and curriculum factors affecting both teaching and learning informs their involvement with young people, which often ranges from pre-school age to 19 years old. The main strands of professional practices are:

- assessment and intervention;
- consultation and problem solving;
- research;
- training;
- personal and group support and counselling.

### Child and adolescent mental health support

Where there are particular concerns relating to a child's emotional development or well-being, help may be sought through teams often known as Child and Adolescent Mental Health Services (CAMHs). A number of professionals work together with parents and families to help with special needs including ADHD, BESD and other problems such as sleep disorders, depression, anxiety and eating disorders. The professional teams may include clinical psychologists, child psychotherapists, a child psychiatrist, social workers and community psychiatric nurses. Individual treatment, group or family therapy may be offered depending on requirements.

In addition to offering appointments, some CAMHs professionals can see you and your child at home if it is difficult to meet elsewhere. They may accept direct contact from parents but in the majority of cases a referral from a GP, school teacher or other professional is required. Again, a number of clinicians work in independent practice. Further information is available from the Royal College of Psychiatrists at www.rcpsych.ac.uk.

## Advice and information (voluntary groups)

There are a number of voluntary groups that exist to provide information for parents and to signpost useful resources. Every local authority has a list. Each also has a Parent Partnership Service (parentpartnership.org.uk) which is established to provide advice and support to parents of children with special educational needs (SEN). They can be contacted through the local authority office or website. Details for some of the more prominent voluntary groups can be found in the Useful Addresses and Associations section in Part 5.

## Therapists

The health therapists that families are most likely to have contact with are physiotherapists, speech and language therapists, occupational therapists and dieticians. Therapists are based in hospitals or health centres and can be contacted through a GP, health visitor or paediatrician referral. Some also operate as independent practitioners.

### Physiotherapists

Physios, as they are often known, treat people with physical problems caused by illness or accident that can give rise to associated special educational needs. They aim to help people improve their range of movement in order to promote health and well-being. In particular, physiotherapists concentrate on problems that affect muscles, bones, the heart, circulation and lungs. Physiotherapy involves a range of treatments, including manipulation, massage, exercise, electrotherapy and hydrotherapy.

### Speech and language therapists

Children who have difficulty producing and using speech, understanding or using language, may need the help of a speech and language therapist. These professionals are also frequently sought to help children who stammer or have other voice problems. The therapists' expertise can also be employed to help children who have problems with feeding, chewing or swallowing. Treatments are generally provided as individual therapy sessions and programmes that can be implemented in school.

### Occupational therapists

Occupational therapists work with individuals who suffer from mentally, physically, developmentally, or emotionally disabling conditions. They use specific, purposeful activity to develop, recover or maintain the daily living, learning and work skills of their patients. Occupational therapists provide help to perform all types of activities, from using a computer to caring for daily needs such as dressing, cooking and eating. Work is based in hospitals, community settings or in a child's home.

### Dieticians

Dieticians help promote good health through proper eating. Their work involves: supervision of the preparation and service of food, development of modified diets and education about good nutritional habits. A key part of their approach when helping children with special educational needs is dietary modification to address issues involving dietary intake.

# A Guide to the Classification of Special Needs

## ATTENTION DEFICIT HYPERACTIVITY DISORDER

*Priya Dhingra, BA, MA, Cert Ed, MSc, C. Psychol*

It is not uncommon to come across children who get distracted by things around them, cannot sit still and get constant comments from teachers to say that they need to focus and concentrate. Some may also need continual supervision for homework and music practice, have high energy levels all day long, shout out during discussions in the classroom and talk persistently. It is also quite usual to see children who do not wait their turn during conversations with peers and adults, and find it hard to play games nicely in recreational time. As a child matures some of these behaviours tend to reduce or change. However, when high levels of impulsivity, hyperactivity and inattention interfere with daily functioning at home and school, there is a possibility that a child might have Attention Deficit Hyperactivity Disorder (ADHD).

ADHD is a condition that affects an individual's ability to control attention and behaviour in an optimal and adaptive manner. It is a childhood disorder that continues through adolescence and adulthood which is frequently associated with educational under-achievement, antisocial behaviour and poor psychosocial adjustment.

### What should you do if you suspect a child has ADHD?

If parents suspect that their child has ADHD, they can raise it with their family doctor or GP. Teachers should raise concerns with the Special Educational Needs Coordinator (SENCo) and a meeting with parents is recommended to explore whether such behaviours are noticed at home too. If parents and teachers are in agreement, a referral needs to be made for a developmental assessment by a paediatrician. Sometimes an Educational Psychologist is involved to conduct observations at home and school to gather additional information concerning behaviour and learning, for the diagnostic assessment.

As a word of caution, many pre-schoolers and young children are very active at one time or another and develop at different rates. They may be very immature at one point, and go through a developmental spurt and calm down later. If difficulties with hyperactivity, impulsivity, and inattention are seen over time, it may be wise to get a medical opinion. However, other factors such as language, learning, emotional and social aspects of a child's development need to be explored too, as they can sometimes present as ADHD features.

## ADHD and age

It should also be noted that ADHD presents differently depending on a child's age, maturity and as the environment requirements for sustained self-control change (Taylor and Sonuga-Barke, 2008). In a pre-school child hyperactivity may involve incessant and demanding extremes of activity. During school years a child may make excessive movements during situations when they are expected to be calm. During adolescence hyperactivity may present as excessive fidgetiness rather than whole body movement. Often inattention diminishes and attention span usually increases with age, but there still tends to be a lag when compared to unaffected individuals and the level needed for everyday attainments.

## Diagnosing ADHD

A diagnosis of ADHD should only be made by a specialist psychiatrist, paediatrician or other appropriately qualified health-care professionals with training and expertise in the diagnosis of ADHD. Initially a full clinical and psychosocial assessment is made of the child or young person. This includes discussion about behaviour and symptoms across home and school settings. Observations, rating scales, schedules, and questionnaires are used to gather information from the family, child (where appropriate), and from relevant school staff.

The two main diagnostic criteria in current use are the International Classification of Mental and Behavioural Disorders 10th revision (ICD-10) and the Diagnostic and Statistical Manual of Mental Disorders 4th edition (DSM-IV). ICD-10 uses a narrower diagnostic category, which includes people with more severe symptoms and impairment. DSM-IV has a broader, more inclusive definition, which includes a number of different ADHD subtypes.

The National Institute of Health and Clinical Excellence (NICE) guidelines are also used by practitioners in the UK. The diagnostic criteria for ADHD in DSM-IV require that symptoms of inattention or hyperactivity should be displayed (to some degree) in at least two settings (ie home and school), and have persisted for at least six months to a degree that is maladaptive and out of line with age expectation. Children meet the criteria for the disorder if they have six or more symptoms of inattention, hyperactivity/ impulsivity, or both. According to the DSM-IV, there are three main subtypes of ADHD:

1 the primarily 'hyperactive-impulsive' type;

2 the primarily 'inattentive' type;

3 the combined type 'combination of hyperactivity, impulsivity, and inattention'.

Some of these signs should have been recognized before the age of 7 years and there needs to be clear evidence of significant impairment in social, academic, and daily living functioning.

ADHD should be considered in all age groups, with symptom criteria adjusted for age-appropriate changes in behaviour.

ADHD tends to co-occur with other developmental disorders such as Oppositional Defiant Disorder, Conduct Disorder, Mood Disorders, Anxiety Disorders, Dyslexia and Specific Learning Difficulties. According to DSM-IV the prevalence rate for ADHD is around 3–5 per cent of children of primary school age.

## Symptoms of ADHD in children

Children who have symptoms of inattention may:

- be easily distracted, miss details, forget things, and frequently switch from one activity to another;
- have difficulty focusing on one thing; ie become bored with a task after only a few minutes, unless they are doing something enjoyable;
- have difficulty focusing attention on organizing and completing a task or learning something new; ie have trouble completing or turning in homework assignments, often losing things (eg, pencils, toys, assignments) needed to complete tasks or activities;
- not seem to listen when spoken to;
- daydream, become easily confused, and move slowly;
- have difficulty processing information as quickly and accurately as others;
- struggle to follow instructions.

Children who have symptoms of hyperactivity may:

- fidget and squirm in their seats;
- talk non-stop;
- dash around, touching or playing with anything and everything in sight;

- have trouble sitting still during dinner, school, and story time;
- be constantly in motion;
- have difficulty doing quiet tasks or activities.

Children who have symptoms of impulsivity may:

- be very impatient;
- blurt out inappropriate comments, show their emotions without restraint, and act without regard for consequences;
- have difficulty waiting for things they want or waiting their turn in games;
- often interrupt conversations or activities of others.

## Cause of ADHD

The main cause of ADHD is unknown. Many studies suggest that genes play a large role based on the research in twin studies. Like other disorders, ADHD probably results from a combination of factors. In addition to genetics, researchers are looking at possible environmental factors such as cigarette smoking and alcohol consumption during pregnancy, brain injuries, and the social environment.

## Managing ADHD

It is important that appropriate steps are taken to help a child or young person with ADHD, as inappropriate treatment and management can lead to poor self-esteem, academic underachievement and social isolation. A one-size-fits-all approach for the management of ADHD does not exist. Each child presents differently and a clear plan needs to be put in place depending on the presenting profile. Some of the commonly used strategies for managing ADHD are as follows:

### Medication

The most common type of medication used for treating ADHD is called a 'stimulant'. Although it may seem unusual to treat ADHD with a medication considered a stimulant, it actually has a calming effect on children with ADHD. For many children, ADHD medications reduce hyperactivity and impulsivity and improve their ability to focus, work, and learn. Any child taking medication must be monitored closely and carefully by parents or caregivers and doctors. As there are side effects to medication, the benefits and risks should be considered carefully.

### Management at school and home

*Establishing appropriate learning environments* – A child with ADHD should be seated away from obvious distractions in the classroom such as doors and windows. Seating a child near the teacher's desk or in the front row of the classroom might help. Allow children to work in pairs rather than groups where possible. Often they find unstructured times difficult and they might need careful supervision at transition times in class or in less structured lessons such as Art and Music. During homework time ensure that the learning environment is free from distractions such as music, television and posters.

*Language and instructions* – Make eye contact while giving instructions. Keep instructions concise and clear. Encourage repeating back of instructions to check understanding. Often explicit instructions help. Use a calm but firm voice.

*Organization and structure* – Provide a clear and uncomplicated structure for the day, lesson and activity. Use visual information to support understanding of structure. Give plenty of warning of any change in routine, eg 'In 5 minutes it will be play time.' Use consistent routines; model and teach these routines. Ensure all materials and equipment are available for the student to avoid wandering around searching and getting distracted. A homework or communication book will ensure that the right homework is written down and can also be used for communication with parents. Timers can be used in the classroom and at home to manage tasks and improve attention span. Tasks need to be short and structured. Increase length and complexity slowly.

When attentional drifts occur, use it as a sign that the child might need extra support or a short break. Students cope better when the task is broken down into manageable parts. For example if the teacher wants the class to write a page, a student with ADHD might be asked to write 5 lines first which is reviewed before continuing. Tasks need to be varied during lessons and homework time, ie an easy task after a very challenging task. Short breaks for physical activity such as a movement break or water break will help in lessons that involve prolonged periods of being seated. Lists and daily task sheets will help a student remember useful information.

*Managing behaviour* – Adults need to remain calm and should employ pre-established consequences for unacceptable behaviour. Keep in mind that it is not always the child's fault if things are not going well; ADHD can make it difficult for an individual to regulate their behaviour. As different adults have different expectations and boundaries, clear expression and consistency are of paramount importance. Clearly set out your expectations of desired behaviour at the beginning of a session, for example, not 'be good today' but 'finish half a page of writing in 15 minutes'. When setting limits, be clear, calm and concise. Also consider rewarding positive behaviours with an appropriate token. Avoid shouting, sarcasm or anger – some children find this reinforcing and will continue the unwanted behaviour. Countdowns are often useful, eg 'Simon, I want you to stop shouting or you will need time out ... 1 ... 2 ... 3 ... 4 ... well done for listening.' Never make threats that cannot be carried through or sanctions that are unrealistic. Use choices and distractions to avoid confrontations. Whole class rewards can be used to encourage peer support.

Involve the child in their own management plan; this is empowering and helps to develop their self-awareness. Give frequent feedback and always try to frame it positively. Feedback such as praise and rewards should be given immediately to be most effective. Ignore minor silly behaviour or disruptions where possible. Provide 'chill out' areas for a child to remove themselves from a situation. This encourages controlled self-time-out. Parents and teachers will benefit from the support of an Educational or Clinical Psychologist when considering appropriate strategies to manage behaviour at school and home.

*Social skills and understanding* – Children with ADHD often misinterpret social cues and language. Thus clear language needs to be used and clarified where necessary. Avoid the use of ambiguous language. A child will benefit from developing awareness of their own physiological responses to triggers, to manage and monitor their behaviour where required. Visual charts and a Feelings Thermometer can be used to regulate and manage behaviour. The practice of self-talk will help children calm down and take control. Deep breathing, counting backwards and visualization will also help in situations where children need to regulate their behaviour. Social skills training can focus on turn taking, listening and conversation skills, to avoid interruptions and to introduce scripts for 'social graces'.

*Reframing technique* – Use of the reframing technique by parents and teachers may help them to see the child with ADHD as having lots of potentially positive characteristics rather than associating the child with largely undesirable behaviours. Reframing involves finding new and positive ways of thinking about a child's problem behaviour to help the family, teacher and child to break cycles of negativity. For example, here are some negative and positive ways of framing characteristics associated with ADHD, with some positive comments to try out:

| Negative | Positive | Reframing in action |
|---|---|---|
| Distractible, eg off task | High level of environmental awareness | 'You notice so many things going on around you. Let's see how we can use those skills in this activity.' |
| Impatient, eg calling out | Goal orientated | 'You're so keen to contribute and get started. I can't wait to hear your ideas when I've finished talking.' |
| Acts without considering consequences, eg getting involved in arguments/sticking up for peer who is in trouble | Willing and able to take risks | 'It's good that you're helping out your friend. Maybe we can think of different ways and times you can use that skill while teachers sort out the classroom problems.' |

Reframing may help reduce levels of parent and teacher stress because they spend less time being angry, exasperated and frustrated and more time thinking positively about the child. This technique is likely to enhance the child's self-esteem and motivation. Children, like adults, are more likely to show positive behaviours and form positive relationships with those who behave in a consistent and positive way towards them.

Parents and teachers can feel exhausted, irritated and angry with a child with ADHD as they feel that all the difficulties lie with the child. However, it should be noted that environmental changes and appropriate management strategies can help relieve adult stress, child frustration, and give a sense of control. ADHD is a manageable childhood disorder if the right strategies are put in place at school and at home.

## References

American Psychiatric Association (2000) *Diagnostic and Statistical Manual of Mental Disorders: Text revision* (4th edn, text revision), American Psychiatric Association, Washington, DC

Hulme, C and Snowling, M J (2009) *Developmental Disorders of Language Learning and Cognition*, Wiley-Blackwell, West Sussex

National Institute for Health and Clinical Excellence (2009) *Attention Deficit Hyperactivity Disorder – Diagnosis and management of ADHD in children, young people and adults*, British Psychological Society and The Royal College of Psychiatrists, Leicester

Taylor, E and Sonuga-Barke, E (2008) Disorders of Attention and Activity in (eds) M Rutter, E Taylor, J S Stevenson *et al, Rutter's Child and Adolescent Psychiatry* (5th edn) Blackwell, London

World Health Organization (1992) *The ICD-10 Classification of Mental and Behavioural Disorders: Clinical descriptions and diagnostic guidelines*, World Health Organization, Geneva

# AUTISM

*Information supplied by The National Autistic Society*

Autism (including Asperger's Syndrome) is a complex developmental disability that affects social and communication skills. People with autism can often have accompanying learning disabilities, but everyone with the condition shares a difficulty in making sense of the world.

In most children with autism, some types of skills will be better than others, so their development will not only be slower than usual but will also be uneven and different from that of other children with learning disabilities.

Autism is a lifelong disability and is not, at present, curable, but there are ways of helping, especially if a child is diagnosed and receives appropriate intervention early in life. Specialized education and structured support can really make a difference to a child's life, helping to maximize skills, minimize any behaviour problems and achieve full potential in adulthood.

Autism affects the way a child communicates and relates to people around him or her. Being a spectrum condition means that, while all children with autism share three main areas of difficulty, their condition will affect them in different ways. The three main areas of difficulty (sometimes known as the 'triad of impairments') are:

1 social interaction (includes difficulty with recognizing and understanding other people's feelings and managing their own. Not understanding how to interact with other people can make it hard to form friendships);

2 social communication (includes difficulty with using and understanding verbal and nonverbal language, such as gestures, facial expressions and tone of voice);

3 social imagination (includes difficulty in the development of imaginative play and having a limited range of imaginative activities, which can be copied and pursued rigidly and repetitively).

In addition to this triad, repetitive behaviour patterns and a resistance to change in routine are notable features. People with autism may also experience over- or under-sensitivity to sounds, touch, tastes, smells, light or colours.

Particular points about autism are worth noting:

- the severity of difficulties differs from person to person, and different aspects of behaviour are more obvious at some ages than others;

- a child's personality, education and social environment can also markedly affect their behaviour;

- children with autism may also have other associated disabilities and learning difficulties, including epilepsy, ADHD, cerebral palsy, dyslexia and dyspraxia. Notably three-quarters of children with autism have mild or severe learning difficulties.

Asperger's Syndrome is a form of autism. People with Asperger's Syndrome are usually at the 'higher-functioning' end of the autism spectrum. Most are of average or above average intelligence and generally have fewer problems with language, often speaking fluently, though their words can sometimes sound formal or stilted. Unfortunately, because their disability is often less obvious, a person with Asperger's Syndrome may be more vulnerable. They can, sadly, be an easy target for teasing or bullying at school.

The causes of autism are still being investigated. Many experts believe that the pattern of behaviour from which autism is diagnosed may not result from a single cause. There is strong evidence to suggest that autism can be caused by a variety of physical factors, all of which affect brain development, and that genetic factors are responsible for some forms of autism. Scientists have been attempting to identify which genes might be implicated in autism for some years. Autism is likely to have multiple genes responsible rather than a single gene. The difficulty of establishing gene involvement is compounded by the interaction of genes and by their interaction with environmental factors. Autism cannot be caused by emotional deprivation or the way a person has been brought up.

It is crucial that autism is recognized early in a child's life to enable effective intervention and management of the condition. Early diagnosis and intervention are also essential to ensure that families and carers have access to appropriate services and professional support.

In most cases, the triad of impairments emerges in the first two to three years of life. Indeed, there are often indications of developmental problems within the first year. However, because autism is a complex condition it is easy to miss important clues.

Autism is a pattern of abnormal development that unfolds over time, so diagnosis depends on obtaining a detailed history of the child's development and a careful assessment of skills and abilities.

In infancy one of the most important indications that autism could be present is the absence, or very delayed development, of drawing the attention of parents and others to objects or events. In typical childhood development, by 12–18 months children are usually pointing at things and trying to engage the interest of the person they are with to invite them to look too. They can also gain attention by bringing toys and making eye contact when doing so. If this behaviour does not occur or begins very late and is limited to the child's own interests, an autism spectrum disorder should be suspected.

If you suspect that autism is present, it is essential that you refer the child for a specialist diagnosis and assessment as early as possible – either to your local GP, the Child Development Centre or Child and Adolescent Mental Health Service or, if you are a teacher, to your local authority's educational psychologist.

The National Autistic Society is the UK's leading charity for people affected by autism. We were founded in 1962 by a group of parents passionate about ensuring a better life for their children. Today we have just under 20,000 members, over 100 branches and provide a wide range of advice, information, support, specialist community and educational services to 100,000 people each year. For more information about autism and education please contact The National Autistic Society, tel 020 7833 2299 or e-mail: nas@nas.org.uk. Website: www.autism.org.uk. Autism Helpline (Mon–Fri, 10 am–4 pm): 0845 070 4004.

# BEHAVIOURAL, EMOTIONAL AND SOCIAL DIFFICULTY (BESD)

*Philip Garner, Professor of Education, SEN and Inclusion*

Behavioural, Emotional and Social Difficulty (BESD) in schools is one of the most high-profile special needs in the UK, both in terms of the level of attention it receives in the general media, and in terms of the concerns expressed about it by teachers and other professionals. Over the last 20 years both groups have continually expressed concern over a perceived rising level of challenging behaviour in schools. For instance, very few general elections go by without there being mention, by all political parties, of concerns regarding deteriorating standards of 'discipline' in schools. And when statutory guidance and sponsored research by UK governments are considered, it is obvious that there is an ongoing preoccupation with this complex area of special needs.

## What is BESD?

The term 'BESD' incorporates a continuum of severity of behaviours. A succinct explanation is provided in Circular 9/94 by the English government, stating that 'Such difficulties lie on the continuum between behaviour which challenges teachers but is within the normal, albeit unacceptable, bounds and that which is indicative of serious mental illness.'

It is not uncommon to encounter pupils who achieve to a very high standard in certain curriculum areas, but frequently display unacceptable behaviour, sometimes of an aggressive nature. More usually, however, BESD is associated with academic under-performance, which causes some to ask whether unwanted behaviour is a result of the child's frustration with his failure to learn. But there can be no doubt that BESD is a special need that presents a barrier to learning, and becomes a cause of serious concern when a range of interventions and strategies employed by mainstream schools does not produce a change in the level of unacceptable behaviour or, as stated in the Code of

Practice, 2001, the pupil 'presents persistent emotional or behavioural difficulties which are not ameliorated by the behaviour management techniques usually employed in the school' (p 53).

The Code of Practice in England (2001) provides a currently applicable official working definition of BESD, stating that:

> 'Pupils with behavioural, emotional and social difficulties cover the full range of ability and continuum of severity. Their behaviours present a barrier to learning and persist despite the implementation of an effective school behaviour policy and personal/social curriculum. They may be withdrawn or isolated, disruptive and disturbing, hyperactive and lack concentration, have immature social skills or present challenging behaviours' (p 93).

As stated, BESD refers to a spectrum of behaviours along a continuum. At the milder end are pupils who have difficulties with social interaction and find it difficult to work in a group or cope in unstructured time. They may have poor concentration, temper outbursts and be verbally and/or physically aggressive to peers. Some pupils display similar signs of low esteem, under-achievement and inappropriate social interaction, but do not have behavioural outbursts. They will be withdrawn, quiet and difficult to communicate with. Many children at one time or another will display at least some of these behaviours, although these will be isolated instances usually associated with the various stages of emotional and social development they are passing through at the time. It is when such behaviour starts to become a dominant feature in the child's life, and is more pronounced or prolonged, that more specialized interventions are needed.

Further along the continuum are pupils who are inclined to be confrontational or openly defiant, sometimes physically aggressive towards their peers or adults and who often present as resentful of authority or angry. Such pupils will more often be unable to concentrate on formal learning, and will sometimes have a low self-esteem. In spite of the severity of their behaviour they do not take responsibility for it or recognize its negative impact.

Finally, there are a smaller number of pupils whose behaviour is such that they are unable to function as part of a classroom or group. Their behaviour is persistent and sometimes physically violent, requiring the use of authorized restraint techniques. Such pupils will also present the full range of achievement levels, although again dominated by those who have a history of chronic under-achievement.

The continuum, expressed in these general terms, encompasses a range of individual 'conditions'. These include Oppositional Defiant Disorder (or ODD, which is especially common in younger children and is characterized by temper tantrums, disobedience, arguing with teachers, parents or other significant adults), Tourette's Syndrome (a condition which begins in early childhood and is manifested by both motor and verbal 'tics', the latter sometimes involving repetitive verbal obscenities), Obsessive Compulsive Disorder (or OCD, characterized by obsessional thoughts and compulsive behaviours, often with attendant anxiety and depression) and Bullying (which often involves pupils with BESD as perpetrators or as victims, the latter often being pupils who are withdrawn, isolated and who are sometimes referred to as the 'silent "E" in BESD').

The principal issue raised by the current term 'BESD' is the variety of interpretations given to it – whilst there may be broad agreement on its basic characteristics, the UK does not have an explicitly applied definition which is consistently utilized. Variations exist from LA to LA, from school to school. Moreover, what is regarded as a 'serious' BESD by one school can be interpreted very differently in another. So, when determining the severity of BESD, teachers and other professionals will normally be informed by such considerations as the nature, persistence, negative impact on the child's learning and on the learning of others.

In terms of incidence, it is difficult to estimate precise numbers of pupils presenting BESD. Cooper (2001) for example, estimates that 'currently at least 10 per cent (and possibly 20 per cent) of school age children in England and Wales experience clinically significant levels of social, emotional and behavioural difficulties'.

## What are the causes of BESD?

Because BESD is essentially a 'broad spectrum' special need encompassing a variety of behaviours, it follows that underlying causes comprise a diverse set of catalysts and explanations. There is certainly evidence in the literature of professionals citing quite different causal factors based on their own training, experience and perspective. It is most often the case that multi-factorial causes are implicated, making subsequent intervention a complicated and long-term process.

Pupils with BESD can be characterized as 'troubled and troubling' children as a result of biological, psychological or social factors; they can be either long-term, chronically present issues or more immediate triggers for unwanted problem behaviour. All three are interrelated and each will vary in its impact on the child over time. Unpacking the relative importance of each of these is of crucial importance, given that an understanding of cause is more likely to result in a more appropriate intervention.

In the case of biological or physical causes, a number of genetic abnormalities, diseases or problems occurring as a result of pre- or post-natal complications can be implicated. A range of psychological factors will also be present, associated with temperament, self-esteem, insecurity and a lack of resilience to social stressors. Social explanations for BESD are common and comprise a wide variety of factors. They will include both family-related and school-related contexts. Amongst the former are such things as divorce or separation, bereavement, unemployment, poor housing and unsatisfactory social relationships.

Ultimately, however, it is important to re-emphasize the interrelationships between the three broad groups of causes highlighted. One of the implications of this is that resulting intervention will invariably comprise a multi-professional approach, involving specialist strategies and skills.

Recognition of the links between the three groups of causal factors is central to the application of the 'ecosystemic' interpretation of BESD (Bronfenbrenner, 1979). When applied to pupil behaviour this attempts to locate an understanding and intervention within a linked set of domains: the 'micro' system (which refers to the pupil in the class-room); the 'meso' system (the whole school); the 'exo' system (which relates to the wider context of family, community and inputs from supporting professionals); and finally, the 'macro' system (which broadly refers to the perceptions, beliefs and cultures of society that define its overall perception of pupils and their behaviour). And more recently it has become popular to link 'behaviour' with 'learning' and associate success in both areas with an ability to establish positive relationships. This has recently formed the basis of government advice regarding the management of BESD in mainstream schools in England.

## How do schools manage pupils with BESD?

Considerable attention has been directed towards addressing the needs of pupils experiencing BESD in mainstream schools in the UK, as well as in alternative specialist settings. A number of major reports and sets of policy guidance have been published in the last decade, most notably those from the committee chaired by Sir Alan Steer (DCSF, 2008; 2009). These place an emphasis on generic behaviour problems, rather than those formally ascertained as BESD. However, 47 separate recommendations are made, stressing the importance of early intervention as well as further professional development in behaviour management skills for teachers. Moreover, the pivotal role of whole-school procedures and policies, as well as effective liaison with parents, community and other professionals are regarded as being essential features of those schools that are successful in meeting the needs of learners who have BESD.

What is apparent from the Steer Report and most other sets of guidance, as well as recent academic research, is that there has been a consistently similar set of advice directed towards teachers and schools that has really changed very little for several decades. In 1989, the Elton Report, *Discipline in Schools*, recommended a set of strategies for dealing with problematic behaviour. These included most of the guidelines set out 20 years later by Steer. They include an emphasis upon:

- recognizing the link between behaviour, learning and the quality of teaching;
- an agreed whole-school policy on behaviour with clear guidelines regarding rules and sanctions;
- understanding that there is no single solution to the problem of poor behaviour, but that consistency is a key element in behaviour management;
- respect has to be given in order to be received: all stakeholders need to operate in a culture of mutual regard;
- support for schools from parents based on a clear understanding of the rights and responsibilities of each;
- the critical role of school-leaders in establishing high standards of learning, teaching and behaviour.

Alongside these generic approaches are a set of strategies and interventions that are utilized by teachers and other professionals who have specific roles in managing BESD, especially in those instances where serious concerns are expressed. These include such approaches as restorative justice, behaviour contracting, person-centred therapy, solution-focused brief therapy and motivational interviewing.

## What provision is available for pupils with more severe BESD?

Pupils who present the most serious challenges to schools on account of the extreme nature of their behaviour and its persistence over time are statistically the most likely to be excluded from mainstream schools. There is, nevertheless, a legal requirement to provide full-time education for such pupils up until 16 years of age. As a result, a range of alternative provision exists. Off-site provision or pupil referral units (PRUs) are intended for short-term strategic placement of BESD pupils, in the expectation that a return to mainstream schooling will follow a period of intensive input to address the priority behaviours identified. Most LAs have PRUs, and the teachers in them work collaboratively with specialist professionals (educational psychologists, therapists, social workers and staff from other behaviour-related agencies) as well as the mainstream schools from which the pupils have been excluded. In some instances dual enrolment forms part of the overall strategy; a pupil receives part of his or her education in a mainstream school and the remainder in an off-site facility.

Separate special schools for pupils with BESD have long been a common feature of the educational landscape. In part this is a recognition that pupils who present the most serious challenging behaviour are unlikely to be included in mainstream schools. They have a number of advantages. Firstly, such schools are geared towards meeting specific behavioural needs, and have the skills and experience to manage extreme and disturbing behaviour. Furthermore, they are able to plan the curriculum in a more individualized way, to meet the needs of specific pupils – in mainstream settings there is always a concern that such adjustments will affect the learning of others and the external profile and reputation of the school.

## Some concluding points

Any consideration of pupils who present characteristics of BESD has to take account of certain contextual issues; recognition of these will serve to ensure that such an emotive and distressing issue, which too frequently evokes unhelpful and even damaging responses, can be tackled in ways that offer more likelihood of adjustment and behaviour change. Thus teachers, parents and others need to understand that pupils identified as having BESD do not behave unacceptably all of the time – there may be extended periods when the pupil demonstrates compliant behaviour. They also need to be aware that 'spontaneous remission', whereby a young person 'grows out' of the unwanted behaviour, is also common. And finally there should be a recognition that BESD is not a condition where instant 'cures' exist – behaviour change takes time.

## Further information

A wide range of useful resources is available electronically. These include:

Behaviour for Learning (http://www.behaviour4learning.ac.uk/Index.aspx)

Behaviour in Schools (Wales) (http://wales.gov.uk/consultations/education/behaviourinschools/?lang=en)

Behaviour in Scottish Schools (http://www.scotland.gov.uk/Publications/2009/11/20101438/0)

The National Strategies (http://nationalstrategies.standards.dcsf.gov.uk/inclusion/behaviourattendanceandseal)

School Discipline and Promoting Positive Behaviour (Northern Ireland) (http://www.deni.gov.uk/index/21-pupils-parents-pg/21-pupils_parents_school_discipline_promoting_positive_behaviour-pg.htm)

Social, Emotional and Behavioural Difficulties Association (http://www.sebda.org/resources.asp)

Teachernet (http://www.teachernet.gov.uk/wholeschool/behaviour/)

### References

Bronfenbrenner, U (1979) *The Ecology of Human Development*, Harvard University Press, Cambridge, MA

Cooper, P (2001) *Dealing with Disruptive Students in the Classroom*, Kogan Page, London

DCSF (2008) *Behaviour Review* (The Steer Report), DCSF, London

DCSF (2009) *Review of Pupil Behaviour. Interim Report 4* (The Steer Report), DCSF, London

DES (1989) *Discipline in Schools* (The Elton Report), HMSO, London

# CEREBRAL PALSY

*Information supplied by SCOPE*

Cerebral palsy is not a disease or an illness. It is the description of a physical impairment that affects movement. The movement problems vary from barely noticeable to extremely severe. No two people with cerebral palsy are the same – it is as individual as people themselves.

Cerebral palsy is most commonly the result of failure of part of the brain to develop, either before birth or in early childhood. This is sometimes because of bleeding or blocked blood vessels, complications in labour, or extreme prematurity. Infections during pregnancy, eg rubella, or in infancy or early childhood, eg meningitis or encephalitis, can also lead to cerebral palsy. Very occasionally it is due to an inherited disorder. In such cases genetic counselling may be helpful. However, it is rare for cerebral palsy to be caused by a genetic link. It is sometimes possible to identify the cause of cerebral palsy, but not always.

The main effect of cerebral palsy is difficulty in movement. Many people with cerebral palsy are hardly affected, others may have problems walking, feeding, talking or using their hands. Some people, for example, are unable to sit up without support and need constant enabling. Sometimes other parts of the brain are also affected, resulting in sight, hearing perception and learning difficulties, and some people are also affected by epilepsy.

People with cerebral palsy often have difficulty controlling their movement and facial expressions. This does not necessarily mean that their mental abilities are in any way impaired. Some are of higher than average intelligence, other people with cerebral palsy have moderate or severe learning difficulties.

Cerebral palsy includes a variety of conditions. The three main types correspond to injuries on different parts of the brain and many people will have a mixture of the following types and effects:

- People with spastic cerebral palsy find that some of the muscles become very stiff and weak, especially under effort. This can affect their control of movement.

- People with athetoid or dyskinetic cerebral palsy have some loss of control of their posture, and tend to make unwanted movements.

- People with ataxic cerebral palsy usually have problems with balance. They may also have shaky hand movements and irregular speech.

Many people with cerebral palsy will have a combination of the above types. The needs of children with cerebral palsy are very wide and often very complex. Some are able to integrate into mainstream schools with minimal support, while others require the help of a welfare assistant, special furniture and adaptations to the environment. The mainstream experience can vary greatly according to the individual challenges faced by each child, the available expertise, resources and environment, and the commitment of all involved. However, the needs of some children cannot easily be met with integrated mainstream provision.

In many cases, it is the complexity of needs as a result of cerebral palsy, for example communication, visuo-motor and visual perceptual problems, physical ability, learning difficulties and medical conditions such as epilepsy and dietary needs, that lead parents to seek out specialist education.

It is now widely agreed that early intervention is very important. The early diagnosis of a disability, coupled with appropriate specialist intervention, can do much to lessen its effects upon the development of children, and thus reduce the potential of the disability to result in functional handicap. This is no less true in the case of cerebral palsy than of any other disability.

The effectiveness of such a strategy in the early years is enhanced greatly by the active participation of the parents and family of a disabled child. Their involvement is central to the success of such programmes. During recent years, there has been a recognition of the role of parents as the prime educators of young children with whom other professional groups must work in genuine partnership.

Access to the National Curriculum is enhanced when children with cerebral palsy have opportunities to develop stable sitting, head control, hand–eye coordination, gross/fine motor skills, effective communication, independence in standing, walking and self-help skills.

Many children need additional time to achieve writing and manipulation activities and, in order to keep pace with their peers, require up-to-date micro-technology and/or communication aids to support their learning.

Methods of teaching vary and professionals from many disciplines can be involved, eg teachers, occupational therapists, physiotherapists, conductors, nursery nurses, speech and language therapists, psychologists, as well as a variety of medical professionals. There are traditional educational methods within mainstream and special schools. Some mainstream schools have special units attached. Multidisciplinary teams of staff are involved in teaching and providing for the needs of individual children. Children attending a mainstream school will usually require time out to attend therapy sessions. This may be within the school or can involve attendance at a child development centre.

Children attending a special school will usually receive their therapy support in the school. Some therapists see the children in their classroom as well as for individual sessions.

An option for some children can be Conductive Education, developed by Professor Andra Peto in Hungary. Conductive Education is a holistic learning system that incorporates teaching and learning, and may help some children with cerebral palsy to become as independent as possible, encompassing all their learning needs.

For further information on cerebral palsy and SCOPE, contact SCOPE Response, PO Box 833, Milton Keynes MK12 5NY, tel: 0808 800 3333 (freephone).

# CYSTIC FIBROSIS

*Information supplied by the Cystic Fibrosis Trust*

Cystic fibrosis (CF) is one of the UK's most common life-threatening inherited diseases, affecting over 8,500 children and young people in the UK. It is caused by a single faulty gene that controls the movement of salt and water through cells in the body. In people with CF the internal organs, especially the digestive system, become clogged with thick, sticky mucus. As recently as the 1960s children with CF did not live very long. However, better understanding and treatment means that today most live into adulthood and half live beyond 38, with the condition kept under control. Cystic fibrosis affects children in different ways and can vary in severity from one month to the next, so it is important to examine the special needs of each child on an individual basis.

One person in 25 is a carrier of the faulty gene that can cause CF in their children. Carriers are, however, completely healthy because they also have a normal gene that overrides the defective gene. If both parents are carriers of CF, any child they have has a 25 per cent chance of having CF (by inheriting faulty genes from both parents), a 50 per cent chance of being completely healthy but being a carrier (by inheriting a faulty gene from one parent and a healthy gene from the other) and a 25 per cent chance of being completely unaffected (by inheriting normal genes from both parents). Screening is now possible to enable prospective parents to find out if either is a carrier and is recommended if there is any history of CF in the family.

## Medical complications

The abnormally thick mucus produced in the lungs of children born with CF can block smaller airways and cause infections, leading to long-term damage. The most noticeable effect is a persistent cough which is non-infectious but may cause distress in front of classmates, particularly if severe, and may lead to coughing up mucus. Digestive problems, in widely varying degrees, may be caused as a result of damage to the pancreas, which produces insulin to regulate sugar levels in the blood and enzymes that aid digestion.

Other less common health problems associated with CF include sinus infections, nasal polyps, osteoporosis, diabetes and liver problems. Sexual maturity may be delayed and boys with CF may become infertile (but not impotent).

## Treatment for cystic fibrosis

Treatment for CF aims to keep the lungs functioning as normally as possible. Physiotherapy and breathing exercises to clear the lungs of thick mucus that attracts infection are a vital part of each child's daily routine. Many will require it two or three times a day, from 15 minutes to an hour at a time, depending on the child's needs. Parents are taught to do physiotherapy as soon as CF is diagnosed, but older children can do part of the treatment themselves and often become completely independent.

Physiotherapy may be combined with nebuliser treatment, in which liquid medication is converted to a fine mist that is inhaled and works directly in the lungs. Antibiotics are also taken regularly to prevent or treat infections. Digestive problems can be alleviated by enzyme treatments taken with meals to aid good absorption of food.

## Special educational needs

A child with CF may have special educational needs if the condition prevents or hinders him or her from making use of educational facilities of a kind provided for children of the same age in schools covered by the Local Authority. Most children with CF can be provided for within a mainstream school without the need for a Statement. Schools should, of course, involve parents and seek their views at all stages.

All schools have the service of a medical officer or equivalent, but not always on site. Teachers, therefore, must be willing to allow parents or other helpers to come into school when a child requires treatment. The school's medical room or another suitable room will need to be made available. Teachers may also need to arrange supervision at mealtimes to ensure that children eat well and take any necessary medication and food supplement capsules.

Cystic fibrosis does not affect a child's intellectual or academic abilities but may mean long periods away from school because of chest infections or hospital stays. However, schools may be able to set work to be done at home or in the hospital if the child is well enough. Physical exercise is usually very good for children with CF because it helps to loosen mucus in the lungs, but teachers should be aware that children may feel unusually tired after a cold or chest infection. Teachers should remember that children with CF may need to use the toilet urgently and more frequently than other pupils. Therefore, consideration should be made for them to leave the classroom for privacy to cough and visit the toilet. As children with CF can pick up CF-related infections from others diagnosed with the condition, it is advisable for them to avoid such contact where possible.

Children with CF may be teased at school because of their persistent cough and the fact that they may be small for their age. Some may also find it embarrassing to take medication in front of their classmates. Friends must be supportive and encouraged to understand the importance of physiotherapy sessions which may sometimes interfere with the social timetable. The adolescent years can be particularly traumatic. Some teen-agers may display rebellious behaviour by neglecting physiotherapy and diet and refusing to recognize the potential seriousness of the condition. Sympathetic counselling can be valuable to help teenagers cope with the stresses associated with delayed sexual maturity, to advise girls of the risks associated with pregnancy and to offer support to boys who face possible infertility.

The pressures of coping with CF can place great strain on family life and relationships. Brothers and sisters may feel resentment at the attention given to their sibling with CF and may feel guilty as a result. This can give rise to bad behaviour, withdrawal or other problems at school. All members of the family will be affected by the psychological pressures aris-ing from the severe nature of CF, uncertainty about the future, genetic aspects and tiring routines. Families may also have to face the prospect of death. Medical advice, support and bereavement counselling are available to help families cope with these pressures.

Teachers can help by meeting parents before a child comes into class and by under-standing the problems that may arise within the family. They may be able to offer practical help by administering medication or supervising children taking it. There are no national guidelines for teachers on giving medication to children at school and teachers are not obliged to do so. If parents consent, however, there is no reason why teachers should not help in this way, provided they are insured by their employer. Teachers can also explain to classmates the reasons for coughing, physiotherapy and so on, and encourage a positive attitude.

Special arrangements can be made for candidates with CF taking examinations. Additional time and supervised breaks may be allowed, or permission given for candi-dates to take examinations in hospital or at home.

For further information parents should contact the Cystic Fibrosis Trust, 11 London Road, Bromley, Kent BR1 1BY, tel: 020 8464 7211, fax: 020 8313 0472, e-mail: enquiries@cftrust.org.uk, website: www.cftrust.org.uk.

# DEAFNESS/HEARING IMPAIRMENT

*Information provided by the National Deaf Children's Society (NDCS)*

## Types of deafness

Conductive deafness is the most common type. It means that sounds cannot pass efficiently through the outer and middle ear to the cochlea and auditory nerve. This is often caused by fluid in the middle ear – a condition known as glue ear or otitis media that affects about one in five children.

Sensori-neural deafness, or nerve deafness as it is sometimes called, usually means that the cochlea is not processing the sound effectively. Often the cause of sensori-neural deafness is not known, but sometimes hereditary factors may be present. Few children are totally deaf. Most children will have some hearing at some frequencies if the sound made is loud enough.

## Causes of permanent deafness

### Causes before birth (pre-natal causes)

Around half of all deaf children born in the UK are deaf as a result of inherited genetic factors. Deafness can be passed down in families, even though there is no immediately apparent family history of deafness. Approximately 70 per cent of these deaf children will encounter no other difficulties arising from their genetic problem. However, the remaining 30 per cent may have disabilities or health problems resulting from the underlying genetic cause of deafness.

### Causes in early childhood (post-natal causes)

Premature birth can increase the risk of a child being deaf or becoming deaf. Babies born prematurely are often prone to infections that can cause deafness. Severe jaundice or a lack of oxygen at some point can cause deafness. Infections later on during early childhood, such as meningitis, measles and mumps, can also be responsible for a child becoming deaf. Although less frequently occurring, deafness can be caused by head injury or exposure to loud noises.

## Communication methods

Children naturally try to learn a language that enables them to be understood. The communication method used by a deaf child will depend on a number of factors, such as the level of his or her hearing loss and which method he or she feels most comfortable with. The most common types of communication used by deaf children are summarized below.

*Auditory-oral approaches.* Auditory-oral approaches aim to develop listening skills and spoken language in deaf children. They emphasize the use of hearing aids, radio aids and cochlear implants to maximize the use of any residual hearing a child has. Most auditory-oral approaches also use lip-reading to help the child's understanding. These approaches are used with children with all levels of deafness, from mild to profound. Auditory-oral approaches do not use sign language or fingerspelling to support understanding of spoken language. The main aim of these approaches is to allow deaf children to develop good, effective speech.

*Sign-bilingualism.* A sign-bilingual approach uses sign language and spoken language. In England the main languages are usually British Sign Language (BSL) and English. If a family speaks another language, children may learn that as a second language, with or without English. When they have become confident in BSL, they can use this as a medium to learn English. BSL also allows them access to the deaf community. Learning English as a second language is essential for children to develop reading and writing, as there is no written form of BSL. The aim of using a sign-bilingual approach is to allow a child to communicate using language and to develop skills in their home language.

*Total communication.* Total communication uses a combination of methods to communicate with deaf children. The aim of the approach is to communicate and teach vocabulary in any way that works. Deaf children and their families are encouraged to use sign language, fingerspelling, natural gestures, lip-reading, body language, speech and amplification (hearing aids or radio aids), to help them communicate effectively.

*Lip-reading.* Lip-reading is the ability to read words from the lip and face patterns of the speaker. Deaf children naturally try to lip read when they are communicating. It's estimated that about 30–40 per cent of speech sounds can be lip-read under the best conditions – with a quiet environment and good lighting.

British Sign Language (BSL) is the language of the British deaf community. Over 70,000 people use the officially recognized language as their first or preferred language. BSL is a visual language, using hand shapes, facial expressions, gestures and body language to communicate, which has developed over hundreds of years. It has a structure and grammar different from that of written and spoken English. The complete language is independent of any other, with a unique vocabulary. Like other languages it has evolved over time and developed regional and national dialects. *Fingerspelling* is used as a part of sign language. It uses the hands to spell out words. Each letter of the alphabet can be indicated using the fingers and palm – specific patterns create individual words.

Deafness itself is not defined as a Special Educational Need. However, there are needs arising from deafness, whether temporary or permanent, that may require special educational provision. For example, deaf children's language and communication development can often be affected by their deafness. They may need extra provision in the form of support from a specialist teacher of deaf children, support from a communication support worker (CSW) or regular speech and language therapy. Specialist equipment such as a radio aid system is also often required. There are various issues to consider when a deaf child attends a school, such as appropriate teaching methods, technical support, language and communication support, as well as social and emotional development.

### Teaching of deaf children

Teachers of deaf children support them in a variety of ways:

- Home visits to newly diagnosed and pre-school children to help parents develop involvement in their child's early education and social development.

- The development of language, whether signed or spoken or both (as in Total Communication approaches).

- Checking of audiological equipment (though parents, support staff and young deaf people could be taught to check hearing and radio aids).

- Advising and training school staff to identify and meet the needs of individual deaf children.

### Speech and language therapy

Speech and language therapists have specialist knowledge about speech and language development (which goes beyond teaching the child to articulate sound) and may work with oral or signing children to develop some competence in lip-reading or British Sign Language (BSL). Some may use Sign Supported English, which is where a sign is used to follow the significant words in an English sentence.

### Specialist equipment

There is a range of technical support now available for deaf children. Such technology can be used to make the teaching and learning process easier. At school a deaf child may use a radio aid system with their hearing aid or cochlea implants to help them pick out the teacher's voice and cut out background noise.

### An acoustically treated environment

The layout and type of classroom can make it easier or harder for a deaf child to learn. An acoustically treated environment is particularly important. Background noise makes it difficult for pupils who use hearing aids or cochlea implants, because their microphone amplifies all noise.

It is very important that there is a whole-school approach to the education of deaf children. This means that all members of staff need to be aware of the needs of deaf children and how to meet these needs. It is also essential that there is a commitment within the school to ensuring that a deaf child has an equal opportunity to participate in every aspect of school life.

*Deaf Friendly Teaching* is a booklet produced by the National Deaf Children's Society (NDCS) for teachers in mainstream schools. It provides information and guidance about working with deaf children. If you would like a copy, please contact the NDCS Freephone helpline.

For further information, please contact: The National Deaf Children's Society, Freephone helpline: 0808 800 8880 (voice and text), open Monday–Thursday 9.30 am–9.30 pm, Friday 9.30 am–5.00 pm, fax: 020 7251 5020, e-mail: helpline@ndcs.org.uk, website: www.ndcs.org.uk.

# DOWN'S SYNDROME

## Background

Down's syndrome is one of the most common genetic causes of learning disability. Around 750 babies are born with the condition each year in the UK. It affects people of all races, religions and economic background equally. Down's syndrome is caused by the presence of an extra copy of chromosome 21 in all or some of a baby's cells, occurs at conception and is irreversible. As yet, no one knows what causes the presence of the extra chromosome 21. Children with Down's syndrome share some common physical characteristics but are all individuals. They will look more like their mother, their father or other family members, than other children with the syndrome. They also vary in personality and ability and will all have a degree of learning disability; some will have additional conditions that result in more complex needs. Although there is no 'cure' for Down's syndrome, there are ways to help children with the condition develop into healthy and fulfilled individuals, able to achieve a level of independence right for them. This includes:

- access to good health care including a range of different specialists;
- early intervention programmes to provide support for children and parents;
- good parenting skills and an ordinary family life;
- education and support groups to provide information and help for parents, friends and families.

Improved education and support has presented more opportunities to people with Down's syndrome. For example, leaving home, forming relationships, gaining employment and leading independent lives. However, it is important to remember that each child is different and it is not possible to predict how individuals will develop.

## Issues that impact on learning and development

Learning and development is delayed in children with Down's syndrome. They usually make progress in most areas but at a slower pace. Children vary in the progress they make and some aspects of development will progress faster than others. Although each child should be treated as an individual, there are recurring patterns in the development of children with Down's syndrome when they are viewed as a group. The recurring patterns can be thought of as a developmental profile of characteristic strengths and weaknesses associated with Down's syndrome. Characteristic strengths include social interaction, visual learning, gesture and mime, and reading ability. Characteristic weaknesses include learning to talk, hearing and vision, learning to calculate and learning from listening, which is considered to be due to verbal short-term memory development.

### Speech and language

Nearly all children and young people with Down's syndrome have delayed language development, with relative strengths in language understanding, compared with expressive language skills. Specific speech and language difficulties can lead to children's cognitive abilities being underestimated. Taking longer to learn to control the muscles needed for speech, difficulty remembering spoken words and effects of early hearing loss may all contribute to expressive language difficulties. Speech and language therapists who provide therapy for children and who guide their teachers/parents with practice activities should be knowledgeable about specific issues and effective interventions for children and young people with Down's syndrome. Teaching that maximizes learning strengths, including addressing motivational factors, using visual and social teaching resources/methods, setting high expectations and providing opportunities to practice skills in enjoyable ways can all help to promote learning and development. All schools will benefit from knowledge of the developmental profile associated with having Down's syndrome and evidence-based interventions to help them meet children's educational needs.

## Hearing

Children with Down's syndrome are prone to colds and often find them more difficult to 'shake off'. The Eustachian tubes, which connect the ear to the nose, can be particularly narrow in children with Down's syndrome and become easily blocked with mucus. This, in turn, can lead to middle ear infections (otitis media) and cause temporary deafness. Usually, when a cold gets better, the Eustachian tube clears and the mucus causing the infection drains away. Sometimes, however, a single infection, or repeated upper respiratory infections such as colds, or infected or enlarged adenoids, can cause more long-term obstruction of the middle ear space which never drains away. Glue ear, as this is known, can occur in all children, but is more frequent in children with Down's syndrome.

## Vision

Up to 50 per cent of people with Down's syndrome will need to wear glasses but 100 per cent have poor visual acuity. Even when a person with Down's syndrome is wearing correctly fitted glasses for either long or short sight, visual acuity is still poor. They see the world differently and are unable to distinguish fine details and sharp contrasts. Therefore it is important for printed material to be big and bold to compensate for this difficulty.

## Lack of muscle tone

Many babies with Down's syndrome have poor muscle tone and tend to be 'floppy' (hypotonic). As a child develops this may contribute to an unsteady or unusual gait. In most cases, reduced muscle tone improves as the child develops. In some children, it can contribute to a delay in acquiring fine and/or gross motor skills. Running, skipping, throwing and catching may be more challenging for a child with Down's syndrome than other children in the class. As with all children, the opportunity to practise is crucial and there is nothing to prevent a child with Down's syndrome acquiring these skills eventually. Poor muscle tone can also affect fine motor skills such as writing. Again, most children will eventually be able to write quite well, but may take longer to acquire such skills.

# DYSCALCULIA

*Information supplied by Dr Steve Chinn, maths learning difficulties consultant and Chair of the BDA Dyscalculia Committee*

## Introduction

Learning difficulties in mathematics is not a new phenomenon. I am certain these learning difficulties experienced by many children and adults existed many years ago. However, in terms of popular educational usage, using the term 'dyscalculia' is a relatively new phenomenon in the learning disabilities field. Research into this construct is relatively limited and a consensus on a definition and an aetiology have yet to be achieved. In a survey of the literature on maths learning difficulties compared to language difficulties Murphy *et al* (2007) found 231 articles on maths learning difficulties compared to 1,077 articles on dyslexia in a 21-year period.

Most teachers have met the child who is totally helpless in maths, but for what combination of reasons does the child have these problems? Is there a pattern or a coherence in those difficulties? The answers to both questions are going to be complex, not least because every child is such an individual mix of abilities, deficits and emotional factors.

So, we have mathematics, we have the child and we have the teacher. Each has a part to play and each interacts with the other two factors. Give one child a calculator and he may cease to have significant maths difficulties. Give another child a set of word problems and suddenly she has serious maths difficulties. Mathematics makes demands on many skills, including mathematical memory, the ability to generalize and short-term and working memories. Once maths learning starts to fail, the child is likely to reduce his or her input, cease to be involved in lessons and learning becomes even less effective.

Mathematics difficulties are about curriculum, motivation, teaching, mathematical intelligence, anxiety and memory. There are enough factors with enough variation in levels of impact to make a single answer to the problem virtually impossible.

So is the dyscalculic child unable ever to grasp maths (whatever 'grasp' means when a C grade in a GCSE paper can be achieved with a score as low as 16 per cent, that is, only one question out of every six needs to be correct)? I think a dyscalculic child may well be one for whom numbers remain meaningless, for whom numbers have no reality or make no sense. For example, the value of numbers is not understood as with the boy who gave a £20 note to the shop assistant and thought he had more money (in value) back because he had more notes and coins in his change than the one note he handed over. This problem may in fact be closer to acalculia, a total inability to do maths.

## Dyscalculia

The UK's official definition remains the one given in the DfES booklet (2001) *The National Numeracy Strategy: Guidance to support pupils with dyslexia and dyscalculia*, which states:

Dyscalculia is a condition that affects the ability to acquire mathematical skills. Dyscalculia learners may have difficulty understanding simple number concepts, lack an intuitive grasp of numbers and have problems learning number facts and procedures. Even if they produce a correct answer or use a correct method, they may do so mechanically and without confidence. Very little is known about the prevalence of dyscalculia, its causes or treatment. Purely dyscalculic learners who have difficulties only with numbers will have cognitive and language abilities in the normal range and may excel in non-mathematical subjects. It is more likely that difficulties with numeracy accompany the language difficulties of dyslexia.

Dyscalculia, like other specific learning difficulties, will have a spectrum or continuum of levels of difficulty. One of the questions one could and should ask is, 'When does the difficulty become significant enough to earn the label "dyscalculia"', which brings me back to the match between the learner, the curriculum and the teacher. I shall avoid the debate on labels, but I would like to introduce the term 'comorbidity' which is alluded to in the definition above. This term is used to describe the co-occurrence of two or more disorders in the same individual. I began my work on the occurrence of maths difficulties in dyslexic students. Recently definitions of dyslexia have focused exclusively on difficulties with language so, although I didn't realize it at the time, I was studying the comorbid conditions of dyslexia and dyscalculia.

For me, a diagnosis is of little use without a prognosis. My experience over the past 30 years of teaching dyslexic students is that the majority have difficulties with maths that can be circumvented, with differing degrees of efficacy, such that some achieve A* at GCSE level while others work diligently to achieve an E or C grade.

The really severe cases I have known, the ones that would definitely qualify as dyscalculic, have to have some skill or skills that enable partial compensation for their overwhelming difficulties in maths. This may be a memory that is able to recall and apply simple procedures. In such cases there is no depth of understanding, but a certain mechanical reliability, even if limited in scope. I would still want to persevere with trying to teach understanding, but that comes with the territory of being a teacher.

So, if we take a simplistic view of dyscalculia as an *unexpected inability* (compared to general abilities) to work to an anticipated standard in maths, then we can start to consider some contributing factors to this situation.

## Why some children fail mathematics

To try to provide a fully comprehensive list would most likely reveal a lack of understanding of the diversity of children. Unlike my experiments when I taught physics, the variables in any study of people are far too many to control, even if one were able to identify them all in the first place. However, let's consider some front-runners.

### Mathematical memory

However gifted a pupil is at working things out from basics, there have to be some facts and procedures retrievable from memory. The skill is to be realistic in understanding what a pupil can and can't learn (usually by rote) and then to find the truly key facts for the pupil to learn if this limited retrieval is an issue.

## Speed of working

This is a classic example of the demands of the subject creating a problem. Speed is not, in my opinion, an intellectual demand. In fact, I think it is a demand that encourages impulsivity and certainly anxiety in many learners. Speed is part of the culture of maths and, as such, it is hard to change the perceptions and expectations of many teachers and parents. The dyslexic learners and the dyscalculic learners I have taught are frequently slow processors of some information and when carrying out some tasks. If the learner perceives the demand for speed to be beyond his capabilities then it is likely he will not attempt the task. We all assess risk (at different levels of acceptability) and we all withdraw when we think the task involves too much risk.

## Reading and writing

The other two Rs. Reading is an example of a sub-skill that suddenly becomes significant as a child moves up through the curriculum. There are no word problems to read when the child is young; then the curriculum introduces them and some children fail. I suspect this is an international problem. Certainly a study in South Africa showed a 50 per cent reduction in correct answers when a number problem was presented in words. The world of maths word problems is frequently bizarre, seldom realistic or anything to do with 'normal' language, and is rarely meaningful to a child.

Some children find writing and/or documenting their work a problem. Again, the child may well perform well in maths when the demands are within her skill range, but she may fail when the new skill of documenting is introduced (and, for some children, vice versa).

It should be noted that the vocabulary of early arithmetic does not help learners. For example, in English we say 'eleven' and 'twelve', which are exceptions to other words for two digit numbers. We say 'thirteen' which implies a three before a ten (and also sounds very much like 'thirty'). 'Twenty three' does suggest a 2 before a 3.

## Thinking styles

I often explain thinking style in maths in my lectures by asking delegates to do some carefully selected maths questions. I then explain that how each question is solved will illustrate the delegates' thinking styles. Usually the split between the two thinking styles, which I will describe below, is close to 50-50. This suggests that teachers are, in this respect, as varied as their students.

Thinking styles have been studied by a number of researchers. Work by my two American colleagues and me in the 1980s led to us describing 'Inchworms' as sequential, procedural, literal thinkers, who often do not have a good 'feel' for numbers and operations. Inchworms like to document, to the point that their paper and pen is almost at comfort blanket level. 'Grasshoppers' are intuitive, flexible in methods used, have a good sense of numbers and operations and their interrelationships and often don't document.

There are several consequences of thinking styles for learners and for teachers and teachers need to be aware that their meticulous, step-by-step explanation of a new topic may not resonate with the grasshopper learner, or their sweeping overview loses the inchworm who fails to see the necessary connections to other ideas and concepts. A further consequence may be that the teacher's appraisal of the pupil and his work is coloured by her own thinking style.

The role of meta-cognition (thinking about how you think) is now receiving more attention in education.

## Short-term and working memory

Dyslexic learners often have very weak short-term and working memories. This is not a unique characteristic of dyslexic learners. Another example is the potential to confuse left and right. However, experience and some research have confirmed that short-term memory and especially working memory are issues.

The use of short-term and of working memory is pervasive in mathematics, not just in mental arithmetic. It affects the ability to do any part of any calculation 'in your head'. It affects how a child analyses data. For example, when trying to predict the 23rd letter in the series 'abcdeabcdeabcdeab', a pupil tried to analyse it in chunks of three, abc, dea, bcd, eab. It was little surprise that he failed to see the pattern.

Pupils with weak short-term memories find it challenging to copy information. For example, if copying from a board they have to look up at the board, track to the correct place, memorize as many items as they can, transfer their gaze to a notebook and write the information in the correct place, then back to the board and the search for the right place. A consequence may be that, if copying maths questions, they mix up the questions as set and create a new set of their own unique questions!

## The affective domain

This domain includes anxiety, expectations, beliefs, attributions, self-esteem and self-concept. These are factors that are difficult to measure, but that does not diminish their capacity to influence learning.

Recent research has shown that working memory (which includes short-term memory) becomes less effective if the learner is anxious. Although a little anxiety may enhance performance, usually it diminishes it. It may well be another maths culture issue. We are judgemental in maths. Work and answers are judged as 'right' or 'wrong'. This judgement is not always delivered discretely, so the learner becomes anxious that he may be wrong (again). Indeed the subject itself consists largely of questions where the answer is 'right' or 'wrong' whatever the teacher may wish to say.

The ethos of the classroom will have a huge effect on anxiety levels in the pupils. Anxiety may result in pupils not taking risks. A good learning classroom teaches pupils how to evaluate and take risks and pupils who avoid risk are often avoiding learning. Children enter maths classrooms with a set of beliefs that will colour their attitude to maths. For example, many children (and adults) believe that only very clever (and boring) people are good at maths. Others may believe as a consequence that they can never be clever enough to be good at maths.

An example of a dangerous expectation is that all children can and will learn the multiplication facts. In my experience, not all children can and, even if they do, the ability to retrieve these facts accurately and quickly (quickly is another expectation) is often transitory. The impact of this failure to meet expectations can be demotivating for the child and distressing for the parent. My informal surveys of teachers as I lecture around the UK suggest that this is a big problem for many children, whether or not they are recognized as dyslexic or dyscalculic.

Perceived failure can affect self-esteem and then self-concept. The decline of these in a child leads them to not being involved in maths. One of my most successful (mathematically) ex-pupils told me how much he hated the words, 'Never mind, you did your best'. His argument was that if he had done his best then he didn't want failure. If he judged that failure was a possibility then he would not try his 'best' and then failure would not be such a blow to self-esteem.

Most dangerous of all is attribution, the way a pupil attributes his or her reasons for success and failure. These attributions control the way each new learning experience is approached. For example, a pupil may assume that because she failed at long division, she will fail at all future maths topics. This is pervasive. She may believe that she is just too stupid to be able to do maths, which is personal. She may think that she can't do the maths lesson today and that she will not be able to do tomorrow's lesson or any other lesson ever again, which is a permanent attribution.

For all of these affect dimensions, children with a learning difficulty will be more susceptible to their inclination to put a negative interpretation on feedback, or pay more heed to the negative as these feedbacks are far more likely in their lives in school.

### How more children can succeed in mathematics

Dr Harry Chasty, a great pioneer and advocate for dyslexics said, 'If the child doesn't learn the way you teach, can you teach her the way she learns?' In this deceptively simple sentence lies a challenge. Certainly that challenge was not an issue for the teachers that taught me back in the 1950s. I had to learn the way they taught. It is a matter of who takes responsibility for the learning. In this first stage of explanation, it has to be the teacher. Later in the process the responsibility transfers to the pupil. Judging the moment for that transition to occur is part of the skill of working with all children, but especially those with specific learning difficulties.

So, what does Harry Chasty mean? Well, I think he means can teachers (and parents) adjust the way that material is presented in that first stage so that communication with each pupil is effective? Can the communication be empathetic for the child? In maths this may mean that I would use a visual model for the concept I was trying to explain. This could be using Base 10 blocks to explain long multiplication or quadratic equations. There is a range of adjustments that can be made to reduce the number of occasions when pupils fail as explained in Chapter 2 of *The Trouble with Maths* (Chinn, 2012a).

The next stage of adjustment requires a reconsideration of some beliefs and a restructuring of some aspects of the maths curriculum, again based on 'Can I teach the way she learns?' The biggest acknowledgement here is that some learners have weak memories for facts and procedures in maths. This problem is compounded if the learner has little understanding of mathematical concepts and relationships. The combination of poor memory and poor conceptual ability is devastating in maths.

Of course, pupils have to learn some facts. The challenge is for teachers to work with the pupils to maximize the benefits of knowing and understanding those facts. For the pupils, learning to extend the use of those facts will provide them with a secure base for building concepts and the continual return to – and use of – key facts will reinforce the retention and retrieval of these facts.

## Finally

Children who have difficulty in learning maths, whether they are labelled as dyscalculic, dyslexic or not labelled at all, obviously need an alternative approach, based on the characteristics of the learner and an adjustment in how mathematical content is structured and presented. It would be foolish to advocate 'the method' but whatever is done it must acknowledge that all children are individuals and will benefit from the responsive flexibility that comes from that acknowledgement.

There will not be just one profile of dyscalculia and maths learning difficulties and some profiles will be hidden all through the school years. Thus, there is a need to address the issues at all times and for all pupils.

## References

Chinn, S (2012a) *The Trouble with Maths: A practical guide to helping learners with numeracy difficulties*, 2nd edn, Routledge, London

Chinn, S (2012b) *More Trouble with Maths: A complete guide to identifying and diagnosing mathematical difficulties*, Routledge/nasen, London

Chinn, S (2011) *The Fear of Maths, A guide for parents and older learners*, 3rd edn, Souvenir Press, London

# DYSLEXIA

## Information supplied by Dyslexia Action

Dyslexia causes difficulties in learning to read, write and spell. Short-term memory, mathematics, concentration, personal organization and sequencing may also be affected. Dyslexia usually arises from a weakness in the processing of language-based information. Biological in origin, it tends to run in families, but environmental factors also contribute.

Dyslexia can occur at any level of intellectual ability. It is not the result of poor motivation, emotional disturbance, sensory impairment or lack of opportunities, but it may occur alongside any of these. The effects of dyslexia can be largely overcome by skilled specialist teaching and the use of compensatory strategies.

Tiny neurological differences in specific areas of the brain of dyslexic people create difficulties in processing information. Differences occur in lower levels, where sensory information is coming into the brain, and in higher levels, where languages and codes are being organized, sequenced and retrieved. Pre-school dyslexic children will often have difficulties with spoken language. They may be late in learning to talk and in learning common sequences, and may confuse sounds. Typically, at five years of age, dyslexic children will have problems with letter knowledge, in linking sounds with symbols and in blending letters. They are also likely to have difficulty in learning by heart such things as the months of the year and songs and rhymes, and in carrying out sequential activities like learning tables. They may become increasingly reluctant to go to school during the first few years, or may develop emotional or behavioural problems.

Unidentified early problems persist and become more complex as they undermine the learning process. Children with dyslexia are puzzling to their parents and to their teachers. Often they appear (because they are) much more able than their work suggests and occasionally it is only the more complex writing and comprehension tasks required at secondary school that expose the problems.

Dyslexia affects some people more severely than others, depending on the amount of neurological difference and the effectiveness of the support they receive. The greater the difference, the greater the help required. The later the condition is identified, the greater its impact is likely to be.

The effects of dyslexia can be alleviated by skilled specialist teaching and committed learning. All children benefit from well-structured, phonically based early learning at school, and from practice to make the learning permanent. For dyslexic children this type of teaching is essential and, because of their difficulties, a multi-sensory approach that integrates seeing, hearing and doing is critical to them. If by the age of six a child is failing to gain early reading, writing and spelling skills (or earlier if dyslexia exists in the family), a psychologist's assessment should be considered. An assessment by an experienced specialist teacher can be very valuable in the early years. The aim is to identify strengths and weaknesses and make recommendations for appropriate helping strategies.

The majority of dyslexic children can, and should, be educated in ordinary schools alongside their peers. They will benefit from specialist teaching to enable them to reach their full potential. Only a tiny minority with severe and complex problems, which are frequently exacerbated by other conditions such as attention deficit disorder or dyspraxia, need to be educated in specialist schools. The key is the quality of teaching by the specialist teacher. Wherever possible dyslexic children should be placed in schools that can nurture their latent talents, as they frequently have strong creative and lateral thinking abilities. If their education is well managed and they are prepared to work hard, they can, and do, succeed in a wide range of careers.

# DYSPRAXIA

*Information supplied by the Dyspraxia Foundation*

The Dyspraxia Foundation defines dyspraxia as 'an impairment or immaturity of the organization of movement and, in many individuals, there may be associated problems with language, perception and thought'. The term normally used is Developmental Dyspraxia or Developmental Co-ordination Disorder.

The condition is thought to affect up to six per cent of the population in varying degrees. It is probable that there is at least one dyspraxic child in every classroom requiring access to a specific treatment programme.

Symptoms are evident from an early age. Youngsters are generally irritable from birth and many exhibit significant feeding problems. They are slow to achieve expected developmental milestones, often not sitting independently by the age of 8 months. Many fail to go through the crawling stage as babies, preferring to 'bottom shuffle' and then walk. Children with dyspraxia usually avoid tasks that require good manual dexterity and depend upon well-developed perceptual skills. Inset puzzles, Lego and jigsaws are difficult.

Between the ages of 3 and 5, children with dyspraxia may demonstrate the following types of behaviour:

- Very high levels of motor activity, including feet swinging and tapping when seated, hand clapping or twisting and an inability to stay in one place for more than 5 minutes.

- High levels of excitability, with a loud/shrill voice. Children may be easily distressed and prone to temper tantrums.

- Awkward movement. Children may constantly bump into objects and fall over. Associated mirror movements, hands flap when running.

- Difficulty pedalling a tricycle or similar toy.

- Poor figure and ground awareness. Children may lack any sense of danger, illustrated, for example, by jumping from an inappropriate height.

- Continued messy eating. Children may spill liquid from drinking cups and prefer to eat with their fingers.

- Avoidance of constructional toys, such as jigsaws or building blocks.

- Poor fine motor skills, demonstrated by difficulty in holding a pencil or using scissors. Drawings may appear immature.

- Lack of imaginative play. Children may show little interest in 'dressing up' or playing appropriately in a home or Wendy House.

- Limited creative play.

- Isolation within the peer group. Rejected by peers, children may prefer adult company.

- Laterality still not established. Problems crossing the midline.

- Persistent language difficulties. Children are often referred to a speech therapist.

- Sensitivity to sensory stimulation, including high levels of noise, being touched or wearing new clothes.

- Limited response to verbal instruction. Children may exhibit a slower response time and have problems with comprehension.
- Limited concentration. Tasks are often left unfinished.

If the condition is not identified, problems can persist throughout school life, causing increasing frustration and a lowering of self-esteem. Between the ages of 5 and 7, behaviour may include the following traits:

- problems adapting to a more structured school routine;
- difficulties with PE (Physical Education);
- slow at dressing and inability to tie shoe laces;
- barely legible handwriting;
- immature drawing and copying skills;
- limited concentration and poor listening skills;
- literal use of language;
- inability to remember more than two to three instructions;
- slow completion of class work;
- continued high levels of motor activity;
- motor stereotypes – hand flapping or clapping when excited;
- tendency to become easily distressed and emotional;
- problems coordinating a knife and fork;
- inability to form relationships with other youngsters, isolation in class;
- sleeping difficulties, including wakefulness at night and nightmares;
- reporting of physical symptoms, such as migraine, headaches or feeling sick.

Poor handwriting is one of the most common symptoms of dyspraxia, and as the child progresses through the education system, requirement for written work increases. By the age of about 8 or 9 the children may have become disaffected and poor school attendance is much in evidence in secondary education.

With access to appropriate treatment, the majority of dyspraxic youngsters can have their needs accommodated within a mainstream setting.

Parents concerned about their children should refer to their GP or health visitor if the child is aged under 5 or to the special needs coordinator if the child is in full-time school-ing. A referral may then be made to an outside professional, for example a paediatrician, educational psychologist, physiotherapist, occupational therapist or speech therapist for assessment.

When an appointment has been made, write down all your concerns. In an unfamiliar setting your child may not behave in the expected manner or give sufficient attention to the tasks set. Assessment usually involves giving a detailed account of your child's developmental history, examination of gross and fine motor skills, and a test of intellectual ability.

Treatment is available from specialists in health and education when the condition has been identified. Movement programmes may be offered by therapists and additional support can be made available in school.

If you require further information about dyspraxia or how to help your child, contact the Dyspraxia Foundation, 8 West Alley, Hitchin, Herts SG5 1EG, tel: 01462 454986, website: www.dyspraxiafoundation.org.uk.

# EPILEPSY

*Information supplied by Epilepsy Action*

Epilepsy is defined as a tendency to have recurrent seizures (sometimes called fits). A seizure is caused by a sudden burst of excess electrical activity in the brain, causing a temporary disruption in the normal message passing between brain cells. This disruption results in the brain's messages becoming halted or mixed up.

The brain is responsible for all the functions of the body, so what is experienced during a seizure will depend on where in the brain the epileptic activity begins and how widely and rapidly it spreads. For this reason, there are many different types of seizure and each person will experience epilepsy in a way that is unique to them.

Epilepsy can begin at any age, but the incidence is higher in childhood. Sometimes the reason epilepsy develops is clear. It could be because of brain damage caused by a difficult birth, a severe blow to the head, a stroke which starves the brain of oxygen, or an infection of the brain such as meningitis. Epilepsy with a known cause is called 'symptomatic' epilepsy. For most people there is no known cause and this is called 'idiopathic' epilepsy.

Children with uncomplicated epilepsy (without additional learning difficulties or physical disabilities) have the same range of intelligence and abilities as children without epilepsy. Many children with the condition are educated in mainstream schools, usually without additional educational support. However, some young people experience behavioural problems and/or learning difficulties. Behavioural problems and learning difficulties in children with epilepsy can have many different causes, including the following.

● The severity of the epilepsy. If seizures are occurring frequently a child's everyday life may be affected.

● Any damage to the brain could cause a number of symptoms. These can include seizures, learning difficulties and behavioural problems.

● The area of the brain in which epileptic activity is occurring. For example, if it is in the part of the brain concerned with memory, then learning difficulties may be experienced.

- The type of seizure. For example, when someone is experiencing a complex partial seizure they may appear to others as if their behaviour is strange or abnormal.

- Sub-clinical seizure activity. This refers to continuous epileptic activity which disrupts brain activity, without a seizure happening. This type of activity is quite rare. It can impair the brain's ability to process, although the child might appear not to be affected.

- The duration of seizures. Prolonged seizure activity may be accompanied by confusion, inappropriate behaviour, etc.

- Anti-epileptic medication. Some anti-epileptic drugs can have a negative effect on a child's behaviour.

- Psychological and social factors, such as family and peer attitudes as well as self-image.

There is also research that suggests that some children with epilepsy experience learning difficulties in specific subject areas, most notably mathematics and reading. The educational psychologist has a role to play in suggesting ways that these can be overcome in order for the child to achieve their full potential.

Some children with severe epilepsy may need to attend a special school. There are very few schools that specifically cater for children with epilepsy. However, schools in St Piers School, Young Epilepsy, St Piers Lane, Surrey, tel: 01342 831348; St Elizabeth's School, Herts, tel: 01279 844270; and the David Lewis School, Cheshire, tel: 01565 640066.

Further information about epilepsy and education can be obtained from Epilepsy Action's epilepsy Helpline, freephone: 0808 800 5050, e-mail: helpline@epilepsy.org.uk, text: 07797 805390 or from our website: www.epilepsy.org.uk.

# GIFTED CHILDREN AND HIGH ABILITY

*Information provided by Potential Plus UK*

Giftedness should not be seen as a property present in a few children but absent from the many; it is broadly the upper 10 per cent of the ability spectrum. However, it is possible that within the top 2 per cent there are individuals whose rapid development can dissociate them from their peers, socially, academically and intellectually. The challenge of gifted children is that of creating learning opportunities appropriate to their ability, age and maturity while at the same time supporting them emotionally and socially within their peer structure. For this to be successful parents and teachers need to work in partnership.

The first issue must be identifying the child who has unusual abilities. Growing knowledge of the brain's complexity and increasing understanding of how learning takes place has led to less reliance being placed on measures that put groups of children in order, high to low. Describing human ability by a single measurement such as a quotient or a score is now seen as simplistic. At least 80 working definitions of giftedness and high ability were developed during the 20th century; each created with its own defined purpose. These include selecting adults for particular high-level tasks, selecting students to attend enrichment programmes, diagnosing reasons for particular pupil behaviours and assessing progress. Hence, for the identification of highly able children there is no one all-embracing definition of what giftedness is, and there are many strategies and diagnostic tests that can be used and that vary across the age range.

## *Identification*

Some parents will have been sorely tested by the insatiable curiosity of their very young child.

For children in the pre-school phase, parents are the people best-placed to observe whether they are developing skills and talents significantly in advance of their peers. Early talking, unusual levels of concentration, and the ability to make creative connections of ideas are good indicators. Parents may encounter problems at toddler group, playgroup or pre-school nursery because staff do not recognize that the child can easily do the things the other children are enjoying doing and so is quickly bored and becomes behaviourally challenging. This should best be managed by discussion between parents and staff as to how adaptable the activities can be.

Once at school some aspects change but others do not. The child is now of an age when an educational assessment can give added professional insight. But as giftedness or high ability does not legally fall in the category of educational special needs, there are limited additional resources available for a child assessed as highly able. If issues have developed, if the child does not want to go to school, is bored at school, is unhappy or has become withdrawn, then parents need to work in partnership with the school, the class teacher and the headteacher to expose the issues in a non-confrontational way. The appropriateness and purpose of an assessment can then be discussed. A case for a LA assessment might be made if behaviour difficulties have developed. If parents are willing to have a private assessment undertaken, this is best done with the full knowledge of the school and an understanding of what will happen in the school as a result of the findings.

If, after discussions with the school, parents feel that they need to know more about how they can manage their child, but the school is not willing to proceed, they can undertake a private assessment. This will provide the parents with additional information about their child's intellectual ability and potential. Parents can then make an informed decision on the way forward, accepting that this may be limited by the school's position.

Schools should have a written policy on how they manage their most able children and it should be openly available on request. It should include how children are identified and what measures are put in place to stretch and challenge them. The policy should have the full support of the staff, the governors and parents.

Identifying older children as having unrecognized abilities, gifts and talents is always a sad occurrence, for it represents a waste of earlier opportunities. If the abilities are not recognized and encouraged early, there is the risk that the child will become withdrawn, or will merge into the crowd, or will develop a disruptive pattern of behaviour, all of which would detract attention from his or her ability that may go on undetected for many years. It is often when schools undertake a formal assessment on the basis of poor behaviour that the truth is revealed – the child is a high-ability low performer!

## Providing the learning for highly able children

Once identified, the highly able child needs challenging learning experiences. The roles of parents and of schools are of equal importance in building this provision. Through parents the child has access to evening, weekend and holiday time activities, and so can be involved with a wide range of ages and expertise that is not found within the school system. This helps to ground the child's emotional and social development.

How learning experiences are managed within school will depend on the child's age as well as the Key Stage of the National Curriculum and the resources available in the school. Teachers in primary schools are used to managing groups of children of widely different abilities, can plan individual extension or enrichment activities for every lesson for the gifted child and can involve him or her in determining appropriate enrichment activities. Where the curriculum allows it, the child can work with other staff or older classes on agreed activities, always remembering that what can happen easily one year may be difficult to secure the next. For some parents the easy solution would appear to be to accelerate the child one or two years. This needs to be viewed with the utmost caution, for older children can be hostile to a younger child being joined to their peer group and also because there are major issues to be faced at the transition from primary to secondary phase.

The structure of the secondary school gives additional scope for differentiating the curriculum and locating pupils in ability sets, but the highly able child still needs to have enrichment activities built into each lesson. The strategies available to a school depend on its unique circumstances, but much good practice has been built up over recent years. Besides a 'Gifted and Talented' policy, schools are expected to have a G and T coordinator, and school inspectors expect that there will be evidence that shows that the policy is working. There has been an ongoing series of government-sponsored projects aimed at enriching the learning experiences of the most able pupils and more information about these can be found on the National Association for Gifted Children's website at www.nagcbritain.org.uk or from the NAGC helpline (tel: 0845 450 0221).

Information on Excellence in Cities and Excellence Clusters is also available from the DCSF website (www.dcsf.gov.uk), which gives the most up-to-date information. These projects are not universal but are targeted on areas of specific educational need. Every state school is expected to have a Gifted Coordinator and a direct approach to the school is needed to make contact with them. In addition, most LAs have an officer who carries a direct responsibility for Gifted and Talented education, and a telephone call to the Local Education Office will reveal who this is.

The British Psychological Society (tel: 0116 254 9568, website: www.bps.org.uk) publishes lists of chartered psychologists who are able to carry out private educational assessments. You can obtain a leaflet with guidance on how to choose an educational psychologist from the NAGC (tel: 0845 450 0221).

# LOSS OF, OR DAMAGE TO, LIMBS

*Information supplied by Reach*

Children may be born without a limb or part of one (limb deficiency), or they may lose all or part of a limb as a result of an accident, or through medical necessity (amputation).

Artificial limbs (prostheses) are usually provided for young children, both to encourage development of strength in the muscles and patterns of movement and, perhaps most important, to encourage independence. Learning to use artificial limbs is self-evidently not a natural process and takes time and practice, according to the motivation and skills of each child. Some may need encouragement, while others may need help to prevent them being too ambitious. For children born with digits missing or who have a partial hand, prostheses are not available or appropriate.

Staff will need to be aware of a child's needs before he or she starts school. Parents will be able to advise on the medical aspects of the limb loss and in most instances a child will be able to explain his or her own needs, eg how he or she operates the arm, what he or she can and cannot do and how much help might be needed. It is important for a pupil to be given the opportunity to say when he or she prefers to wear or remove the artificial limb, for example for PE, or during hot weather when the residual limb may become uncomfortably hot in the prosthesis.

A child who is fitted with a prosthesis will be in regular contact with a prosthesist, who will be able to advise on any problems in using the prosthesis, or in new tasks to be learnt. As children grow, prostheses need to be replaced regularly. If the child has had an amputation, he or she may need surgery from time to time to check the growth of the residual limb.

There are no learning difficulties specifically associated with limb deficiency or amputation. However, teachers may have to seek extra time for students sitting examinations if it is considered that the student's writing speed is affected by the limb loss. Written forms of language can be produced on typewriters, personal computers or a voice-activated computer system, and access to word-processing can be tailored to the requirements of the pupil. Other solutions include accessing the word processor via single or multiple switches, which may be in the form of rollerballs or joysticks.

The artificial arms usually supplied to children are made from metal or plastic and have a grasp mechanism. They are normally covered in foam and toning plastic to improve the appearance. With practice pupils develop the skills needed to use the arm and grasp mechanism. Most children do not learn to write with their artificial arm. Some prefer to use their own ways of managing instead of, or as well as, using an artificial arm. A pupil's preference is important but it is also advisable to check with the parents, prosthesist and/ or occupational therapist to ensure a consistent approach.

Children with no upper limbs who do not use artificial arms have to learn methods of managing their own personal needs. Initially they may require assistance, but with time many of them develop the skills needed to be fully independent. Children who have lost one or both legs, above or below the knee, will be able to use artificial limbs, but are still likely to have some mobility difficulties. Some may use sticks or crutches and some may use a wheelchair. Mobility needs should be taken into account when considering emergency procedures.

Children who have limb deficiency should be encouraged to take part in PE as far as possible. Physical fitness is as important for these pupils as for all others. Children will often develop strategies for participating within their limits but may need encouragement. If advice is needed, a physiotherapist will be able to help. If the child chooses to participate without the artificial limb, it is important it is stored safely and securely. If the limb is hidden as a prank, this can be very distressing for the child.

Children who lose a limb following an accident or through medical necessity often find it difficult to adjust to their impairment and changed body image. They, their parents and possibly siblings may need counselling to help them work through the emotional stress of the loss of a limb. Emotional stress is an almost universal experience among amputees, their families and carers.

Any child who is physically 'different' is at risk of being teased. It may be helpful to ensure that the child concerned has a simple explanation and is ready to satisfy the curiosity of his or her peers. A matter-of-fact attitude on the part of the adults will help to reduce any embarrassment felt by a pupil and his or her peer group.

Good communication between parents, professionals and the pupil must be encouraged to ensure proper resources are in place. The expertise of parents and pupil should be utilized, and inter-agency collaboration will help smooth the way for the pupil's academic and social development. The transition from school to adult life can often be a stressful time and transitional planning is therefore essential.

Further information is available from: Chief Operations Officer, Reach Charity Ltd, Association for Children with Upper Limb Deficiency, PO Box 54, Helston, Cornwall TR13 8WD, tel: 0845 130 6225; Limbless Association, Roehampton Rehabilitation Centre, Roehampton Lane, London SW15 5PR, tel: 020 8788 1777.

# MUSCULAR DYSTROPHY

*Information supplied by the Muscular Dystrophy Campaign*

Muscular dystrophy (MD) is a name given to many different conditions that have in common the breakdown of muscle fibres, leading to weak and wasted muscles. More than 60,000 children and adults in the UK have MD or a related neuromuscular condition. A further 300,000 people in the UK are indirectly affected as relations or carers.

Each of these neuromuscular conditions has a different cause; they are mostly genetic, but some are autoimmune (where a person's immune system attacks healthy cells within the body itself). Symptoms of some disorders show very early on, even at birth, but in others symptoms may only start to show later in childhood or adulthood. Severity is variable: several conditions are very disabling or life-threatening; the rest can cause moderate or mild disability. Most of the conditions cause progressive weakening of the muscles but some remain stable. Different conditions affect different muscles and various other body systems. The inheritance risks vary. There can also be a wide variation in the degree of severity not only between one type of dystrophy and another but also between individuals with the same type.

In some conditions, particularly Duchenne muscular dystrophy (DMD) and myotonic dystrophy, some individuals may have a degree of intellectual impairment. This may be reflected particularly in poor reading ability, word comprehension and memory skills. This intellectual impairment is not directly related to muscle weakness, however, and is not progressive.

Children's educational needs depend, of course, on the individual concerned and the nature of their condition and disability. Some children may need to attend special schools but many will be able to continue with mainstream schooling right through to college or university. Help needed within school will also vary widely, depending on the physical limitations of the individual. Many children with a significant disability will need a great deal of support.

Some conditions also have other complications which need to be carefully monitored, such as heart and breathing problems and allergy to anaesthesia. Muscle weakness can also cause additional mobility problems such as contractures (tightening of joints) and scoliosis (curvature of the spine).

Anyone can be affected by these conditions. They are usually inherited from the parent(s) but can appear out of the blue, in a family with no history of the condition. Males and/or females can be affected, depending on the genetic cause of the condition. For example, DMD is usually inherited from the mother by the son. Apart from very rare exceptions females are the only carriers of DMD and can themselves be manifesting carriers. In myotonic dystrophy either the mother or the father is affected and can pass the gene on. In spinal muscular atrophy neither parent is affected but both must carry the faulty gene for it to be passed on to their children. The conditions are not infectious.

It is not possible to 'catch' muscular dystrophy or any of the related conditions. However, if someone is found to be affected, their relatives might also have the condition because the disrupted gene may run in the family.

Although there are as yet no treatments or cures available for the majority, physiotherapy is helpful and symptoms can be alleviated through careful management. However, it is possible to treat the symptoms of myotonia congenita effectively. Immunological treatment is possible for polymyositis, dermatomyositis, myasthenia gravis and other immunological neuromuscular conditions. These treatments may involve the use of immunosuppressive drugs such as steroids, plasma exchange and intravenous immunoglobin.

Researchers are trying to find treatments and cures for other conditions. Where the cause is genetic, identification of the genetic fault is the first vital step towards understanding the condition and then finding a treatment. Muscular Dystrophy Campaign researchers are at the forefront of international research; they already know the genetic faults responsible for several conditions and are investigating several possible treatments.

Guidance for primary and secondary schools entitled 'Inclusive education for children with muscular dystrophy and other neuromuscular conditions' is available from the Muscular Dystrophy Campaign, 61 Southwark Street, London SE1 0HL, tel: 020 7803 4800, freephone: 0800 652 6352, e-mail: info@muscular-dystrophy.org, website: www.muscular-dystrophy.org.

# SPEECH AND LANGUAGE DIFFICULTIES

*Information supplied by Afasic*

The ability to use language and communicate effectively is the basis of all learning and social interaction. Without these skills, education would not achieve its goals. It follows that the development of language and communication skills is central to all education.

The vast majority of children with special educational needs have one or other kind of communication difficulty. There is also a group of children who do not develop language skills normally, irrespective of any obvious intellectual or physical disability. These children are often said to have a specific or primary speech or language impairment, which may be in isolation or alongside another disability.

It is estimated that one in 500 school-age children will have severe long-term impairments, while at least 6 per cent will experience some degree of difficulty at some time that could interfere with their educational progress.

## Characteristics

Some children are unable to understand or express themselves clearly, while others have near normal understanding but experience difficulty in speaking intelligibly. Some may not be able to form words and sentences correctly, have limited vocabulary, may produce strings of unintelligible sounds or repeat spoken language correctly without knowing the meaning of what they are saying. Some will have difficulty with the beginnings and endings of words. Others may display 'autistic tendencies'.

## Identification of difficulties

Any of the following can be an indication of a language impairment:

- late onset of speech;
- a discrepancy between verbal and non-verbal skills or between receptive and expressive language;
- lack of concentration;
- history of 'glue-ear';
- difficulty with fine and/or gross motor skills;
- poor short-term memory;
- word-finding difficulties;
- poor interaction with peers.

As language skills develop very rapidly in the early years, much is gained if difficulties are identified as early as possible; 2 to 3 years of age is not too early. Where help is provided at this age, a child is often able to join a mainstream school at 5 years of age.

If the difficulties are not tackled in the early years, and the child struggles through primary schooling, difficulties can be seriously compounded by the time secondary age is reached. In a mainstream school the child is unlikely to be able to master the necessary conceptual understanding and complex social interactions expected in such a setting and may well become confused, disorientated, suffer emotional stress and succumb to bullying. Special schooling is then likely to be the only way to begin to provide effective help.

## Assessment of difficulties

If there is cause for concern and a speech and language therapist has not already been seen, referral should be arranged following discussion with the parent(s). It is obviously important to identify a child's particular strengths and weaknesses at the first possible opportunity. Speech and language therapists have the skills to undertake such an assessment and to advise how any weakness may be overcome. Where a child's difficulties are particularly severe it is likely that a full assessment has taken place, or is under way, and that a statement has been drawn up.

## Ways to help

Those with severe difficulties are best helped in a special school or language unit or class, with teachers and speech and language therapists working very closely in partnership. In the latter, intensive language work can take place with integration into the host school as and when appropriate. There are about 400 such units throughout the country but few, as yet, are available for secondary-aged pupils.

Even where difficulties are not said to be severe, input from a speech and language therapist is recommended, as different approaches and programmes can be discussed, the most appropriate selected and queries clarified. Advice from an occupational therapist and/or physiotherapist should be sought for those with coordination difficulties.

Because these children do not acquire language spontaneously as others do, they need to be taught appropriate skills in a structured setting.

- A planned approach should be used to teach speaking and listening skills and reading and writing for all pupils.

- Activities should encourage the development of turn-taking, rhythms and rhyme, and the building up of self-esteem and confidence.

- Where a child has difficulty in learning the order of a task, it helps to structure the sequence of skills and to simplify each step.

- The use of computers and a combination of sight, sound, touch or movement can be valuable.

- Small group work (four to eight pupils) is essential to achieve National Curriculum targets successfully.

- Social skills and the use of social or functional language must be developed.

It can be especially helpful to relate work to a child's own interests or family.

For further information please send a stamped, addressed envelope to Afasic, 2nd Floor, 50–52 Great Sutton Street, London EC1V ODJ.

# SPINA BIFIDA AND/OR HYDROCEPHALUS

*Information supplied by SHINE*

## What is spina bifida?

Spina bifida is a congenital condition that affects babies very early in pregnancy. It is a fault in the development of the spine, when one or more vertebrae fail to close properly. Spina bifida usually affects the lower limbs, where there may be reduced mobility, a lack of sensation of pain and temperature and perhaps problems with circulation. Many people with spina bifida will have continence problems, which need to be managed effectively if self-image is not to be damaged.

## What is hydrocephalus?

Hydrocephalus happens when the fluid in the brain cannot drain away into the bloodstream because the pathways are blocked. The excess pressure must be relieved quickly to minimize damage.

New drainage pathways are opened, either by inserting a fine tube (called a shunt) inside a space in the brain or by making a small hole in the floor of one of these spaces. This operation is called a ventriculostomy.

Many people with spina bifida also have hydrocephalus, but it can occur by itself, especially in babies born prematurely, or after meningitis, a head injury or stroke. Hydrocephalus may affect motor skills, vision, speech and language, and behaviour. Neither spina bifida nor hydrocephalus is associated with any particular level of general intelligence.

## Educational issues for children with spina bifida and/or hydrocephalus

### Time off in hospital

Children with spina bifida and/or hydrocephalus may require repeated admission to hospital or hospital visits as out-patients. During prolonged stays in hospital, arrangements will probably need to be made for formal education to be continued.

## Physical access

Consideration must be given to access issues, especially wheelchair access, or access to the curriculum through specialist equipment or classroom assistance before a child starts at a particular school. Accessible toilet facilities may also be necessary. For pupils with spina bifida who manage their own continence, or need assistance with this, the privacy of toilet facilities must also be considered.

## Learning

Hydrocephalus, whether it has or has not been shunted, may affect 1) a child's coordination and visual-spatial perception, 2) short-term memory, concentration and the ability to solve problems, and to conceptualize, and 3) social and emotional development and peer relationships.

### 1. Coordination and perception

Some children appear to be clumsy and have balance problems. Many tire very easily. Hand–eye coordination may be poor, and there is often a weak handgrip.

Visuo-spatial perception may be affected, resulting in a distorted view of the world. There may, for instance, be difficulty in distinguishing between a step and a line drawn on the ground. Many children have squints, some may have tunnel vision, or nystagmus. Work in mathematics, especially abstract concepts, and geography may be affected.

Careful observation is needed to identify ways in which visual problems (squints, tunnel vision) may be affecting children's performance, eg in copying from the board and organizing their belongings, as they may have poor organizational skills.

Help and understanding may be needed in the following situations:

- walking long distances and walking up and down stairs;
- colouring-in and hand-writing; using scissors and other tools; fastening buttons; tying laces;
- moving in crowded spaces without bumping into furniture or other people;
- 'finding' objects that are mixed up with other objects, interpreting diagrams and maps;
- noticing things on their desk/table that are immediately in front or to one side;
- 'tuning in' to one voice, against a background of chatter and hypersensitivity to noises like clapping, laughter or lawn mowers.

### 2. Memory, problem-solving and conceptualization

Long-term memory for details of events may be very good. However, many children have short-term memory problems, especially in retaining spoken words long enough to understand what they mean. The speed at which a child with hydrocephalus processes information may also be slower than for others. The perceived 'verbal' ability of many children can lead others to presume that they understand the instructions and conversations when this may not be so. Most children will have short concentration spans. Many will have problems in self-correcting, expressing observations and giving explanations, and these children will find it difficult to 'make connections' between different items of information. Most children will need extra time and help to learn new ideas and to develop the thinking strategies they need to deal with unfamiliar information. Allowing extra time for information to be absorbed before moving on to the next point is a useful approach.

Again for some children, some abilities can improve if appropriate experiences are provided. However, unless they are also helped to recognize their own competencies and what is expected of them, many will still experience a great deal of anxiety in relatively unfamiliar situations, which may include formal tests.

Help and understanding may be needed in the following situations:

- concentrating on tasks and self-monitoring;
- switching from one activity to another;
- finding their way in an unfamiliar environment;
- understanding and remembering verbal instructions;
- giving clear accounts – there can be a tendency to focus on isolated, unconnected details;
- self-organization – where to start, what to do next;
- problem-solving – reluctance to engage in 'difficult' work without help;
- thinking ahead – a tendency to act or speak before they think.

### 3. Social and emotional behaviour

Hydrocephalus is sometimes linked with developmental delay in physical development in infancy and also in language development.

Although some children with hydrocephalus are very 'sociable', they may have problems in adjusting their own behaviour to different social contexts. Some can tend to treat everyone as a 'friend'. Some may be very shy, or overly domineering with their peers. Lack of self-esteem is common and some people become withdrawn and depressed, while others show challenging behaviours.

Children with hydrocephalus can be helped to learn social skills and have more confidence in themselves, and the chances of this teaching being effective are greater if begun before the beginning of Key Stage 2.

Help may be needed to develop skills in the following areas:

- self-inhibition, eg learning to wait their turn to speak;
- addressing different people in appropriate ways;
- peer relationships;
- anticipating unfamiliar situations;
- participating in family and classroom chores;
- initiation of discussion.

## Support in mainstream schools

Open and trusting relationships between parents and teachers are essential, as is a problem-solving approach to any perceived difficulties.

Good school–home partnerships will ensure that information relating to possible medical problems and physical difficulties is shared and understood, and that the 'strategies' to be used to solve behavioural problems are consistent. Behavioural problems may be evident in school but not at home, and vice versa. It is important not to attribute blame in either context. No strategy will succeed unless the child is also involved.

If learning support assistant time is available in class, target it on developing the skills the children will need to work and socialize independently. Independent skills should be encouraged; eg as children develop the ability to listen to whole-class instructions and carry them out, the assistant may begin to use prompts instead of repeating the whole instructions on a one-to-one basis.

Make a point of observing and noting the outcomes of the approaches that are used, and to modify them as necessary after discussions. If the children can begin to think positively about the skills and knowledge they are developing, this will provide the confidence for more difficult tasks.

SHINE produces books titled *Hydrocephalus and You* and *Your Child and Hydrocephalus*. These are available from: Helpline and Information, SHINE, 42 Park Road, Peterborough PE1 2UQ, tel/helpline: 01733 55988, e-mail: info@shinecharity.org.uk, website: shinecharity.org.uk.

# VISUAL IMPAIRMENT

*Information supplied by the Royal National Institute for the Blind*

There are an estimated 25,000 blind and partially sighted children and young people under the age of 16 in the UK today. Approaching 50 per cent of this number have additional sensory, physical or learning needs that affect their education.

While visual impairment is a 'low-incidence' disability with only about two children in every thousand being blind or partially sighted, these children have very individual and important information and support needs.

Although a few children have no sight at all, most have some vision. For example, some can tell the difference between light and dark, some have central vision and can only see things in front of them, while others can see objects to one side but are unable to see the detail of things directly in front of them. Some children see everything as a vague blur, others as a patchwork of blanks and defined areas. Some see better in bright light, some when it is darker, others find it difficult to adjust between light and dark.

Some children's vision is affected not by a problem with the eyes themselves, but with the processing of visual information in the brain. This is known as cerebral visual impairment (CVI) and can make it difficult for children to interpret and understand what they are seeing. Ongoing functional vision assessment (observing the child's response to different visual stimuli) can be helpful in understanding the impact of CVI on a child's ability to see.

### *Children who are blind or partially sighted but have no other significant additional needs*

The majority of blind and partially sighted children whose main disability is visual impairment attend mainstream schools. For most of these children, inclusion will be appropriate throughout their education.

Whilst mainstream education for blind and partially sighted children is now the norm, some may need a certain level of special school education. A small number of specialist schools cater specifically for blind and partially sighted children. However, of the blind and partially sighted children who attend special schools, most attend Local Authority (LA) special schools that cater for diverse ranges of special educational need and disability.

Each child should be assessed as soon as possible so that the level of educational support needed can be planned in conjunction with the LA visual impairment specialist. RNIB can provide names of LA visual impairment specialists and also offers a wide variety of assessment services.

Whether in a mainstream or special school, a child with a visual impairment will need some specialized materials, equipment, or adaptations to the resources and materials used by their fully sighted peers. This is required in order to maximize their learning potential and to provide access to the National Curriculum.

Children with some residual vision may be able to use enlarged materials, whether enlarged on a photocopier or specially printed in a larger print size. All examination boards provide pre-enlarged exam papers, and all Key Stage test papers are available in both enlarged and modified enlarged formats. Many diagrams, maps, photos and pictures in learning materials will need to be simplified or presented in an alternative way for children with sight problems.

If visual impairment prevents children from reading enlarged print, they may learn to read and write Braille and may also make extensive use of audio material. In addition there are organizations, including RNIB, which can offer advice and information on a range of access technology solutions. Examples include:

- A closed-circuit television (CCTV). This enables a student to place a regular piece of print underneath a small moving camera, while the CCTV shows the enlarged print on a monitor. The student can then move the camera across a page and read a whole page of standard print.

- Computer packages that can convert words on a computer screen into synthesized speech, and read computer files back to a blind or partially sighted student.

- Devices that can be attached to a computer and allow the user to have a Braille display of what is on the computer screen.

- Packages that can convert computer text into a Braille printout.

- Portable Braille note-takers, which allow individuals to Braille information into a small machine and retrieve it later by connecting it to a computer. Print copies can then be produced for a sighted teacher.

RNIB offers advice, in-service training, curriculum advice and support and help in setting up new inclusion schemes to LA staff. For individual schools and pupils, RNIB has facilities for trying out special equipment and can help with particular aspects of the curriculum. For more information, visit rnib.org.uk/curriculum.

The decision on what type of school is appropriate depends on many factors and not just the extent of a child's vision or how well he or she uses this. The ability of a school to include a child socially is as important as meeting their educational needs within the National Curriculum.

## Blind and partially sighted children with additional needs

Owing to the range of causes of visual impairment, approximately 50 per cent of children with a sight problem may also have a hearing impairment, learning difficulty, physical difficulty or a combination of impairments.

A full multidisciplinary assessment of all of the child's educational needs will determine whether a special or mainstream school is most appropriate. It is very important that the LA visual impairment teaching service is included in this assessment process.

Most children with complex needs and visual impairment go to special schools within their local authority area. In exceptional circumstances, however, children sometimes attend residential schools further from home. Each LA has its own approach to educating children with sight problems and complex needs. There are a small number of special schools for blind and partially sighted children with additional needs, including two RNIB schools.

Technology is also used extensively with blind and partially sighted children with additional needs, particularly in the form of multi-sensory rooms using lights and sounds to stimulate the child. Touch screens, communication aids with adapted tactile access and switch technology can also help develop communication skills and provide access to the National Curriculum.

A large number of books, DVDs and factsheets have been published by RNIB and others about the education of blind and partially sighted children, many of which are available from RNIB. For details of any aspect of the education of a blind or partially sighted child, including the services mentioned above, please contact the RNIB Helpline: 0303 123 9999 or e-mail: children@rnib.org.uk.

# The Special Educational Needs Code of Practice

John Friel, Barrister-at-law, Gray's Inn

The Special Educational Needs (SEN) Code of Practice was introduced as part of a substantial reform by the 1993 Education Act. For parents of children with special educational needs, the 1993 Act gave both parents and children new specific rights, including rights of appeal. Alongside those rights of appeal was the Code of Practice, which provided guidance to all schools. The initial Code, to be used by parents and all concerned, was issued in 1994. It was replaced by a revised Code of Practice in November 2001.

The 1996 Education Act clarified previous Education Acts, but has now been subject to later variations. These include the Learning Skills Act 2000 and the Special Educational Needs and Disability Discrimination Act 2001.

The purpose of the Code of Practice is to give practical guidance on the discharge of functions in relation to children with special educational needs (under the Education Act 1996), to LAs, governing bodies of all maintained schools, teachers, parents and all interested parties. The Code sets out guidance on policies and procedures aimed at enabling pupils with special educational needs to reach their full potential.

The Code makes it clear that the vast majority of children will be assisted in a main-stream setting. In addition, some children at some time will require further help from SEN services and other agencies. A small minority of children who have special educational needs of a severe or complex nature will need Statements. The basic intention behind the Code is to set out guidelines in order to ascertain:

- whether children have special educational needs;
- whether they require special educational provision;

- if so at what level; and

- whether a Statement is or will be necessary.

*Editor's note:* A nationwide consultation on approaches to special educational needs and disability began in 2011, which affects the legislation and the Code of Practice. For further details see Section 1.5

# Principles of the Code of Practice

The Code is intended to help schools and LAs obtain the best value from the considerable resources and expertise they invest in helping children with special educational needs. It considers the rights and duties introduced by the 2001 Act and Regulations, as well as the Learning Skills Act 2000.

## *Fundamental principles*

The general principles are that:

- Children with special educational needs should have their needs met.
- The special educational needs of children will normally be met in mainstream schools or settings.
- The views of the child should be sought and taken into account.
- Parents have a vital role to play in supporting a child's education.
- Children with special educational needs should be offered full access to a broad, balanced and relevant education, including an appropriate curriculum at foundation stage and the National Curriculum.

The Code sets out a number of critical success factors, which are as follows:

- All resources in a school setting should be managed and deployed to ensure that all children's needs are met.
- LA schools and settings should work together to ensure that any child's special educational needs are identified early.
- LA schools and settings should exploit best practice when devising their interventions.
- The wishes of the child concerned should be taken into account in the light of his or her age and understanding.
- Parents and professionals should work in partnership.
- The views of individual parents should be taken into account.

- Interventions for each child should be reviewed regularly and assessed for their impact and effectiveness.

- There should be close cooperation between all relevant agencies together with a multidisciplinary approach.

- LAs should meet the prescribed time limits set out in the Regulations.

- Where children require Statements these should be clear and detailed; the LA should meet the prescribed time limits and should monitor the arrangements and review the Statement annually.

The Code of Practice defines the role of the LA and its statutory duties extensively. Equally, it defines the role of the school governing body and its statutory duties. It considers SEN policies in early education settings at schools and includes a useful table (paragraph 1.39) of roles and responsibilities.

The current Code is far more detailed and complex than the earlier Code. The 1994 Code provided a clear five-stage assessment of children with special educational needs. Stages 1 and 3 were the school-based interventions (Stage 3 bringing in outside intervention). Stages 4 and 5 were statutory assessment and a Statement. The current Code introduces the idea of School Action and School Action Plus, which are much vaguer concepts than a five-stage Code of Practice.

The Code is divided into a number of sections. The first defines principles and policies and thereafter outlines the system of identification and intervention. It begins with identification, assessment and provision in early education settings, then in the primary phase and finally in the secondary sector. Statutory assessments are dealt with in Chapter 7 of the Code. Statements of Special Educational Needs are dealt with in Chapter 8 and annual reviews in Chapter 9. Chapter 10 describes working in partnership with other agencies, including where a child transfers from the school sector into further education.

Overall, the Code seeks to make schools more accountable for children with special educational needs and the funds invested in them. The previous Code could be described as far more precise about intervention on behalf of the child and more concerned with ensuring that some definition of his or her learning difficulties is set out. The current Code has abandoned the useful detailed guidance on certain learning difficulties contained in Chapter 3 of its predecessor.

Significant criticisms were made of the current Code of Practice in its draft form, and it was withdrawn in draft on a number of occasions. Some of these criticisms were valid. First, it is too complicated for parents and for teachers. Second, it uses unnecessarily complicated language. Overall, the document is far more concerned with administration and accountability than the first Code.

The current Code places greater obligations than the previous version on all schools to make sure that the Special Educational Needs Coordinator (SENCo) in primary and secondary schools is given a substantial management role and has sufficient time to carry out the required duties. In seeking greater levels of accountability and clearer evidence of intervention, the Code is likely to create problems in cases where schools do not comply with its requirements. Local Authorities may well claim in cases where parents seek Statements of Special Educational Needs that there is insufficient information. However, the legal position is that a Statement depends not on the availability of information, but on whether a Statement is necessary for the child (Section 323, the assessment provisions, and Section 324, the Statement provisions of the 1996 Act, make this quite clear).

## School Action and School Action Plus

The Code incorporates a two-stage procedure: School Action and School Action Plus. Although the criteria for primary and for secondary level differ slightly, the overall principles are the same.

*School Action* depends on the identification by the SENCo or a member of staff that the child requires an intervention additional to, or different from, that normally provided by the school. The criteria outlined at secondary level are that the child:

- makes little or no progress even when teaching approaches are targeted particularly at a pupil's identified area of weakness;

- shows signs of difficulty in developing literacy or mathematics skills that result in poor attainment in some curriculum areas;

- has persistent emotional and/or behavioural difficulties that are not ameliorated;

- has sensory or physical problems and continues to make little or no progress despite specialist equipment;

- has communication and/or interaction difficulties and continues to make little or no progress despite the provision of a differentiated curriculum.

The Code provides for consultation and cooperation with parents. It also requires an individual education plan, examples of which are found in the SEN Toolkit, an associated document published by the Department for Education. The Individual Education Plan should include information about:

- the short-term targets set for or by the pupil;

- teaching strategies to be used;

- provision to be put in place;

- when the plan is to be reviewed;

- success and/or exit criteria;

- outcomes.

The next stage is *School Action Plus*. This stage follows a review of intervention under School Action, which would normally bring in, when needed, external support services provided by the LA and/or outside agencies. The triggers for this are defined in the Code of Practice at secondary level (Chapter 6.64) as being that the child:

- continues to make little or no progress in specific areas over a long period;

- continues working at National Curriculum level substantially below that expected of pupils of a similar age;

- continues to have difficulty in developing literacy and mathematics skills;

- has emotional or behavioural difficulties that substantially and regularly interfere with his or her own learning and/or that of the class group despite intervention;

- has sensory or physical needs that require additional specialist equipment or regular advice or visits providing direct intervention of pupil or staff;

- has ongoing communication or social interaction difficulties that impede the development of social relationships and cause substantial barriers to learning.

The Code of Practice allows that for a very small number of pupils the help given by schools through Action Plus may not be sufficient to enable the pupil to make adequate progress.

Schools can now themselves seek a statutory assessment. The terms upon which they can seek such an assessment are defined on pages 72 and 73 of the Code of Practice (Chapter 6.72).

It should be noted that the expectation of the Code of Practice is for a very complex and sophisticated intervention at Action Plus. Practical experience suggests that this may not be available in all cases. For example, where children or staff require specific help or disability equipment, they may in reality only be provided with aids as a result of a Statement or a statutory assessment under Section 323. The current Code of Practice expects an enormous amount of schools. It remains to be seen whether schools can deliver such a sophisticated service.

## Statutory assessment and Statement

Chapter 7 of the Code deals with the statutory assessment of special educational needs, the evidence to be provided by the school or the early education setting and referral by another agency. Considerations for parents who wish to request an assessment are important in this section (pages 78–79 of the Code, Chapter 7.21 to 7.29). Many of the parents consulting this Guide will be considering making such a request.

Chapter 7.23 sets out the principles on which parents should request an assessment. First, parents should believe that their child's needs are not being met through school-based intervention or that the needs are so substantial that a mainstream school could not meet them effectively without the use of outside resources. The Code points out that parents should clearly set out the reasons for their request. They should also provide information about the provision that the child has already received. However, the Code is silent on issues arising from certain cases that frequently come to the attention of LAs, and the Special Educational Needs Tribunal. These are cases where children have not received any or adequate intervention because their problems have been under-estimated or missed altogether.

The previous Code included detailed criteria for dealing with individual categories of disability, ie emotional and behavioural difficulties and specific learning difficulties, including dyslexia. The current Code does not address matters in similar detail. However, the previous Code omitted some obvious categories.

The current Code provides an improvement on the previous version in that it includes a section on children who need an immediate referral for a statutory assessment. Obviously this refers to children with the most severe difficulties, and this new, more substantial section of the Code is a welcome addition.

## *Evidence in deciding whether to make a statutory assessment*

Pages 81–89 of this Code cover the evidence that a LA should consider before making a decision to conduct a statutory assessment. This includes, with guidance, some consideration of certain learning difficulties, but not in the same detail or complexity as the previous Code.

The evidence to be considered by the LA includes:

- Evidence that the school has responded appropriately to requirements of the National Curriculum especially in relation to inclusion.

- Evidence provided by the child's school, parents and other professionals involved with the child as to the nature, extent and cause of the child's learning difficulties.

- Evidence of action already taken by the child's school to meet and overcome those difficulties.

- Evidence of the rate and style of the child's progress.

- Evidence that where some progress has been made, it has been the result only of additional efforts and instruction at a sustained level not usually commensurate with provision through School Action Plus.

The Code clearly requires specific evidence of attainment and requires LAs to seek clear, recorded evidence of the child's academic attainment. Overall, the LA should consider the case for a statutory assessment where the balance of evidence presented to, and assessed by, it suggests that the child's learning difficulties:

- have not responded to relevant and purposeful measures taken by the school or by an external specialist;

- may call for special educational provision that could not reasonably be provided within the resources normally available to mainstream maintained schools and settings in the area.

The new document improves on the previous Code by seeking the child's views. It also points out that each child is unique and that the questions asked by the LA should reflect the particular circumstances of the child.

The Code then covers some areas of strengths and difficulties such as: communication and interaction; vocation and learning behaviour; emotional and social development; sensory and/or physical needs; and medical conditions. However, it covers these issues in a much broader sense than the previous Code and the guidance it gives is far more general. For example, autism, dyslexia, dyspraxia and hearing impairment are covered in Chapter 7.55 to 7.57; the previous Code covered specific learning difficulties including dyslexia very effectively and accurately in greater depth.

## Criteria for considering intervention

In dealing with children with, for example, dyslexia, dyspraxia, language delay, other learning difficulties or language and communication problems, the types of intervention are set out as follows:

- Flexible teaching and arrangements.

- Help in acquiring, comprehending and using language.

- Help in articulation.

- Help in acquiring literacy skills.

- Help in using augmentative and alternative means of communication.

- Help in using different means of communication confidently and competently for a range of purposes, including formal situations.

- Help in organizing and coordinating oral and written language.

- Support to compensate for the impact of communication difficulty on learning in English as an additional language.

- Help in expressing, comprehending and using the child's own language, where English is not his or her first language.

The Code goes on to state that if some or all of these programmes can be provided for a child by the school in collaboration with the LA or external services, then the LA may conclude that intervention should be provided at School Action Plus and be monitored to see if that action is effective. It would then be appropriate for the LA to conclude that a statutory assessment was not necessary. If, on the other hand, the school support and services had already provided these interventions through School Action Plus and the child had not made acceptable progress, then a statutory assessment should be considered.

There is one difficulty with the Code worth noting here. It makes no reference to the necessity of a Statement in cases where there has been no intervention and where there is evidence that sufficient support is not available. In most such cases a Statement should be necessary, but the Code does not address this point.

If one turns to the provision for Statements in Chapter 8 of the Code, particularly the criteria for deciding to draw up a Statement, and contrasts this with the provisions relating to a statutory assessment, it is clear that where children will require greater intervention than is normally available, a Statement should be made. There is therefore a clear internal conflict in the Code between cases in which there is lack of evidence of adequate intervention by the school together with insufficient evidence that there will be future adequate intervention, and cases where the LA is bound to draw up a Statement.

Generally speaking, the Code seems to overemphasize the requirement of a school to provide detailed compliance documentation, and places insufficient emphasis to the child's interest. The law, however, lies clearly in the other direction. The statutory considerations in Sections 323 and 324 are based on the whole child R v Secretary of State for Education ex parte E (1992) FLR p 377.

The test as outlined by the Court of Appeal in that leading case is far simpler. As Balcombe in ex parte E pointed out, the real test is whether the school, with or without assistance on assessment from the LA, can provide from its own resources (which include the resources normally provided to the school through LA services) adequate intervention to deal with the child's needs. If so, no Statement is necessary. If, however, outside intervention over and above that which is normal is required, then a Statement is necessary. The current Code has made the test extremely complex, and to some degree ignores the guidance of the Courts on these issues.

In outlining considerations for a Statement, the Code accurately sets out the law. A Statement makes a diagnosis of the child's learning difficulties and the prescription to meet his or her needs. If the LA can provide what is needed together with the school within the normal resources, no Statement is necessary. If it cannot, then a Statement is necessary. Normally, of course, Statements are required, as the Code makes clear, for children with severe and complex learning difficulties, but a Statement can be required for a child solely with a severe learning difficulty or a complex learning difficulty.

Chapter 10 of the Code discusses partnership with other agencies and covers future progress. It is to be noted that the Connexions service brought in under the Learning Skills Act is an important development. The intention of this chapter is to make sure that for children with Statements there is smooth cooperation between other agencies, particularly for the more disabled child who will require continuous support, and for those who will require support well into further and higher education. To this extent, again the Code is a great improvement.

## Criteria for residential placement

The current Code provides clearer guidance which, overall, is of considerable assistance to parents who are seeking a residential school or a specialist independent school. Many of the schools in this guide provide for children with greater disabilities, and for such schools the changes in the Code of Practice that relate to these issues are extremely important. In essence, the Code takes the following approach:

1  If a child requires multi-professional intervention by Health, Social Services and the Education Authority, the Code requires that specific arrangements are put in place.

2  If a parent is seeking a residential placement, the Code states that if the child's needs cannot be met in local day provision, or the child requires a consistent programme both during and after school hours that cannot be provided by parents with support from other agencies, these are the main factors in considering a residential placement.

In practice this means that where it is accepted or established that a consistent programme of after school hours is needed (a waking day curriculum), where a local authority has not established the existence of combined provision from Social Services and Health, the parent is entitled to rely on these provisions of the Code. In particular, the Code provides at pages 104–05, paragraphs 8:44 to 8:48 that the Statement should set out the non-educational needs that the LA either proposes to meet or is satisfied will be met by arrangement or by other action with Health Services, Social Services or some other body. The provision should also be set out in the Statement, but can only be set out if the Local Authority is satisfied that it will be made available by either Social Services or Health or the LA proposes itself to make such provision available (paragraph 8:44).

When looking at the criteria, a parent who has care of their child where there is not joint funding for an independent placement with Health and/or Social Services should consider that the important questions are:

1  Is it established that the child has severe or multiple special educational needs that cannot be met in local day provision?

2  Is it established that the child has severe or multiple needs that require a consistent programme during the waking day, which cannot be provided by parents with support from other agencies?

First, the child's needs for a waking day curriculum must be established. In considering such cases, it is extremely important to examine the extent of Health support, Social Services support, its competence and consistency. Ultimately, these are issues for the Special Educational Needs and Disability Tribunal.

## Disability Discrimination Act 1995 – Code of Practice

The Code of Practice on disability discrimination is available from the Disability Rights Commission. It is to be read together with the Code of Practice Special Educational Needs. However, for the purposes of this book, the Disability Code of Practice has applied fully in education since September 2002. It is frankly of minor importance, because parents who are seeking a specialist placement will not normally wish to bring proceedings in disability discrimination. However, the Code is of some relevance, particularly if parents wish to establish a case for an alternative school, and that the current school is making an unlawful provision that is discriminatory for their child.

## The structure of the Code

The Code is divided into some 10 chapters, explaining the different aspects of disability discrimination.

Prior to the coming into force of the 2001 Act, disability discrimination was excluded from education. However, for parents, the provisions of the 1995 Act in relation to discrimination in relation to goods, facilities and services is probably the most relevant. Section 19 declares that it is unlawful for the provider of services to discriminate against a disabled person in the ways provided in the Section. For the purposes of the Act, a school/Local Authority or independent school is a provider of services, ie school holidays, outings, equipment, sports, etc.

A good example of a breach of the provisions of the Act is the case DRC/00/138: refusal of permission to go on school trips to a young person who suffered from diabetes. The young person, who was 15 years old, suffered from diabetes and had recently had a hypoglycaemic attack while away on a school trip. The school took the view that the attack was a result of his mismanagement of his diabetes. They banned him from future school trips merely as a result of one attack. The young person's paediatrician stated that she had never come across such poor treatment by a school of a diabetic pupil. The young person's lawyers argued that he had been treated unfairly, and had suffered detriment. The court awarded damages on the basis that the young person had been discriminated against on both counts, and made a declaration of discrimination and an award of damages under the Act. Damages were quite substantial, totalling £3,000 for the denial of a school trip.

## Disability discrimination in primary and secondary education

It is now unlawful for those responsible for a school, including an independent school, to discriminate against a disabled person:

1  in the arrangements it makes for determining an admission to the school as a pupil;

2  in the terms in which it offers to admit a child to the school as a pupil;

3  by refusing or deliberately omitting to accept an application of admission to the school as a pupil;

4  in the education or associated services provided or offered to pupils at school;

5  in exclusions.

The Disability Code of Practice states in summary that education or associated services cover all aspects of school life including:

1  preparation for entry into school;

2  the curriculum;

3  teaching and learning;

4  classroom and organization;

5  timetabling;

6  grouping of pupils;

7  homework;

8  access to school facilities;

9  activities to supplement the curriculum, eg a drama group;

10  school sport;

11  school policies;

12  breaks and lunchtimes;

13  the serving of school meals;

14  interaction with peers;

15  assessment of exam arrangements;

16  school discipline and sanctions;

17  school clubs and activities;

18  school trips;

19  the school's arrangements for working with other agencies;

20  preparation of pupils for the next phase of education.

The responsible body is in relation to a maintained school, the LA or the governing body. In relation to student referral units the LA is the responsible body, as it is in relation to nursery schools. In relation to independent schools, it is the proprietor. The definition of discrimination and the test of discrimination are complex and are not set out in detail in this work. A claim for damages can be made in relation to provision of services as set out above, but aside from further and higher education, the Act restricts the right to redress to certain statutory bodies. In relation to admissions, the body would normally be the admissions of appeal panel, and in relation to exclusions it would be the exclusions appeal panel set up by statute. As regards other acts of discrimination that are not concerned with the provision of services, the normal body to determine these issues is the Special Educational Needs and Disability Tribunal, which covers discrimination by all responsible educational bodies, with (as set out above) the exception of claims relating to admissions, or permanent exclusions which are dealt with by the relevant independent panels.

The Tribunal has a limited jurisdiction, but if it considers a claim is well founded, it may declare that a person has been unlawfully discriminated against, and if it does so it may make such an order as it considers reasonable in all the circumstances of the case. The power to make such orders is intended to be exercised with a view to obviating or reducing the adverse effects of the discrimination, rather than, as in failure to provide services, compensation by way of damages, which also applies in further and higher education. The Tribunal's jurisdiction, thus, is limited.

Overall, such claims will have a limited role in relation to parents reading this work and seeking a school that offers specialist education or specialist facilities.

# The Changing Legal Framework of SEN and Disability

John Friel, Barrister-at-law, Gray's Inn

In its publication about the newly proposed SEN and disability laws, the coalition government states that it is committed to improve services for vulnerable children and support families. It was with this reform in mind that a consultation Green Paper was published soon after the coalition took office. The Paper was a rather lengthy complex document and quite repetitive in parts, but a proposal for improvements was generally welcomed.

As a result of the Green Paper, the Government set up a number of pathfinder schemes, intended to tighten up the assessment process, with a view to making Health, Education and Children's Services more cohesive and parent friendly.

There were, however, a number of difficulties with the pathfinder schemes, not least that they were set up before any criteria were put in place to assess their outcome. The method of assessment was put in place much later, after the schemes started. In addition, it is fairly clear from evidence given to the Parliamentary Select Committee for Education, who reported on proposed changes in the legislation in December 2012, that the pathfinders did not really address the issue of Post-16/Post-19 up-to-25 education. That has, thankfully, now changed.

Following detailed representations about the Green Paper, many were unfortunately found to be, in fact, quite justifiably negative. The comments were later largely supported by the Parliamentary Select Committee for Education in its report of December 2012 and the Government proceeded to propose draft legislation issued in September 2012. This was before the end of the Path Finder Scheme – a somewhat strange decision. At the same time, the Minister responsible for children with special educational needs left the Government in September 2012, and was replaced by a new Minister for Children and Families, Mr Edward Timpson MP. Following his appointment in September 2012, the proposed changes in the system were sent to the Parliamentary Select Committee for what is called pre-legislative scrutiny.

One highly likely reason why the proposed legislation was sent to the Parliamentary Select Committee was that the September published Bill, for the first time ever, actually reduced the rights of parents of children with special educational needs and disabilities. A number of important parental rights and individual rights that related to ensuring that children's needs were assessed, that their statements were up to date and appropriate to their needs, and that the provision needed by an individual child was made available and was delivered, were set to be cut back by the original proposals of September 2012.

Not surprisingly, it appears that the new Minister, Mr Timpson, together with the Secretary of State, Mr Michael Gove, were aware of the strong criticism of these proposals. They were very probably aware that the original changes to help children with SEN in the law were introduced in the 1981 Education Act, under the first government of Baroness Thatcher. For those reasons it appears that matters were sent to the Parliamentary Select Committee on Education, whose report, December 2012, is both comprehensive and wholly justified in the criticisms made of the original proposed legislation.

There remain a number of serious concerns about the current proposed legislation. Although parents' rights have been restored, there still appears to be considerable defects in the current proposals. These proposals are now before Parliament, but not in the final form. The current proposals are:

1 A new system as proposed under the Children's School and Families Bill 2013, the proposed Act itself is not in force and remains subject to Parliamentary amendment and scrutiny.

2 Regulations to be made under the new Act when it comes into force, which are a matter of concern, because some parent and child rights are contained in regulation, and are no longer contained in statute, as they are in the 1996 Act.

3 A new Code of Practice on special educational needs is proposed. However it appears at the moment in draft form, to be seriously deficient.

4 There is a positive benefit in the sense that Post-16 to Post-19 education up-to-25, now falls into the system that includes an appeal system to the Special Educational Needs and Disability Tribunal. Previously once a child or young person post 16 or 19, left a school and went to a college, or went outside education for a temporary period, there were no rights at all to come back into the system, and the system that existed was both convoluted and unfair.

The general article produced on the 27th March, by the Children and Families Bill team in the Department of Education states that: '*The Government is transforming the system for children and young people with special educational needs (SEN) including those who are disabled, so that services consistently support the best outcomes for them*'. This is unfortunately somewhat of an overstatement. While it is true that the system will be changed, the proposed system is not transformed, it is very much the same, albeit extended.

Parents can still only appeal education issues, there are no appeal rights proposed currently against social services, which is extremely important for the most disabled children, and Health (appeals do exist against social services in Scotland and will very probably in Wales).

An introduction of personal budgets could be very helpful, but the draft Code of Practice is attempting to restrict their use, and it is not at all clear that a personal budget will actually purchase the services required.

The current information published by DFE claims:

*The bill will extend the SEN system from birth to 25, giving children, young people and their parents greater control and choice in decisions, and ensuring needs are properly met. It takes forward the reform programme set out in support and aspiration: a new approach to special educational needs and disability: progress and next steps including by:*

- *replacing old statements with new birth-to-25 education, health and care plan;*

- *offering families personal budgets; and*

- *improving co-operation between all the services that support children and their families, particularly requiring local authorities and health authorities to work together.*

## How in fact do these proposals affect processes or practical applications presently in existence?

| Statements/current position | New ECH plans/new proposals |
| --- | --- |
| Request for statutory assessment/6 weeks to decision | Request for EHC plans/6 weeks to decision |
| Legal test whether it is necessary | Legal test whether it is necessary |
| Advices/6 weeks: | Advices/6 weeks: |
| • child's parent | • child's parent |
| • education advice | • education advice |
| • medical advice | • medical advice |
| • psychological advice | • psychological advice |
| • social care | • social care |
| Any other advice LA considers appropriate including teacher of the deaf/teacher of the visually impaired | Any other advice LA considers appropriate including teacher of the deaf/teacher of the visually impaired |
| Statements | New EHC plan |

*The difference is the time for the parents' negotiation is removed completely and that a right to a note in lieu (of a statement – or EHC plan, as proposed) is also removed.*

| Statements/current position | New ECH plans/new proposals |
| --- | --- |
| If no statement, parent receives note in lieu | If no EHC plan parent receives nothing |
| After assessment/if statement proposed/ 8 weeks negotiation period with parent gives 15 days for an initial response | After assessment/if EHC plan is proposed/parent is giving 15 days for comments then finalization |
| Total 26 weeks from request | Total 20 weeks for request |

**The difference is the time for the parents' negotiation is removed completely and that a right to a note in lieu (of a statement – or EHC plan, as proposed) is also removed.**

## Rights of Appeal

Rights of appeal remain as they are currently, which include:

- A right to request a statutory assessment.

- An appeal against a refusal to conduct a statutory assessment.

- An appeal against a refusal following an assessment to make an EHC plan.

- Appeals against EHC plans.

- Appeals following annual reviews.

- Appeals against decisions to cease to maintain statements.

- Appeals against amendments.

- Overall, no specific changes. However, in relation to appeals following annual reviews, there is now no obligation which currently exists, to make a decision following an annual review. This would appear to be a reduction in parents' rights, rather than an increase, despite the Government's position that the system is improved.

A further complex new procedure to be brought in, is the introduction of mediation which is purely voluntary at the moment. If you do not want mediation, (*mediation in essence creates two appeals*), you have to apply for a certificate to say you do not wish it.

The current system does not provide for mediators to be formally trained, and does not offer a clear set of rules and guidance for this field. Moreover, a mediation now and in the future could well be conducted by former heads of local authority education departments or head teachers who work locally and is unlikely to be a system which brings in a great deal of trust. The system is also complicated because if you do not want mediation, and it is likely that many will not, the adviser must give a certificate within three days of being informed that mediation is not sought. This delays all appeals.

# What are the main changes?

1  New Education Health and Care Plans (EHCs). On the current proposals these plans are still only enforceable on education, and education is the only aspect that can be appealed against, hence no change.

2  It is therefore not legally a Health Education and Care Plan as there is no appeal against Health and Education, and they do not have the same legal obligation to deliver.

3  There is no single means of redress or appeal against the whole plan, only Education.

4  The EHC plan does go up to 25 years, but stops if the young person enters an apprenticeship or goes to university.

5  Personal budgets are introduced, and the regulation proposed does state that it should ensure the amount of direct payment under the personal budget must be sufficient to ensure the school full cost of the provision. However, you cannot appeal a personal budget on current proposals, and if in fact it cannot deliver there seems to be no mechanism for sorting matters out. Finally, the draft Code of Practice states: *'Personal budgets must not be used to fund a school place'*.

No doubt parents seeking an independent special needs school or independent school with specialist provision will bear this fact in mind. But whether the Code of Practice is actually giving appropriate legal advice to local authorities on this issue is doubtful. This will obstruct part funding agreements. However, the draft Code of Practice prevents the funding of part payment or payment for a school place using a personal budget.

## The local offer

One major change is the local offer. Parents should not be confused by statements being made by local authorities at the moment that this offer is a provision guarantee – it is not. It is being said therefore that EHC plans need not to be made in the individual child's case. The local offer is an explanation of the provision a local authority will offer in its local area, and it must include the following:

● Arrangements for requesting an EHC plan assessment.

● Arrangements for identifying and assessing a young person's needs.

● Details of educational provision.

● Details of training and apprenticeships.

● Details of Section 17 social care arrangements/children's services arrangements.

● Details of short breaks to include breaks for carers of the disabled.

Overall, as the local offer does make local authorities more accountable to the local parents and children in their area, and clearly is an attempt to show in local terms, what provision is actually available, to monitor it, and seek to have it improved by local action, this *is* a positive development.

### Changes which are adverse

1   The Code of Practice seems to abolish Individual Education Plans (IEPs), and there is no standard tracking system outlined in the Code of Practice: this may, however, change.

2   In relation to annual reviews, there are significant changes for the worse: they include:

  - No right to reports before an annual review which currently exists.

  - No right to a head teacher's report before an annual review, so parents have less information as a matter of course.

  - No time limit for a decision following an annual review.

  - No requirement to make a decision following the annual review which prevents parents exercising a right of appeal.

  - The proposed Code of Practice removes the definitions of adequate progress, both at primary and secondary level, which are superbly helpful when determining whether a child needs a statement or a statement needs amendment. The absence of a definition of adequate progress removes a baseline from which parents can argue, to show that the child has not made appropriate progress and needs are not being met.

3   The standard form of statements is abolished. EHC plans may then differ from local authority to local authority, in effect creating a postcode lottery.

## Transitional arrangements

For those with statements, there are no clear transitional arrangements. It is clear that once the legislation comes into force, there will be no further statutory assessments under the current system, and assessments will be for EHC plans. It is stated that there is consultation on the approach proposed. It is also quite clear from statements made by education officers, that it is thought simply because the law has changed they can refuse to honour statements (subject to the fact that there are some regressive changes, which are for the worse). In fact the law is not proposed to change significantly, as noted previously. The statutory test is the same, rights of appeal are the same. What has changed is that the attempt to change the system has in fact, as many suggested to the Parliamentary Select Committee, produced a system that is highly likely to be more complex.

# Children with Special Educational Needs – The Legal Implications

John Friel, Barrister-at-law, Gray's Inn

The Special Educational Needs and Disability Act 2001 has made some amendments to rights and duties in relation to children in this field. In particular, it brings into play the Disability Rights Commission and the provisions of the Disability Discrimination Act 1995 in education, when education has previously been exempt. .

There is a Code of Practice on disability discrimination in education, but in relation to the issues arising for parents reading this Guide disability discrimination issues will normally not be particularly relevant. The 2001 Act effectively:

- Strengthens the specific duty to educate in a mainstream school, if the child can be so educated, and if the parents so wish.

- Creates a needed mediation system, to which parents may have recourse when they are in dispute with a Local Authority over a Statement. However, the mediation system should not delay or deny an appeal.

- Brings in rights to raise disability discrimination issues in exclusion appeals. Parents who are paying fees for an independent school education may note that these schools are now subject, like state schools, to claims that they have discriminated against disabled children. While damages cannot be claimed, extensive changes may be required by the school to meet a disability discrimination claim.

- Brings the full weight of the Disability Discrimination Act into further and higher education, an area in which it is likely to have a long-term substantial effect.

## How do you enforce your rights?

Despite alterations to the law, and two new Codes of Practice, the principles as to how parents can obtain adequate assistance for their children remain unchanged. In some cases, the new Code of Practice may be of assistance, for example if a school is discriminating against particular disabilities by making no provision for them. Therefore the Code of Practice on Disability Discrimination should not be ignored and should be obtained. However, the chief concern for parents reading this Guide is clearly the enforcement of their child's rights.

For parents of children with more severe disabilities there will probably be no debate about whether or not a Statement is required. The issue in this case will be how the child's difficulties are to be addressed, and where he or she should be educated. For parents of children who have obviously severe and complex learning difficulties (but not profound and multiple handicaps), and who will go on, if assisted properly, to take a role in normal life, the situation will not be the same as for a severely disabled child. The school may, of course, identify the child's problem, but it may not. Thus the parent may be seeking a statutory assessment under s.323, or alternatively, having reached the point where everybody agrees a Statement is necessary, be seeking to argue that they require much more for their child than the LA is prepared to offer.

The principles upon which parents should prepare a case are exactly the same whether the issue concerns the necessity of a Statement or its content. However, the considerations and the level of preparation will be different if there is no Statement.

### Preparation of your case

Before a parent or an Education Authority can know whether there is a legal obligation to make provision (under the Education Act 1996, s.324) for a Statement of Special Educational Needs or even for a statutory assessment, the child's needs must first be assessed.

### Identification of children with special educational needs

The Code of Practice and the 1996 Act require a LA to exercise its powers with a view to securing or identifying that those children who have special educational needs and for whom it is necessary for the authority to determine the special educational provision required are so identified. If the authority forms the opinion that the child's special educational needs require, or probably require, a Statement, then they will conduct an assessment. The school itself can now request an assessment.

However, a major problem arises where the LA has failed to identify children with special educational needs. Many requests for Statements still come from parents. Thus where a parent requests statutory assessment, unless that parent has evidence that it is required, the LA will inevitably refuse. The terms of the new Code of Practice make it clear that the LA will be entitled to refuse unless the request is supported by substantial evidence.

The 2001 Act allows schools to request a statutory assessment as well as permitting LAs to conduct an assessment under s.323. Therefore it is likely to be more rather than less difficult for parents to obtain a statutory assessment and/or a Statement in circumstances where neither the LA nor the school has requested an assessment. Regrettably, this can only be done if the case is prepared properly by the parent.

## Preparing a request for an assessment

If possible, a parent who can afford independent advice should consider such advice essential. Where there is no support or little support by a school for a statutory assessment and evidence that the school has simply not fulfilled its role adequately, or where the LA requires clearly identified intervention by the school and there is none, parents will not be able to obtain a Statement or even a statutory assessment unless they are prepared to obtain adequate independent reports.

Unfortunately, for parents who have limited means, this is difficult. For those who are on Income Support, the legal help scheme (available from some specialist solicitors) provides a means whereby independent reports can be obtained. However, parents seeking such advice should ideally use specialist education solicitors because the Legal Services Commission has changed matters and procedure in legal aid cases. Legal aid is now only available from approved solicitors. For parents with very limited means (ie those on Income Support), this remains one route.

Another route for those with limited income is the National Health Service. A number of hospitals – for example the Munro Centre and Liverpool Alder Hey – have clinical/educational psychologists who can provide a detailed and appropriate report. There are also some charities that provide assessments or funds for them. An example is the Dyslexia Institute Bursary Fund, which will provide funds for an assessment. However, this and other charities do not generally provide such assessments for the purposes of seeking a statutory assessment but in order to establish a level of need. IPSEA (the Independent Panel of Special Needs Advisors) remains a valuable service.

On the assumption that adequate funds are available, reports must be obtained. It should be remembered that experts need to earn a living but are not, in comparison with other services today, generally expensive. Independent experts should be used.

Parents should also bear in mind that they are asking the LA to provide, in the form of a Statement, a potential substantial and valuable benefit. The cost of education at the state schools listed in this Guide or the independent schools with specialist help is considerable. All these schools provide a sophisticated, expensive and complex service to assist children with varying learning difficulties. Nobody would approach a claim where, for example, they had been run over in the street and suffered substantial damages, on the basis of amateur and inadequate preparation. Parents must take great care to prepare their child's case adequately.

Many children with special educational needs have conditions that require medical treatment or the supervision of doctors. In all such cases medical reports should be obtained. For those with physical difficulties and associated brain damage, that may include reports from a paediatrician, physiotherapist, occupational therapist and speech therapist. However, it should be borne in mind that increasingly NHS speech therapy reports do not advise on the child's level of need, but rather what is on offer from the Local Health Service. Because provision from Local Health Services varies nationally, the advice also varies in quality. In some cases it is excellent; in others the authority may only say what will be made available, not what is needed.

The legal duty of the Local Authority is to provide for the special educational needs of the child. Thus what is on offer from the Health Service is not necessarily what a Local Authority is obliged to provide. In cases of Statements of Special Educational Needs, the law requires the LA to pay for a provision irrespective of resources. If provision is not locally available, the LA must pay for the provision to be made from elsewhere: see East Sussex County Council *ex parte* T (1998) Education Law Reports p 198. The House of Lords differentiated the duties in education from duties in social services.

The Courts have strengthened parents' rights in this field. A Statement must have a diagnosis of and a prescription of the child's special educational needs: see R *v* Secretary of State for Education *ex parte* E (1992) Family Law Reports p 377. Further Statements must be specific so that provision in a Statement is ascertainable, identifiable and quantified. Although the Code of Practice and the Regulations make this point quite clearly, the major failing by LAs is to so identify the provision. In L *v* Clarke & Somerset (1998) Education Law Reports p 128 and Bromley *v* The SENT (1999) Education Law Reports p 260 CA, both the High Court and the Court of Appeal confirmed that Statements must be detailed, quantified and specific.

This is an important consideration in dealing with a child's learning difficulties. Parents will need to seek evidence – both at the assessment stage and at the statementing stage – that the intervention is detailed, sufficiently quantified, and sufficiently specific to ameliorate the child's learning difficulties. Evidence that such intervention is not available provides grounds for a case for a statutory assessment and means that it should succeed, irrespective of the vagueness of the Code of Practice on this issue. It should also establish a case for the parent on an appeal against a Statement.

Thus the expert must address the following questions:

- What are the child's needs in the area of expertise required? For example, an educational psychologist will need to comment on requirements for specialist reports, eg from speech therapists, occupational therapists, etc.

- What is the provision required to meet the needs?

- What provision is available at the local school?

- What provision is required for the child? If this is an assessment case, is this likely to be available in the local school or LA?

- What provision does the expert advise?

As far as occupational therapists, physiotherapists, speech therapists, paediatricians and other specialists are concerned, the same questions arise within their area of expertise. In cases of autistic children or children with emotional and behavioural problems or mental health problems, a report from a consultant child psychiatrist or child and adolescent psychiatrist can be essential. Regrettably, there are few good experts available nationally. However, in cases where such a skill is involved, attention should be given to such reports.

## Involvement of the child and the role of Social Services and educational welfare services

The Code of Practice now requires the views of the child to be sought. While this is a good and appropriate development, it can lead to difficulties. Parents may be understandably overanxious. At the same time there is a risk that schools and LAs may put pressure on children to make statements in support of the institution.

Where children are capable of expressing their views – and some children may not be able to do so – use of the guidance given in the Children Act for the interviewing of young people by the LA is essential. This guidance is to ensure that children are not over-influenced by the interviewer, or pressurized into saying things with which they do not agree. Recent experience has shown that attempts have been made both by parents and by local authorities to influence children in expressing their views. Children with special educational needs are generally vulnerable and may well be unduly subject to pressure.

Unfortunately, Social Services intervention is often notable by its absence. Children with considerable learning difficulties who are likely to be disabled for life or for a substantial period often have no Social Services care plan or intervention in place for them. Section 17 of the Children Act provides a general power to assess children who are in need. Assessment provisions of the Act normally require that children should be assessed at the same time as a Statement of Special Educational Needs is put into place or a statutory assessment takes place.

In London Borough of Bromley v The SENT (1999) Education Law Reports p 260 the Court of Appeal emphasizes that there is no border between Social Services needs, medical needs and educational needs that are clear and defined. Children who require a waking day curriculum or a 24-hour curriculum may be as much in need of a whole multi-professional approach (educational, medical and practical) as they are in need of education. Less able children will develop independence skills and communication skills but may never be fully independent or fully able to communicate, and thus the working day curriculum is educational.

If available, reports should be sought from Social Services. In more complex cases involving children with severe and complex difficulties, an independent social worker's report may be required if the Social Services reports are inadequate or if there has been no Social Services intervention.

## What is a Statement?

A Statement is a document that clearly defines a child's educational needs and the intervention to meet those needs. It must be specific, quantified and effective. Case law in this area has been considered above.

### The process of assessment

The process of assessment is governed by Regulation. The LA should normally seek:

- educational advice;
- advice from an educational psychologist;
- advice from Social Services;
- medical advice;
- advice from any specialist services providing assistance to the child.

The Act creates a definite timetable that is often dishonoured. The Code of Practice time-table is set out at the end of this section and is laid out clearly in the current Regulations and in the Code of Practice. The Education (Special Educational Needs) England Consolidation Regulations 2001 SI 3455 clearly state the time limits. Once a Local Authority has completed an assessment it is under obligation to serve a draft Statement. The parent then has the right to require meetings and representations. It is at this time, once a Statement has been finalized, that mediation should be considered. The time limits for an appeal to the Tribunal are extremely strict. Appeals should be made within two months of the date of service of the final Statement, and it is only in exceptional circumstances that a Tribunal can extend the time.

The structure of the Act requires the parent to prepare the case in advance. If the parent is seeking to catch up, difficulties will ensue.

## Experts

A major difficulty of seeking expert advice is that even though there are a large number of psychologists available for private consultation, few are prepared to assist in special educational needs appeal cases. Some who offer their services in these instances do not have the forensic skills to do so. Parents seeking to put forward a case in support of an application for a place at one of the schools in this Guide are well advised to seek expert legal guidance. If that is not available to them, advice from charities that have good working knowledge of complex difficulties should be sought. For example, the British Dyslexia Association provides an advisory and representation service, as does the National Autistic Society. Parents should appreciate that these are complex, difficult and sophisticated cases which normally require expert preparation and support.

Experience suggests that the documents from the Special Educational Needs Tribunal indicating that parents can easily prepare a case and can represent themselves are unrealistic. Children who require a Statement will normally have complex difficulties. Although it is possible for parents to prepare cases properly, experience has shown that the task is often substantially underestimated. Many appeals to the High Court have arisen where parents were unrepresented, and for that reason the Tribunal has not been able to address key issues in their case and consequently has made quite substantial mistakes. The Tribunal system is obviously designed to hear very complex cases and decide them quickly. It does so without great cost in comparison to normal cases of this complexity and importance. However, because the documentation of the Tribunal attempts to help parents – and ensure that cases are decided quickly and efficiently in the child's interest – it disguises the basic complexity of many cases. Some cases will be simple, but a parent reading this publication would require expensive specialist provision. Cases of this nature are not easy, and few parents have been able to come away from a Tribunal feeling that they have handled cases on their own adequately. A number have complained after the hearing that the Tribunal publications on this issue are misleading and that they did not understand the difficulty and complexity of cases. For the reader of this Guide cases should be presented either with legal assistance, or at least with assistance from one of the major charities that provide representation of an experienced and competent nature.

A surprising number of appeals to the High Court are settled, resulting in a rehearing. If argued, they have usually resulted in a remission to the Special Educational Needs Tribunal. The overall experience indicates that parents are better at preparing cases like this with professional legal advice and with adequate reports than they are attempting to prepare without such guidance. The Tribunal carries out good work, in difficult circumstances, to the best of its ability.

## The Code of Practice timetable

The LA must decide whether or not to make a statutory assessment within six weeks of the date that the request was lodged. The LA then has 10 weeks to undertake the statutory assessment process. The decision about whether or not to make a Statement must be finalized within two weeks of completing the statutory assessment, allowing eight weeks to gather information, seek professional advice and make a decision. The LA then has a further two weeks to notify the parents of its decision and to make a proposed Statement if appropriate. Otherwise a note in lieu, explaining why the Statement was refused, must be provided. A final Statement must be agreed within eight weeks of the issue of the proposed Statement.

## Enforcing your rights – the SEN Tribunal

The 1996 Education Act, as amended by the 2001 Act, provides parents with a right of appeal to the Special Educational Needs and Disability Tribunal. Most relevant to the present Act are the appeal rights as follows:

1  It provides the parents with an appeal against a refusal to make a statutory assessment.

2  It provides the parents with a right of appeal where the authority has conducted an assessment and has either refused to make a Statement, or has refused to amend a Statement. The powers of the Tribunal when a Statement has been refused are different from the powers when a Statement is amended or when one

is refused following assessment. In one case the Tribunal can order a Statement to be made or reconsidered, in the other they can order the Statement to be amended.

3  Appeal against the contents of the Statement, including the school.

4  In certain limited circumstances, an appeal providing a right to change the name of the school contained in the Statement so long as the parent wishes to change the name to another state-operated school of whatever type.

5  If a parent claims disability discrimination against a school, but not damages.

Although there are a number of charities that assist parents with the preparation of a case, such as the British Dyslexia Association, and IPSEA, in general, because of the financial costs of independent specialist education, or even of specialist state education, parents are advised to seek specialist legal advice in this field if possible. If they cannot access such advice, then they should obtain at least specialist help and assistance from one of the recognized charities. While a Tribunal does its best to assist unrepresented parents, the major criticism from unrepresented parents and indeed from a number of charitable representatives, is that the Tribunal is not listening sufficiently to the lay person. From my personal experience, normally Tribunals do their best to ensure fair play. But handling difficult cases, for children with special educational needs, many of whom have severe difficulties, is a very onerous task, the more so if you present a case for your own child. Generally, the view is that the parents are assisted by representation, if possible legal representation, and that a specialist can assist preparation of the case greatly. Equally, parents will be advised if their hopes are unrealistic. I do not intend in this chapter to promote the interest of lawyers, but it is necessary to point out that a constant feeling of parents who have appeared on their own in Tribunals is how difficult presenting the case has been.

I would, however, comment that the Tribunal's own material suggests to parents that the procedure is relatively easy, parent friendly and not over-legalistic. This description is certainly considered by most to be over-optimistic, though well intentioned. There is no doubt that taking a case to a Tribunal involves a difficult personal decision as well as a great deal of time, effort and work.

# Disability Discrimination and Education – The Equality Act

John Friel, Barrister-at-law, Gray's Inn

The Equality Act 2010 protects pupils and prospective pupils from various forms of disability discrimination. The new Act consolidates and in some respects modifies and extends previous legislation based on the Disability Discrimination Act 1995. Whilst there are some significant differences between the two Acts, the general thrust is essentially the same. Thus previous case law and statutory definitions remain appropriate in many cases.

At the outset of a discussion of how the equality act protects pupils with special needs and disabilities from discrimination it is useful to consider the definition and meaning of SEN and disability.

## Definition of disability

The 2010 Act requires much more than formal equality of treatment for pupils in the context of disability and SEN. As Lady Hale put it:

> The 1995 Act... [and this now is the same for the 2010 Act] does not regard the differences between disabled peoples and others as irrelevant. It does not expect each to be treated in the same way. It expects reasonable adjustments to be made to cater for the special needs of disabled persons. It necessarily entails an element of favourable treatment.
>
> *Source: Archibald v Fife Council 2004 ICR Page 954 at paragraph 47*

It is important to remember that disability is not necessarily the same as having a Special Educational Need (SEN), which requires a Statement or an Education Health and Care Plan (EHCP) as outlined in the current proposed legislation. Though the two will often match, they operate independently. If the new EHCPs are less frequently provided than Statements, there is little doubt that disability discrimination, under the Equality Act, will become a major tool for parents in enforcing their rights in dealings with maintained and independent schools.

## Meaning of disability

Whether a person does or does not have a disability is a crucial issue to determine. In order to qualify as disabled in accordance with the Act there are four essential elements that must be present:

1   The individual must have a physical or mental impairment.

2   The impairment must have an effect on his or her ability to carry out normal day-to-day activities.

3   The effect must be adverse and substantial.

4   The effect must be long term.

To be considered a disability all four criteria must be met. There are certain conditions that are deemed to meet all of these criteria and therefore require no debate such as HIV, multiple sclerosis and severe disfigurements. Other disabilities such as ASD or Dyslexia must be proved. However, generally speaking, most pupils with Special Educational Needs will be defined as disabled under the Act.

For the purposes of determining a disability, current guidance issued suggests that the normal day-to-day activities affected are to be considered in general things people do on a regular basis, ie shopping, reading, writing, having a conversation on the telephone, and similar activities.

## The scope of the Act in education

The scope of the Act means that it is unlawful for a school's governing body, whether independent or maintained, to discriminate against or victimize a disabled pupil in 5 broad areas:

● Admissions, whether in the arrangements for determining admissions, the terms of admission or a refusal to admit.

● The provision of education.

● The provision of access to a benefit facility or service.

- Exclusions.

- Subjecting the pupil to any other detriment.

This clearly covers a very broad range of activity encompassing all aspects of school life including the curriculum, timetable, access to school facilities, school sports, assessment and examination arrangements, discipline and sanctions, and work experience.

The responsible body of the school will be liable for acts of discrimination committed by its employees in the course of their employment or by its agents acting with its authority, unless it has done all it can to prevent such acts. Those individuals may also be individually liable.

## Forms of discrimination

Under the 2010 Act there are now no fewer than six forms of prohibited conduct. They are:

1 Direct discrimination when a pupil is treated less favourably because of a disability. It can include the less favourable treatment of a pupil because of another person's disability (associative discrimination).

For example, if a pupil is treated detrimentally because they have ASD – eg being denied a part in the school play because it is assumed they wouldn't be able to take part because of their disability.

Associative discrimination is when less favourable treatment is meted out to a person because of another person's disability, rather than because of his/her own. It is concerned with a person being treated less favourably because of 'a protected characteristic', rather than because of 'his disability'. Thus, for example, it would be unlawful to treat a pupil less favourably because his mother had a disability.

2 Discrimination arising from the disability when a pupil is unjustifiably treated unfavourably for a reason connected with disability. Here, lack of knowledge of a disability is a defence as the example below shows.

A key difference between this form of discrimination and direct discrimination is the availability of a justification defence. Take the example of a school that refused to permit a child with Tourette's Syndrome to attend a school trip at a museum for fear that the child would disrupt other visitors to the museum. If this was based on stereotypical assumptions about Tourette's, this might amount to direct discrimination and could not be justified as a matter of law. However, if there was clear evidence that the child with Tourette's did in fact often shout abusive language in public places, and the school would also have prohibited any other child who was liable to utter abuse, this would tend to indicate that it was (*prima facie*) discrimination arising from disability; the school might accordingly be able to justify its decision. However, the scope of justification is much more proscribed than it was under the 1995 Act. Any tribunal would need to decide for itself whether the treatment was a proportionate means of achieving a legitimate aim.

3 Indirect discrimination when a general and ostensibly neutral policy unjustifiably discriminates against a disabled person, placing them at a particular disadvantage when compared to others.

An example of indirect discrimination may be a uniform policy. The same policy applies to everyone, but there are various ways in which this might disadvantage pupils with certain disabilities. For instance, if the required uniform is available only in synthetic material, this may exacerbate eczema.

4 Failure to make reasonable adjustments, which occurs when a provision criterion or practice places disabled persons at a substantial disadvantage when compared with others, and the responsible body fails to take reasonable steps to remove the disadvantage. The duty to make reasonable adjustments does not, in the schools context, in any way extend to physical features. The 2010 Act extends to the provision of auxiliary aids and services and this provision is now in force as of September 2012 (see the separate information in this chapter on auxiliary aids).

Section 20 of the 2010 Act sets out in broad terms the duty to make reasonable adjustments. This may be a most important duty for parents as reasonable adjustments are often required to allow pupils with SENs and disabilities an equal opportunity at school. For example, additional time in examinations may be required for a pupil with dyslexia.

Factors to be taken into account, when deciding what are reasonable adjustments for a school to make would include:

- The extent to which support will be provided to a disabled pupil under a Statement of Special Educational Needs.
- The resources of the school and the availability of financial or other assistance.
- The financial and other costs of making the adjustment.
- The extent to which a particular step would be effective in overcoming the substantial disadvantage suffered by the disabled pupil.
- The practicality of the adjustment.
- The effect of the disability on the individual.
- Health and safety requirements.
- The need to maintain academic, musical, sporting and other standards.
- The interest of pupils and other prospective pupils.

5 Harassment is another form of discrimination, which occurs when unwanted conduct related to a disability violates a person's dignity or creates an intimidating, hostile, degrading, humiliating or offensive environment for him or her.

**6** Victimization is discrimination, which occurs when a person is subjected to detriment because he has done or has believed to have done something which is protected by the act. These can be things such as bringing proceedings under the Act or making a complaint.

## Enforcements

Claims for disability discrimination against schools, whether in the independent sector or the maintained sector are to be enforced in the First-tier Tribunal (formerly the Special Educational Needs and Disability Tribunal). Claims must be bought within six months of the decision or act complained of. However the Tribunal has a general power to extend time, if the application notice is late, and a request for an extension of time can be made. The First-Tier Tribunal may make any order it thinks reasonable, except the payment of financial compensation.

Claims against Local Authorities that retain a general jurisdiction should be made in the County Court – which now falls within the scope of Part 3 of the 2010 Act – which covers all public functions and is not a claim before the First-Tier Tribunal.

## Auxiliary aids etc

Auxiliary aids and resources are now specific issue for both maintained schools and independent schools. The new duty is contained in Section 20 (5) of the Equality Act which states:

> A requirement, where a disabled person, would but for the provision of an auxiliary aid, be put at a substantial disadvantage in relation to a relevant matter in comparison with persons who are not disabled, to take such steps as it was reasonable to have to provide the auxiliary aid.

Auxiliary aids are special pieces of equipment that improve accessibility such as a special chair, adaptive text, or a special computer or software, and auxiliary services are services to improve access often involving the provision of a helper/assistant or possibly therapy. This requirement came into force from 1 September 2012.

The duty is subject to cost and practicality considerations. But in some cases no charge can be made. As mentioned previously, there are disabled persons who do not have Special Educational Needs or a Statement. This is important because schools are not funded for this duty. They are normally funded for Statements for Special Educational Needs.

Parents of children with SEN may therefore be able to use this duty as a lever to persuade a school to give more help, particularly where the child does not have a Statement or as a method of requesting a Statutory Assessment instituted by the school. In addition for a child with a vague Statement, this could act as a lever to persuade the school to recommend changes to the Statement at Annual Review. If the school does not cooperate, parents can request the provision of an auxiliary aid or service; if it is reasonable to supply it, it has to be supplied whether in the independent sector or the maintained sector at no cost.

The test is whether the child will be placed at a substantial disadvantage compared with other people who are not disabled. It must be borne in mind that one-off decisions and one-off actions are also caught by the act. For example, if a school has a practice of designating parking places for senior members of staff or for members of staff, this may have to extend to covering parents of pupils with special educational needs who have mobility and safety problems.

The requirement involves making the changes to overcome barriers created by physical features and the environment. For example, glass doors at the end of a corridor might present a hazard for a visually impaired child. Putting signs or indicators on the door so they are much more visible is likely to be a reasonable adjustment.

A third example is providing extra equipment or assistance. While in the past these have been paid for under a statement by Local Authorities who included some aids and services, in their Statements schools may potentially have to provide aids and services from their delegated funds if parents show it is reasonable to do so.

Independent schools are not immune from these new duties and they will need to make provision from the schools budget for auxiliary aids and services. These will include a number of things, most commonly teaching assistant support. The act also makes it unlawful to require any payment or make any charge for making a 'reasonable adjustment in any circumstances'.

## Implications of the Equality Act / duties

For a parent seeking a school, the implications of the Equality Act duties apply chiefly at two stages prior to – and after – admission:

### Prior to admission

Admission policies need to make reasonable adjustments for a disabled child and the mere fact a child is disabled or has a SEN that amounts to disability, and will require specific arrangements and adjustments which can be made is no reason to refuse admission.

It would be advisable for any school to spell out quite clearly what they can offer on their website or prospectus. Parents will need to know in sufficient detail at the outset what is an additional support for which there is a charge and what is the support, contained in the ordinary fees. At this stage, a charge obviously can be made for extra provision.

It is highly advisable that both parents and school meet to discuss in some detail the admission of a pupil with a disability or SEN.

## After admission

Schools will have to consider the definition of disability very carefully, particularly when a child's needs emerge after a placement at the school. Simply telling parents that they cannot meet needs or attempting to exclude a child for these reasons or indeed for reasons associated with a disability, simply will not work under the Equality Act.

So far as parents are concerned, there are obviously issues arising from the discovery of a Special Educational Need, as to whether a school can, within the terms of the Equality Act duty, then charge for an auxiliary aid or service. As already indicated, the answer to this and other questions will be determined on a case-by-case basis. Unfortunately one has to say, when such issues arise, parents would be well advised to seek considered legal advice.

# A Parents' Guide to Admissions Procedures for Children with Special Educational Needs

Veale Wasbrough Vizards

For all parents, getting their child into their first choice of school can seem complicated and challenging. For parents of children with special educational needs (SEN) it can be even more so. This article examines procedures for children who have Statements of SEN and for those with SEN, but no Statement, who are seeking admission to maintained schools, special schools or independent schools.

Special educational needs provision is not, as many people believe, a matter just for special schools. It should be possible for the needs of most children with SEN to be met in ordinary ('mainstream') schools. It might be assumed that the term 'mainstream school' refers to any school that is not a special school. In fact the Education Act 1996 defines a mainstream school as any school that is not a special school or an independent school. City Technology Colleges, City Colleges for the Technology of the Arts, and Academies are classified as independent schools but all count as mainstream schools for these purposes, as do Pupil Referral Units.

Ever since the Warnock Committee Report in 1978, one of the main principles of SEN policy is that children with special educational needs should be educated in mainstream schools whenever possible. This is reinforced by legislation and the SEN Code of Practice.

## The law regarding admissions

Under the School Standards and Framework Act 1998, Local Authorities (LAs) must make arrangements to allow parents: a) to express a preference as to the maintained school,

City Technology College or Academy, at which they wish education be provided for their child; and b) to give reasons for this preference. The LA also has a duty to provide advice and assistance to parents to help with this process. Under the 2012 School Admissions Code, LAs must put in place a scheme to coordinate all admissions (except in year admissions from the admissions year 2013/14 and subsequently). However, this does not apply to nursery schools or special schools. The Admission Authority of the school must comply with the parental preference, subject to certain conditions (see below). The admissions procedures for children with Statements are different. So how does the law on admissions procedures affect children with SEN? This is dependent on whether or not the child has a Statement of Special Educational Needs and on the representations the parents make as to where their child should be educated.

## SEN – children without a Statement of Special Educational Needs

In the maintained sector, children who have SEN but do not have a Statement must be educated in mainstream schools, except in very specific circumstances as outlined below. The School Admissions Code 2012 states that pupils with SEN but without Statements must be treated in at least the same way as all other applicants, but protocols must include arrangements for ensuring that, where there is prior need for particular support or reasonable adjustments, such children are placed quickly. The admission authority must consider all such applications on the basis of the school's published admission criteria as part of the normal admissions procedures. In fact, many LAs and schools give priority to children with SEN in their admission oversubscription criteria.

Despite the clear direction for children with SEN to be educated in mainstream schools, there may be a small number of exceptional cases where a child has SEN but does not have a Statement, where it is more appropriate for the child to attend a special school. These exceptional circumstances are set out in section 316A(2) of the Education Act 1996 and include situations where an assessment for a Statement is taking place or where a child is a hospital patient and is admitted to a hospital school, which is classed as a special school.

## SEN – children with a Statement of Special Educational Needs

Again, in the maintained sector, if a child who would normally attend school has a Statement, that child must be educated in a mainstream school unless: a) this is contrary to the wishes of the parents; or b) it is incompatible with the provision of efficient education for other children, or is an inefficient use of resources. These are the only reasons why the LA can refuse to arrange mainstream education. The LA needs to take reasonable steps to prevent 'incompatibility' in a particular school or across its mainstream schools. Efficient education means providing for each child a suitable and appropriate education in terms of a child's age, ability, aptitude and any SEN that he or she may have.

Cases must be considered on their individual merits. For example, if a child's needs are such that they pose a threat to the safety of other children or if the education of other children is seriously affected, this would be incompatible with the efficient education of other children but only if there are no reasonable steps that could be taken to overcome the incompatibility. The term 'other children' means children with whom the child with the Statement would be likely to come into contact on a regular day-to-day basis, such as the child's class if in primary school or the tutor group and subject classes if in secondary school. 'Other children' does not mean children in other schools or pupils who will only occasionally come into contact with the child.

OFSTED monitors how admission authorities operate their procedures in relation to children with SEN, and the Secretary of State can act if it is believed that the maintained school or the LA is acting unreasonably by refusing to admit children with SEN. Reasonable steps might include one-to-one support, counselling, special equipment or occasional sessions in a special needs unit. Whether one of these steps is 'reasonable' will depend on a number of factors including cost and practicality. With regard to school numbers, maintained schools named on a Statement cannot refuse to take a child because the school is full. However, before naming a school, the LA should consider whether the school is already nominally full. Admitting children over the planned number may be incompatible with the provision of efficient education or the efficient use of resources.

LAs also have to ensure that they comply with the legislation on infant class sizes. The School Standard and Framework Act 1998 imposes a limit of 30 pupils per infant class. Children with a Statement that specifies a school and who are admitted outside the normal admission round (that is, for example, in the middle of a term or at the start of the Summer term), do not have to be counted as part of this maximum limit. Also, pupils who are registered at a special school or who are usually educated in a special unit but come into the mainstream school for certain classes are not to be counted for these purposes.

## Expressing a preference

Parents of a child with a Statement have the right to express a preference as to where their child is educated and to give reasons for their preference. This preference will affect the duties on the LA when naming a school in the child's Statement.

## Mainstream provision

### 1. Expressing a preference for a maintained mainstream school

If the parents of a child with a Statement express a preference for a maintained school, the LA has a duty to name the parents' preferred school unless: a) the school is unsuitable to the child's age, ability or aptitude or to his or her special educational needs; or b) the attendance of the child at the school would be incompatible with the provision of efficient education for the children with whom the child would be educated, or the efficient use of resources. LAs must explain to parents the arrangements that allow them to express their preference. Before naming a maintained school in a child's Statement, the LA must consult the school and send it a copy of the draft Statement together with all the appendices that go to inform the Statement. If the school is outside the LA area, then the LA must also consult the LA responsible for the school. Consultation does not mean that either the school or the other LA has a veto. If a maintained school is named in a child's Statement, the school must admit the child. It is the LA where the child resides that is the admissions authority in these circumstances.

*2. Parents may also express a preference for an Academy*

Before naming an Academy in a child's Statement, the LA has to consult the Academy concerned. The Academy's funding agreement with the Secretary of State will usually provide for the Academy to consent to being named in a Statement except where admitting the child would be incompatible with the provision of efficient education for other children and where no reasonable steps may be made to secure compatibility. Where there is a disagreement between an Academy and the LA over the proposal to name an Academy in a Statement, the matter can be referred to the Secretary of State who can direct the Academy to admit the child.

*3. When parents do not express a preference for an individual mainstream school*

Where parents request mainstream education for their child but do not express a preference for a particular school, the LA must decide which mainstream school should be named in the Statement. All the mainstream schools in that area will be reviewed. Mainstream education can be refused in only a small number of cases by using the efficient education ground as set out above.

**Non-mainstream provision**

Where a child has a Statement and the child's parents do not want him or her to go to a mainstream school, the duty of the LA to provide a place in a mainstream school does not apply, although the LA still has the option to name a mainstream school in the child's Statement. The parents can appeal against such a decision to the First-tier Tribunal (Health, Education and Social Care (SEND Tribunal)). There should be strong and clear reasons for going against the parents' wishes.

*1. Where parents express a preference for a maintained special school*

The LA must name the parents' preferred choice of maintained special school in the child's Statement unless the school is unsuitable or the child's inclusion would be incompatible with efficient education (see above).

   The LA must consult the school before naming it in a Statement, including sending the school a copy of the draft Statement. Where a maintained special school is named in a child's Statement, the school must admit the child. Where the LA does not name the parents' preferred choice of special school in the Statement, the LA must consider the request for special school education in the light of the general duty set out in Section 9 of the Education Act 1996 (see above).

*2. Where parents make representations for an independent or non-maintained school*

Parents are able to make representations for an independent school or a non-maintained special school to be named in their child's Statement. However, this is not the same as being able to express a preference as there is no implied duty on the LA to name the school requested. The LA must consider such a request in the light of Section 9 of the Education Act 1996. This sets out the general principle, now reinforced by the Human Rights Act 1998, that pupils must be educated in accordance with their parents' wishes so far as this is compatible with; a) the provision of efficient instruction and training; or

b) the avoidance of unreasonable public expenditure. It is unusual for the LA to agree, as costs will usually be high. The LA must be satisfied that the child's interests require education at a non-maintained school and that education at the particular school is appropriate. When an LA names an independent or non-maintained special school in a child's Statement, it must pay all the fees. If the LA does not agree to name the independent or non-maintained special school in the child's Statement, it must name another school, mainstream or special, and the parents have the right of appeal to the SEND Tribunal.

Parents who have children with a Statement of SEN have the right to educate their child, at their own expense, at an independent school or non-maintained special school if they so choose and it is agreed with the school. Even if the parents are paying for their child to be educated at an independent school, the LA still has a duty to make and maintain the Statement and review it on an annual basis, and ensure that the child is receiving efficient SEN provision.

Parents should look to the individual non-maintained school's admission policy for details of that school's admissions criteria. Under the Education (Independent Schools Standards) (England) Regulations 2010 as amended, it is mandatory for independent schools to have an admissions policy, which should include a section on equal treatment and must be compliant with the Equality Act 2010.

*3. Where parents do not express a preference for an individual special school*
If parents tell the LA that they do not want their child to be educated in mainstream provision but do not indicate a preferred choice of school, the LA must decide which school should be named in the child's Statement.

## Parents' right of appeal

Under the 1996 Education Act, parents have the right of appeal to the SEND Tribunal if they disagree with the school named in Part 4 of their child's Statement or with Part 2 describing the child's SEN and Part 3 stating the special educational provision that the LA thinks the child should receive. For children with SEN but no Statement, the usual admissions appeals procedures for maintained schools apply as set out in the School Admissions Appeals Code.

Where the LA refuses the parent's request to name an Academy in the Statement, the parent can appeal to the SEND Tribunal. The Academy is bound by the decision of the Tribunal in accordance with the provision in its Funding Agreement. If the Tribunal does name an Academy, the Secretary of State expects the child to be admitted and is likely to issue a direction to that effect if the Academy is still reluctant to agree. If an independent school refuses admission to a child with SEN, there is no access to an Independent Appeal Panel as in the maintained sector. However, it may be possible to make a claim for disability discrimination to the SEND Tribunal. If discrimination is found, the Tribunal has the power to order the school to admit the child. Very few cases have been brought so far. Other sections in this Guide provide more details of the process for appeal to the SEND Tribunal.

## *Sources*

School Admissions Code 2012.

DCSF SEN Code of Practice, DfES/0581/2001.

DCSF SEN Toolkit, DfES/0558/2001.

Inclusive Schooling – Children with SEN, DfES/0774/2001.

Removing Barriers to Achievement, DfES/0117/2004.

## *Legislation*

Education Act 1996.

Schools Standards and Framework Act 1998.

Equality Act 2010.

Education (Independent School Standards) (England) Regulations 2010 as amended.

Education and Skills Act 2008.

The Schools Admissions (Admissions Arrangements and Co-ordination of Admission Arrangements) (England) Regulations 2012.

The Schools Admissions (Appeals Arrangements) (England) Regulations 2012.

The Schools Admissions (Infant Class Sizes) (England) Regulations 2012.

# Independent Schools and Special Educational Needs

Veale Wasbrough Vizards

Most children with special educational needs (SEN) are educated in 'mainstream' state or independent schools, alongside children without special needs.

Section 146 of the Education and Skills Act 2008 (in force as of 1 September 2009) has removed the need for an independent school to obtain the approval of the Secretary of State before it can admit a child who has a Statement of Special Educational Needs. Schools admitting a child without a Statement are still required by general law to detect when a child has learning difficulties and deal with them appropriately.

Unlike a state school where legal relationships are regulated by public law, the legal relationships in the independent sector are governed by a private contract between the school and the parents. This is known as the 'parent contract'. Good examples of these contracts will include a form that seeks full information (in confidence) from parents about:

- any learning difficulty, disability, medical condition or allergy affecting the child;
- any learning difficulty affecting other members of the family, since certain conditions are often inherited.

Parents are encouraged to provide the school with as much information as possible, whether or not the forms ask about these matters, and to have confidence that the information will be used constructively to ensure the child receives the right support and can integrate successfully. Conversely, to withhold information or play down the extent of a child's needs can undermine the essential working relationship between parents and school.

The admission process to an independent school will vary according to whether a school is more or less academically selective. Most independent schools set entry tests, and a school that is oversubscribed will often use the test results to produce a rank order for interviews. The law now requires a school to make reasonable adjustments to its admission procedures to ensure that a child with SEN or a disability is not disadvantaged during the admissions process. Therefore, parents applying for a place should let the school know in good time if their child will need special arrangements, such as wheel-chair access to the examination room, large-print or Braille test papers, quick access to a toilet or extra time to complete the test. An application of this kind should be backed up by written evidence, such as the report of an educational psychologist sent in advance in good time. The twin themes of 'full information' and 'as much notice as possible' run throughout this Guide and apply most of all to the admissions process.

Both state and independent schools have the same responsibility to recognize when a child may have a learning difficulty or disability (SEN) and to refer the child or provide appropriately for the difficulty. Methods may differ between the sectors:

- A state school is expected to follow each stage of the SEN Code of Practice and to meet the requirements of a Statement of SEN where one is issued by the LA.

- An independent school will normally carry out screening tests and then consult with parents if there are indications that a further assessment is needed. The assessment may be carried out by the school's SEN Coordinator (SENCo), or the child may be referred to an educational psychologist.

- The LA remains responsible for making and maintaining the Statement and ensuring that the needs of a statemented child at a mainstream independent school are being met, and the LA has a statutory right to enter school premises at any reasonable time for the purpose of monitoring the SEN provision being made for that child.

There are many cases where parents have not disclosed – or have not realized – that their child has a special need or learning difficulty, which starts to manifest itself in the first term or perhaps later on. Symptoms may include deteriorating or violent behaviour, loss of concentration or motivation in class and poor quality homework. Schools and parents need to recognize that this kind of behaviour may be a symptom of a special educational need or disability that must be referred for assessment. Not doing this and treating the behaviour solely as a disciplinary matter is potentially an error that can lead to litigation under the provisions of the Equality Act 2010.

The expert who assesses the child's needs should be asked to make clear recommenda-tions as to future provision and management. Sometimes the expert's report discloses a level of SEN or disability that a mainstream independent school cannot provide for, even after making reasonable adjustments. The same may be true of the psychologist's list of recommendations.

An independent school faced with this problem, and often being pressed by parents to persevere, must consider whether it is going to be able to meet the child's needs as diagnosed and assessed. Careful consideration should be given to the evidence and the reasonable adjustments that can be made to the school's policies, procedures and practices and the cost of making those adjustments. There should be consultation with the parents and the parents are encouraged to refer the child to the LA for assessment for a Statement.

There are cases when the headteacher of an independent school makes a conscientious decision that the child must leave because the school cannot cope with his or her needs but the parents wish to challenge the head's judgement. The parents should ask for a copy of the school's complaints procedure or seek legal advice on whether the school has operated its own procedures correctly.

Parents who consider that their child has a disability and has been treated differently from other children have the right to apply to the First-tier Tribunal (Health, Education and Social Care (SEND Tribunal)).

In a recent case, a boy's behaviour at an independent school was disruptive over a long period of time. The school had provided a great deal of support and employed a number of strategies but even so his behaviour was affecting the education of other children to an unacceptable degree and he was excluded. His parents applied to the Tribunal claiming the school had discriminated against their son on grounds of his behavioural disorder, which was a disability. The tribunal held:

- in most respects the school had done all it could. The exclusion, although discriminatory, was justified and therefore lawful; but

- detentions imposed on the boy for failure to hand in homework on time were unjustified discrimination because his lack of personal organization was a symptom of his disorder and the school had not provided any support systems that might have helped him to overcome this.

A mainstream independent school is likely to find that the greatest difficulty arises with disorders such as attention deficit hyperactivity disorder (ADHD) and also behavioural, emotional and social disorders (BESD). In the interests of the child as much as the school, assessments should be carried out when the symptoms become apparent. It will normally be a condition of attendance at an independent school that parents pay the cost of tests and assessments. If they are unwilling to cooperate in having their child assessed or following recommendations it may become necessary for an independent school, after consultation and appropriate warnings, to require them to remove their child.

The duty to make reasonable adjustments requires schools to take positive steps to ensure that disabled pupils can fully participate in education and other services and facilities which the school offers. Previously, independent schools have been able to charge parents for such adjustments that amount to an auxiliary aid or service.

From September 2012 reasonable adjustments includes the provision of auxiliary aids and services; thus it includes things such as teaching assistant support and care for children with disabilities. Schools are no longer able to charge for auxiliary aids and services where they amount to a reasonable adjustment.

Schools therefore need to consult with parents during the admissions process, or subsequently if special educational needs or a disability become apparent, taking into account various factors to determine whether the additional support required amounts to a reasonable adjustment and should be provided from the school's own resources.

## Sources

School Admission Appeals Code 2012.

DCSF SEN Code of Practice, DfES/0581/2001.

DCSF SEN Toolkit, DfES/0558/2001.

Inclusive Schooling – Children with SEN, DfES/0774/2001.

Removing Barriers to Achievement, DfES/0117/2004.

## Legislation

Education Act 1996.

Schools Standards and Framework Act 1998.

The School Admissions (Infant Class Sizes) (England) Regulations 2012.

Education (Independent Schools Standards) (England) Regulations 2010 as amended.

Education and Skills Act 2008.

Equality Act 2010.

# Help for Parents Wrestling with SEN legislation

Melinda Nettleton, SEN Legal

As a solicitor specializing in Special Educational Needs, Disability and Social Care, and a mother of a child with Special Educational Needs, I know from first-hand experience that when I was pregnant, I had all of the usual baby books on the shelf, but nothing on Special Educational Needs. Nobody, not even a solicitor, says to themselves, 'I do hope that I am going to have an opportunity to wrestle with the SEN legislation, regulations and Code of Practice'.

At the time of going to press, the Children and Families Bill is currently passing through Parliament. The Government has also issued a draft Code of Practice, draft regulations and briefing notes. Although big, bold changes are suggested, and hopes raised, the reality does not match the expectations. As the new legislation will not be in force for another year, I am going to deal with the current position, which will exist for at least another twelve months. Parents would be well advised to take action under the current known framework, rather than to wait for the new legislation to come in to effect.

There is no 'if we can afford it' in the current legislation. The law does not allow Local Authorities to refuse to put provision in place on the grounds of cost once they have evidence that it is needed.

However, there is no legal obligation for the Local Authority to provide the best possible provision or to maximize your child's potential. Children have a legally enforceable right to provision which genuinely and adequately meets their needs, but there is no entitlement to Rolls Royce provision.

The core reality is that Local Authorities have fixed budgets for children with Special Educational Needs. Most Local Authority officers are therefore balancing their legal obligations with budgetary constraints and operate with a central consideration of delivering services within the local authority's budget.

No one ever rings a solicitor especially in this field to tell them how happy they are with their Local Authority. There must be *happy parents*. Unfortunately, we experience some Local Authorities putting efforts into avoiding Statutory Assessments by refusal and misinformation and telling parents and SENCos, 'We don't do Statements in our LA', or, 'You won't get a Statement for Dyslexia', or, 'You won't get a Statement because he/she is not bad enough'.

Local Authorities also sometimes tell parents and SENCos in the independent sector that they are not entitled to a Statutory Assessment. This is also incorrect.

The content of a Statement of Special Needs depends on the expert advisers who contribute to the Statutory Assessment. When undertaking a Statutory Assessment, Local Authorities normally obtain evidence from their own Educational Psychologists and the NHS Trusts. These reports often do not sufficiently particularize the level of provision required and may only deal with what the Local Authority or Health Service is prepared to offer, which is not necessarily what is required for the child's learning difficulty. Here, it is important to bear in mind that Section 322 of the Education Act 1996 links both your Local Authority and your local NHS Trust. An NHS Trust is normally required to comply with the Local Authority's request for help (subject to a lack of resources proviso). Hence, local NHS Trusts are not quite as independent of Local Authorities as many parents may believe.

The evidence produced by Statutory Assessments can often be woolly and fail to specify clearly the additional provision that the child needs, and so fail to quantify the hours of Speech and Language Therapy (SALT), Occupational Therapy (OT) or Physiotherapy support needed. If the provision needed is not specified in the reports, then it cannot be quantified in the Statement and there is therefore not a legal duty to provide it. The same applies to the Local Authority's Educational Psychologist, who will rarely quantify the amount of specialist teacher input (for example, the duration and frequency of specialist Dyslexia teaching, or ASD advisory teacher input. Teacher of the Deaf input and teacher of the Visually Impaired input is also frequently not specified). Learning support assistant provision and staff training requirements are also not usually quantified.

If the evidence is not there, it is difficult to say that the critical mass of provision required is such that a specialist provision, such as the specialist schools for SEN listed in this Guide, are needed.

When advice from the LA's Educational Psychologists and the NHS Trusts are given in such a way that they do not give details of the provision needed, it is also difficult for parents to insist that officers write Statements in the way that they should.

In addition, if a Statement of Special Educational Needs is vaguely worded, it is very difficult to say the totality of the provision required (ie critical mass), is such that placement at a specialist school, such as those listed in this Guide, is necessary.

Independent expert evidence enables parents to ensure that their child's Statement of Special Educational Needs is sufficiently detailed and contains all of the provision required to meet their needs.

Good experienced professionals undertaking independent work tend to be extremely busy people with full diaries. Appointments need to be booked well in advance.

To help your child, you need to develop a really good understanding of the SEN system; only those children who have parents who are informed about their legal rights and have some understanding of evidence will get what is really needed for their children.

## Statutory Assessment

The initial step is a request for a Statutory Assessment. If you are going to request a Statutory Assessment, then do so *in writing* to your Local Authority. It is also possible for your school to make a request.

Once a request has been made, the Education (Special Educational Needs) (England) (Consolidation) Regulations 2001 lay down a statutory timetable which has to be followed. The timetable is:

- Making a decision as to whether to undertake a Statutory Assessment (*6 weeks*);

- Undertaking the assessment (this is when a variety of professionals will need to see your child) (*10 weeks*);

- Drafting the proposed Statement (*2 weeks*);

- Negotiating about the text of the proposed Statement (*8 weeks*).

This totals 26 weeks. Officers sometimes overrun this timescale and have to be reminded that the Regulations are statutory in nature and that this timetable must be complied with.

## The Format of a Statement of SEN

The sections of a Statement of Special Educational Needs are interlinked. You could also describe the parts of the statement as having a *'domino effect'*. This is because Part 2, is held by the Courts to be the equivalent of a medical diagnosis and Part 3 as a prescription for all the needs diagnosed in Part 2.

The Courts have then held that the school named in Part 4 of a Statement must be capable of making the provisions set out in Part 3. The key to Part 4 (School Placement) is therefore Part 3 (The Prescription). In turn, the key to Part 3 is Part 2 (Diagnosis). The structure is extremely important and means that no appeal to the SEN Tribunal is ever simply about Part 4 (School Placement).

If a Statement is vaguely worded, or omits areas of need in Part 2, then Part 3 of the Statement is likely to be 'light on provision'. If Part 3 of the Statement is light on provision, or is vaguely worded, there is no requirement to provide very much at all, then it is difficult to say that the totality of the provision required is such that the specialist placement of your choice should be named in Part 4.

## Discussion with your Local Authority v the SEND Tribunal

Parents often negotiate with Local Authority officers for considerable periods, in the hope of avoiding SEND Tribunal proceedings and persuading officers to accept their point of view. Here, it is important to bear in mind that LA officers are trying to deliver a service within budgetary constraints, and many officers, in the current recession, will have seen a reduction in their budget. To be seen by their employer as being good at their job, they have to deliver a service within the LA budget. It explains why parents have difficulty in securing provision at every level.

An Appeal to the SEND Tribunal can prove as fast, if not faster, than lengthy and protracted negotiation with your Local Authority. From the date of submission of an appeal to the eventual hearing takes some four to five months, and in many cases, for example, Phase Transfer (in which a child moves from one Phase of Education to another, such as Primary to Secondary school cases, a great deal less. This contrasts sharply with the months and years it takes parents involved with negotiations (often with an unsuccessful outcome), leading to an appeal in any event. The SEND Tribunal has the advantage of speed. Provision delayed is provision denied.

The other problem with negotiation is that it does not extend the two-month appeal period. If negotiations go beyond the critical two-month deadline, then the right to appeal to the SEND Tribunal is lost.

The Practice Direction of the SEND Tribunal requires the Tribunal to consider the child's needs as at the date of the hearing. The SEND Tribunal is not concerned about the niceties of negotiation, correspondence and whether a number of meetings have taken place or not. The issue the Tribunal considers is a very simple black and white one, what are the child's needs as at the date of the hearing?

The SEND Tribunal is an independent judicial body, like an Employment Tribunal (the Chair of the Tribunal panel, for example, carries the status of a County Court Judge). The Special Educational Needs and Disability Tribunal is based in Darlington. It is independent of parents, Local Authorities and schools. The decisions of the SEND Tribunal have to be complied with by the Local Authority.

The SEND Tribunal make decisions on the evidence before it, and on the basis of an ever-increasing body of legislation, case law and statutory regulations which apply, together with the Practice Directions of the SEND Tribunal. SEND Tribunals are becoming far more complex in the way they deal with cases.

If you do decide to appeal to the SEND Tribunal, it is ultimately up to you whether you present your own case, or seek professional representation by a Solicitor/ Barrister. There is no legal requirement either way, and it is certainly not the case that Tribunals prefer parents to represent themselves. Parents are entitled to represent themselves if they wish, but they should be aware that Local Authorities are often represented, either by an officer of the Authority, who is likely to have experience of SEND Tribunals, a solicitor (usually from the Local Authority's legal department) or a specialist barrister in the field of Education Law.

Our experience suggests that the more expensive provision sought by the parent, the more effort the Local Authority will make in contesting the provision sought. Expensive placements are rarely straightforward appeals. Our experience suggests a direct relationship between the costs of the provision sought and the effort with which the Local Authority will contest the appeal.

On this point, Brian Lamb OBE, the Chairman of the Special Educational Consortium and author of the Lamb Inquiry into Special Educational Needs and Parental Confidence (a Government Inquiry) commented on 19 January 2010, when giving evidence to the Select Committee: 'Unrepresented parents are unable to properly handle the Tribunal system'.

The SEND Tribunal hearing is ultimately a formal judicial process. The Tribunal operates on the basis of evidence and complex law and the presence of solicitors and barristers, especially those that specialize in education law, who will fight your corner and apply their knowledge and experience, can make a massive difference in terms of your prospects of success.

## Evidence

All judicial cases are based on evidence which is the key to a successful case; it is the fundamental building block of any argument and you cannot expect to succeed without it. The Local Authority can draw upon the expert evidence of their own professional experts, and the Local NHS Trust (Section 322 of the Education Act 1996 creates a link).

In some cases, staff from the child's school will attend, and give evidence against the parental case. Parents often find this incredibly upsetting, particularly when they feel they have spent time building up a good working relationship with staff. It is very difficult for employees to give evidence against their current employer, particularly in the current financial climate.

There are many good educational and medical professionals working with children with Special Educational Needs. However, not all are familiar with the SEND Tribunal's very specific requirements set out in the SEND Tribunal's Practice Direction, issued by Judge John Aitken in February 2010, relating to the specificity and quantification of provision, listing of documents and a Statement of Truth or the Case Law. Expert witness work is a specialization within its own right, and treatment is very different to report writing for these specific, judicial purposes. It is always worth checking that the experts you approach are familiar with the 2010 Practice Direction and are willing both to comply with its requirements, particularly including the requirement of specificity, and are willing to attend any SEND Tribunal hearing. Assessments which do not provide quantified advice, or experts who will not attend a hearing, are of little practical use.

Qualitatively, evidence differs. Teacher assessments, although they are said to be mediated, are largely expressions of opinion, and are very different to the standardized assessments undertaken by Clinical and Educational Psychologists, which are scientifically validated. There is an enormous qualitative difference.

It will also be argued, that the evidence of professionals who do not normally work in the field of education, such as Doctors and Clinical Psychologists, should carry less weight because they are unfamiliar with current practice in education. This is something to take into consideration when preparing for a case.

## Representation

If you intend to use a solicitor or barrister, then you should certainly choose one that specializes in education law. In terms of lawyers, the day of the all-rounder has long gone. As in medicine, you would not expect a consultant in rheumatology to undertake your brain surgery.

There are also lay representatives, some of whom have impressive websites. Lay representatives are not lawyers, and they are of variable quality. They are not regulated by any professional body.

When choosing a representative for an Education Law issue, the questions you should be asking are:

- How many appeals to the SEND Tribunal does the practice undertake per year?

- What is the success rate for the practice?

- Does the practice actually specialize in education law, or is this one practice area amongst many?

- Does the practice come independently recommended by, for example, a parents' or support group?

- What level of experience do the individual practitioners have in education law?

- Does the practice ever undertake work for Local Authorities?

If you are considering hiring a lay representative, then I suggest you ask them similar questions.

Education is an expensive commodity and if you were to consider the cost of what you are seeking for your child over the lifetime of the placement, (multiply the number of years your child will be in education in an independent specialist placement, by the sum of money to be paid each year in school fees, and other related costs), the sum reached is often large – in the region of £200,000–300,000, although it can reach over £750,000 over the lifetime of the placement, in very complex cases. The money spent on a specialist solicitor or barrister, to ensure your child receives an adequate standard of education, will be far more modest. If you were injured in a car accident, you would expect to use a highly specialist team of personal injury lawyers and good expert evidence to obtain a similar level of damages. The same principle can be applied in the educational context, to achieve a desired result.

## Post 16/18 Situation

The position of Post 16/18 without a Statement of Special Educational Needs is opaque and makes the situation before 16 with a Statement look like a shining model of user-friendly clarity. The best advice is to retain the advice of a Statement of Special Educational Needs as long as possible. A Statement can continue until 19.

For those with severe learning difficulties, who lack capability to manage their own affairs, parents are well advised to seek a Deputyship Order in the Court of Protection as their child approaches 18, in order to be able to manage their child's financial affairs, as well as health and welfare, as they were able to do before the age of 18. The Court of Protection process takes quite some time – parents are well advised to apply shortly after a child/young person's 17th birthday.

Section 139A of the Learning & Skills Act 2000 places Local Authorities under a duty to arrange a Learning Difficulties assessment for Statemented pupils who they expect to leave school at 16/19. Updated Statutory Guidance was issued on 20 December 2012 to reflect the decision made in the case of Alloway v London Borough of Bromley dated 17 September 2008 (2008 EWHC 2499 Admin) which was successfully argued by John Friel. That decision required greater precision than hitherto in the identification of the young person's needs and appropriate provision to meet them (ie not as precise as a Statement, but similar).

For those who will be attending University, Student Finance England, which receives applications for Disabled Student Allowance, does not accept what was in a Statement or in a Section 139A assessment and continues to require fresh Post 16 reports, confirming conditions which have existed, in some cases, since pre-school Statements.

## Legal Aid

The issue of legal aid is often raised by parents. Before someone can be granted legal aid, they must satisfy a financial means assessment. The case must also satisfy a merits test of whether it has a reasonable chance of succeeding.

Legal Aid can provide advice and assistance in preparing an appeal to the First-tier Tribunal (SEN and Disability), but it does not cover having a lawyer to act as a formal legal representative before the Tribunal (that is acting as an advocate).

A parent seeking to access Legal Aid for an SEN case can go online via www.gov.uk/legalaid to find out if they are eligible. Alternatively, they can contact the Civil Legal Advice (CLA) Service on 0845 345 4 345. If the CLA assesses a person as eligible, the legal advice will normally be provided by phone, online or by post unless the specialist advice provider assesses them unsuitable to have advice in this way.

## Top Tips for Statementing

1 Local policies cannot and do not override legislation, case law or the Code of Practice. The SEND Tribunal is not bound by your Local Authority's policies.

2 There is no 'if we can afford it' clause anywhere in the legislation, Code of Practice or case law.

3 Be aware your child's needs may not be the prime motivator for your LA's actions/ advice/ suggestions.
   LAs are increasingly reluctant to provide for specialist provision/placement.

4 The SEND Tribunal looks at the child's needs as at the date of the hearing, not the past. Whether you had meetings and corresponded nicely is irrelevant.

5 A SEND Tribunal only takes four to five months from start to finish, and in many cases, such as Phase Transfer cases, a great deal less. It can be quicker than negotiation with your Local Authority. Provision delayed is provision denied.

6 Think about the person giving you advice. Always consider asking the following:

- Is the individual a qualified lawyer?

- Just how many successful cases have they run for parents in the SEND Tribunal?

- Does their pay cheque come from the Local Authority? Is there a conflict of interest?

Assess critically any advice which you are given. For example, Parent Partnership will never have undertaken an appeal to the SEND Tribunal for a parent. Further, they are paid by your Local Authority. Your SENCO and head teacher are also unlikely to have ever successfully run an appeal for a parent to a SEND Tribunal.

7 Be organized and manage information. The following may help:

- Keep a large ring binder file with all reports and correspondence in date order.

- Confirm in writing what has been said to you on the phone or at meetings.

- Keep a diary of who you spoke to, date and time and what you agreed.

- Take contemporaneous notes at meetings.

Remember that the purpose of a letter is not always to benefit the recipient. Its purpose may be to record information.

So, where are we now? My son, now grown up, has a First in Philosophy. Not bad for a language disorder. All that speech and language therapy, occupational therapy and specialist Dyslexia teaching, in settings named in this Guide (thanks to a successful outcome at the SEND Tribunal) really does work.

# 1.11

# An Introduction to Assessment

## Dr Richard Lansdown MA, PGCE, DipPsych, PhD, FBPsS

The psychological assessment of a child thought to have special educational needs is an exercise in problem solving.

First, one has to pose a 'why' question, examples of which are:

- Why is he or she not reading as well as we expect?

- Why is he or she unable to get on well with other children?

- Why is he or she having such difficulty with written work?

The problem then is to answer these questions in a way that will give indications for the child's educational future.

## The first step

The very first step is to gather some general information, which involves taking a brief medical, social and educational history, usually from parents. Information on milestones like walking and talking, hearing and vision, serious illnesses or accidents is essential. Whether there is a history of learning difficulties of any kind in the family may be relevant, and details on how many schools have been attended are also sought.

Next comes current information: what do the present teachers say about the child's attainment and behaviour? Is there any specific concern, eg maths or reading, or is the worry more general? What are the child's interests? What is the child's behaviour like at home? Are there any problems with sleeping or eating or with making and keeping friends?

At this stage it is usually helpful to have some formal rating of a child's behaviour. This can be obtained from standardized questionnaires, which allow one to compare the child in question with others of the same age.

Equally important, especially in view of the Code of Practice that was published in 2001, is to listen to the child. For example, what does he or she see as a problem? What are the good or bad points about the school?

## The first hypothesis

Once this information has been gathered, a preliminary hypothesis can be made. For example, consider these five 9-year-olds:

- Peter Doe was born after a difficult delivery and he has always been slow in his milestones. His hearing and vision are normal but he has not been able to keep up with his peers in school work and has been kept down a year in primary school. He prefers to play with younger children. He used to sleep well but now says that it is hard to get to sleep, especially in term time.

- Mary Doe was a normal toddler, very bubbly and outgoing as a young child, and has always had a wide circle of friends. She was a little late in talking but is very agile and swims like a fish. She has recently been reluctant to go to school, complaining of headaches or tummy aches, and her reports have been encouraging but consistent in pointing to a difficulty with reading and spelling.

- Jenny Doe has severe cerebral palsy and has no speech. She can swipe at an object with a closed fist but cannot hold or manipulate a pencil. Her parents report that she seems able to understand a great deal but they admit that they may be biased.

- John Doe is described as having been a good baby, but not at all cuddly, with normal motor milestones, no illnesses but some language delay. He is solitary at school and has only one friend in the neighbourhood who shares his interest in trains. By choice, he reads nothing but train books, including out-of-date timetables, and will spend hours at a station. He hates change of any kind.

- Michael Doe was adopted when he was 5 years old. When with his birth parents, he was neglected and abused physically and mentally. He is now aggressive, very active with a short concentration span and finds it hard to make friends. His teachers say he is bright but they cannot get him to stay on task long enough.

Each of these yields a different hypothesis. The next step is to test them, using tests and/or observations.

## Testing the hypotheses

An intelligence test is the usual starting point for children with learning difficulties of any kind. Two are commonly used in the UK: the Wechsler Scales and the British Ability Scales. Both follow the same pattern of asking that children undertake a range of tasks, which include verbal and non-verbal reasoning, memory, general knowledge, vocabulary and so on. The results are then aggregated to yield an IQ, with 100 as an average score. About 80 per cent of children score between 80 and 120. As a very rough rule of thumb, a score below 70 is an indication of learning difficulties, but it is of the utmost importance to note that this is only an indication, not a ticket to a special school.

There has been much criticism of intelligence tests, and it is true that they have to be used with caution, especially with children from cultures different from that on which the test was standardized. Caution has to be exercised also when quoting an overall IQ, since this can mask significant differences between verbal and non-verbal skills. What is more, an IQ is not as precise a measure as height or weight: there is an expected variation of plus or minus about 6 points, so a given IQ of 100 could be seen to represent a 'true' score of between 94 and 106.

It should be remembered that the tests have been devised for and standardized on able-bodied children, so if one is assessing a child with disabilities one is comparing that child with children without disabilities.

Much can be learnt from the scores on such a test, but also from the way the child approaches the task. Does he rush at everything, showing no sense of planning or reflection on what he is doing? Does she persist, even when the tasks are getting hard? How does he react to failure?

But an IQ is only a beginning. One needs next to look at other relevant areas, depending on the question being asked.

### Peter: global or specific problems?

Peter's history suggests global difficulties, but to check on this one would supplement the intelligence test with others that look at reading and maths, writing and drawing. If they all point in the same direction, one begins to firm up on a diagnosis of learning difficulty, but it may be helpful also to consider his behaviour. Here rating scales completed by parents and teachers are useful.

### Mary: dyslexia?

Mary is reported to have problems with reading and spelling, so one must test those skills. Here we run into the difficulty of defining what we mean by reading. Some tests simply look at the child's ability to read single words out of context; this is useful as a screen, but if there are difficulties it should be supplemented with a test of reading comprehension: how well does the child understand what is read? How much can he or she use context to guess at difficult words or phrases? Spelling mistakes can also give a clue to the next area of investigation: a child who writes 'mite' for 'might' and 'dun' for 'done' may have a weakness in visual memory.

If Mary's reading and/or spelling are poor when compared with her IQ, and if there are no reasons in her educational, medical or social history to explain the discrepancy, then the hypothesis of specific reading difficulty or dyslexia is likely to be upheld. It is common at this stage to assess the child's phonological awareness, which means in essence finding out how well he or she copes with language-related sounds. There are batteries of tests to examine this, most of which include asking the child to detect words that rhyme, picking out words according to their ending sound or saying as many words as possible that begin with a certain letter in a short time. The rationale is that children diagnosed as dyslexic have often been found to have a weakness in such skills.

If it is thought that the child has a memory weakness, then there are tests that examine his or her memory, differentiating between visual and auditory channels.

A rating of Mary's behaviour may also be helpful, but equally important may be to look at how she sees herself. Here one uses a self-concept scale, which gives some idea of whether she perceives herself as socially or academically a success, or possibly whether she feels supported at home.

A note on dyscalculia. Much is made of dyslexia, less of the maths equivalent, which is known as dyscalculia. Relatively little work has been done in this area. There is some suggestion that it is related to spatial skills. The approach is similar to that used for dyslexia, with more detailed assessments of mathematical knowledge being carried out.

### Jenny: a test for the tester?

Jenny is quite a different matter. There are no tests standardized on children with cerebral palsy and so one normally uses instruments devised for the able-bodied and interprets them in the light of the child's disability. At first it may seem impossible even to begin testing a child with no language and no hand control, but much can be learnt if the child can point, and swiping with a fist is often enough. For example, the British Picture Vocabulary Test consists of a series of pages with four pictures on each. The tester says a word and the child has to indicate the appropriate picture on that page. In this way one can assess vocabulary even in a child who has no speech at all. There are similar tests for spatial skills, and even one new scale that claims to assess general intelligence.

The interpretation of such tests is very much a matter of experience, for one has to take into account the fact that children with physical disabilities have not had the opportunities to learn that their able-bodied peers have.

### John: autism?

From his history, John is possibly autistic. Here one starts not with any formal testing but with a careful and detailed consideration of what he has done in the past and what he does now. Observations from teachers and parents are all important. One approach is to take the criteria for autism given in one of the classification systems and to look to see to what extent the child's behaviour matches them. (There are two classification systems in use in the UK. DSM IV is a US system; ICD X is European. They both give detailed lists of criteria for the whole range of psychiatric disorders.)

Once it has been established that a child can be so classified, tests can be useful, and indeed are essential, to allow recommendations for the type of school that will be the best. Standard intelligence and attainment tests can often be used, although it may be necessary to rely on non-verbal scales for some children.

Behaviour ratings are also helpful, especially those that focus on activity levels, for autistic children are often overactive.

### Michael: brain injury?

Michael's history is one of neglect and trauma. It is now known that adverse environmental conditions in the first two years of life can affect the actual structure of the brain, and even if he does not have any established injury his behaviour is consistent with someone who does.

In his case it is advisable to give the standard battery of tests of intelligence, memory, reading and maths but also to look carefully at what is known as his executive functioning, by which is meant how well, or badly, he organizes himself, how impulsive he is, how well he seems to be able to learn from mistakes and so on. There are questionnaires for parents and teachers to complete and individually administered tests as well.

This is a relatively new area but already ways of helping such children are being developed.

These five examples have been chosen to show that not only are different tests used according to the question put but different weights are assigned to test or assessment approaches as well. The art of assessment is not simply in coming up with answers; it lies crucially in asking the right question.

## Some miscellaneous points

1 A note on IQ (intelligence quotient) and reading age. Psychologists usually report the results of intelligence tests using an IQ or standard score. This computation allows an age correction to be applied to children's responses: a six-year-old answering 20 out of 30 items correctly is clearly brighter than a nine-year-old who has the same raw score. Reading test results are sometimes expressed as standard scores as well (and the purists say they should be), but they are often given as a reading age that indicates the level reached by an average child of those years.

2 What effect is there when a child feels unwell, or if he or she does not like the psychologist? It is unwise to test a child who is unwell, and most unwise to rely on scores of one who is emotionally upset. The personality of the psychologist can make a difference, but if he or she has been properly trained this should be relatively small.

3 Are scores stable over time? The older the child, the more stable the IQ will be. But a test is a snapshot, taken at one time, giving a picture of a child on that occasion, and although large changes are relatively unusual in older children, they can occur and a retest after two years is advisable. (NB There can also be a practice effect on tests; that is, if a child is given the same test again within a few weeks, the scores on the second occasion tend to be higher by up to 8 points on the full-scale IQ.)

4   Is IQ that important in explaining school success or failure? Yes and no. There is no doubt that, in general, children with high IQs do better in school than those at the lower end, which is hardly surprising. But factors within children such as motivation, organization and persistence play a major part, as do good teaching and support from home.

5   Do all intelligence tests give similar IQ scores? Again, yes and no. They are likely to give more or less similar scores but the variation can be considerable. The IQ is basically a figure derived from a comparison of the child being tested with the sample on whom the test was standardized. So test A, standardized on group A, will not necessarily give the same results as test B, standardized on group B. Of relevance here is the fact that tests get out of date and should be restandardized every 20 years or so.

6   What does an IQ of 100 really mean? When a test standardized on a British population is used, it indicates that the child has scored at an average level when compared with a sample of children chosen to be representative of the whole of the UK, geographically, ethnically and socially.

7   Why are IQ scores generally preferred to mental ages? Mental ages are sometimes helpful but they can be misleading. Say three children have a mental age of a 9-year-old. There is all the difference in the world between a 4-year-old, a 9-year-old and a 15-year-old with that mental age.

8   Does IQ predict success in areas other than the academic? Not really; many other factors come into play, like the ability to get on with other people and creative ability.

9   Should we, then, talk of many different types of intelligence? It is reasonable to distinguish between practical and academic abilities: one person may be outstanding at running a greengrocery business, always giving the right change and managing to balance the books, but may have been hopeless at the more sophisticated maths at school. Some people are brilliant at school work but hopeless socially. Musical or artistic skills also seem frequently to be distinct, ie a child can be very talented in either of these areas but will not necessarily do well in mainstream school subjects.

**1.12**

# Choosing a School for Your Child's Special Educational Needs

David Urani, Consultant Educational Psychologist

The Special Educational Needs Code of Practice defines special educational needs in the following way: 'Children have special educational needs if they have a learning difficulty which calls for special educational provision to be made for them.'

In recent years the general thrust in special needs education has been one of 'inclusion': the belief that the majority of children with special needs will and can be catered for within a mainstream school setting. This, however, is not always the case. Situations do arise whereby a child's special educational needs cannot be effectively met within a mainstream context, due to the complexity or unique nature of the needs involved. In such a situation, a range of more specialist provision will need to be considered.

## Types of specialist provision

### Special needs units

Units are based on mainstream school sites. They enable children to access specialist support from the unit, as well as having the possibility of regular integration into a mainstream class. In some cases children can be enrolled in the unit, but in fact spend most of their time in a mainstream setting.

### Local Authority special schools

Some children may require the intensive and specialist support provided by special schools. LA special schools (including grant maintained special schools) offer smaller class sizes, teachers with specialist training, high levels of one-to-one and small group support, and on-site input from therapists and other professionals where necessary. Special schools usually have the resources to cater for children with more severe learning, emotional/behavioural or medical needs.

Special schools fall into two broad categories. Some specialize in dealing with a specific need, for example dyslexia or autism. Other schools cater for a variety of children who may have different specific diagnoses but broadly fit a more general description, such as moderate learning difficulties (MLD) or severe learning difficulties (SLD).

In the main, LA special schools are day provisions where the child can continue to live at home. In exceptional circumstances, where the special need is relatively rare, complex or the appropriate school is not near the child's home, residential provision can be offered.

Depending on the child's progress, some children in special schools can be given the opportunity to integrate into local mainstream schools with support. In a few cases, it is possible for the child to return to full-time mainstream education with support.

## Independent special schools

There are a smaller number of independent special schools in the UK that offer specialist provision for children with special educational needs.

Being independent, fees are charged for children to attend. While some schools will accept private fee-paying students, in the main the costs are too prohibitive for most parents. Many independent special schools have a policy of only considering children who have a Statement of Special Educational Needs, where the child's LA is prepared to fund the placement. In some instances, funding may be arranged through other agencies such as Social Services or Health, depending on the specific needs and circumstances of the child.

Independent special schools are designated by the Secretary of State for Education, and are recognized by LAs as providing for a particular aspect of special needs education. In cases where the school does not have official approval to take a certain category of special need child, LAs will not be in a position to support the placement. In exceptional circumstances, it is possible to gain permission from the Secretary of State for a child to attend a non-designated school.

Another category of independent special school, Non-Maintained Special Schools, are also approved by the Secretary of State but are wholly funded by charitable organizations (eg Barnardo's, National Autistic Society).

## Alternative provisions

In very exceptional circumstances, such as chronic illness, some children's learning needs cannot be met in a school setting. With prior approval from the LA, tuition can be offered at home or in hospital. Tuition, however, is often only provided on a part-time basis, and is seen as a short-term arrangement.

Some parents choose to implement an intensive home-based programme, supervised by a non-LA organization. An example of this is the Lovaas/Applied Behavioural Analysis interventions used for young autistic children. These programmes are either funded by parents, or can be funded by the LA through a child's Statement.

Parents should be aware, however, that most LAs are reluctant to fund such pro-grammes, commonly referred to as 'education otherwise'. It is frequently the LA's view that most children with special needs can be catered for from within the Authority's own maintained provision.

## Selecting a school

Parents are frequently in the position of having to assess the suitability of a school in meeting their child's special needs. The decision as to which school to choose can be a daunting task. The following are some aspects to consider prior to contacting a potential school:

- What is the LA recommending as suitable to your child's needs? Is there a choice? Do you accept that the school/s being offered is/are appropriate?

- What are the opinions of professionals such as teachers, educational psychologists, therapists or medical consultants regarding the type of school needed for your child?

- Many support groups or professional organizations (eg Royal Institute for the Blind, National Autistic Society) are there to help parents and are able to offer advice in their area of expertise.

- Consulting organizations such as Gabbitas or IPSEA for a list of possible schools can be a good place to start a search.

- Schools often publish a prospectus for parents. Many schools have their own website.

- Has the school had a recent Ofsted inspection and is the report available for you to see? (Ofsted publishes its reports on the internet at www.ofsted.gov.uk.)

Once you have narrowed down the schools you think may be suited to your child's needs, the next step is to visit the schools and see what they have to offer. It is advisable not to take your child on an initial visit, as it may create unrealistic expectations within the child of attending the school. The following are a few things to consider:

- Don't limit your list to only one school. The more schools you see, the greater your chances are of finding the most appropriate one for your child.

- The most vital question to ask before taking things further is whether the school actually has a place to offer. Many schools are often full, or may have a waiting list.

- How far is the school from home? Will transport be an issue? Will boarding need to be considered?

- Does the school only cater for your child's specific area of need (eg visual impairment) or is it more generalist (eg MLD)? What are the special needs of the other children in the school?

- What is the physical learning environment like? Is the school modified for children with physical impairments? Is the playground safe and easy to supervise?

- Is the school well-resourced in terms of learning materials and teaching aids? What level of access is there to computers?

- What are the class sizes and the adult to child ratio? What is the training expertise of the teaching and supporting staff? Is there access to other professionals such as psychologists and speech and language therapists if needed?

- Are there opportunities for mainstream integration? If so, are there children in the school who are on an integration programme?

- Were you able to see children in a lesson? If so, did the children appear to be stimulated and interested? How did the teacher deal with unforeseen circumstances such as a child misbehaving?

- What are the residential facilities like for boarding pupils? Are there extracurricular activities on offer?

- With older children, is there a work experience/life skills component to the curriculum? What links does the school have with post-secondary colleges?

It is more than likely that you will have further questions to ask after seeing a school for the first time. A second visit is always a good idea, especially if you're unsure. If you feel certain of your choice, take your child along. Ultimately he or she is the one who will be attending and it may well be that you haven't considered some aspect of the school from his or her perspective. For support, it is also helpful to take a friend or a trusted professional who knows your child and can provide a more objective opinion.

## Making an application to a school

If as parents you are paying the fees, the application process is relatively uncomplicated and is made directly to the school.

With a Statemented child the situation is very different. You will need to ascertain if the LA is prepared to fund a place in the school you have chosen. Even when you have found a school, and the school is prepared to offer a place, the LA is under no legal obligation to support the placement if it believes an appropriate provision can be found from within its own resources.

Disagreements between parents and LAs regarding school placement can arise. In some instances this can lead to an appeal by parents to an independent First-tier Tribunal (Health, Education and Social Care (SEND Tribunal)). This can be a very drawn out and expensive option, and should be seen as a last resort.

Advice from professionals such as educational solicitors or independent educational psychologists experienced in Tribunal appeals is strongly recommended before proceeding with this route.

# Welfare Benefits

Rundip Thind from Disability Rights UK

This chapter is a brief introduction to the benefits that you may be able to claim if your child has a physical disability, a learning disability, developmental delays or behavioural problems. The chapter also outlines benefits that can be claimed independently by the disabled person once they reach age 16. Lastly, a brief introduction has been included on Universal Credit which will replace a range of means-tested benefits and tax credits for working age families nationwide from October 2013. Universal Credit is being phased in over four years so the current benefits as they stand will not entirely be replaced until 2017.

## Getting advice

The benefits system need not be daunting or confusing. You can get information and advice from a number of sources. In the first instance you could contact your local Jobcentre Plus office, or call the Benefit Enquiry Line on 0800 882200 (a national telephone helpline about benefits for people with disabilities).

You can get independent advice from a Citizens Advice Bureau, DIAL (Disability Information and Advice Line) or local advice centre. There are also a number of books that give information or advice about benefits. The Disability Rights UK provides information about welfare benefits and tax credits that disabled people can claim. It publishes the Disability Rights Handbook and a range of other publications every year (see useful addresses at the end of the book).

The information in this chapter uses the benefit rates current from April 2013.

## Benefits for your child

### Child Benefit

You are entitled to receive Child Benefit if you are responsible for a dependent child. You do not have to be the child's parent. You can receive Child Benefit for a child aged under

16, or a young person aged under 20 if they are in full-time, non-advanced education (ie more than 12 hours a week at school or college) or in approved unwaged training. A 19-year-old can only be included if they started such education or approved training before their 19th birthday. You may not be entitled to Child Benefit if your child is in local authority care for more than eight weeks (unless the child regularly stays with you for at least a day a week, midnight to midnight), or if you receive a fostering allowance for that child. Child Benefit is administered by HM Revenue & Customs.

### Amounts
Only or eldest child     £20.30
Each other child          £13.40

The value of your Child Benefit is reduced through a tapered income tax charge if you or your partner are individually earning more than £50,000 for the tax year. Your Child Benefit will not be withdrawn but continues to be paid in full. Instead the value of it will be clawed back through taxation, starting at £50,000 and increasing at a rate of 1 per cent of the Child Benefit in payment per £100 of the annual income of you or your partner. If you are earning more than £60,000 for the tax year, the value of your Child Benefit will be nil because of the tax claw back.

To claim Child Benefit, contact the Child Benefit helpline (0845 302 144; textphone 0845 302 1474).

## Child Tax Credit

Child Tax Credit is paid to families both in and out of work. It is paid in addition to Child Benefit. Although Child Tax Credit is affected by your family income, it is by no means aimed only at low-income families. The amount of Tax Credit you can get depends on your individual circumstances. As a rough guide, if you have one child and your gross annual income is below £26,000 you can probably get Tax Credits. This figure could be higher, if for example, you have a disabled child or pay for childcare. HM Revenue & Customs administers Child Tax Credit. You can claim it on form TC600 which is available from the Tax Credit Helpline (0345 300 3900; textphone 0345 300 3909).

Between April 2013 and end of 2017 Child Tax Credit will be replaced by Universal Credit. Universal Credit will be introduced nationally for new claimants from October 2013. For more information on Universal Credit please see the section 'Future Changes' in this chapter further below.

## Disability Living Allowance

The most important benefit for anyone looking after a disabled child is Disability Living Allowance. It is assessed purely on the child's needs; your financial circumstances are irrelevant. It is not taxable and it is paid on top of any other benefits you may receive. In fact, your other benefits or tax credits may actually be increased when your child receives Disability Living Allowance. The benefit is assessed and paid in two parts. The 'care component' helps with the extra costs of providing personal care, and the 'mobility component' helps with the extra costs of going out.

The care component can be paid if your child needs extra attention (in connection with his or her bodily functions) or supervision (to maintain his or her safety). Obviously, all children need different amounts of attention or supervision at different stages in their development. However, to get the care component you have to show that your child needs attention or supervision that is 'substantially in excess' of that normally needed by other children of the same age and sex. The care component can be claimed at any age, but your child must have needed the extra attention or supervision for at least three months before any benefit is paid. The care component is paid at three different rates, depending on whether the extra attention or supervision is needed for just a portion of the day, throughout the day or night, or around the clock. A simple way of building up a picture of your child's extra needs would be to make a short diary. This diary could provide details of a typical day or week in your child's life, outlining all the things that you need to do for him or her, why you need to do them and how long they take. You could include a copy of the diary with the claim form to provide a clearer account of your child's extra attention and supervision needs.

The mobility component is paid at two different rates and is designed to help with the costs of going out and getting around. The higher rate can be paid from the age of three.

### Amounts

| Care component | | Mobility component | |
|---|---|---|---|
| Highest | £79.15 | Higher | £55.25 |
| Middle | £53.00 | Lower | £21.00 |
| Lowest | £21.00 | | |

Your child will normally be awarded Disability Living Allowance for a fixed period. You will need to re-apply before the award expires: a renewal form should be sent to you automatically. If your child is approaching the age of 16, he or she will be invited to claim Personal Independence Payment. This is a new benefit replacing Disability Living Allowance from April 2013 for adults aged 16–64. More information is available further on in this chapter. Disability Living Allowance will continue to apply to children as long as they are aged under 16.

If you think your child may be entitled to Disability Living Allowance, you should make a claim. You can phone the Benefit Enquiry Line on 0800 882200 and ask them to send you a claim-pack (the DLA1: Child). If you are awarded benefit, it can be paid from the date of this phone call. You can also claim online (www.gov.uk/dla-disability-living-allowance-benefit/how-to-claim). The claim-pack that you will receive can seem quite complicated, so seek advice if you are not sure how to fill it in.

It is also worthwhile to get the support of any professionals who are involved with your child, in particular paediatricians, nurses or GPs. There is a page in the claim-pack that they can complete. If you have made a diary of your child's extra care or supervision needs, you should provide them with a copy, in case they are approached later to provide further information.

If your child gets the higher rate of mobility component, you will also be entitled to exemption from road tax for one car, and you may be able to hire or buy a car under the Motability scheme (telephone 0845 456 4566). You can also apply to your local authority for a Blue Badge for concessionary parking. Even if your child doesn't get the higher rate mobility component, you may still be able to get a Blue Badge if your child has 'a permanent and substantial disability which causes inability to walk or very considerable difficulty in walking' or is registered blind.

# Benefits that can be claimed from age 16

On reaching the age of 16, a young disabled person can claim benefit in their own right. If the young person claims benefit in their own right, they will cease to be your dependant for benefit purposes. If you are claiming Child Benefit or Child Tax Credit for a young person you will no longer be able to do so. Any benefits will be paid in the young person's name, though if the young person is unable to handle their own claim, an 'appointee' can act for them.

The below information is aimed at disabled young people claiming in their own right independently.

### Personal Independence Payment

The Government is replacing Disability Living Allowance with a new benefit called Personal Independence Payment for adults aged 16–64. Personal Independence Payment is being introduced over a number of years, starting from April 2013.

From April 2013, Personal Independence Payment is being piloted for new claims in parts of northern England only. From 10 June 2013, all new claims for adults aged between 16 and 64 will be for Personal Independence Payment. From October 2013, if you report a change of circumstances, reach the end of an existing award of Disability Living Allowance or in some cases are approaching the age of 16, then you will be invited to claim Personal Independence Payment.

If you have reached your 16th birthday on 10 June 2013 and are not already receiving Disability Living Allowance, you will need to claim Personal Independence Payment instead.

If you reach 16 before 7 October 2013 and if your current Disability Living Allowance award is ending, you will be asked to complete a Disability Living Allowance renewal form. If you reach 16 on or after 7 October 2013 you will be reassessed for Personal Independence Payment.

Personal Independence Payment is tax free, not means tested and you do not need to have paid national insurance contributions to be entitled to it.

The benefit is assessed and paid in two parts. The daily living component is for help participating in everyday life. Your ability to carry out daily living activities is assessed by focusing on activities such as preparing food, taking nutrition, washing and bathing, managing toilet needs or incontinence. There are ten types of such activity.

The mobility component is assessed by focusing on two types of activity. These are planning and following journeys and moving around.

Each component is paid at either a standard rate or an enhanced rate.

**Amounts**

| *Daily living component* | | *Mobility component* | |
|---|---|---|---|
| Enhanced | £79.15 | Enhanced | £55.25 |
| Standard | £53.00 | Standard | £21.00 |

You can make a new claim for Personal Independence Payment by telephoning 0800 917 222. If you need extra help or are unable to telephone to start the claim, you can request a paper version of the initial claim form. This captures the same basic information that would have been taken over the phone. Once the claim has been registered you will be sent a PIP 1003 'How your disability affects you' form for completion.

You can get a free tax disc if you get the enhanced mobility component of personal independence payment (PIP). You can also get a 50 per cent discount on your road tax if you receive the standard mobility component of PIP. In England, if you have been awarded 8 points or more in the 'moving around' activity of personal independence payment (PIP) you can also get a Blue Badge. Contact your local authority to apply for a Blue Badge.

### Employment and Support Allowance

Employment and Support Allowance (ESA) is a benefit for people whose ability to work is limited by their disability or health condition. There are two types of the benefit; contributory ESA and income-related ESA.

## Contributory ESA

Contributory ESA can only be paid if you have paid enough National Insurance contributions in specific years.

Contributory ESA cannot usually be paid to a student under 19 who is at school or college and is attending classes for 21 hours or more a week. Lunch breaks, breaks between lessons, free periods and periods of private (unsupervised) study or homework do not count. When calculating the 21 hours you should also ignore any time spent in study that would not be suitable for a person of your age who does not have a physical or mental disability. So, if you receive a lot of support to follow a course, or if the course is taught in such a way that would make it unsuitable for a non-disabled person, then you may still be entitled to contributory ESA.

From age 19 there are no rules that limit the hours you can study.

## Income-related ESA

Income-related ESA can be paid if you have no other income or only a small income. It can be paid by itself, or it can top up contributory ESA if you are entitled to it. It cannot be paid if you have more than £16,000 in savings; any savings between £6,000 and £15,999 will reduce the amount of benefit paid.

Income-related ESA can include extra amounts called premiums which are paid to more severely disabled people. The enhanced disability premium is payable if you receive the highest-rate care component of Disability Living Allowance or the enhanced daily living component of Personal Independence Payment; the severe disability premium is payable if you are living alone and receive the middle or highest-rate care component of Disability Living Allowance or the daily living component of Personal Independence Payment (as long as no one is getting Carer's Allowance for looking after you).

As a full-time student, you can only get income-related ESA if you are getting Disability Living Allowance or Personal Independence Payment. If you are in higher education or you are aged 19 or over and in higher or further education you will be automatically treated as having limited capability for work. This means you will not be assessed for your entitlement to ESA but instead you will be assessed to determine whether you should be awarded the work related activity component or the support component.

Between April 2013 and end of 2017 income-related ESA will be replaced by Universal Credit. Universal Credit will be introduced nationally for new claimants from October 2013. For more information on Universal Credit please see the section 'Future Changes' in this chapter further below.

## Claiming ESA

The quickest way to apply for ESA is by calling the Jobcentre Plus claim-line (0800 055 6688; textphone 0800 023 4888). You can also download the claim-form (ESA1) from www.gov.uk/employment-support-allowance/how-to-claim.

You will need a fit note from your GP. It is possible for a new claim for ESA to be back-dated for up to three months as long as you would have qualified for it at that time. You will need to ask your doctor to confirm that you were not fit for work during this period.

The first 13 weeks of the claim is the assessment phase. During this time ESA will be paid at a lower level. During this assessment phase you will undergo a 'work-focused interview' and a 'work capability assessment'. At the work focused interview a personal adviser will discuss work prospects with you. The work capability assessment will usually start with you being sent the form (the ESA50) to complete. The time limit for completing and returning form ESA50 is four weeks. You should seek advice if you are not sure how to fill this in. A follow-up face-to-face assessment with a health-care professional may then be arranged. The work capability assessment will determine whether you remain on ESA and, if you do, which of two groups of claimants you will be placed in: the 'support group' or the 'work-related activity group'. If you are placed in the support group you do not have to undertake work-related activities, although you can volunteer to do so. You receive a higher rate of ESA than if you are placed in the work-related activity group. If you are placed in the work-related activity group, you must meet work-related conditions including attending monthly work-focused interviews; if you fail to meet the conditions, your ESA payment may be reduced.

If you are found not to have a limited capability for work at the work capability assessment, you can ask the decision maker to reconsider the decision or appeal straight away. You can do this within one calendar month of the date of the decision letter. You will not be entitled to ESA while your request for a reconsideration is being dealt with. If you appeal straight away your ESA can be paid up to the appeal hearing. Appeal forms (the GL24) can be obtained from Jobcentre Plus offices. From October 2013 the Government intends to introduce mandatory reconsiderations which will mean you will need to claim Jobseekers Allowance while the reconsideration is being dealt with.

### Amounts

| *Assessment period* | | *After 13 weeks* | |
|---|---|---|---|
| (aged under 25) | £56.80 | Work-related activity group | £100.15 |
| (aged 25 or over) | £71.70 | Support group | £106.50 |

## Benefits for carers

### Carer's Allowance

Carer's Allowance is a benefit paid for people who regularly spend at least 35 hours a week caring for a severely disabled person. You can claim Carer's Allowance if you are caring for a young person who receives Disability Living Allowance care component at the middle or highest rate or Personal Independence Payment daily living component (at either rate). You do not have to be related or live with the disabled person.

Carer's Allowance is a taxable benefit. It is not means tested and does not depend on national insurance contributions.

You cannot receive Carer's Allowance if you are in full-time education. You are generally treated as being in full-time education if your course is described as such by the educational establishment; even if your course is not described as full-time you will be treated as in full-time education if the course involves supervised study of 21 hours or more a week. If you work, you must not earn more than £100 a week. It does not matter for how many hours you work as long as you are below this earnings limit and you are still providing care for at least 35 hours per week. To calculate your net earnings, deduct tax, National Insurance contributions and half of your contributions towards an occupational or personal pension. You are also allowed to deduct care costs up to a maximum of half your net earnings.

Carer's Allowance is paid at £59.75 per week, and while you are receiving the allowance your National Insurance contribution record will be protected. Your Carer's Allowance will be taken into account if you (or your partner) are also claiming Income Support, Income-related Employment and Support Allowance or income-based Job-seeker's Allowance, but these benefits will also be increased by an additional carer's premium. To claim Carer's Allowance, get a claim form from your local Jobcentre Plus office, call the DWP Benefit Enquiry Line freephone on 0800 882200 or claim online (www.gov.uk/carers-allowance/how-to-claim).

# Other benefits

## *National Insurance contributory benefits*

If you are unable to work, unemployed, widowed, pregnant or retired, you may be entitled to some benefits through the payment of National Insurance contributions. Employment and Support Allowance, contribution-based Jobseeker's Allowance, Maternity Allowance and State Pension can be payable if you have paid enough contributions. In the case of bereavement benefits (for widows, widowers and surviving civil partners), your late husband's, wife's or civil partner's contributions are relevant.

If you qualify, these benefits are paid to you as an individual. It does not matter if you have savings, or (except for bereavement benefits) a partner who is in full-time work. However, if these benefits are your family's only or main source of income, you will usually need to claim a top-up from a means-tested benefit, such as Income Support, as well (Employment and Support Allowance has its own means-tested element). To claim any of these benefits call the Jobcentre Plus claim-line 0800 055 6688 (or textphone 0800 023 4888).

## *Income Support, Income-based Jobseeker's Allowance and Pension Credit*

Income Support and income-based Jobseeker's Allowance are the benefits for people who do not have enough money to live on and who are not in full-time work. You will not be entitled to these benefits if you have savings or capital above £16,000. If you have savings or capital of more than £6,000, your benefit will be reduced. Pension Credit is the equivalent benefit for people who have reached the qualifying age, which is being raised from 60 to 66 between April 2010 and April 2020.

Income Support can only be claimed by certain people. This includes lone parents with a child under 5 or carers. If you do not fit into any of the categories for which Income Support can be paid, you will have to claim income-based Jobseeker's Allowance (if you are able to work) or income-related Employment and Support Allowance (if you are not) instead. To claim Income Support call the Jobcentre Plus claim-line 0800 055 6688 (or textphone 0800 023 4888).

Income-based Jobseeker's Allowance is paid to people who are required to be available for, and actively seeking, work. You can be sanctioned, and have your benefit reduced or taken away altogether, if you refuse the offer of a job or leave a job without 'just cause'. To claim income-based Jobseeker's Allowance call the Jobcentre Plus claim-line 0800 055 6688 (or textphone 0800 023 4888).

Pension Credit can be paid to people who have reached state pension age, which is being increased from 60 to 66 between 2010 and 2020. To find out your exact state pension age, call the Pension Service on 0845 6060265 or visit www.gov.uk/calculate-state-pension. Pension credit consists of a 'guarantee credit', which is similar to Income Support, and a top-up 'savings credit' for those aged 65 or over. There is no upper capital limit above which you cannot claim Pension Credit. To claim Pension Credit contact the Pension Service application line (0800 99 1234).

If you are an owner-occupier Income Support, income-based Jobseeker's Allowance, income-related Employment and Support Allowance and the guarantee credit of Pension Credit are important as they provide direct help with your mortgage costs (You can also get support for mortgage interest as well as certain charges if you receive Universal Credit, however, the housing element will not be paid if you are doing any paid work).

If you receive Income Support, income-related Employment and Support Allowance or income-based Jobseeker's Allowance, you will be entitled to free school meals, vouchers for milk, fresh fruit or vegetables for children under 4, free prescriptions, NHS dental treatment and vouchers for glasses, wigs and fabric supports. You can also claim a refund of your fares to hospital.

Between April 2013 and end of 2017 Income Support and income-based Jobseeker's Allowance will be replaced by Universal Credit. Universal Credit will be introduced nationally for new claimants from October 2013. For more information on Universal Credit please see the section 'Future Changes' in this chapter further below.

## Housing Benefit and Council Tax Reduction

Housing Benefit helps with your rent if you are a tenant. Council Tax Reduction helps with your Council Tax bill, regardless of whether you own your home or rent. Housing Benefit and Council Tax Reduction can be payable if you are unemployed or working. Both are administered by your council.

If you are receiving Income Support, income-related Employment and Support Allowance, income-based Jobseeker's Allowance or the guarantee credit of Pension Credit, you will be entitled to the maximum allowable Housing Benefit. Otherwise the amount of help you get will depend on the level of your family's income. The amount you get may be reduced if you have any other adults living with you. Contact your local council for the claim form.

The amount of Council Tax reduction you get depends on where you live as each council runs their own scheme.

Between April 2013 and end of 2017 Housing Benefit will be replaced by the Universal Credit. Universal Credit will be introduced nationally for new claimants from October 2013. For more information on Universal Credit please see the section 'Future Changes' in this chapter further below.

## Health benefits

If you receive Income Support, income-related Employment and Support Allowance, income-based Jobseeker's Allowance or the guarantee credit of Pension Credit, you will automatically qualify for help with prescription charges, hospital travel costs, dental treatment and glasses.

If you receive Working Tax Credit or Child Tax Credit, you may get assistance with the above medical costs, depending on how your Tax Credit has been worked out – if you are entitled to help you should be sent a Tax Credit exemption certificate.

If you are not in receipt of these benefits, you can still claim help with medical costs on grounds of low income. Ask for form HC1, which you can get from your local Jobcentre Plus office, or by calling the Prescription Pricing Division: 0845 850 1166.

### Working Tax Credit

You can claim Working Tax Credit if you are working for 16 hours or more a week and you are a single parent responsible for a dependent child or young person, or if you are a couple responsible for a dependent child or young person and one of you works at least 16 hours a week where the other partner is in hospital or prison or entitled to carer's allowance or counts as 'incapacitated'. If the other partner does not fall into any of these exception categories then you must work at least 24 hours a week between you. This means that if you both work, one of you must do 16 hours a week and the other must do at least eight hours a week. If only one of you works, that person must work at least 24 hours a week. You can also claim Working Tax Credit if you are working for 16 hours or more a week and meet the criteria for a disabled worker or if you are aged 60 or over. Otherwise you can only qualify if you are aged 25 or over and usually work at least 30 hours a week. The amount that you receive depends on your family circum-stances and the level of your earnings. Working Tax Credit and Child Tax Credit are administered by HM Revenue & Customs. They are calculated and awarded on an annual basis.

You can claim Tax Credits on form TC600 which is available from the Tax Credit Helpline (0345 300 3900; textphone 0345 300 3909).

Between April 2013 and the end of 2017 Working Tax Credit will be replaced by the Universal Credit. Universal Credit will be introduced nationally for new claimants from October 2013. For more information on Universal Credit please see the section 'Future Changes' in this chapter further below.

## Would you be better off in work?

If you are thinking about starting work you can visit a Citizens Advice Bureau or any other local advice centre to ask for a 'better off' calculation, comparing your current rate of benefit with what you could be entitled to once you start work. When you make your decision remember to take into account your extra expenses and costs of going out to work, as well as other factors such as the possible loss of free school meals and milk vouchers.

## Future Changes

### Universal Credit

Universal Credit is a new single benefit for people who are looking for work or are on a low income. Between April 2013 and the end of 2017 Universal Credit will replace income-based Jobseeker's Allowance, income-related Employment and Support Allowance, Income Support, Working Tax Credit, Child Tax Credit and Housing Benefit. Universal Credit will be introduced nationally for new claimants from October 2013, initially in one district per region. This will cover both new claims and natural migrations following a change of circumstances. Universal Credit has already been introduced from April 2013 in selected 'pathfinder' areas to test that the processes are robust and reliable before the national roll-out commences.

If you are already getting income-based Jobseeker's Allowance, income-related Employment and Support Allowance, Income Support, Working Tax Credit, Child Tax Credit or Housing Benefit you will be moved over at a later date.

Universal Credit will consist of a standard allowance with additional amounts for children, housing and other needs and circumstances such as disability, childcare and caring.

The awards will be calculated on an ongoing basis and will go up or down each month in response to changes in income and other factors. If you are employed and paid through PAYE, the new 'REAL Time Information' system will allow DWP to automatically adjust your Universal Credit award if your wages change. You have to notify DWP directly of other changes of circumstances affecting your award as they occur.

Most full-time students will not be eligible for Universal Credit. However there are exceptions to the exclusion which include disabled students. Universal Credit will be limited to students who are both on disability living allowance and have a limited capability for work.

You can make a claim for Universal Credit online. If you cannot claim online, face-to-face and telephone support will be available.

## Getting further advice

This chapter can only give a very brief introduction to the benefits and tax credits that you may be entitled to. If you would like to find out more, contact a local Citizens Advice Bureau, DIAL or other advice centre. If you believe that the Department for Work and Pensions has made a mistake about your benefit, you should contact them and explain why you think the decision is wrong. You could ask them to reconsider the decision and you may also be able to appeal to an independent tribunal, but there are very strict time limits – get independent advice.

# 1.14

# Access Arrangements, Reasonable Adjustments and Special Consideration

The document 'Access Arrangements and Reasonable Adjustments' is produced by the Joint Council for Qualifications (JCQ). The rules and regulations are designed to facilitate access to qualifications for candidates who are eligible for adjustments in examinations. The regulations in force as at September 2013 are valid for the academic year 1 September 2013 to 31 August 2014. They apply to General and Vocational qualifications. The regulations are reviewed throughout the year and revised annually before publication in September. There are two categories of adjustment:

1 *Access Arrangements*. These are agreed before an examination or assessment. They allow candidates with special educational needs, disabilities or temporary injuries to access the examination(s). Access arrangements allow candidates to show what they know and can do without changing the demands of the assessment; examples include the provision of a reader, a scribe or a word processor. An access arrangement which meets the need of a disabled candidate would be a 'reasonable adjustment' for that candidate.

2 *Reasonable Adjustments*. A reasonable adjustment required by a candidate will usually be an access arrangement, but it may include other adjustments that are not included in the JCQ document. Reasonable adjustments should be applied for in the same way as access arrangements. Where a candidate has substantial needs, advice must be sought from the relevant awarding body.

It should be noted that the information shown here is necessarily only a very brief introduction. For a copy of the document, which includes examples of how Access Arrangements might apply, visit the JCQ website at http://www.jcq.org.uk/exams-office/

access-arrangements-and-special-consideration. Day-to-day enquiries about interpretation of the Regulations should be made to the JCQ. Subject specific enquiries or advice on the suitability of a particular specification should be made to the individual awarding body concerned.

**Assessment and Qualifications Alliance**
Stag Hill House, Guildford,
Surrey GU2 5XJ
Tel: 0844 209 6614
Fax: 01483 300152
Website: www.aqa.org.uk

**Council for the Curriculum Examinations and Assessment (CCEA)**
29 Clarendon Road, Belfast BT1 3BG
Tel: 02890 261200
Fax: 02890 261234
Website: www.ccea.org.uk

**Edexcel**
190 High Holborn, London WC1V 7BH
Tel: 0844 463 2535
Website: www.edexcel.com

**JCQ**
29 Great Peter Street
London SW1P 3LW
Tel: 020 7638 4137
Website: www.jcq.org.uk

**OCR**
Syndicate Buildings, 1 Hills Road,
Cambridge CB1 2EU
Tel: 01223 553998
Fax: 01223 553051
Website: www.ocr.org.uk

**Welsh Joint Education Committee**
245 Western Avenue, Cardiff CF5 2YX
Tel: 02920 265155 or 02929 265135
Website: www.wjec.co.uk

# Children with Special Educational Needs – Guidance for Families Overseas

(This chapter has been updated with the kind assistance of Lydia Parbury, Special Needs and Disability Adviser at the Diplomatic Service Families Association.)

## Leaving the UK

Parents leaving the UK, for example on a temporary posting, face key decisions about their children's education, including whether their child should accompany them or, alternatively, remain at a boarding school in the UK. In cases where a child has special educational needs, wider issues must also be considered. If you expect to live overseas for a period, the following points may be helpful in planning your child's education.

Whether your child will accompany you or remain in the UK for his or her education depends on many factors, including:

- your individual circumstances;
- expected length of stay outside the UK;
- continuity – are you likely to move again before returning to the UK?
- your child's age;
- the nature and severity of your child's special needs;

● availability and accessibility of suitable education provision and, where appropriate, medical provision and therapy in the UK and in the host country;

● your child's ability to cope with change.

It is also wise to ensure that you have a thorough understanding of the culture and attitudes towards special needs or disabilities in the country in which you will be living. You may also wish to check the general levels of physical access available to people with mobility difficulties; some travel guides provide good information on this point.

If your child has a Statement of Special Educational Needs, check with your Local Authority (LA) the position with reference to the maintenance of that Statement. This may vary from one LA to another and according to your child's individual circumstances. If your child has been attending a day school, for example, will the LA maintain a place for him or her while you are away from the UK? What happens upon your return? Depending on circumstances, funding may be shared between the LA and Local Health Authority, and arrangements may be complex. It is wise to send a copy of your child's annual review, or its equivalent, back to the LA for their records while you are away. Remember too that your child would normally have a Transition Review at age 14, which will influence the next vital years in education. You should be aware that your child will not be able to have this review if he or she is abroad.

If you plan to take your child with you, life in your host country may offer a number of advantages and disadvantages. The benefits might include:

● better salary and employment conditions;

● better climate;

● availability of domestic help;

● good provision for your child's particular needs;

● local tax concessions;

● higher welfare benefits;

● better housing;

● travel opportunities that will broaden your child's horizons and experiences;

● better medical provision.

Against this, however, there may be drawbacks, including:

● isolation;

● absence of support groups;

● lack of family support;

● language barriers;

- loss of welfare benefits;
- limited special needs provision;
- lack of facilities for the disabled;
- unsuitable climate;
- housing (perhaps in a flat with no garden);
- setbacks in your child's progress;
- lack of networking opportunities to share help and ideas;
- poorer medical provision.

Above all, avoid making hasty decisions. Give yourself time to make an informed choice and to consider the benefits and drawbacks for the whole family.

## Points to remember

1  If your child is having extra help at school, make sure you take an up-to-date Individual Education Plan (IEP) with you. The IEP can then be adjusted at any new school abroad.

2  Find out as much as you can with reference to the host country in which you expect to live, for example:
   - What provision is available for your child's needs? Consider any medical care as well as educational provision.
   - Is there an appropriate centre/support group where you can obtain information and advice?
   - Is your child/are you entitled to any state benefits or tax concessions?

Some countries may offer highly advanced provision, others almost none. Your support group in the UK, if one exists, may be able to advise you or put you in touch with 'sister groups' in the host country or with other members of the association who have lived abroad. If experienced in working in the host country, your employer/your partner's employer may be able to guide you. It may also be worth consulting international organizations such as the European Dyslexia Association or the British Embassy/High Commission or the British Council office in your host city/country for any other useful information.

The internet offers a wealth of information. Most schools now have prospectuses and information available online. Use the schools' websites to find out about those which might be of interest to you.

3  If you know the area in which you will be living, try to make contact with sources of help, such as:
   - a local doctor or hospital;
   - local authority or equivalent;

- any English-speaking organization, for example an expatriates' club. There may also be a local special needs group online;
- any organization for the disabled. Even if it does not focus specifically on your child's particular needs, it may still be able to offer support and direct you to other appropriate organizations.

4  You may wish to consider educating your child at home. If so, make sure you have all the support you need before committing yourself. The internet is a good source of help, but check whether you will have access to it in your new destination. At the time of writing there are several useful website addresses with details of the National Curriculum and support groups. For general information try the website of the Department for Education at www.education.gov.uk.

5  Talk over the move and possible changes in routine with your child. Take care also to talk to siblings about their concerns.

6  Keep a written record of the help you seek – names and contact numbers.

7  Try to obtain some basic training in the treatment of the type of special needs presented by your child and research why your child has the condition or learning difficulty.

8  Keep your employer and/or your partner's employer fully briefed about your child's special needs. Most companies now have a family-friendly policy. Might either employer offer any help to meet additional costs associated with your child's education?

9  Take with you any reference books about the condition or learning difficulty that affects your child, or make a note of useful website addresses.

10  Join any organization in your home country that can keep you up to date with developments and improvements in provision for the special needs your child has.

11  State clearly what you want and need for your child. Do not assume that friends and colleagues understand the kind of help and support you and your child require. Remember too that you will not be alone: at least 20 per cent of children will at some time in their lives present special needs in some form.

12  Remember to take with you all relevant and up-to-date papers concerning your child's special needs. Also ensure you update your records whilst abroad.

13  Finally, be realistic about the level of involvement you have had with your child's needs and the extent of support given by the school and other sources. How will your child cope under different circumstances?

## Returning to the UK

If you are returning to the UK after being resident abroad, it is wise to contact in advance the LA for the area in which you intend to live and ask for an assessment of your child's needs. However, be aware that you will need to confirm your address in the UK before the LA can discuss schools with you or make an assessment, and that the reintegration process back into UK education may be a difficult process taking a number of weeks. At the same time, contact your support group in the UK to ensure that you are fully up to date with DFE regulations on special needs provision.

## Educating your child in the UK

If you live overseas, either as a British expatriate or as a citizen of another country, but wish to have your child educated in the UK, there are a number of points to consider.

The UK offers a variety of boarding education options. The independent (fee-paying) sector offers a wide choice of boarding education with varying levels of provision for special needs. Few mainstream independent schools have children with Statements of Special Educational Needs. Many, however, have children with mild or moderate specific learning difficulties. Some schools have dedicated units to cater for children requiring special tuition and usually operate on a withdrawal basis, which means that children are withdrawn from certain lessons during the school day to have special tuition for their particular needs. Other schools offer more limited assistance, for example through extra lessons from a visiting teacher. Annual fees at independent boarding schools in 2014 generally range from £12,000 to £20,000+ at preparatory level and from £18,000 to £25,000+ at senior level.

Where a child's needs are more complex or severe, and where a child has a Statement of Special Educational Needs, a special school may be more appropriate. Residential special schools usually provide for a particular type of special need. Because of the highly specialist teaching and facilities offered by independent special schools, fees are often substantial. Where the LA agrees that a child should attend a particular school, it will normally pay the fees (sometimes in conjunction with Social Services or Health Services), provided that the school is one that has been approved by the Secretary of State for Education and Skills. In some cases, the fees are paid by parents. Parents with no right of abode in the UK should expect to meet the full cost of fees.

State-maintained boarding schools are few in number and are open only to UK and EU nationals and others with a right of residence in the UK. Fees are charged only for the cost of boarding at these schools, while tuition is free. Annual fees are therefore generally no more than £6,000 and in some cases considerably less. As indicated above, parents should take care to find out exactly how much help will be offered to a child with special needs.

In most cases, parents based overseas should expect to meet the cost of the fees for a boarding place. A boarding allowance is made for British parents employed by the Foreign & Commonwealth Office or by HM Forces. British parents living overseas may be eligible for LA support for a child being educated in the UK, but are strongly advised to take independent advice in accordance with their individual circumstances.

Non-British children of statutory school age, who are nationals of a member state of the European Union (EU) or of Iceland, Norway or Liechtenstein and who are being educated in the UK (whether accompanied by their parents or not), have the same rights to education in the UK as British citizens. Under reciprocal arrangements within the EU, those who hold the equivalent of a Statement of Special Educational Needs made in another EU country may be eligible for support from the LA covering the area of the UK in which they will be living, but parents should seek advice according to their particular circumstances. In practice, children who come to the UK unaccompanied may be more likely to attend a boarding school in the independent sector, for which parents will normally be required to meet the fees.

Unaccompanied children of statutory school age who do not have a right of abode in the UK are not normally allowed entry to take up a place at a state-maintained school. Entry to the UK for purposes of receiving an education is only permitted if the student can demonstrate that he or she has been accepted for a course of study at an independent educational institution.

It may be helpful to obtain a clear assessment of a child's needs in the home country for use in finding suitable UK schools. Some schools will reassess the child before offering a place.

### Points to remember about boarding education in the UK for parents resident overseas

The choice of a suitable boarding school requires careful research. As well as providing suitable provision for your child's special needs, the school must meet your child's wider needs and offer an environment in which he or she will feel happy and at home. Find out as much as possible about schools in which you are interested and visit them before making a choice. Consider in particular:

- *Your child's academic background.* If your child has been educated in the British system, it should not be difficult to join a school in the UK. Entry from a different national system is possible but may be less straightforward.

- *Your child's level of English.* Is additional support required?

- *Length of stay.* If the stay in the UK is expected to be relatively short, an international school may be more appropriate.

- *Location.* You may prefer a location that enables your child to be near friends or relatives, but most parts of the UK are well served by air, road and rail links, so it is not necessary to limit your search to schools close to major airports.

Further advice on the choice of a suitable mainstream school is given in Part 4.1.
Also bear in mind the following points:

- If your child is attending a boarding school in the UK while you are overseas, he or she must have a guardian in the UK, preferably living near the school, who will take responsibility for your child at weekends and other times when your child is out of school. While some residential special schools offer 52-week placements, most schools have three school holidays plus half-term holidays and exeats (weekends out of school). You may have friends or relatives in the UK able to care for your child during these periods, but this arrangement is not always suitable and may limit your choice of schools. If you have no contacts in the UK, talk to a reputable guardianship service provider such as Gabbitas who can find a family able to offer your child a safe and welcoming home-from-home and take care of other travel and administrative arrangements.

● Your child may require an escort during travel, which will incur additional costs. Some airlines issue a card to travellers who require special care and will provide the facilities requested free of charge each time a booking is made. Children with parents in the Forces may be entitled to have escorts provided by the British Red Cross or the Soldier, Sailor and Airforce Families Association (SSAFA).

● While you should receive regular progress reports from your child's school and guardian, communication with your child on a day-to-day basis may be difficult if his or her special needs give him or her limited or no speech unless he or she can use e-mail.

## Children accompanying their parents to the UK

Children accompanying parents who have the right of abode in, or leave to enter, the UK will normally be treated as dependants. Upon taking up residence in the UK, overseas parents living in the UK have the same right as anyone else with a right of abode in the UK to apply for a place at a maintained school. They also, therefore, have the same entitlement to have their child's educational needs met by their LA.

Whatever your requirements, you are strongly advised to seek specialist guidance in accordance with your own individual circumstances and the specific needs of your child. Further information may be available from your child's school, from any parents' support group to which you currently belong or from one of the associations listed at the back of this book.

# Education and Training for Young People with Disabilities or Learning Difficulties after Age 16

If you are nearly 16 years old, you will probably be thinking about education and training options ahead. You will need to consider what you are best at and what you would most like to do. You may also need to consider any extra support that you may need because of your disability or learning difficulty. This chapter explains the options available to you and the support you can expect because of your disability or learning difficulty.

## What choices are available at 16?

### School sixth form

You may be able to stay at your current school if it has a sixth form or you might want to go to a different sixth form for a particular course or better support. At sixth form you can take an academic course such as A levels, or a work-based course such as a National Vocational Qualification (NVQ). Your school should be able to give you advice about your options. If you are leaving your school, your Connexions Personal Adviser (PA) can help you to find a new place to learn or train (see below).

### Link courses

Many schools offer 'link courses'. These courses are based at school, but students attend a local further education college for part of their studies.

## Further education (FE) colleges

You may find that your local FE college offers a wider range of courses than is available at your school. These might include:

- Academic courses (GCSEs, A and AS levels).

- Work-based or work-related courses (National Vocational Qualifications (NVQs), including RSA, Edexcel or City & Guilds Institute qualifications).

- General courses to prepare you for adult life. These courses may not always lead to a qualification.

It is important to find a course that you like and to ensure that the college can offer you any extra support you need because of your disability or learning difficulty.

## Specialist colleges

You may find that your support needs cannot be met in a local school or college. If this is the case, there are specialist colleges that have extensive experience of teaching students with a particular type of disability or a range of different disabilities. These colleges are located around the country and recruit nationally, so you may have to travel to get there. Many specialist colleges are residential and can help you to learn to live away from home. Some colleges offer a range of education options, including those listed above under further education colleges.

Information on specialist residential colleges is given in Part 2.4 of this guide and the COPE Directory (of Post-16 residential education and training for young people with special educational needs). Your local careers/Connexions service should have a copy of the COPE Directory and they should be able to help you find the best college. You can also contact the Association of National Specialist Colleges (NATSPEC) for details of their colleges.

## Higher education

Once you have completed A levels or an equivalent qualification you may want to go on to higher education to study for a Higher National Certificate (HNC), Higher National Diploma (HND) Foundation Degree (FD) or a degree. Your school or college should be able to give advice on how to apply for higher education.

## Work-based learning opportunities

Work-based learning for young people is organized by the Local Authority. Young people are able to take up these opportunities when they leave school at 16 or 17.

- *Employment preparation,* which does not necessarily lead to a particular qualification, eg life skills training.

- *Entry to Employment (E2E)*, which provides high-quality work-based learning below NVQ Level 2 for young people at the pre-apprenticeship stage.

- *Apprenticeships,* which give school leavers training while they work within an industry. There are different levels of Apprenticeship available but they all lead to *National Vocational Qualifications (NVQs), Key Skills* qualifications and, in most cases, a technical certificate such as a *BTEC* or *City & Guilds.*

Your local careers/Connexions service can give you information on work-based learning opportunities in your area. If you want to know more about apprenticeships you should contact the National Apprenticeship Service (NAS), www.apprenticeships.org.uk. For information on training programmes for adults contact your local Jobcentre Plus.

## Paid time off for study or training

You can get 'reasonable' paid time off from work to study if you are 16 or 17 and employed but do not yet have a Level 2 qualification. The types of qualification you could study for include GCSEs, NVQs and BTECs. The study or training could be at a local college, by distance learning or in the workplace. Contact your local careers/Connexions service for further information.

# How do I find out what's available? Can anyone help me?

## Careers education at school

You should be given help to prepare for your future in Year 9. There may be a teacher who is responsible for careers education. There may also be a Connexions PA who comes into your school. The school should have access to careers information, such as books and leaflets about further education, training and careers. This information should be given to you in your preferred format. For example, if you read Braille, you should be given access to this information in Braille.

## Guidance on careers and future learning

From Year 9 onwards you may need independent information, advice and guidance on your future work or learning. This information is available from your local careers/ Connexions service.

In England every young person aged 13–19 should have access to a Connexions Personal Adviser (PA). If you have a disability you can continue to use Connexions until the age of 25. Connexions support young people at all times, especially at times of transition. Connexions services have access to a wide range of information about careers, employment and further study. Connexions PAs can help you to write a Career Action Plan, which includes your goals in education and employment and the steps you need to take to get there. They can advise you about different jobs available and the type of training or course required for the job of your choice. They can also tell you about courses in local schools and colleges and can direct you to your local careers library.

### Transition plan

If you have a Statement of Special Educational Needs (SEN), it should be reviewed every year. When you are 14 you should be involved in writing a transition plan that will help you think about what to do when you reach 16. Your Connexions PA or careers adviser should be able to assist you in finding another school, college, or training course if you are unable to stay at your school after 16. It is important that your Connexions PA or careers adviser helps you look at all of your options to choose what is most appropriate for you. Your Connexions PA or careers adviser should also attend your transition review meeting, which will be held at school. Your Connexions PA can help if you are having problems getting the support you need from your school or Local Authority (LA). Your parents or guardians should also be involved in ensuring that there is a good transition plan.

If you have a Statement of Special Educational Needs (SEN), your LA has a duty to arrange for you to have a Section 139a assessment. If you do not have a Statement of SEN but have a disability or learning difficulty and are likely to go on to college, training or university, your LA has the power to arrange a Section 139a assessment for you. Section 139a will set out your learning needs and the provision required to meet those needs.

### Social Services and Health Authority support

Arrangements for personal and medical care come from different sources. If you have a Statement of SEN your LA must work with the local Social Services and local Health Authority to meet your needs. This is particularly important when your transition plan is written and again when you are due to leave school.

Local Social Services or social work departments are required to provide certain services to young people and adults with disabilities. If you are worried that the department is not getting involved in your transition plan, you can contact your local Social Services or the social work department directly. Your Connexions PA can also speak to the different agencies involved and ensure that everything is paid for before you begin your course.

## How do I find out about courses?

### National Database of Accredited Qualifications

This is a searchable online database of qualifications accredited by the regulators of external exams, in England (Ofqual), Wales (DCELLS) and Northern Ireland (CCEA), www.accreditedqualifications.org.uk. You should be able to use this database at your local careers/Connexions service.

### Learndirect freephone (0800 100 900)

This is a free telephone helpline set up by the Government. The helpline can give information about course providers and qualifications needed to pursue particular careers. They can also tell you where you can get careers advice in your local area. See also www.learndirect.co.uk.

# Will I get the support or help I need because of my disability or learning difficulty?

### What happens to my Statement when I reach age 16?

A Statement of Special Educational Needs (SEN) sets out the type of educational support you need at school. The school has a legal duty to provide the support specified in your statement.

When you reach 16 your Statement will only continue to be a legal document if you stay at school. If you go to college, your Statement will no longer give you a legal right to the support it sets out. But your college will have a legal duty to assess your needs and provide you with the support you need.

### School

If you stay on in the same school or move to a different school, your Statement of SEN will continue to be a legal document and you should continue to get the support you had previously. As long as you remain at a school, your Local Authority (LA) must ensure that you receive the support you need.

### Local further education (FE) colleges

Local FE colleges receive money from their funding bodies to pay for additional support needed by students with disabilities or learning difficulties, for example additional study support for dyslexia students, an interpreter for deaf students or materials in alternative formats. Most FE colleges also offer study programmes specifically for people with learning difficulties, which include specialist help. These may be Basic Skills courses, which aim to develop numeracy and literacy skills, or Independent Living Skills courses that prepare students generally for adult life. Disability or Learning Support Coordinators are available at local FE colleges and their job is to coordinate disability support within the college. Before you start your course the college should look at what you will need to take part in the course. Sometimes you may need to have an assessment to find out what support suits you best. You should contact the college Disability or Learning Support Coordinator to discuss your individual support arrangements.

### Specialist further education (FE) colleges

Specialist FE colleges provide education exclusively for people with disabilities. Some specialist colleges provide education for students with any type of disability, while others provide education for students with specific disabilities. Going to a specialist college can give you access to specialist equipment, support and teaching that your local college may be unable to provide.

### Work-based learning

If you want to take up work-based learning when you leave school, you should be given enough support to enable you to take part in and complete successfully the training outlined in your Individual Training Plan. When you attend college, the college must ensure that you have the support you need to make the most of your studies. Your college also has a duty to ensure that you have the support you need while on work placements. If you are on an apprenticeship, you can apply for Access to Work to help meet the costs of any support you need while at work. For further information, contact the National Apprenticeship Agency (NAS).

## How is education and training after the age of 16 funded?

### Education up to 19

Sources of funding for education up to the age of 19 vary according to the type of education chosen.

### School

Your Local Authority will pay for your education if you stay at a school until you are 19. If you have a Statement of SEN you should continue to receive the support it sets out.

### Local further education (FE) colleges

In England, your Local Authority will also pay for your education up to the age of 19 at local or specialist FE colleges. If you have a Section 139a assessment, your Local Authority can pay for your education up to the age of 25. Courses for adult learners will be funded by the Skills Funding Agency (SFA). In Wales, the Department for Education, Lifelong Learning and Skills (DELLS) funds all further education.

In England and Wales you will not have to pay any tuition fees if you are studying full time at a further education college and are aged 16–19 years or up to 25 if you are studying for your first full Level 3 qualification, or at any age if you are studying for your first Level 2 qualification.

In Scotland, further education colleges receive funding from the Scottish Further Education Funding Council (SFEFC). You will not pay fees if you are a full-time student and meet the residency conditions. A college should not accept you unless it can offer the support that you need because of your disability or learning difficulty and must provide any equipment or extra support services you need. An assessment may be needed to find out exactly what is required.

## Education over 19

Funding for education should not stop when you reach 18 or 19. If you start a full-time course before you are 19, you should be funded until the end of your course. If you start a course once you are over 19, you may still be exempt from paying tuition fees. Colleges operate a fee-waiver scheme, whereby students on certain means-tested benefits do not have to pay tuition fees. Sometimes individual colleges will also waive or reduce the fees for students who do not receive any of these benefits but who nevertheless find it difficult to meet their course fees.

## Independent specialist colleges

If your disability-related needs can be met at a local FE college, then it is unlikely that you will receive government funding for a place at a specialist college. However, the Local Authority will fund a specialist place for a student up to the age of 25 if they have a Section 139a assessment and their needs cannot be met at a local college. When applying for funding you will need to provide certain forms of evidence that your needs cannot be met in a local FE college. Your Connexion PA can approach the funding bodies on your behalf.

Social Services may also pay or contribute towards a specialist place where the provision includes a strong care component.

In Scotland you may be able to obtain funding for a placement in an independent college through a bursary from the education department of your local council.

## Transport help and costs

Local Authorities (LAs) must publish an integrated transport plan and transport policy for learners aged 16–19. They also have a duty to make financial support or transport services provision available to students aged 16–18 and those aged 19 or over if they continue to attend a course they began before they were 19. This is to ensure they are not prevented from attending school or college because their fares are too high or because transport provision is inadequate. LAs are also required to produce a transport policy statement for post-19 disabled learners. When creating this policy they must consider their duty to provide suitable education and training that meets the reasonable needs of disabled learners aged 19 to 25.

To search for your local transportation policy, visit www.direct.gov.uk. LAs cannot refuse to help with transport costs on policy grounds without considering your individual circumstances.

Social Services also have the power to pay for transport, but may take their resources into account when deciding whether to provide transport.

FE colleges have Learner Support Funds (LSF) for students who face financial hardship. If your transport costs are very high, you can apply to the LSF for extra money.

In Scotland you should contact your college to see if you could get help with travel costs through a bursary. Learner Support Funds may be asked to contribute some of your EMA (see below).

## Benefits

When you are 16, you may be able to claim certain benefits in your own right, even if you are still studying. These include Employment and Support Allowance (ESA) and Disability Living Allowance (DLA). If you need help with the calculations or what you can claim, you should contact a local welfare rights unit or Citizens Advice.

## Bursary scheme

A bursary scheme exists for students aged between 16 and 19 years facing financial hardship while in full-time education.

Schools, colleges and training providers will be responsible for awarding bursaries. In most cases they decide on the amount, when it's paid and whether it's linked to behaviour or attendance, although there are exceptions. For example, those most in need (those in care, care leavers or those claiming income support) are guaranteed a bursary of £1,200.

# Applying to Higher Education – Guidance for Disabled People

For many people the prospect of entering higher education is becoming more attractive. Everyone considering entry to college or university should ask questions about courses and facilities. However, disabled students are likely to have other concerns too. These might include, for example, provision of learning materials in accessible formats such as Braille, wheelchair access to lecture halls or the extent to which an institution will understand the difficulties encountered by a student with dyslexia.

## What is higher education?

Higher education is any course that leads to a certain level of qualification. It includes the following.

*Undergraduate studies leading to:*

- a first degree (BSc, BA, BEd, LLB, BDS, MBBS, BEng, BMus, or at some Scottish universities BMed);

- undergraduate Master's degree (MEng, MSci, MPharm, MPhys, MA in Scotland);

- a National Vocational Qualification (NVQ4 or 5) linked with a degree, a diploma of higher education (DipHE) or job-related courses such as Diploma in Nursing;

- a Higher National Diploma (HND) or Higher National Certificate (HNC), often more work-related than other undergraduate qualifications;

- foundation degree or other vocational courses.

*Postgraduate studies leading to:*

- a Master's degree (MA, MSc, MEd, MPhil);
- a doctorate (PhD or DPhil);
- a Postgraduate Certificate of Education (PGCE);
- other postgraduate diplomas.

These courses are offered in universities and colleges around the country. Some further education colleges also offer higher education courses.

## Higher education – is it for me?

You could go into higher education for a number of reasons. This might be in preparation for a chosen career, for the experience, to study a subject you enjoy or to develop a new interest. Higher education can also offer opportunities to take up other activities, gain independence and meet new people.

## Will I get the funding I need?

Money is a big issue for all students. If you have study-related needs because of your disability, you may be eligible for Disabled Students' Allowances to help pay for additional costs such as equipment, non-medical helper support or travel. Contact Skill for further information on funding disabled students in higher education and claiming Disabled Students' Allowances.

## How do I choose the right course?

You should start your search for a university or college like any other student – by choosing a course to study. There are several questions to consider, including:

- Is the course essential for your proposed work or career plans? Would it be helpful?
- Could you still pursue your ambitions with a degree or HND in any subject?
- What subjects are you interested in? Does the content of your course reflect your interests?
- Would you prefer to study full time or part time?
- Which teaching methods are used?
- Which assessment methods are used?
- What level of course do you require?

- Can you fulfil the entry requirements? Is there a related course with different requirements?
- Are you seeking a course that includes work experience or study abroad?

## Where should I study?

You may be tempted to apply only to institutions that have good provision for disabled students. But choosing the right institution and course for you as an individual is very important. A good way to start is to prepare a list of places that offer the courses that interest you. Then think through the following issues:

| | |
|---|---|
| *Academic considerations:* | Facilities and reputation of the college? Academic support, eg personal tutor? Library facilities? |
| *Location:* | Near home, or away from home? Campus or city site? Near to transport? |
| *Money:* | How much are the fees? What bursaries and scholarships are available? |
| *Student community:* | How many students are there? What age groups? |
| *Recreation and leisure:* | Town facilities, sports, hobbies, students' union? |
| *Access:* | To lecture theatres and teaching rooms? To the library, photocopier, etc? To a parking space? To the bar and canteen? To sports facilities? In other ways, eg induction loops, clear signs, good lighting? |
| *Experience:* | Other disabled students? Staff attitude to you as a disabled person? |
| *Accommodation:* | Is it accessible? Would you be integrated with other students? Could equipment be installed or adaptations made? Would a room be provided for your personal assistant? What are the fire procedures for disabled students? |
| *Disability support:* | Talk to the disabled student's adviser about the support available. Is there a suitable centre available locally for medical treatment? Any particular facilities for disabled students, eg Braille embosser, dyslexia support tutor, sign language interpreter unit, campus minibus, note-takers? If these are not available, can they be arranged in time for the start of your course? |

# How do I find out more about a college or university?

### Website and prospectus

All colleges and universities have websites where you can find listings of courses and information on student services, visits and open days.

Prospectuses are produced which provide information about the general facilities as well as course details. Most also give some details of facilities for disabled students. They may also give a contact name for the disability coordinator.

### Disability equality scheme

All higher education institutions are required to produce a disability equality scheme that sets out how they intend to improve disability equality for staff and students. The scheme can also give information on the general support provided for disabled people. You could ask for a copy to be sent along with the prospectus, or read it on the institution's website.

### Student union or association

The student union or association may produce its own information about the college or university and may have its own disability support structures and policy.

### Making contact

If your questions are not answered by the prospectus, website or other written information, you could contact the institution. For information on disability-related provision contact the disability coordinator, who is responsible for services for disabled students.

### Skill's 'Into Higher Education'

You can search this online database for the contact details of disability coordinators and the disability equality scheme at the institutions you are interested in; see: www.skill.org.uk.

### Making a visit

The best way to find out what a university or college is like is to visit. Many places welcome early informal 'information visits'. Try to visit during term time or semester, when you are more likely to meet other students and will be able to form a more accurate picture.

# How do I apply?

### The application form

Applications for most courses are made through the Universities and Colleges Admissions Service (UCAS). Most UCAS applications are now made online.

## *Your disability*

As part of UCAS online applications you are asked to choose a disability category. Some people worry that disclosing a disability at this stage may leave them vulnerable to discrimination. However, Part 4 of the Disability Discrimination Act (DDA) 1995 exists to protect disabled people against discrimination in education. (It is worth remembering that if you do experience discrimination, you will only be protected by the DDA 1995 if the university or college knows or 'could reasonably have known' about your disability. For more information about the DDA, contact Skill.) You may also wish to consider the following when making your mind up about disclosing your disability:

- If you need additional disability-related support from the university or college, you may wish to disclose your disability at an early stage to ensure that the support is in place from the beginning of the course.

- You may have had an unusual academic career because of your disability, eg taking exams later than usual. Disclosing your disability may help to explain this.

- Your disability may not affect your study. Similarly, if you are receiving support from a source other than the university or college, you may feel that disclosing your disability is unnecessary.

- If you choose not to disclose your disability at application stage, you should still be given opportunities to do so once you have been accepted onto the course.

The decision about what to write is yours and you must feel comfortable with it. Beware of using terms that admissions tutors may not understand. The institution is interested in two things: how your disability may affect your studies and what kind of support you will need.

If you cannot fill in the form yourself because of your disability, ask someone to type or write your answers for you. Your referee can explain in his or her confidential report the method used and the reasons for it.

## Selection interviews

If you are invited to attend an interview, let the institution know if you need any particular access arrangements. You may be asked about your disability, for example about adapting course material to suit your needs. Be prepared to speak clearly and confidently about potential problems and solutions. It is best if these points have already been discussed during your information visit.

## Admissions tests

Some institutions have introduced admissions tests for their most popular subjects. If you are required to sit an admissions test you may want to discuss your access needs with the institution's disability coordinator.

## Offers

Admissions tutors decide whether to offer you a place and the offer will usually be a conditional offer. This means that your exam results must meet the UCAS point and grade requirements of the course.

## Rejections

Institutions rarely give reasons for a rejection. If you think you have been rejected because of your disability, contact the institution to request the reason. If you believe you have been discriminated against you have the right to make a complaint. Contact Skill for more information on how to proceed. If the institution is unable to meet your needs, UCAS will allow you to substitute another choice of institution.

## Do I need support?

Do not be afraid to use support. It does not make you different from other students; it is intended to enable you to study and participate with other students. You can always change your support arrangements, eg if your needs change or if the support turns out to be unsuitable.

## How do I find out more?

There are many websites and directories containing information about higher education courses. A list of suggested titles is given in the Bibliography in Part 5.

## PART TWO

# SPECIAL SCHOOLS AND COLLEGES – INDEPENDENT AND NON-MAINTAINED

**2.1**

# Notes on the Directory

## Type of school

Part 2 of *Schools for Special Needs* contains two directories covering establishments in England, Scotland, Northern Ireland and Wales:

1 Independent and non-maintained schools

2 Colleges and other provision at 16+

### Independent and non-maintained schools

The term 'special school' covers a wide range of different types of school. Special schools that are provided by a Local Authority (LA) (maintained special schools) are listed in Part 3. 'Nonmaintained special school' is a technical term which is often abbreviated as NMSS. These schools take pupils with Statements and must comply with detailed regulations. Matters covered in the regulations include admission arrangements, governing body, teaching staff and many other aspects. They must be constituted as registered charities and, although they are not funded directly by a Local Authority, all or most of their pupils are placed by the LA under a Statement, and the LA pays all fees. Some of these schools provide residential accommodation. Where this is for 52 weeks in the year, the school will be registered as a Children's Home and will be inspected by Ofsted accordingly. Independent special schools may be charities but are not required to be. They may be owned either by an individual or by a limited company or group of companies. The proportion of children placed by parents or by LAs will vary from school to school. These schools are classified as 'Independent Schools' and will be equipped to take children with particular types of special needs, whether they have a Statement or not.

### Colleges and other provision at 16+

These are divided between maintained, non-maintained and independent. Maintained provision is listed in Part 3. Some establishments will be residential communities registered under the Care Standards Act and will provide care and educational opportunities for people from 16 until well into adulthood.

# Entries in the directory

Every effort has been made to compile a comprehensive list of schools and provision at 16+. Each entry includes the school name, address, web address (where available), and the age range and gender of students accepted. Schools may be independent or non-maintained, or in Scotland voluntary aided or grant aided. The status of each school is given where known. Entries also indicate whether or not the school offers 52-week care.

The types of need for which a school or college makes provision are shown in abbreviated form. A key to the abbreviations used is given below. The principal types of special needs catered for are shown in bold (in addition to catering for the special needs specified, all schools and colleges recognize their responsibilities under the Disability Discrimination Act 1995 to consider the needs of all disabled children and to make reasonable adjustments to facilitate the admission of such children to the school). Please note that this information is intended as a guide only. For further information contact schools directly.

# Key to abbreviations used in the directory

## *Special needs provision*

| | | | | |
|---|---|---|---|---|
| ADD | Attention Deficit Disorder | | EPI | Epilepsy |
| ADHD | Attention Deficit Hyperactivity Disorder | | HEA | Health Problems (eg heart defect, asthma) |
| ASD | Autistic Spectrum Disorder | | HI | Hearing Impairment |
| ASP | Asperger's Syndrome | | IM | Impaired Mobility |
| BESD | Behavioural, Emotional and Social Disorders | | MLD | Moderate Learning Difficulties |
| CB | Challenging Behaviour | | PMLD | Profound and Multiple Learning Difficulties |
| CP | Cerebral Palsy | | SLD | Severe Learning Difficulties |
| DOW | Down's Syndrome | | SP&LD | Speech and Language Difficulties |
| DYC | Dyscalculia | | | |
| DYP | Dyspraxia | | TOU | Tourette's Syndrome |
| DYS | Dyslexia | | VI | Visual Impairment |

## *Wheelchair access*

W       Wheelchair access (unspecified)
WA1     School is fully wheelchair accessible in all areas
WA2     Main teaching areas are wheelchair accessible
WA3     No permanent access for wheelchairs; temporary ramps available

## *Symbol*

+       Registered with CReSTeD (see Part 5.1)

## 2.2

# Directory of Independent and Non-Maintained Special Schools

# England

## BERKSHIRE

**ANNIE LAWSON SCHOOL**
Nine Mile Ride, Ravens Wood
Village, Crowthorne,
Berkshire RG45 6BQ
*Type:* Co-educational Boarding
and Day 11–19
*Special needs:* ASD **ASP** CB
CP EPI HEA HI **PMLD SLD**
SP&LD VI
*Wheelchair access:* W
*Independent Special*

**ELLESMERE COLLEGE**
Hermitage, Thatcham,
Berkshire RG18 9NU
*Website:* www.priorscourt.org.uk
*Type:* Co-educational Boarding
and Day 5–19
*Special needs:* ADHD ASD **ASP**
CB EPI HEA MLD SLD SP&LD
*Wheelchair access:* WA2
*Independent Special*

**HEATHERMOUNT SCHOOL**
Devenish Road, Ascot,
Berkshire SL5 9PG
*Type:* Co-educational Boarding
and Day 3–19
*Special needs:* **ASD** ASP
*Wheelchair access:* W
*Non-maintained*

**HIGH CLOSE SCHOOL
(BARNARDO'S)**
Wiltshire Road, Wokingham,
Berkshire RG40 1TT
*Website:* www.barnardos.org.uk/
highcloseschool
*Type:* Co-educational Boarding
and Day 9–16
*Special needs:* **ADD ADHD**
ASD ASP **BESD CB** DYC DYP
DYS HEA MLD SP&LD
*Wheelchair access:* WA1
*Non-maintained*

**MARY HARE SCHOOL FOR
THE DEAF**
Arlington Manor, Snelsmore
Common, Newbury, Berkshire
RG14 3BQ
*Website:* www.maryhare.org.uk
*Type:* Co-educational Boarding
and Day 11–19
*Special needs:* **HI**
*Wheelchair access:* WA2
*Non-maintained*

**PRIOR'S COURT SCHOOL\***
Hermitage, Thatcham,
Berkshire RG18 9NU
*Website:* www.priorscourt.org.uk
*Type:* Co-educational Boarding
and Day 5–19
*Special needs:* **ASD** CB EPI
MLD SLD SP&LD
*Wheelchair access:* WA2
*Independent Special*

**THAMES VALLEY SCHOOL\***
Conwy Close, Tilehurst,
Reading, Berkshire RG30
*Website:* www.
thamesvalleyfreeschool.co.uk
*Type:* Co-educational Day Only
4–16
*Special needs:* **ASD ASP** CB
*Independent Special*

# BRISTOL

**BELGRAVE SCHOOL**
10 Upper Belgrave Road,
Clifton, Bristol BS8 2XH
*Website:*
www.belgrave-school.org
*Type:* Co-educational Day Only
5–13
*Special needs:* ADD ASD ASP
DYC DYP **DYS** SP&LD
*Wheelchair access:* WA3
*Independent Special*

**NAS ANDERSON SCHOOL\***
Rookery Lane, Pilning,
Bristol BS35 4JN
*Website:* www.autism.org.uk/
andersonschool
*Type:* Co-educational Boarding
and Day 10–16
*Special needs:* **ASD ASP** CB
*Independent Special*
*52-week care*

**ST CHRISTOPHER'S SCHOOL**
Carisbrooke Lodge, Westbury
Park, Bristol BS6 7JE
*Website:*
www.st-christophers.bristol.sch.uk
*Type:* Co-educational Boarding
Only 5–19
*Special needs:* ASD CB CP EPI
**PMLD SLD**
*Wheelchair access:* WA1
*Independent Special*
*52-week care*

**SHEILING SCHOOL,
CAMPHILL COMMUNITY
THORNBURY**
Thornbury Park, Park Road,
Thornbury, Bristol BS35 1HP
*Website:*
www.sheilingschool.org.uk
*Type:* Co-educational Boarding
and Day 7–19
*Special needs:* ADD ADHD ASD
ASP BESD CP DOW DYP EPI
HEA MLD SLD SP&LD
*Wheelchair access:* WA2

# BUCKINGHAMSHIRE

**MACINTYRE SCHOOL
WINGRAVE**
Leighton Road, Wingrave,
Aylesbury, Buckinghamshire
HP22 4PA
*Website:*
www.macintyrecharity.org
*Type:* Co-educational Boarding
and Day 10–19
*Special needs:* ASD CB EPI
PMLD **SLD** SP&LD
*Wheelchair access:* WA1
*Independent Special*
*52-week care*

**PENN SCHOOL**
Church Road, Penn, High
Wycombe, Buckinghamshire
HP10 8LZ
*Website:*
www.pennschool.bucks.sch.uk
*Type:* Co-educational Day and
Boarding 11–19
*Special needs:* **ASD** ASP
SP&LD
*Non-maintained*

**WALNUT TREE LODGE
SCHOOL**
Avenue Farm Lane, Wilden,
Buckinghamshire MK44 2PY
*Type:* Co-educational Day Only
11–16
*Special needs:* BESD
*Independent Special*

# CAMBRIDGESHIRE

**CHARTWELL HOUSE SCHOOL**
Goodens Lane,
Newton, Wisbech,
Cambridgeshire PE13 5HQ
*Website:*
www.thechartwellgroup.co.uk
*Type:* Boys Boarding Only 10–16
*Special needs:* ADD ADHD ASP
**BESD** CB DYC DYP DYS MLD
TOU
*Wheelchair access:* WA2
*Independent Special*
*52-week care*

**DOWNHAM LODGE SCHOOL**
1 Second Drove,
Little Downham, Ely,
Cambridgeshire CB6 2UD
*Website:*
www.thechartwellgroup.co.uk/
downham-lodge-little-
downham.html
*Type:* Boys Boarding and
Day 10–16
*Special needs:* BESD

**STATION SCHOOL**
5 Station Approach, March,
Cambridgeshire PE15 8SJ
*Type:* Co-educational Day Only
11–16
*Special needs:* BESD
*Wheelchair access:* W

# CHESHIRE

**ACORNS SCHOOL**
19b Hibbert Lane,
Marple, Stockport,
Cheshire SK6 7NN
*Type:* Co-educational Day Only
5–16
*Special needs:* BESD

**CHAIGELEY SCHOOL**
Lymm Road, Thelwall,
Warrington, Cheshire WA4 2TE
*Type:* Boys Boarding and Day
8–16
*Special needs:* ADD ADHD
**BESD**
*Wheelchair access:* W
*Non-maintained*

**CORNERSTONES**
2 Victoria Road,
Grappenhell, Warrington,
Cheshire WA4 2EN
*Type:* Boys Day Only 8–18
*Special needs:* **ASD ASP BESD**
**CB EPI SLD** SP&LD
*Wheelchair access:* WA3
*52-week care*

**THE DAVID LEWIS SCHOOL**
Mill Lane, Warford, Nr Alderley
Edge, Cheshire SK9 7UD
*Website:* www.davidlewis.org.uk
*Type:* Co-educational Boarding
and Day 7–19
*Special needs:* ASD **ASP CP**
**EPI PMLD SLD** SP&LD
*Wheelchair access:* WA1
*Non-maintained*
*52-week care*

**DELAMERE FOREST SCHOOL**
Blakemere Lane, Norley,
Frodsham, Warrington,
Cheshire WA6 6NP
*Type:* Co-educational Boarding
and Day 6–17 (Jewish boarders
only)
*Special needs:* ADD ADHD
**ASD** ASP BESD DOW DYP DYS
EPI HEA **MLD** SP&LD TOU

**HALTON SCHOOL**
31 Main Street, Halton Village,
Halton, Runcorn,
Cheshire WA7 2AN
*Type:* Co-educational Day Only
7–14
*Special needs:* ADD ADHD
**BESD** CB DYC DYP DYS MLD
*Wheelchair access:* W

**LAMBS GRANGE
RESIDENTIAL AND DAY
EDUCATION AND CARE**
Forest Road, Cuddington,
Cheshire CW8 2EH
*Website:* www.lambs-group.co.uk
*Type:* Co-educational Boarding
and Day 14–19
*Special needs:* ASD **ASP** CB
EPI PMLD SLD SP&LD
*Wheelchair access:* W
*52-week care*

**ROYAL SCHOOL
MANCHESTER**
Stanley Road, Cheadle Hulme,
Cheadle, Cheshire SK8 6RQ
*Website:* www.seashelltrust.org.uk
*Type:* Co-educational Boarding
and Day 2–22
*Special needs:* ASD **ASP** CB
CP DOW EPI HEA **HI IM PMLD
SLD** SP&LD VI
*Wheelchair access:* WA2
*Non-maintained*
*52-week care*

**THE ST JOHN VIANNEY
SCHOOL**
(Lower School), Didsbury Road,
Heaton Mersey, Stockport,
Cheshire SK4 2AA
*Website:* www.stjohnvianney.co.uk
*Type:* Co-educational Day Only
5–11
*Special needs:* **ADD** ADHD ASD
ASP CP **DOW** DYP **MLD** SP&LD
*Wheelchair access:* W

# CUMBRIA

**APPLETREE SCHOOL**
Natland, Kendal,
Cumbria LA9 7QS
*Website:*
www.appletreeschool.co.uk
*Type:* Co-educational Boarding
Only 6–12
*Special needs:* **ADD ADHD**
**BESD CB** DYP DYS **MLD**
SP&LD
*Wheelchair access:* WA2
*Independent Special*
*52-week care*

**EDEN GROVE SCHOOL**
Bolton, Appleby,
Cumbria CA16 6AJ
*Website:* www.priorygroup.com/
edengrove
*Type:* Co-educational Boarding
and Day 8–19
*Special needs:* **ADHD** ASD ASP
**BESD** CB MLD SP&LD TOU
*Wheelchair access:* W
*Independent Special*
*52-week care*

**WHINFELL CARE**
Kendal, Cumbria
*Website:*
www.whinfellschool.co.uk
*Type:* Boys Boarding Only
11–19
*Special needs:* **ADD ADHD**
**ASD ASP BESD CB DYP DYS**
**MLD SLD** SP&LD **TOU**
*Wheelchair access:* WA3
*52-week care*

**WINGS SCHOOL**
Whassett, Milnthorpe,
Cumbria LA7 7DN
*Website:*
www.wingsschool.co.uk
*Type:* Co-educational Boarding
Only 11–17
*Special needs:* ADD ADHD ASP
**BESD** DYP DYS MLD
*Wheelchair access:* WA3
*Independent Special*
*52-week care*

**WITHERSLACK HALL**
Witherslack,
Grange-over-Sands,
Cumbria LA11 6SD
*Website:*
www.witherslackhallschool.co.uk
*Type:* Boys Day and Boarding
10–19
*Special needs:* **ADD ADHD**
**ASD ASP BESD CB** DYP **DYS**
**MLD** SP&LD
*Independent Special*
*52-week care*

# DERBYSHIRE

**ALDERWASLEY HALL**
**SCHOOL AND CALLOW PARK**
**COLLEGE**
Alderwasley, Belper,
Derbyshire DE56 2SR
*Website:*
www.alderwasleyhall.com
*Type:* Co-educational Day and
Boarding 5–19
*Special needs:* ADD ADHD
**ASD ASP BESD CB DYC DYP**
DYS EPI HEA HI SP&LD VI
*Wheelchair access:* WA2
*Independent Special*
*52-week care*

**EASTWOOD GRANGE**
**SCHOOL**
Milken Lane, Ashover,
Nr Chesterfield,
Derbyshire S45 0BA
*Website:* www.priorygroup.com
*Type:* Boys Day and Boarding
11–16
*Special needs:* **ADD** ADHD
**BESD CB**
*Wheelchair access:* W
*Independent Special*
*52-week care*

**NEW DIRECTION SCHOOL**
Ringer Lane, Clowne,
Chesterfield,
Derbyshire S43 4BX
*Type:* Co-educational 11–16
*Special needs:* ASD ASP BESD
MLD SLD
*Independent Special*

**PEGASUS SCHOOL**
Caldwell Hall, Main Street,
Swadlincote, Caldwell,
Derbyshire DE12 6RS
*Website:* www.senadgroup.com/
pegasus
*Type:* Co-educational Day and
Boarding 8–19 (Places for up to
23 students.)
*Special needs:* **ADD ADHD**
ASD **ASP** BESD **CB** DOW DYP
**EPI HEA HI IM** MLD **PMLD SLD**
SP&LD **TOU** VI
*Wheelchair access:* WA3
*Independent Special*
*52-week care*

**ROYAL SCHOOL FOR THE DEAF DERBY***
Ashbourne Road, Derby,
Derbyshire DE22 3BH
*Website:* www.rsd-derby.org.uk
*Type:* Co-educational Boarding and Day 3–19
*Special needs:* **HI**
*Wheelchair access:* WA1
*Non-maintained*

**THE TRUST CENTRE**
C/O Alderwasley Hall School,
Alderwasley, Belper,
Derbyshire DE56 2SR
*Website:*
www.thetrustcentre.com
*Type:* Co-educational Day and Boarding 9–19
*Special needs:* **BESD CB** CP **EPI HEA HI IM** SP&LD VI W
*Independent Special*
*52-week care*

# DEVON

**CHELFHAM MILL SCHOOL**
Chelfham, Barnstaple,
Devon EX32 7LA
*Website:*
www.chelfhammillschool.co.uk
*Type:* Boys Boarding and Day 7–16
*Special needs:* ADD **ADHD ASD ASP BESD CB** DYS EPI MLD TOU
*Wheelchair access:* W
*Independent Special*
*52-week care*

**CHELFHAM SENIOR SCHOOL**
Bere Alston, Yelverton,
Devon PL20 7EX
*Website:*
www.prioryeducation.com
*Type:* Boys Boarding and Day 7–19
*Special needs:* ADD **ADHD** ASD ASP **BESD** CB MLD SP&LD **TOU**
*Wheelchair access:* W
*Independent Special*
*52-week care*

**DAME HANNAH ROGERS SCHOOL**
Woodland Road, Ivybridge,
Devon PL21 9HQ
*Website:* www.damehannah.com
*Type:* Co-educational Boarding and Day 5–19
*Special needs:* **CP** EPI HEA IM **MLD PMLD SLD** SP&LD VI
*Wheelchair access:* W WA1
*Non-maintained*
*52-week care*

**NAS BROOMHAYES SCHOOL**
The National Autistic Society,
Kingsley House,
Alverdiscott Road, Bideford,
Devon EX39 4PL
*Website:* www.autism.org.uk/
broomhayes
*Type:* Co-educational Day and Boarding 12–25 (Students can be admitted up to the age of 18 years but there is provision for residential accommodation up to 25)
*Special needs:* **ASD ASP**
*Wheelchair access:* W
*Independent Special*
*52-week care*

**ROYAL WEST OF ENGLAND SCHOOL FOR THE DEAF**
50 Topsham Road, Exeter,
Devon EX2 4NF
*Website:* www.rsd-exeter.ac.uk
*Type:* Co-educational Boarding and Day 3–19
*Special needs:* BESD CP **HI** MLD SLD VI

**VRANCH HOUSE SCHOOL**
Pinhoe Road, Exeter,
Devon EX4 8AD
*Type:* Co-educational Day Only 2–12
*Special needs:* **CP** MLD PMLD SP&LD
*Wheelchair access:* W

**THE WEST OF ENGLAND SCHOOL AND COLLEGE FOR PUPILS WITH LITTLE OR NO SIGHT**
Countess Wear, Exeter,
Devon EX2 6HA
*Website:*
www.westengland.org.uk
*Type:* Co-educational Boarding and Day 2–22
*Special needs:* VI
*Wheelchair access:* W

**WHITSTONE HEAD SCHOOL**
Whitstone, Holsworthy,
Devon EX22 6TJ
*Website:*
www.whitstoneheadschool.ik.org
*Type:* Co-educational Boarding and Day 10–16
*Special needs:* **ADD ADHD ASD ASP BESD** DYS HEA MLD TOU
*Wheelchair access:* WA3
*Non-maintained*

# DORSET

### THE FORUM SCHOOL
Shillingstone, Dorset DT11 0QS
*Website:* www.cambiangroup.
com/specialist_education
*Type:* Co-educational Boarding
Only 7–19 (Mixed gender
7–19 years)
*Special needs:* **ASD CB** EPI
HEA **MLD** SP&LD
*Wheelchair access:* WA1
*Independent Special*
*38 and 52-week care*

### LANGSIDE SCHOOL
Langside Avenue, Parkstone,
Poole, Dorset BH12 5BN
*Type:* Co-educational Day Only
2–18
*Special needs:* CP EPI HEA
**PMLD SLD** VI
*Wheelchair access:* WA1

### PHILIP GREEN MEMORIAL
### SCHOOL
Boveridge House, Cranborne,
Wimborne, Dorset BH21 5RU
*Website:* www.pgmschool.org.uk
*Type:* Co-educational Boarding
and Day 11–19
*Special needs:* ADD ASD ASP
BESD CB DOW DYP EPI HEA HI
**MLD SLD** SP&LD
*Independent Special*

### PORTFIELD SCHOOL
Parley Lane, Christchurch,
Dorset BH23 6BP
*Website:* www.twas.org.uk
*Type:* Co-educational Boarding
and Day (45 students are at
the main school at Parley and
14 students attend Lifeskills.)
*Special needs:* ASD **ASP**
*Wheelchair access:* W
*Non-maintained*
*52-week care*

### PURBECK VIEW SCHOOL
Northbrook Road, Swanage,
Dorset BH19 1PR
*Website:* www.cambiangroup.
com/specialist_education
*Type:* Co-educational 7–19
(Mixed gender
9–19 years)
*Special needs:* **ASD CB** EPI
HEA **MLD** SP&LD
*Independent Special*
*38 and 52-week care*

### VICTORIA EDUCATION
### CENTRE
12 Lindsay Road, Branksome
Park, Poole, Dorset BH13 6AS
*Type:* Co-educational Day and
Boarding
*Special needs:* **CP DYP** DYS
EPI **HEA** HI **MLD** SLD SP&LD
*Wheelchair access:* WA1
*Non-maintained*

# ESSEX

### DOUCECROFT SCHOOL
Abbotts Lane, Colchester,
Essex CO6 3QL
*Website:*
www.essexautistic.org.uk
*Type:* Co-educational Boarding
and Day 2–19
*Special needs:* **ASD ASP**
*Wheelchair access:* W

### JACQUES HALL
Harwich Road, Bradfield,
Manningtree, Essex CO11 2XW
*Website:* www.priorygroup.com
*Type:* Co-educational Boarding
and Day 11–18
*Special needs:* **ADD ADHD**
ASD **BESD** CB MLD SP&LD
TOU
*Wheelchair access:* W
*Independent Special*
*52-week care*

### THE RYES COLLEGE &
### COMMUNITY
Ryes Lane, Little Henny,
Sudbury, Essex CO10 7EA
*Website:*
www.theryescollege.org.uk
*Type:* Co-educational Boarding
Only 7–16
*Special needs:* **ADD ADHD**
**ASD ASP BESD CB** CP DYS
EPI HEA **MLD PMLD SLD**
SP&LD **TOU**
*Independent Special*
*52-week care*

### ST JOHN'S RC SCHOOL
Turpins Lane, Woodford Bridge,
Essex IG8 8AX
*Website:*
www.stjohnsrcschool.co.uk
*Type:* Co-educational Day Only
5–19
*Special needs:* **MLD** SLD SP&LD
*Non-maintained*

### WOODCROFT SCHOOL
Whitakers Way, Loughton,
Essex IG10 1SQ
*Website:*
www.woodcroftschool.net
*Type:* Co-educational Day Only
2–12
*Special needs:* ADD ADHD ASD
**ASP CB** DYP DYS EPI HEA
MLD **SLD** SP&LD TOU
*Wheelchair access:* WA3
*Independent Special*

# GLOUCESTERSHIRE

**COTSWOLD CHINE SCHOOL***
Box, Stroud, Gloucestershire
GL6 9AG
*Website:*
www.cotswold-chine.org.uk
*Type:* Co-educational
Boarding and Day 9–19
(and exceptionally from 8)
*Special needs:* **ADD ADHD**
**ASD ASP BESD** CB DYP EPI
**MLD** SLD SP&LD TOU
*Wheelchair access:* WA3
*Independent Special*

**MARLOWE EDUCATION UNIT**
Hartpury Old School,
Gloucester Road, Hartpury,
Gloucestershire GL19 3BG
*Type:* Co-educational Day Only
8–16
*Special needs:* **BESD**

**ST ROSE'S SCHOOL**
Stratford Lawn, Stroud,
Gloucestershire GL5 4AP
*Website:* www.stroses.org.uk
*Type:* Co-educational Boarding
and Day 2–19
*Special needs:* ASP **CP** DOW
**DYP EPI** HEA HI **IM MLD PMLD**
SLD SP&LD VI
*Wheelchair access:* WA2
*Non-maintained*

**WILLIAM MORRIS HOUSE
CAMPHILL COMMUNITY**
William Morris House,
Eastington, Stonehouse,
Gloucestershire GL10 3S
*Website:* www.wmcc.ac.uk
*Special needs:* ASD ASP DOW
**MLD**

# HAMPSHIRE

**COXLEASE SCHOOL**
High Coxlease House,
Clay Hill, Lyndhurst,
Hampshire SO43 7DE
*Website:* www.priorygroup.com/
coxlease
*Type:* Co-educational Boarding
and Day 9–18
*Special needs:* **ADD ADHD**
ASD ASP **BESD** CB MLD TOU
*Wheelchair access:* W
*Independent Special*
*52-week care*

**GRATELEY HOUSE SCHOOL**
Grateley, Andover,
Hampshire SP11 8TA
*Website:* www.cambiangroup.
com/specialist_education
*Type:* Co-educational Boarding
and Day 9–19 (Mixed gender
9–19 years)
*Special needs:* ADHD **ASP CB**
DYC DYP DYS EPI MLD
SP&LD **TOU**
*Independent Special*

**HILL HOUSE SCHOOL**
Rope Hill, Boldre, Lymington,
Hampshire SO41 8NE
*Website:* www.cambiangroup.
com/specialist_education
*Type:* Co-educational Boarding
Only 11–19 (Mixed gender
11–19 years)
*Special needs:* **ASD CB EPI**
HEA **MLD SLD** SP&LD
*Independent Special*
*52-week care*

**HOPE LODGE SCHOOL**
22 Midanbury Lane, Bitterne
Park, Southampton, Hampshire
SO18 4HP
*Website:* www.has.org.uk
*Type:* Co-educational Boarding
and Day 4–19
*Special needs:* **ASD ASP** SLD
SP&LD
*Wheelchair access:* WA2
*Independent Special*
*52-week care*

**LODDON SCHOOL**
Wildmoor, Sherfield-on-Loddon,
Hook, Hampshire RG27 0JD
*Website:*
www.Loddon-school.co.uk
*Type:* Co-educational Boarding
Only 8–18
*Special needs:* **ADD ADHD**
ASD **ASP** BESD CB DOW **EPI**
**SLD** SP&LD VI *52-week care*

**ROSEWOOD SCHOOL**
The Bradbury Centre, 300
Aldermoor Road, Southampton,
Hampshire SO16 5NA
*Website:* www.roseroad.co.uk
*Type:* Co-educational Day Only
2–19
*Special needs:* CP EPI HEA HI
IM **PMLD** SLD SP&LD VI
*Wheelchair access:* WA1

**ST EDWARD'S SCHOOL**
Melchet Court, Sherfield English,
Romsey, Hampshire S051 6ZR
*Website:* www.melchetcourt.com
*Type:* Boys Boarding and Day
10–17
*Special needs:* ADD ADHD ASD
ASP BESD DYS MLD SP&LD
*Wheelchair access:* WA3
*Independent Special*

### THE SHEILING SCHOOL RINGWOOD
Horton Road, Ashley, Ringwood, Hampshire BH24 2EB
*Website:*
www.sheilingschool.co.uk
*Type:* Co-educational Boarding and Day 6–19
*Special needs:* ADD ADHD ASD BESD CB CP DOW DYP EPI HEA IM MLD **SLD** SP&LD
*Wheelchair access:* WA2
*Independent Special*

### SOUTHERN ENGLAND PSYCHOLOGICAL SERVICES
Fair Oak, Eastleigh, Hampshire SO50 7DE
*Website:* www.drludwigfredlowenstein.com
*Type:* Co-educational Boarding and Day 5–16
*Special needs:* ADD ADHD **ASP ASP BESD** DOW **DYC DYP DYS** MLD **SLD**
*Wheelchair access:* W
*Independent Special*

### SOUTHLANDS SCHOOL
Vicar's Hill, Boldre, Lymington, Hampshire SO41 5QB
*Website:* www.cambiangroup.com
*Type:* Boys Boarding and Day 7–16 (Boys 7–16 years)
*Special needs:* **ASP** CB DYC DYP DYS EPI HEA SP&LD TOU
*Independent Special*

### STANBRIDGE EARLS SCHOOL+ *(now closed)*
Stanbridge Lane, Romsey, Hampshire SO51 0ZS
*Website:* www.stanbridgeearls.co.uk
*Type:* Co-educational Boarding and Day 10–19
*Special needs:* **DYC DYP DYS** SP&LD
*Wheelchair access:* WA2

### TADLEY HORIZON
Tadley Common Road, Tadley, Basingstoke, Hampshire RG26 3TB
*Website:* www.priorygroup.com
*Type:* Co-educational Boarding and Day 5–19
*Special needs:* ADD ADHD ASD **ASP** CB EPI MLD SP&LD
*Wheelchair access:* W
*Independent Special*
*52-week care*

### TRELOAR SCHOOL AND COLLEGE*
London Road, Holybourne, Alton, Hampshire GU34 4GL
*Website:* www.treloar.org.uk
*Type:* Co-educational Boarding and Day 7–25
*Special needs:* **CP** DYP DYS EPI HEA HI IM **MLD PMLD** SLD SP&LD VI
*Wheelchair access:* WA1
*Non-maintained*

# HEREFORDSHIRE

### BARRS COURT SCHOOL
Barrs Court Road, Hereford, Herefordshire HR1 1EQ
*Website:* www.barrscourt.hereford.sch.uk
*Type:* Co-educational Day Only 11–19
*Special needs:* **PMLD SLD**
*Wheelchair access:* W

### QUEENSWOOD SCHOOL
Callow Hills Farm, Hereford Road, Ledbury, Herefordshire HR8 2PZ
*Website:* www.priorygroup.com/
*Type:* Co-educational Boarding Only
*Special needs:* **BESD**
*Wheelchair access:* W
*Independent Special*
*52-week care*

# HERTFORDSHIRE

### MELDRETH MANOR
Fenny Lane, Meldreth, Nr Royston, Hertfordshire SG8 6LG
*Website:* www.scope.org.uk/education
*Type:* Co-educational Boarding and Day 9–19
*Special needs:* **CP** EPI HI **PMLD** SLD SP&LD VI
*Wheelchair access:* WA1
*Independent Special*
*52-week care*

### NAS RADLETT LODGE SCHOOL*
Harper Lane, Radlett, Hertfordshire WD7 9HW
*Website:* www.autism.org.uk/radlettlodge
*Type:* Co-educational Day and Boarding 4–19
*Special needs:* **ASD ASP** CB
*Wheelchair access:* WA2
*Independent Special*

### ST ELIZABETH'S SCHOOL*
South End, Much Hadham, Hertfordshire SG10 6EW
*Website:* www.stelizabeths.org.uk
*Type:* Co-educational Boarding and Day 5–19
*Special needs:* ADD ADHD **ASD** ASP BESD **CB** CP DOW DYP DYS **EPI** HEA IM **MLD PMLD SLD** SP&LD TOU
*Wheelchair access:* WA1
*Non-maintained*

# ISLE OF WIGHT

### ST CATHERINE'S SCHOOL
Grove Road, Ventnor,
Isle of Wight PO38 1TT
*Website:*
www.stcatherines.org.uk
*Type:* Co-educational Boarding
and Day 11–19
*Special needs:* ADD ADHD ASD
ASP CB DYC DYP DYS EPI HEA
HI MLD SP&LD VI
*Wheelchair access:* WA3
*Independent Special*

# KENT

### BASTON HOUSE SCHOOL
Baston Road, Hayes, Bromley,
Kent BR2 7AB
*Website:* www.
bastonhouseschool.org.uk
*Type:* Co-educational Day Only
2–16
*Special needs:* **ASD** ASP
*Independent Special*

### BREWOOD SECONDARY SCHOOL
86 London Road, Deal,
Kent CT14 9TR
*Type:* Co-educational Day Only
7–16
*Special needs:* ADD ADHD ASP
**BESD** DYC DYP DYS HI **MLD**
SP&LD TOU VI
*Wheelchair access:* WA2

### BROWN'S SCHOOL+
Cannock House, Hawstead
Lane, Chelsfield, Kent BR6 7PH
*Website:*
www.brownsschool.co.uk
*Type:* Co-educational Day Only
6–16
*Special needs:* **DYP DYS**
*Independent Special*

### CALDECOTT COMMUNITY
Ashford, Kent TN25 6SP
*Website:* www.
caldecottfoundation.co.uk
*Type:* Co-educational Boarding
and Day 5–16
*Special needs:* ADHD **BESD**
DYS MLD

### DORTON HOUSE SCHOOL
Royal London Society for
the Blind, Seal, Sevenoaks,
Kent TN15 0ED
*Website:* www.rlsb.org.uk
*Type:* Co-educational Boarding
and Day 5–16
*Special needs:* **VI**

### EAST COURT SCHOOL+
Victoria Parade, Ramsgate,
Kent CT11 8ED
*Website:*
www.eastcourtschool.co.uk
*Type:* Co-educational Boarding
and Day 7–13
*Special needs:* DYC DYP **DYS**
*Wheelchair access:* WA3

### GREAT OAKS SMALL SCHOOL
Ebbsfleet Farmhouse, Ebbsfleet
Lane, Minster, Kent CT12 5DL
*Type:* Co-educational Day Only
18–11
*Special needs:* **ADD ADHD
ASD ASP**
*Wheelchair access:* W
*Independent Special*

### HEATH FARM SCHOOL
Heath Farm, Charing Heath,
Ashford, Kent TN27 0AX
*Type:* Co-educational Day Only
5–18
*Special needs:* **BESD**

### HYTHE HOUSE EDUCATION
Power Station Road, Sheerness,
Kent ME12 3AB
*Website:* www.
hythehousesupport.co.uk
*Type:* Boys Day Only 6–16
*Wheelchair access:* WA2

### LEARNING OPPORTUNITIES CENTRE PRIMARY
The Street, Womenswold,
Canterbury, Kent CT4 6HE
*Type:* Co-educational Day Only
7–12
*Special needs:* ADD ADHD ASP
**BESD** DYP DYS

### LITTLE ACORNS SCHOOL
London Beach Farm, Ashford
Road, St Michaels, Tenterden,
Kent TN30 6SR
*Type:* Co-educational Boarding
Only 5–11
*Special needs:* **ADD ADHD**
ASD ASP **BESD** CB DYP DYS
HI MLD SLD SP&LD TOU VI
*Wheelchair access:* W
*Independent Special*
*52-week care*

**MEADOWS SCHOOL (BARNARDO'S)**
London Road, Southborough, Kent TN4 0RJ
*Website:* www.barnardos.org.uk/meadowsschool
*Type:* Co-educational Boarding and Day 11–19
*Special needs:* **ADD ADHD** ASD ASP **BESD MLD**

**NAS HELEN ALLISON SCHOOL\***
The National Autistic Society, Longfield Road, Meopham, Kent DA13 0EW
*Website:* www.autism.org.uk/helenallison
*Type:* Co-educational Boarding and Day 5–19
*Special needs:* **ASD** ASP CB
*Wheelchair access:* WA3

**NASH COLLEGE**
Croydon Road, Hayes, Bromley, Kent BR2 7AG
*Type:* Co-educational Boarding and Day 5–16
*Special needs:* **CP** EPI **PMLD** VI
*Wheelchair access:* W

**THE OLD PRIORY SCHOOL**
Priory Road, Ramsgate, Kent CT11 9PG
*Type:* Boys Day Only 11–16
*Special needs:* **BESD**
*Wheelchair access:* WA3

**THE QUEST SCHOOL FOR AUTISTIC CHILDREN**
The Old Stables, Church Farm, Church Road, Offham, West Malling, Kent ME19 5NX
*Type:* Co-educational Day Only 5–14
*Special needs:* **ASD ASP**
*Wheelchair access:* WA1

**RIPPLEVALE SCHOOL**
Chapel Lane, Ripple, Deal, Kent CT14 8JG
*Website:* www.ripplevaleschool.co.uk
*Type:* Boys Boarding and Day 7–16
*Special needs:* **ADD** ADHD **ASD ASP BESD CB DYC DYP DYS** EPI HEA HI **MLD** SP&LD **TOU**
*Wheelchair access:* WA3
*Independent Special*

**TRINITY SCHOOL+**
13 New Road, Rochester, Kent ME1 1BG
*Website:* www.trinityschool.info
*Type:* Co-educational Day Only 6–16
*Special needs:* ADD **ASD ASP DYC DYP DYS** SP&LD
*Wheelchair access:* WA1
*Independent Special*

**WESTWOOD SCHOOL**
479 Margate Road, Broadstairs, Kent CT10 2QA
*Website:* www.actionforchildren.org.uk
*Type:* Co-educational Day Only 11–16
*Special needs:* ADHD ASD ASP **BESD CB** MLD
*Wheelchair access:* WA2
*Non-maintained*

# LANCASHIRE

**APPLEGATE**
51–53 Albert Rd, Colne, Lancashire BB8 0BP
*Website:* www.northern-care.co.uk
*Type:* Boys Boarding Only 11–17
*Special needs:* **BESD CB**

**BELFORD COLLEGE**
Grange Avenue, Werneth, Oldham, Lancashire OL8 4EL
*Type:* Co-educational Day Only 16–99

**BELMONT SCHOOL**
Hasligdon Road, Rawtenstall, Lancashire BB4 6RX
*Website:* www.belmont-school.co.uk
*Type:* Boys Boarding and Day 8–16
*Special needs:* **BESD**
*Non-maintained*

**THE BIRCHES**
106 Breck Rd, Poulton le Fylde, Lancashire FY6 7HT
*Website:* www.northern-care.co.uk
*Type:* Boys Boarding Only 11–17
*Special needs:* **BESD CB**

**BIRTENSHAW SCHOOL**
Darwen Road, Bromley Cross, Bolton, Lancashire BL7 9AB
*Website:* www.birtenshaw.org.uk
*Type:* Co-educational Day Only 3–19 (3–19yrs)
*Special needs:* **ADD** ADHD **ASD ASP CB CP DOW EPI HEA** HI **IM PMLD SLD** SP&LD VI
*Wheelchair access:* WA2
*Non-maintained*
*52-week care*

**CEDAR HOUSE SCHOOL**
Bentham, Lancashire LA2 7DB
*Website:* www.cedarhouseschool.co.uk
*Type:* Co-educational Boarding and Day 7–16
*Special needs:* ADD ADHD ASD ASP **BESD CB** CP DYC DYP DYS EPI HEA MLD SP&LD TOU
*Wheelchair access:* WA2
*Independent Special*

**CROOKHEY HALL SCHOOL**
Garstang Road, Cockerham, Lancaster, Lancashire LA2 0HA
*Type:* Boys Day Only 11–16
*Special needs:* **ADD ADHD ASD** ASP **BESD CB DYS MLD PMLD SLD**
*Wheelchair access:* WA3
*Independent Special*

## CUMBERLAND SCHOOL
Church Road, Bamber Bridge, Preston, Lancashire PR5 6EP
*Website:* www.cumberlandschool.co.uk
*Type:* Co-educational Day Only 11–16
*Special needs:* **BESD**
*Independent Special*

## EMMANUEL CHRISTIAN SCHOOL
Fylde Community, Blackpool, Lancashire FY3 0BE
*Type:* Co-educational Day Only 5–16

## MILL HOUSE
Farington Moss, Leyland, Lancashire PR26 6PS
*Website:* www.northern-care.co.uk
*Type:* Boys Boarding Only 11–17
*Special needs:* **BESD CB**

## THE NOOK SCHOOL
The Nook, Knotts Lane, Colne, Lancashire BB8 8HH
*Website:* www.northern-care.co.uk
*Type:* Boys Boarding Only 8–13
*Special needs:* **BESD** CB
*52-week care*

## NUGENT HOUSE SCHOOL*
Carr Mill Road, Billinge, Wigan, St Helens, Lancashire WN5 7TT
*Website:* www.nugenthouse.co.uk
*Type:* Boys Boarding Only 7–19
*Special needs:* ADD ADHD **ASD** ASP **BESD CB** DYP **DYS** TOU
*Wheelchair access:* W
*Independent Special*
*52-week care*

## OLIVER HOUSE
Hallgate, Astley Village, Chorley, Lancashire PR7 1XA
*Type:* Co-educational 6–19
*Special needs:* ASD DYC DYP DYS EPI SLD
*Independent Special*

## PENNSYLVANIA HOUSE
1 Barclay Avenue, Blackpool, Lancashire FY3 4HH
*Website:* www.northern-care.co.uk
*Type:* Boys Boarding Only 11–17
*Special needs:* **BESD CB**

## PONTVILLE SCHOOL
Black Moss Lane, Ormskirk, Lancashire L39 4TW
*Website:* www.pontville.co.uk
*Type:* Co-educational Boarding and Day 5–19
*Special needs:* ADD ADHD **ASD ASP** DYP EPI HEA MLD SP&LD
*Wheelchair access:* W
*Independent Special*

## PRIMROSE COTTAGE
Hudcar Lane, Bury, Lancashire
*Website:* www.northern-care.co.uk
*Type:* Girls Boarding Only 11–17
*Special needs:* **BESD CB**

## PROGRESS SCHOOL
Suites 1–5 Centurion House, Centurion Way, Leyland, Lancashire PR25 3GR
*Website:* www.progressschool.co.uk
*Type:* Co-educational Boarding Only 7–19
*Special needs:* CB SLD
*52-week care*

## RED ROSE SCHOOL
28–30 North Promenade, St Annes on Sea, Lytham St Annes, Lancashire FY8 2NQ
*Type:* Co-educational Day Only 7–16
*Special needs:* **ADHD ASD ASP DYC DYP DYS** SP&LD **TOU**
*Wheelchair access:* WA2

## RIDGWAY PARK SCHOOL
Jenny Browns Point, Silverdale, Carnforth, Lancashire LA5 0UA
*Type:* Co-educational Boarding Only 11–16
*Special needs:* ADHD ASD **BESD**
*Wheelchair access:* WA3
*52-week care*

## ROSSENDALE SCHOOL
Bamford Road, Ramsbottom, Lancashire BL0 0RT
*Website:* www.priorygroup.com
*Type:* Co-educational Boarding and Day 8–16
*Special needs:* **ADD ADHD ASD ASP BESD CB DYP** DYS EPI TOU
*Wheelchair access:* WA3
*Independent Special*

## UNDERLEY GARDEN SCHOOL
Kirkby Lonsdale, Carnforth, Lancashire LA6 2DZ
*Website:* www.underleygardenschool.co.uk
*Type:* Co-educational Boarding Only 9–19
*Special needs:* ADD **ADHD** ASD **ASP BESD CB** DOW DYC DYP DYS EPI HEA HI **MLD SLD** SP&LD TOU VI
*Wheelchair access:* WA2
*Independent Special*
*52-week care*

## UNDERLEY HALL SCHOOL
Kirkby Lonsdale, Carnforth, Lancashire LA6 2HE
*Website:* www.underleyhallschool.co.uk
*Type:* Co-educational Boarding and Day 9–19
*Special needs:* **ADD ADHD** ASP **BESD CB** DYP DYS **MLD** SP&LD
*Wheelchair access:* WA3
*Independent Special*
*52-week care*

## WATERLOO LODGE SCHOOL
Preston Road, Chorley, Lancashire PR6 7AX
*Type:* Co-educational Day Only 11–16
*Special needs:* **ADHD** ASD **BESD CB** DYP DYS HI SP&LD
*Wheelchair access:* WA3

## WESTMORLAND SCHOOL
Weldbank Lane, Chorley, Lancashire PR7 3NQ
*Website:* www.westmorlandschool.co.uk
*Type:* Co-educational Day Only 5–11 (32 Day pupils, co-educational)
*Special needs:* **ADD ADHD** ASD **ASP BESD CB DYS MLD** SP&LD
*Independent Special*
*52-week care*

# LEICESTERSHIRE

**LEWIS CHARLTON SCHOOL**
North Street, Ashby-de-la-
Zouch, Leicestershire LE65 1HU
*Type:* Co-educational Day Only
11–16
*Special needs:* **BESD**
*Wheelchair access:* WA2

**SKETCHLEY HORIZON**
Manor Way, Sketchley Village,
Burbage,
Leicestershire LE10 3HT
*Website:*
www.prioryeducation.com
*Type:* Co-educational Day Only
8–16
*Special needs:* ASD **ASP**
*Wheelchair access:* WA3

# LINCOLNSHIRE

**KISIMUL SCHOOL – OLD
VICARAGE\***
The Old Vicarage, High Street,
Swinderby,
Lincolnshire LN6 9LU
*Website:* www.kisimul.co.uk
*Type:* Co-educational Boarding
and Day 8–19
*Special needs:* ASD **CB** DOW
EPI HI **SLD** SP&LD
*Wheelchair access:* WA1
*Independent Special*
*52-week care*

# NORTH LINCOLNSHIRE

**BARTON SCHOOL\***
Barrow Road, Barton-Upon-
Humber, North Lincolnshire
DN18 6DA
*Website:*
www.optionsgroup.co.uk
*Type:* Co-educational Boarding
and Day 8–19
*Special needs:* ADD ADHD
**ASD ASP CB EPI** HEA MLD
PMLD **SLD** SP&LD
*Wheelchair access:* WA1
*Independent Special*
*52-week care*

# LONDON

**ABINGDON HOUSE SCHOOL**
4–6 Abingdon Road,
London W8 6AF
*Website:* www.
abingdonhouseschool.co.uk
*Type:* Co-educational Day Only
4–11
*Special needs:* **ADD ADHD
ASD DYC DYP DYS**
*Wheelchair access:* W
*Independent Special*

**BLOSSOM HOUSE SCHOOL+**
8A The Drive, Wimbledon,
London SW20 8TG
*Website:*
www.blossomhouseschool.co.uk
*Type:* Co-educational Day Only
3–16
*Special needs:* ASD ASP DYP
DYS SP&LD
*Wheelchair access:* WA2
*Independent Special*

**CENTRE ACADEMY***
92 St John's Hill, Battersea,
London SW11 1SH
*Website:* www.centreacademy.net
*Type:* Co-educational Day Only
7–19
*Special needs:* **ADD ADHD
ASD ASP DYP DYS MLD**
SP&LD
*Wheelchair access:* WA1
*Independent Special*

**THE CHELSEA GROUP OF
CHILDREN**
The Gatehouse, Magdalen Road,
Wandsworth, London SW18 3NP
*Type:* Co-educational Day Only
4–11
*Special needs:* ADD ADHD ASD
**ASP** CB DYC DYP DYS **MLD**
SP&LD
*Independent Special*

**FAIRLEY HOUSE SCHOOL*+**
30 Causton Street, London
SW1P 4AU
*Website:* www.fairleyhouse.org.uk
*Type:* Co-educational Day
Only 5–14
(Junior Department – Year 2–5
Senior Department – Year 6–9)
*Special needs:* **DYC DYP DYS**
HEA SP&LD
*Wheelchair access:* WA1

**FREDERICK HUGH HOUSE***
48 Old Church Street,
London SW3 5BY
*Website:*
www.frederickhughhouse.com
*Type:* Co-educational Day Only
(Currently registered for children
aged 4–11 years with special
needs but with a vision to take
our children through to 18 years
old.)
*Special needs:* **ADD ADHD
ASD ASP CP DOW DYC DYP
DYS EPI IM MLD** SP&LD TOU
*Wheelchair access:* WA1
*Independent Special*

**HORNSEY CONDUCTIVE
EDUCATION CENTRE**
54 Muswell Hill,
London N10 3ST
*Website:*
www.hornseytrust.org.uk
*Type:* Co-educational Day Only
*Special needs:* **CP**
*Wheelchair access:* WA1

**KESTREL HOUSE SCHOOL**
104 Crouch Hill, Crouch End,
London N8 9EA
*Type:* Co-educational Day Only
2–12
*Special needs:* ADD ADHD
**ASD ASP** DYP MLD SLD
SP&LD
*Wheelchair access:* WA3
*Independent Special*

**KISHARON DAY SCHOOL**
1011 Finchley Road,
London NW11 7HB
*Website:* www.kisharon.org.uk
*Type:* Co-educational Day Only
5–19 (Jewish pupils only)
*Special needs:* ADHD ASD **ASP**
BESD CP **DOW MLD** SP&LD

**THE LONDON CENTRE FOR
CHILDREN WITH CEREBRAL
PALSY**
54 Muswell Hill,
London N10 3ST
*Website:* www.cplondon.org.uk
*Type:* Co-educational Day Only
*Special needs:* **CP IM**
*Wheelchair access:* W
*Independent Special*

**THE MOAT SCHOOL+**
Bishop's Avenue, Fulham,
London SW6 6EG
*Website:*
www.moatschool.org.uk
*Type:* Co-educational Day Only
11–16
*Special needs:* **DYC DYP DYS**
*Wheelchair access:* W
*Independent Special*

**PARAYHOUSE SCHOOL**
New Kings School Annex, New
Kings Road, London SW6 4LY
*Website:* www.parayhouse.com
*Type:* Co-educational Day Only
7–16
*Special needs:* ADD ADHD ASD
ASP BESD CB DOW DYP DYS
EPI HEA HI **MLD** SP&LD TOU
*Wheelchair access:* WA3
*Non-maintained*

**THE SPEECH, LANGUAGE &
HEARING CENTRE**
1–5 Christopher Place, Chalton
Street, London NW1 1JF
*Website:* www.
speech-lang.org.uk
*Type:* Co-educational Day Only
*Special needs:* ADD ADHD ASD
ASP BESD CB DYP **HI** MLD
SP&LD
*Wheelchair access:* WA1
*Independent Special*

**TREE HOUSE**
The TreeHouse Trust, Woodside
Avenue, London N10 3JA
*Type:* Co-educational Day Only
3–11
*Special needs:* ASD **ASP**
SP&LD

# GREATER MANCHESTER

### AIM HABONIM
401 Bury Road, Salford,
Greater Manchester M7 2BT
*Type:* Co-educational Day Only
*Special needs:* SLD
*Independent Special*

### DIDSBURY SCHOOL
611 Wilmslow Road, Didsbury,
Manchester, Greater
Manchester M20 6AD
*Website:*
www.advancedchildcare.co.uk
*Type:* Co-educational Boarding
and Day
*Special needs:* ADHD **BESD**
MLD

### INSCAPE HOUSE SALFORD
Silkhey Grove, Worsley,
Greater Manchester M28 7FG
*Website:* www.
togethertrust.org.uk
*Type:* Co-educational Day Only
5–19
*Non-maintained*

### LIMES MEADOWS
73 Taunton Rd,
Ashton under Lyne,
Greater Manchester OL7 9DU
*Website:*
www.northern-care.co.uk
*Type:* Boys Boarding Only
11–17
*Special needs:* **BESD CB**

### THE ST JOHN VIANNEY
SCHOOL
Rye Bank Road, Firswood,
Stretford, Greater Manchester
M16 0EX
*Website:*
www.stjohnvianneyschool.ik.org
*Type:* Co-educational Day Only
5–19
*Special needs:* **MLD**
*Wheelchair access:* W
*Independent Special*

# MERSEYSIDE

### CLARENCE HIGH SCHOOL
West Lane, Freshfield, Formby,
Merseyside L37 7AZ
*Website:*
www.clarencehighschool.co.uk
*Type:* Co-educational Boarding
and Day 9–19
*Special needs:* ADD ADHD **ASP**
**BESD** CB **DYS** TOU
*Wheelchair access:* W
*Independent Special*

### LAKESIDE SCHOOL
Naylors Road, Liverpool,
Merseyside L27 2YA
*Website:*
www.lakesideschool.co.uk
*Type:* Co-educational Day and
Boarding 5–13
*Special needs:* ADD **ADHD**
**ASD ASP** BESD **CB** DOW **DYC**
**DYP DYS** EPI HEA HI IM MLD
SP&LD TOU VI
*Wheelchair access:* WA1
*Independent Special*
52-week care

### PETERHOUSE SCHOOL
Preston New Road, Southport,
Merseyside PR9 8PA
*Website:* www.
autisminitiatives.org
*Type:* Co-educational Boarding
and Day 5–19
*Special needs:* **ASD ASP**
*Wheelchair access:* WA2
*Non-maintained*
52-week care

### ROYAL SCHOOL FOR THE
BLIND
Church Road North, Wavertree,
Liverpool, Merseyside L15 6TQ
*Website:* www.rsblind.org.uk/
index.
*Type:* Co-educational Boarding
and Day 2–19
*Special needs:* BESD **MLD**
**PMLD SLD** VI
*Wheelchair access:* W
*Independent Special*

### ST VINCENT'S SCHOOL, A
SPECIALIST SCHOOL FOR
SENSORY IMPAIRMENT AND
OTHER NEEDS
Yew Tree Lane, West Derby,
Liverpool, Merseyside L12 9HN
*Website:* www.stvin.com
*Type:* Co-educational Boarding
and Day 4–19
*Special needs:* ASD ASP CP
DYS EPI HI MLD SP&LD **VI**
*Wheelchair access:* WA2
*Non-maintained*

### WALTON PROGRESSIVE
SCHOOL
European Lifestyles Education
Sevices, Rice Lane, Liverpool,
Merseyside L9 1NR
*Type:* Co-educational Day Only
8–19
*Special needs:* **ADD ADHD**
**ASD ASP CB EPI** HI **IM** PMLD
**SLD** SP&LD VI
*Wheelchair access:* WA1
*Independent Special*

**WARGRAVE HOUSE SCHOOL**
449 Wargrave Road,
Newton-le-Willows,
Merseyside WA12 8RS
*Website:*
www.wargravehouse.com
*Type:* Co-educational Boarding
and Day 5–19
*Special needs:* **ASD ASP**

**WEST KIRBY RESIDENTIAL SCHOOL**
Meols Drive, West Kirby, Wirral,
Merseyside CH48 5DH
*Type:* Co-educational Boarding
and Day 5–18
*Special needs:* **ADD ADHD
ASD ASP BESD CB** DYP DYS
EPI HI MLD SP&LD TOU VI
*Wheelchair access:* WA1
*Non-maintained*

# MIDDLESEX

**HILLINGDON MANOR SCHOOL**
Moorcroft Complex, Harlington
Road, Hillingdon, Uxbridge,
Middlesex UB8 3HD
*Type:* Co-educational Day Only
6–19
*Special needs:* ASD **ASP** SLD
*Independent Special*

**NAS SYBIL ELGAR SCHOOL\***
The National Autistic Society,
Havelock Road, Southall,
Middlesex UB2 4NY
*Website:* www.autism.org.uk/
sybilelgar
*Type:* Co-educational Day and
Boarding 14–19
*Special needs:* **ASD ASP** CB
*Wheelchair access:* WA1
*Independent Special*

**PIELD HEATH SCHOOL**
Pield Heath Road, Uxbridge,
Middlesex UB8 3NW
*Type:* Co-educational Boarding
and Day 7–19
*Special needs:* ADD ASD ASP
CP DOW DYP EPI HEA **MLD**
PMLD **SLD** SP&LD VI

**RNIB SUNSHINE HOUSE SCHOOL\***
33 Dene Road, Northwood,
Middlesex HA6 2DD
*Website:* www.rnib.org.uk/
sunshinehouse
*Type:* Co-educational Day and
Boarding 2–11 (Children from
the ages of 5 to 14 years can
board Monday to Thursday for
up to 50 weeks per year.)
*Special needs:* CP EPI HEA HI
IM **PMLD SLD** SP&LD **VI**
*Wheelchair access:* WA1
*Non-maintained*

# NORFOLK

**EAGLE HOUSE – NORFOLK SCHOOL**
Andrews Furlong, Mill Road,
Banham, Norwich,
Norfolk NR16 2HU
*Website:* www.
eaglehousenorfolk.co.uk
*Type:* Co-educational Boarding
and Day 4–19
*Special needs:* ADD ADHD ASD
**ASP** CB EPI MLD SLD SP&LD
*Wheelchair access:* WA3
*Independent Special*
*52-week care*

**SHERIDAN SCHOOL**
Thetford Road, Northwold,
Thetford, Norfolk IP26 5LQ
*Website:* www.priorygroup.com/
locations-results/item/
sheridan-school---thetford
*Type:* Co-educational 10–19
*Special needs:* ADD ADHD ASP
**BESD CB** DYS MLD SP&LD
*Wheelchair access:* WA3
*Independent Special*
*52-week care*

# NORTHAMPTONSHIRE

**POTTERSPURY LODGE SCHOOL\***
Potterspury Lodge, Towcester,
Northamptonshire NN12 7LL
*Website:*
www.potterspurylodge.co.uk
*Type:* Boys Boarding and
Day 8–18
*Special needs:* ADD ADHD
**ASD ASP BESD**
*Wheelchair access:* WA2
*Independent Special*

**THORNBY HALL THERAPEUTIC COMMUNITY**
Naseby Road, Thornby,
Northamptonshire NN6 8SW
*Type:* Co-educational Boarding
Only 12–18
*Special needs:* BESD CB
*Wheelchair access:* WA3
*Independent Special*
*52-week care*

# NORTHUMBERLAND

**NUNNYKIRK CENTRE FOR DYSLEXIA**
Netherwitton, Morpeth,
Northumberland NE61 4PB
*Type:* Co-educational Boarding
and Day 7–16
*Special needs:* **DYS**

# NOTTINGHAMSHIRE

**GLENDALE HOUSE**
255 Tamworth Rd, Long Eaton,
Nottinghamshire NG10 1AS
*Website:*
www.northern-care.co.uk
*Type:* Co-educational Boarding
Only 11–17
*Special needs:* **BESD CB**

**HOPE HOUSE SCHOOL**
Barnby Road, Newark,
Nottinghamshire NG24 3NE
*Website:*
www.hopehouseschool.co.uk
*Type:* Co-educational 5–14
*Special needs:* ASD **ASP**
*Independent Special*

**I CAN'S DAWN HOUSE SCHOOL\***
Helmsley Road, Rainworth,
Mansfield, Nottinghamshire
NG21 0DQ
*Website:*
www.dawnhouseschool.org.uk
*Type:* Co-educational Boarding
and Day 5–19
*Special needs:* ASP SP&LD
*Wheelchair access:* WA1
*Non-maintained*

**ORCHARD SCHOOL**
South Leverton, Retford,
Nottinghamshire DN22 0DJ
*Website:* www.orchardspecial.
shropshire.sch.uk
*Type:* Co-educational Day Only
2–16
*Special needs:* ASD DYS SLD

**RUTLAND HOUSE SCHOOL**
1 Elm Bank, Mapperley Road,
Nottingham, Nottinghamshire
NG3 5AJ
*Website:*
www.scope.org.uk/rutland
*Type:* Co-educational Boarding
and Day 5–19
*Special needs:* **CP EPI** HI IM
PMLD SP&LD **VI**
*Wheelchair access:* WA2
*Independent Special*
*52-week care*

**SUTHERLAND HOUSE SCHOOL (CARLTON)**
Sutherland Road, Nottingham, Nottinghamshire NG3 7AP
*Website:*
www.sutherlandhouse.org.uk
*Type:* Co-educational
Day Only 3–19
*Special needs:* ASD **ASP**
*Wheelchair access:* WA2
*Non-maintained*

**SUTHERLAND HOUSE SCHOOL (SECONDARY DEPARTMENT)**
'Westward', 68 Cyprus Road, Mapperley Park, Nottinghamshire NG3 5ED
*Type:* Co-educational Day Only 11–16
*Special needs:* ASD **ASP**

**WINGS EAST SCHOOL**
Kirklington Hall, Kirklington, Newark, Nottinghamshire NG22 8NB
*Website:*
www.wingseastschool.co.uk
*Type:* Co-educational Boarding Only 11–17
*Special needs:* **ADD ADHD ASD BESD DYP DYS MLD**
*Independent Special*
*52-week care*

# OXFORDSHIRE

**ACTION FOR CHILDREN PARKLANDS CAMPUS***
Action for Children, Near Appleton, Abingdon, Oxfordshire OX13 5QB
*Website:* www.actionforchildren. org.uk/parklands
*Type:* Co-educational Boarding and Day 11–19
*Special needs:* ADHD ASD **BESD**
*Non-maintained*
*52-week care*

**ACTION FOR CHILDREN PENHURST SCHOOL**
New Street, Chipping Norton, Oxfordshire OX7 5LN
*Website:* www.actionforchildren. org.uk/schools
*Type:* Co-educational Boarding and Day 5–19
*Special needs:* CP EPI HI IM **PMLD** SLD SP&LD **VI**
*Non-maintained*
*52-week care*

**CHILWORTH HOUSE SCHOOL**
Thame Road, Wheatley, Oxford, Oxfordshire OX33 1JP
*Website:* www. chilworthhouseschool.com
*Type:* Co-educational Day Only 5–14
*Special needs:* **ADD ADHD ASD ASP BESD CB DYS MLD**
*Independent Special*

**CHILWORTH HOUSE UPPER SCHOOL**
Grooms Farm, Thame Road, Wheatley, Oxfordshire OX33 1JP
*Website:* www.witherslackgroup. co.uk/chilworth-house-upper-school
*Type:* Co-educational Day Only 11–16
*Special needs:* **ADD ADHD ASD ASP BESD CB**
*Independent Special*

**HILLCREST PARK SCHOOL**
Southcombe, Chipping Norton, Oxfordshire OX7 5QH
*Type:* Co-educational Day Only 8–16
*Special needs:* ADD ADHD **BESD CB** MLD SLD
*Wheelchair access:* W

**MULBERRY BUSH SCHOOL***
Abingdon Road, Standlake, Witney, Oxfordshire OX29 7RW
*Website:* www.mulberrybush. org.uk
*Type:* Co-educational Boarding Only 5–13
*Special needs:* ADD **ADHD BESD** DYP DYS
*Wheelchair access:* WA2
*Non-maintained*

**SWALCLIFFE PARK SCHOOL TRUST***
Swalcliffe, Banbury, Oxfordshire OX15 5EP
*Website:*
www.swalcliffepark.co.uk
*Type:* Boys Boarding and Day 11–19
*Special needs:* ADD ADHD **ASD ASP** BESD DYC DYP DYS SP&LD TOU
*Wheelchair access:* WA2
*Non-maintained*

**THE UNICORN SCHOOL***
20 Marcham Road, Abingdon, Oxfordshire OX14 1AA
*Website:*
www.unicorndyslexia.co.uk
*Type:* Co-educational Day Only 6–13
*Special needs:* ADD ADHD **DYC DYP DYS** SP&LD
*Independent Special*

# RUTLAND

**THE GRANGE THERAPEUTIC SCHOOL**
15–17 Somerby Road,
Knossington, Oakham,
Rutland LE15 8LY
*Type:* Boys Boarding and
Day 8–16
*Special needs:* **BESD**
*Wheelchair access:* W
*Independent Special*

# SHROPSHIRE

**CRUCKTON HALL\***
Cruckton, Shrewsbury,
Shropshire SY5 8PR
*Website:* www.cruckton.com
*Type:* Boys Boarding and
Day 7–19
*Special needs:* **ADD ADHD
ASD ASP BESD** CB DYC DYP
DYS EPI HI MLD
*Wheelchair access:* WA3
*52-week care*

**HIGFORD SCHOOL\***
Higford Hall, Nr Shifnal,
Shropshire TF11 9ET
*Website:*
www.optionsgroup.co.uk
*Type:* Co-educational Boarding
and Day 8–19
*Special needs:* ADD ADHD
**ASD ASP CB EPI HEA** HI IM
MLD PMLD SLD **SP&LD** VI
*Wheelchair access:* W
*Independent Special*
*52-week care*

**HIGHLEA SCHOOL**
Astbury Lane, Chelmarsh,
Bridgenorth, Shropshire
WV16 6AX
*Type:* Co-educational

**LEARNING FOR LIFE**
Station Road, Bridgnorth,
Shropshire WV16 6SS
*Type:* Co-educational Day
Only 11–16

**OVERLEY HALL SCHOOL**
Wellington, Shropshire TF6 5HE
*Website:* www.overleyhall.com
*Type:* Co-educational Boarding
Only 9–19
*Special needs:* ADHD ASD **ASP**
CB DOW **EPI** HI PMLD **SLD**
SP&LD
*Wheelchair access:* WA2
*Independent Special*
*52-week care*

**YOUNG OPTIONS COLLEGE\***
Lamledge Lane, Shifnal,
Shropshire TF11 8SD
*Website:*
www.optionsgroup.co.uk
*Type:* Co-educational Day and
Boarding 7–19
*Special needs:* ADD ADHD ASP
**BESD** CB HEA
*Wheelchair access:* WA1
*Independent Special*
*52-week care*

# SOMERSET

**EDINGTON AND SHAPWICK SCHOOL+**
Shapwick Manor, 21 Station Road,
Shapwick, Somerset TA7 9NJ
*Website:*
www.edingtonshapwick.co.uk
*Type:* Co-educational Boarding
and Day 8–18
*Special needs:* DYC DYP **DYS**
*Wheelchair access:* WA3
*Independent Special*

**FARLEIGH COLLEGE MELLS**
Newbury, Nr Mells, Somerset,
Somerset BA11 3RG
*Website:* www.priorygroup.com
*Type:* Co-educational Boarding
and Day 11–19
*Special needs:* ADD ADHD ASD
**ASP** CB DYC DYP DYS
*Wheelchair access:* WA1
*Independent Special*

**THE LIBRA SCHOOL**
Edgemoor Court, South
Radworthy, South Molton,
Somerset EX36 3LN
*Type:* Co-educational Day
Only 8–18
*Special needs:* BESD
*Independent Special*

**THE MARCHANT-HOLLIDAY SCHOOL***
North Cheriton, Templecombe, Somerset BA8 0AH
Website: www.marchantholliday.co.uk
Type: Boys Boarding and Day 5–13
Special needs: **ADD ADHD ASD ASP BESD CB** DYC DYP DYS IM MLD SLD SP&LD TOU
Wheelchair access: W
Independent Special

**MARK COLLEGE+**
Mark, Highbridge, Somerset TA9 4NP
Website: www.markcollege. somerset.sch.uk
Type: Co-educational Boarding and Day 10–19
Special needs: ADD **DYC DYP DYS** SP&LD
Wheelchair access: WA2
Independent Special

**MERRYHAY ACADEMY**
Merryhay House, Ilton Business Park, Ilton, Ilminster, Somerset TA19 9DU
Type: Co-educational Day and Boarding 11–16
Special needs: **ADD ADHD** ASD **ASP BESD CB** DYP DYS MLD
Wheelchair access: WA3
Independent Special
52-week care

# STAFFORDSHIRE

**BLADON HOUSE SCHOOL**
Newton Solney, Burton upon Trent, Staffordshire DE15 0TA
Website: www.bladonhouse.com
Type: Co-educational Day and Boarding 5–19
Special needs: **ADD ADHD** ASD **ASP** BESD **CB** CP **DOW DYC DYP EPI** HEA **HI** IM **MLD PMLD SLD** SP&LD **TOU**
Wheelchair access: WA3
Independent Special
52-week care

**DRAYCOTT MOOR COLLEGE**
Draycott Old Road, Draycott in the Moors, Stoke-on-Trent, Staffordshire ST11 9AH
Type: Co-educational Day Only 11–16
Special needs: BESD
Independent Special

**MAPLE HAYES SCHOOL**
Abnalls Lane, Lichfield, Staffordshire WS13 8BL
Website: www.dyslexia.gb.com
Type: Co-educational Day Only 7–17
Special needs: **DYS**
Wheelchair access: W
Independent Special

**ROACHES SCHOOL**
Tunstall Road, Knypersley, Stoke On Trent, Staffordshire ST8 7AB
Type: Co-educational Boarding and Day 5–16
Special needs: **BESD**
52-week care

**RUGELEY HORIZON SCHOOL**
Blithbury Road, Blithbury, Rugeley, Staffordshire WS15 3JQ
Website: www.prioryeducation.com
Type: Co-educational Boarding and Day 4–19
Special needs: ASD **ASP**
Wheelchair access: WA1
Independent Special

**YOUNG OPTIONS PATHWAY COLLEGE STOKE***
Phoenix House, Marlborough Road, Longton, Stoke-on-Trent, Staffordshire ST13 1EJ
Website: www.optionsgroup.co.uk
Type: Co-educational Boarding and Day 11–19
Special needs: ADD ADHD **BESD** CB **HEA** MLD
Independent Special
52-week care

# STOKE

**AIDENSWOOD**
47 Liverpool Rd East, Kidsgrove, Stoke on Trent, Stoke SY10 9DD
Website: www.northern-care.co.uk
Type: Boys Boarding Only 11–17
Special needs: **BESD CB**

# SUFFOLK

### BRAMFIELD HOUSE
Walpole Road, Bramfield,
Halesworth, Suffolk IP19 9AB
*Type:* Boys Boarding and Day
10–16
*Special needs:* BESD MLD

### CENTRE ACADEMY EAST ANGLIA*+
Church Road, Brettenham,
Ipswich, Suffolk IP7 7QR
*Website:* www.
centreacademy.net
*Type:* Co-educational Day and
Boarding 8–19
*Special needs:* **ADD ADHD
ASD ASP DYC DYP DYS MLD**
SP&LD *Independent Special*

# SURREY

### CORNFIELD SCHOOL
53 Hanworth Road, Redhill,
Surrey RH1 5HS
*Type:* Girls Boarding and
Day 11–18
*Special needs:* BESD
*Wheelchair access:* WA1
*Independent Special*
*52-week care*

### EAGLE HOUSE SCHOOL MITCHAM
224 London Road, Mitcham,
Surrey CR4 3HD
*Website:* www.
eaglehouseschool.co.uk
*Type:* Co-educational Day
Only 4–19
*Special needs:* ADD ADHD
**ASD ASP** DYP MLD SLD
SP&LD
*Wheelchair access:* WA3
*Independent Special*

### GRAFHAM GRANGE SCHOOL
Grafham, Bramley, Guildford,
Surrey GU5 0LH
*Website:* www.ggset.co.uk
*Type:* Boys Day and Boarding
10–18
*Special needs:* ADD ADHD ASD
ASP **BESD CB** DYS MLD
SP&LD
*Wheelchair access:* W
*Non-maintained*

### I CAN CENTRE WITH MEATH SCHOOL*
Brox Road, Ottershaw,
Surrey KT16 0LF
*Website:* www.ican.org.uk
*Type:* Co-educational Day and
Boarding 4–11
*Special needs:* ADD **ASP** DYP
EPI HEA HI IM SP&LD VI
*Wheelchair access:* WA1
*Non-maintained*

### THE JIGSAW SCHOOL
Dunsfold Park, Stovolds Hill,
Cranleigh, Surrey GU6 8TB
*Type:* Co-educational Day
Only 4–16
*Special needs:* ASD **ASP**
*Independent Special*

### KISIMUL SCHOOL – WOODSTOCK HOUSE*
Woodstock Lane North, Long
Ditton, Surrey KT6 5HN
*Website:* www.kisimul.co.uk
*Type:* Co-educational Day and
Boarding 8–19
*Special needs:* ASD **CB** DOW
**EPI SLD** SP&LD
*Wheelchair access:* WA1
*Independent Special*
*52-week care*

### KNOWL HILL SCHOOL+
School Lane, Pirbright, Surrey
GU24 0JN
*Website:* www.knowlhill.org.uk
*Type:* Co-educational Day Only
7–16
*Special needs:* DYC DYP **DYS**
*Wheelchair access:* W

### THE LINK PRIMARY SCHOOL
138 Croydon Road, Beddington,
Croydon, Surrey CR0 4PG
*Website:* www.link.ik.org
*Type:* Co-educational Day
Only 6–12
*Special needs:* ASD ASP DOW
DYP DYS MLD SP&LD
*Wheelchair access:* WA3
*Non-maintained*

### THE LINK SECONDARY SCHOOL
82–86 Croydon Road,
Beddington, Surrey CR0 4PD
*Website:*
www.link-sec.sutton.sch.uk
*Type:* Co-educational Day Only
11–19
*Special needs:* ASD ASP
SP&LD
*Wheelchair access:* WA2

**LITTLE DAVID'S SCHOOL**
(Timebridge Centre), Fieldway,
New Addington, Croydon,
Surrey CR0 9AZ
*Type:* Co-educational Day
Only 3–12
*Special needs:* **ADD ADHD**
ASD **ASP BESD CB** DYS **MLD
PMLD SLD** SP&LD
*Wheelchair access:* WA3
*Independent Special*

**MOON HALL COLLEGE AND
BURYS COURT**
Flanchford Road, Leigh,
Reigate, Surrey RH2 8RE
*Website:*
www.moonhall.surrey.sch.uk
*Type:* Co-educational Boarding
and Day 11–16
*Special needs:* **DYS**
*Wheelchair access:* WA3

**MOON HALL SCHOOL+**
Feldemore, Holmbury St Mary,
Dorking, Surrey RH5 6LQ
*Website:* www.
belmont-school.org
*Type:* Co-educational Boarding
and Day 2–13
*Special needs:* DYC DYP DYS
*Independent Special*

**MOOR HOUSE SCHOOL**
Hurst Green, Oxted,
Surrey RH8 9AQ
*Website:*
www.moorhouse.surrey.sch.uk
*Type:* Co-educational Boarding
Only 7–16
*Special needs:* DYC DYP DYS
SP&LD

**MORE HOUSE SCHOOL+**
Moons Hill, Frensham, Farnham,
Surrey GU10 3AP
*Type:* Boys Boarding and
Day 9–18
*Special needs:* **DYC DYP DYS**
SP&LD

**MRCS EDUCATIONAL UNIT**
61 Lodge Road, Croydon,
Surrey CR20 2PH
*Type:* Boys Day Only 11–16
*Special needs:* **ADD ADHD
BESD DYS HEA MLD SLD**
SP&LD **TOU**

**RUTHERFORD SCHOOL**
1A Melville Avenue, South
Croydon, Surrey CR2 7HZ
*Website:*
www.garwoodfoundation.org.uk
*Type:* Co-educational Day Only
2–19
*Special needs:* **CP EPI HEA HI
IM PMLD SLD** VI
*Wheelchair access:* WA2
*Independent Special*

**ST DOMINIC'S SCHOOL**
Hambledon, Godalming,
Surrey GU8 4DX
*Website:*
www.stdominicsschool.org.uk
*Type:* Co-educational Boarding
and Day 8–16
*Special needs:* ADD ADHD ASD
ASP DYC DYP DYS EPI HEA
SP&LD
*Wheelchair access:* W
*Non-maintained*

**ST JOSEPH'S SPECIALIST
SCHOOL & COLLEGE\***
Amlets Lane, Cranleigh,
Surrey GU6 7DH
*Website:* www.st-
josephscranleigh.surrey.sch.uk
*Type:* Co-educational Boarding
and Day 5–19
*Special needs:* ADD **ADHD
ASD** ASP **CB DOW MLD SLD**
SP&LD
*Wheelchair access:* WA1
*Non-maintained*

**ST PIERS SCHOOL, YOUNG
EPILEPSY**
St Piers Lane, Lingfield,
Surrey RH7 6PW
*Website:* www.ncype.org.uk
*Type:* Co-educational Boarding
and Day 5–19
*Special needs:* ADHD ASD ASP
BESD CB DOW **EPI** HI MLD
PMLD SLD SP&LD TOU
*Wheelchair access:* WA1
*Independent Special*
*52-week care*

**THE SCHOOL FOR
PROFOUND EDUCATION\***
Tadworth Court, Tadworth,
Surrey KT20 5RU
*Website:* www.thechildrenstrust.
org.uk/profoundeducation
*Type:* Co-educational Boarding
and Day 5–19 (There is
additional college provision
for 19 to 25 year olds.)
*Special needs:* CP EPI HEA HI
IM **PMLD** VI
*Wheelchair access:* WA1
*Non-maintained*
*52-week care*

**UNSTED PARK SCHOOL**
Mustead Heath Road,
Godalming, Surrey GU7 1UW
*Website:*
www.prioryeducation.com
*Type:* Co-educational Boarding
and Day 7–16
*Special needs:* ASD ASP
*Wheelchair access:* WA2
*Independent Special*

# EAST SUSSEX

### CHAILEY HERITAGE FOUNDATION*
Haywards Heath Road,
NORTH CHAILEY, Nr Lewes,
East Sussex BN8 4EF
*Website:* www.chs.org.uk
*Type:* Co-educational Boarding
and Day 3–19 (The school also
offers a Young Adults' Transition
Service for young disabled
adults aged 19–25.)
*Special needs:* ASD **CP** EPI
**HEA** HI **IM** MLD PMLD SLD
SP&LD VI
*Wheelchair access:* WA1
*Non-maintained*
*52-week care*

### THE FIRS
2 The Green, St Leonards on
Sea, East Sussex
*Website:*
www.northern-care.co.uk
*Type:* Boys Boarding
Only 11–17
*Special needs:* **BESD CB**

### FREWEN COLLEGE+
Brickwall, Rye Road, Northiam,
Rye, East Sussex TN31 6NL
*Website:*
www.frewencollege.co.uk
*Type:* Co-educational Boarding
and Day 5–16
*Special needs:* ASP **DYC DYP
DYS** SP&LD
*Wheelchair access:* W
*Independent Special*

### HAMILTON LODGE SCHOOL FOR DEAF CHILDREN
Walpole Road, Brighton,
East Sussex BN2 0LS
*Website:*
hamiltonlodgeschool.co.uk
*Type:* Co-educational Boarding
and Day 5–18
*Special needs:* **HI**
*Wheelchair access:* WA2
*Non-maintained*

### THE LIONCARE SCHOOL
c/o The Lioncare Group,
Lioncare House, 58a
Livingstone Road, Hove,
East Sussex BN3 3WL
*Website:* www.lioncare.co.uk
*Type:* Co-educational Day Only
7–16
*Special needs:* **ADD ADHD
ASD** ASP **BESD CB DYS** HEA
HI **MLD PMLD** SLD SP&LD VI
*Wheelchair access:* WA3
*Independent Special*
*52-week care*

### NORTHEASE MANOR+
Rodmell, Lewes, East Sussex
BN7 3EY
*Website:* www.northease.co.uk
*Type:* Co-educational Boarding
and Day 10–17
*Special needs:* DYC DYP **DYS**

### OWLSWICK SCHOOL
Newhaven Road, Kingston,
Lewes, East Sussex BN7 3NF
*Website:*
www.owlswickschool.co.uk
*Type:* Co-educational Boarding
Only 10–18
*Special needs:* ADD **ADHD
BESD** DYS **MLD**
*52-week care*

### ST JOHN'S SCHOOL & COLLEGE
Firle Road, Seaford,
East Sussex BN25 2HU
*Website:* www.st-johns.co.uk
*Type:* Co-educational Boarding
and Day 7–22
*Special needs:* ADD ASD ASP
**BESD** DOW **MLD SLD** TOU
*Non-maintained*

### ST MARY'S WRESTWOOD CHILDREN'S TRUST*
Wrestwood Road,
Bexhill-on-Sea, East Sussex
TN40 2LU
*Website:*
www.stmarysbexhill.org
*Type:* Co-educational Boarding
and Day 7–19
*Special needs:* ADD **ASD** ASP
CP HI **MLD** VI
*Non-maintained*

# WEST SUSSEX

### BRANTRIDGE SCHOOL
Staplefield Place, Staplefield,
Haywards Heath, West Sussex
RH17 6EQ
*Website:*
www.brantridge-school.co.uk
*Type:* Boys Boarding Only 13–6
*Special needs:* ADD ADHD ASD
ASP **BESD** CB MLD SP&LD
*Wheelchair access:* W
*Non-maintained*

### FARNEY CLOSE SCHOOL
Bolney Court, Bolney, Haywards
Heath, West Sussex RH17 5RD
*Website:* www.farneyclose.co.uk
*Type:* Co-educational Boarding
and Day 11–16
*Special needs:* ADD ADHD ASP
**BESD** MLD

### HILLCREST SLINFORD
Stane Street, Slinford,
Nr Horsham,
West Sussex RH13 0QX
*Type:* Boys Boarding Only
11–16
*Special needs:* ADD **ADHD
BESD CB**
*Wheelchair access:* WA3
*52-week care*

**INGFIELD MANOR SCHOOL**
Ingfield Manor Drive, Five Oaks,
Billingshurst, West Sussex
RH14 9AX
*Website:* www.scope.org.uk
*Type:* Co-educational Day and
Boarding 3–19
*Special needs:* **CP** IM SP&LD
*Wheelchair access:* WA2
*Independent Special*

**KINGS MANOR COMMUNITY
COLLEGE**
Kingston Lane, Shoreham-by-
Sea, Shoreham-by-Sea,
West Sussex BN43 6YT
*Website:* www.
kingsmanor.w-sussex.sch.uk
*Type:* Co-educational Boarding
Only 11–16
*Special needs:* ADD **ADHD**
BESD **DYP** DYS EPI HEA MLD

**MUNTHAM HOUSE SCHOOL**
Barns Green, Horsham,
West Sussex RH13 7NJ
*Website:* www.
munthamhouse.w-sussex.sch.uk
*Type:* Boys Boarding and
Day 8–18
*Special needs:* ADD **ADHD** ASD
ASP **BESD CB**
*Wheelchair access:* WA3

**PHILPOTS MANOR SCHOOL***
West Hoathly, East Grinstead,
West Sussex RH19 4PR
*Website:*
www.philpotsmanorschool.co.uk
*Type:* Co-educational Boarding
and Day 7–19
*Special needs:* ADD ADHD ASD
ASP **BESD** CB DOW DYC DYP
DYS EPI MLD SP&LD TOU
*Wheelchair access:* WA3
*Independent Special*

**SOUTHWAYS SCHOOL**
The Vale House, Findon Road,
Findon, Worthing, West Sussex
BN14 0RA
*Website:*
families-for-children.co.uk
*Type:* Co-educational Day
Only 7–11
*Special needs:* **BESD**
*Wheelchair access:* W
*Independent Special*

# TYNE AND WEAR

**NORTHERN COUNTIES
SCHOOL**
Great North Road,
Newcastle-Upon-Tyne,
Tyne and Wear NE2 3BB
*Website:* www.
northern-counties-school.co.uk
*Type:* Co-educational Boarding
and Day 3–19
*Special needs:* **HI** MLD
**PMLD VI**
*Wheelchair access:* W

**PARKSIDE HOUSE SCHOOL**
Station Road, Backworth,
Tyne and Wear NE27 0AB
*Type:* 11–16
*Special needs:* BESD MLD
*Independent Special*

**PERCY HEDLEY SCHOOL**
Station Road, Forest Hall,
Newcastle-upon-Tyne,
Tyne and Wear NE12 8YY
*Website:*
www.percyhedley.org.uk
*Type:* Co-educational Day and
Boarding 3–19
*Special needs:* ADHD ASD ASP
**CP** DYP HI IM SP&LD VI
*Wheelchair access:* WA1
*Non-maintained*

**TALBOT HOUSE SPECIAL
SCHOOL**
Hexham Road, Walbottle,
Newcastle Upon Tyne, Tyne and
Wear NE15 8HW
*Website:*
www.talbothouseschool.org
*Type:* Co-educational Day and
Boarding 7–18
*Special needs:* **ADD ADHD
BESD CB** DYP MLD TOU
*Wheelchair access:* WA2
*Non-maintained*
*52-week care*

**THORNHILL PARK SCHOOL**
21 Thornhill Park, Sunderland,
Tyne and Wear SR2 7LA
*Type:* Co-educational Boarding
and Day 2–19
*Special needs:* **ASD ASP**
*Wheelchair access:* W
*52-week care*

# WARWICKSHIRE

### ARC SCHOOL
Church End, Ansley,
Nr Nuneaton, Warwickshire
CV10 0QR
*Type:* Co-educational Day
Only 11–16
*Special needs:* BESD
*Independent Special*

### THE OLD SCHOOL
Church End, Ansley, Nr
Nuneaton, Warwickshire
CV10 0QR
*Type:* Co-educational Day
Only 11–16
*Special needs:* **BESD**

### RNIB PEARS CENTRE FOR SPECIALIST LEARNING*
Wheelwright Lane, Ash Green,
Coventry, Warwickshire CV7
9RA
*Website:* www.rnib.org.uk/
pearscentre
*Type:* Co-educational Boarding
and Day 4–19
*Special needs:* ASD BESD CB
CP DOW EPI HEA HI **IM PMLD
SLD** SP&LD **VI**
*Wheelchair access:* WA1
*Non-maintained*
*52-week care*

### WATHEN GRANGE SCHOOL
C/O Complete Care (Warks) Ltd,
34 Lillington Road, Leamington
Spa, Warwickshire CV32 5YY
*Website:* www.
wathengrange.com/index.php
*Type:* Co-educational Day and
Boarding 12–16
*Special needs:* **BESD** CB
*Wheelchair access:* WA1
*Independent Special*
*52-week care*

# WEST MIDLANDS

### NATIONAL INSTITUTE OF CONDUCTIVE EDUCATION
Cannon Hill House, Russell
Road, Moseley, Birmingham,
West Midlands B13 8RD
*Website:* www.
conductive-education.org.uk
*Type:* Co-educational Day Only
1–11
*Special needs:* ASD **CP** DYP
HEA IM MLD SP&LD
*Wheelchair access:* WA2
*Independent Special*

### NEW HALL PROJECT 20/20
The Huntingtree Park Centre,
Halesowen, West Midlands
B63 4HY
*Type:* Co-educational Day
Only 14–16

### THE ROYAL WOLVERHAMPTON SCHOOL+
Penn Road, Wolverhampton,
West Midlands WV3 0EG
*Website:*
www.theroyalschool.co.uk
*Type:* Co-educational Boarding
and Day 2–18
*Special needs:* ADD ADHD
DYP **DYS**

### SECOND CHANCES AT THE VINE TRUST WALSALL
33 Lower Hall Lane, Walsall,
West Midlands WS1 1RR
*Type:* Co-educational Day
Only 14–16
*Wheelchair access:* W

### SUNFIELD SCHOOL*
Clent Grove, Woodman Lane,
Stourbridge, West Midlands
DY9 9PB
*Website:* www.sunfield.org.uk
*Type:* Co-educational Boarding
and Day 6–19
*Special needs:* ADD **ADHD
ASD** ASP **CB** DOW EPI HEA
**MLD** PMLD **SLD** SP&LD TOU
*Independent Special*
*52-week care*

# WILTSHIRE

**APPLEFORD SCHOOL+**
Elston Lane, Shrewton,
Salisbury, Wiltshire SP3 4HL
*Website:*
www.applefordschool.org
*Type:* Co-educational Boarding
and Day 7–14
*Special needs:* ADD ADHD **DYC**
DYP **DYS** MLD SP&LD
*Wheelchair access:* WA3
*Independent Special*

**BELMONT SCHOOL**
School Lane, Salisbury,
Wiltshire SP1 3YA
*Type:* Co-educational Day
Only 11–16
*Special needs:* **BESD**
*Wheelchair access:* WA3

**BURTON HILL SCHOOL**
Malmesbury,
Wiltshire SN16 0EG
*Website:* www.shaftesburysoc.
org.uk/burtonhill
*Type:* Co-educational Boarding
and Day 11–20
*Special needs:* ASD **CP** HEA HI
**IM MLD PMLD SLD** SP&LD VI
*Wheelchair access:* WA1
*Non-maintained*

**CALDER HOUSE SCHOOL+**
Thickwood Lane, Colerne,
Chippenham,
Wiltshire SN14 8BN
*Website:*
www.calderhouseschool.co.uk
*Type:* Co-educational Day
Only 5–13
*Special needs:* DYC **DYP DYS**
HEA SP&LD
*Wheelchair access:* WA3

**COTSWOLD COMMUNITY**
Spine Road West, Ashton
Keynes, Swindon,
Wiltshire SN6 6QU
*Website:* www.
actionforchildren.org.uk/schools
*Type:* Boys Boarding and
Day 9–18
*Special needs:* ADD ADHD ASP
**BESD** CB DYS HI MLD
*Wheelchair access:* WA1
*Independent Special*
*52-week care*

**TUMBLEWOOD PROJECT
SCHOOL**
The Laurels, 4 Hawkeridge
Road, Heywood, Westbury,
Wiltshire BA13 4LF
*Type:* Girls Day Only 11–18
*Special needs:* **BESD**
*Wheelchair access:* WA2
*52-week care*

**WESSEX COLLEGE**
Wessex House, 76 Boreham
Road, Warminster, Wiltshire
BA12 9JN
*Type:* Co-educational Day
Only 11–16
*Special needs:* BESD

# WORCESTERSHIRE

**NEW COLLEGE WORCESTER***
Whittington Road, Worcester,
Worcestershire WR5 2JX
*Website:*
www.newcollegeworcester.co.uk
*Type:* Co-educational Boarding
and Day 11–19
*Special needs:* ASP DYP DYS
HEA HI IM VI
*Wheelchair access:* W
*Independent Special*

# NORTH YORKSHIRE

### BRECKENBROUGH SCHOOL*
Sandhutton, Thirsk, North
Yorkshire YO7 4EN
*Website:*
www.breckenbrough.org.uk
*Type:* Boys Boarding and Day
9–19
*Special needs:* ADD ADHD
**ASD ASP BESD** TOU
*Wheelchair access:* WA3
*Non-maintained*

### SPRING HILL SCHOOL (BARNARDO'S)
Palace Road, Ripon, North
Yorkshire HG4 3HN
*Website:* www.barnardos.org.uk/
springhillschool
*Type:* Co-educational Boarding
and Day 9–19
*Special needs:* **ADD ADHD
ASD ASP BESD CB** DOW DYP
DYS EPI HEA HI **MLD** SLD
SP&LD TOU VI
*Wheelchair access:* WA2
*Non-maintained*
*52-week care*

# SOUTH YORKSHIRE

### DONCASTER SCHOOL FOR THE DEAF*
Leger Way, Doncaster,
South Yorkshire DN2 6AY
*Website:* www.
deaf-school.co.uk
*Type:* Co-educational Boarding
and Day 3–19
*Special needs:* ADHD BESD
CP DYS **HI** MLD PMLD SLD
SP&LD
*Wheelchair access:* WA1
*Independent Special*
*52-week care*

### FULLERTON HOUSE SCHOOL
off Tickhill Square, Denaby,
Doncaster, South Yorkshire
DN12 4AR
*Website:*
www.hesleygroup.co.uk
*Type:* Co-educational Boarding
Only 8–19
*Special needs:* ASD EPI SLD
SP&LD

### NAS ROBERT OGDEN SCHOOL*
Clayton Lane, Thurnscoe,
Rotherham, South Yorkshire
S63 0BG
*Website:* www.autism.org.uk/
robertogden
*Type:* Co-educational Boarding
and Day 5–19
*Special needs:* **ASD ASP** CB
*Wheelchair access:* WA2
*Independent Special*
*52-week care*

### PACES CONDUCTIVE EDUCATION
Pack Horse Lane, High Green,
Sheffield, South Yorkshire
S35 3HY
*Website:*
www.paces-school.org.uk/
*Type:* Co-educational
*Special needs:* **CP** HEA HI MLD
SLD SP&LD VI
*Wheelchair access:* W
*Non-maintained*

### WILSIC HALL SCHOOL
Wadworth, Doncaster,
South Yorkshire DN11 9AG
*Website:*
www.wilsichallschool.co.uk
*Type:* Co-educational Boarding
Only 11–19
*Special needs:* ASD **ASP** CB
SLD SP&LD
*Wheelchair access:* WA3
*Independent Special*
*52-week care*

# WEST YORKSHIRE

**DENBY GRANGE SCHOOL**
Off Stocksmoor Road, Midgley,
Wakefield, West Yorkshire
WF4 4JQ
*Type:* Co-educational Day
Only 11–16
*Special needs:* ADD ADHD
**BESD CB** MLD
*Wheelchair access:* WA1
*Independent Special*

**HOLLY BANK SCHOOL**
Roe Head, Far Common Road,
Mirfield, West Yorkshire
WF14 0DQ
*Website:*
www.hollybanktrust.com
*Type:* Co-educational Boarding
and Day 5–19
*Special needs:* **CP** EPI **IM** MLD
**PMLD SLD** SP&LD VI
*Wheelchair access:* WA2
*Non-maintained*
*52-week care*

**NORSETT HOUSE**
West View, Boothtown, Halifax,
West Yorkshire HX3 6PG
*Website:*
www.northern-care.co.uk
*Type:* Boys Boarding Only
11–17
*Special needs:* **BESD CB**

**ST JOHN'S CATHOLIC
SCHOOL FOR THE DEAF\***
Church Street, Boston Spa,
West Yorkshire LS23 6DF
*Website:* www.stjohns.org.uk
*Type:* Co-educational Boarding
and Day 4–19
*Special needs:* ADHD ASD ASP
CP DYP DYS EPI **HI** IM MLD
SP&LD VI
*Wheelchair access:* WA2
*Non-maintained*

**WILLIAM HENRY SMITH
SCHOOL**
Boothroyd Lane, Brighouse,
West Yorkshire HD6 3JW
*Website:* www.whsschool.org.uk
*Type:* Boys Boarding and
Day 8–16
*Special needs:* ADD ADHD
**BESD** CB DYS
*Wheelchair access:* WA2
*Non-maintained*

# YORK

**NEW HAVEN**
3 Wilton Rd, Hornsea, York
HU18 1QU
*Website:*
www.northern-care.co.uk
*Type:* Boys Boarding Only
11–17
*Special needs:* **BESD CB**

# Scotland

## ABERDEENSHIRE

### CAMPHILL SCHOOL ABERDEEN
Central Office, Murtle Estate,
Bieldside, Aberdeen,
Aberdeenshire AB15 9EP
*Website:*
www.camphillschools.org.uk
*Type:* Co-educational Boarding
and Day 3–19
*Special needs:* ADD ADHD
**ASD ASP BESD** CP DOW DYP
DYS EPI HEA HI **MLD PMLD
SLD** SP&LD TOU VI
*Wheelchair access:* WA2
*Independent Special*

### LINN MOOR RESIDENTIAL SCHOOL
Peterculter, Aberdeen,
Aberdeenshire AB14 0PJ
*Website:*
www.linnmoorschool.co.uk
*Type:* Co-educational Boarding
Only 5–18
*Special needs:* ASD ASP CB
**MLD** PMLD SLD
*Wheelchair access:* WA1
*52-week care*

### OAKBANK SCHOOL
Midstocket Road, Aberdeen,
Aberdeenshire AB15 5XP
*Type:* Co-educational Boarding
and Day 12–18
*Special needs:* ADHD **BESD**

## NORTH AYRSHIRE

### GEILSLAND SCHOOL
Beith, North Ayrshire KA15 1HD
*Type:* Boys Boarding Only
14–18
*Special needs:* **BESD** MLD

### SEAFIELD SCHOOL
86 Eglinton Road, Ardrossan,
North Ayrshire KA22 8NL
*Type:* Boys Boarding and Day
7–17
*Special needs:* ADD ADHD ASP
**BESD** DYS MLD
*Wheelchair access:* W

# EAST AYRSHIRE

**NAS DALDORCH HOUSE
SCHOOL\***
Sorn Road, Catrine,
East Ayrshire KA5 6NA
*Website:* www.autism.org.uk/
daldorch
*Type:* Co-educational Boarding
and Day 5–21 (We offer primary
and secondary education for
students up to the age of 18,
and continuing education and
supported living for young
people up to the age of 25.)
*Special needs:* **ASD ASP** CB
*Independent Special*
*52-week care*

# CLACKMANNANSHIRE

**NEW STRUAN SCHOOL**
A Centre for Autism,
100 Smithfield Loan, Alloa,
Clackmannanshire FK101NP
*Website:*
www.autism-in-scotland.org.uk
*Type:* Co-educational Boarding
and Day 5–19
*Special needs:* **ASD ASP**
*Wheelchair access:* WA1

# DUMFRIES & GALLOWAY

**WOODLANDS SCHOOL**
Merton Hall, Wigtownshire,
Dumfries & Galloway DG8 6QL
*Type:* Boys Boarding Only 7–17
*Special needs:* ADD ADHD
**BESD** MLD SP&LD

# FALKIRK

**BARNARDO'S LECROPT**
School & Family Support
Service, 108 Glasgow Road,
Camelon, Falkirk FK1 4HS
*Type:* Co-educational Day
Only 5–12
*Special needs:* ADD **ADHD** ASD
ASP **BESD CB** DYC DYP DYS
SP&LD TOU
*Wheelchair access:* WA1

# FIFE

**FALKLAND HOUSE SCHOOL**
Falkland Estate, Falkland,
Cupar, Fife KY15 7AE
*Website:* www.
falklandhouseschool.org
*Type:* Boys Boarding and Day
*Special needs:* ADHD ASP
BESD TOU
*Independent Special*

**HILLSIDE SCHOOL**
Hillside, Aberdour, Fife KY3 0RH
*Type:* Boys Boarding
Only 11–16
*Special needs:* ADD ADHD
BESD DYS MLD
*Wheelchair access:* WA3
*52-week care*

**STARLEY HALL**
Aberdour Road, Burntisland,
Fife KY3 0AG
*Website:*
www.starleyhallschool.co.uk
*Type:* Co-educational Boarding
Only 11–16
*Special needs:* **ADD ADHD** ASP
BESD TOU
*52-week care*

**SYCAMORE SCHOOL**
6 Bellyeoman Road,
Dunfermline, Fife KY1 3HD
*Special needs:* ASD **BESD**

# GLASGOW

**EAST PARK SCHOOL**
1092 Maryhill Road,
Glasgow G20 9TD
*Type:* Co-educational Boarding
and Day 5–19
*Special needs:* ADHD ASD **ASP**
**CB** CP **EPI HEA** IM **PMLD** SLD
SP&LD VI
*Wheelchair access:* WA1
*52-week care*

**SPRINGBOIG ST JOHN'S**
1190 Edinburgh Road,
Glasgow G32 4EH
*Type:* Boys Boarding
Only 14–17
*Special needs:* BESD

# LANARKSHIRE

**PARK VIEW**
73 Grange St, Clayton le Moors,
Lanarkshire BB5 5PJ
*Website:*
www.northern-care.co.uk
*Type:* Boys Day Only 11–17
*Special needs:* **BESD CB**

# NORTH LANARKSHIRE

**ST PHILLIP'S SCHOOL**
Plains, Airdrie, North
Lanarkshire ML6 7SF
*Website:* www.
stphilipsschoolplains.org.uk
*Type:* Boys Boarding and
Day 10–16
*Special needs:* ADD ADHD
**BESD** MLD

# SOUTH LANARKSHIRE

**NAS DALDORCH SATELLITE
SCHOOL**
St Leonards, East Kilbride,
South Lanarkshire
*Website:*
www.autism.org.uk/daldorch
*Type:* Co-educational Boarding
Only 5–19
*Special needs:* **ASD ASP**
*Independent Special
52-week care*

**STANMORE HOUSE
RESIDENTIAL SCHOOL**
Lanark, South Lanarkshire
ML11 7RR
*Type:* Co-educational Boarding
and Day 2–18
*Special needs:* **CP** EPI PMLD
SLD

# LOTHIAN

**DONALDSON'S COLLEGE
FOR THE DEAF**
West Coates, Edinburgh,
Lothian EH12 5JJ
*Website:*
www.donaldsons.org.uk
*Type:* Co-educational Boarding
and Day 3–19
*Special needs:* **ASD** ASP **HI**
SP&LD
*Wheelchair access:* W

**HARMENY SCHOOL**
45 Mansfield Road, Balerno,
Lothian EH14 7JY
*Website:* www.harmeny.org.uk
*Type:* Co-educational Day and
Boarding 6–13
*Special needs:* ADD **ADHD** ASP
**BESD** CB DYC DYS MLD
SP&LD
*Wheelchair access:* WA3
*52-week care*

**MOORE HOUSE SCHOOL**
Edinburgh Road, Bathgate,
Lothian EH48 1EX
*Type:* Co-educational Day and
Boarding 11–16
*Special needs:* **ADHD BESD
CB** MLD
*Wheelchair access:* W
*Independent Special
52-week care*

**THE ROYAL BLIND SCHOOL,
EDINBURGH**
Craigmillar Park, Edinburgh,
Lothian EH16 5NA
*Website:* www.royalblind.org
*Type:* Co-educational Boarding
and Day 5–19
*Special needs:* ADD ASD ASP
BESD CB CP DOW DYS EPI
HEA HI IM MLD PMLD SLD
SP&LD VI

# PERTH AND KINROSS

**OCHIL TOWER (RUDOLF
STEINER) SCHOOL**
140 High Street, Auchterarder,
Perth and Kinross PH3 1AD
*Website:*
www.ochiltowerschool.org.uk
*Type:* Co-educational Boarding
and Day 5–18
*Special needs:* ADD ADHD
ASD ASP BESD CB DOW DYC
DYP DYS **MLD** PMLD **SLD**
SP&LD TOU
*Independent Special*

**SEAMAB HOUSE SCHOOL**
Rumbling Bridge, Kinross,
Perth and Kinross KY13 0PT
*Type:* Co-educational Boarding
and Day 5–12
*Special needs:* **BESD** CB
*Wheelchair access:* WA2
*52-week care*

# PERTHSHIRE

**THE NEW SCHOOL**
Butterstone, Dunkeld, Perthshire
PH8 0HJ
*Website:* http://www.
thenewschool.co.uk
*Type:* Co-educational Boarding
and Day 12–20
*Special needs:* **ADD ADHD
ASD ASP DYC DYP DYS EPI**
HEA **MLD** TOU
*Wheelchair access:* W
*Independent Special*

# RENFREWSHIRE

**GOOD SHEPHERD CENTRE**
Greenock Road, Bishopton,
Renfrewshire PA7 5PF
*Website:*
www.goodshepherdcentre.co.uk
*Type:* Girls Boarding and Day
12–16
*Special needs:* **BESD** MLD
*Wheelchair access:* W
*52-week care*

**KIBBLE CENTRE**
Goudie Street, Paisley,
Renfrewshire PA3 2LG
*Website:* www.kibble.org
*Type:* Boys Boarding and Day
12–17
*Special needs:* ADD ADHD ASD
ASP **BESD** CB DYP DYS EPI
**MLD** TOU
*Wheelchair access:* WA2
*52-week care*

# STIRLING

**BALLIKINRAIN RESIDENTIAL
SCHOOL**
Fintry Road, Balfron,
Stirlingshire, Stirling G63 0LL
*Website:* www.ballikinrain.org
*Type:* Boys Boarding and Day
8–14
*Special needs:* ADD ADHD ASD
ASP **BESD CB** DYC DYP DYS
MLD
*Wheelchair access:* WA3
*Independent Special*
*52-week care*

**SNOWDON SCHOOL**
31 Spittal Street,
Stirling FK8 1DU
*Type:* Girls Boarding Only
12–18
*Special needs:* ADD ADHD ASD
ASP **BESD** CB DYS
*Wheelchair access:* WA3
*Independent Special*
*52-week care*

# STRATHCLYDE

**CORSEFORD SCHOOL**
Howwood Road, Milliken Park,
Kilbarchan, Strathclyde
PA10 2NT
*Type:* Co-educational Day and
Boarding

# Wales

## CARDIFF

**CRAIG-Y-PARC SCHOOL**
Heol y Parc, Pentyrch, Cardiff
CF15 9NB
*Website:* www.scope.org.uk
*Type:* Co-educational Boarding
and Day 3–19
*Special needs:* CP **IM PMLD**
*Wheelchair access:* WA1

## DYFED

**YSGOL RHYDYGORS+**
Llanstephan Road, Johnstown,
Carmarthen, Dyfed SA31 3NQ

## FLINTSHIRE

**KINSALE SCHOOL\***
Kinsale Hall, Llanerach-y-mor,
Holywell, Flintshire CH8 9DX
*Website:*
www.optionsgroup.co.uk
*Type:* Co-educational Day and
Boarding 8–19
*Special needs:* ADD ADHD
**ASD ASP CB EPI** HEA **MLD**
PMLD SLD SP&LD
*Wheelchair access:* W
*Independent Special*
*52-week care*

# MONMOUTHSHIRE

**TALOCHER SCHOOL**
Talocher Farm, Wonastow Road,
Monmouth, Monmouthshire
NP25 4DN
*Website:* www.priorygroup.com
*Type:* Co-educational Day Only
11–18
*Special needs:* **BESD**
*Wheelchair access:* W
*Independent Special*
*52-week care*

# PEMBROKESHIRE

**ST DAVID'S EDUCATION UNIT**
Pembroke House, Brawdy
Business Park, Haverfordwest,
Pembrokeshire SA62 6NP
*Type:* Co-educational Day Only
8–17

# POWYS

**HILLCREST PENTWYN
SCHOOL**
Clyro, Hereford, Powys HR3 5SE
*Website:*
www.hillcrestcare.co.uk
*Type:* Boys Boarding Only
11–17
*Special needs:* ADD ADHD
**BESD CB DYC** DYP **DYS**
*Wheelchair access:* WA2
*Independent Special*
*52-week care*

**MACINTYRE SCHOOL
WOMASTON**
Womaston School, Walton,
Presteigne, Powys LD8 2PT
*Type:* Co-educational Boarding
Only 14–19
*Special needs:* ADD ADHD ASD
**ASP CB** CP DOW DYP EPI IM
MLD **PMLD SLD**
*Wheelchair access:* WA1
*Independent Special*
*52-week care*

# VALE OF GLAMORGAN

### ACTION FOR CHILDREN HEADLANDS SCHOOL*
2 St Augustines Road, Penarth, Vale of Glamorgan CF64 1YY
*Website:* www.actionforchildren. org.uk/headlands
*Type:* Co-educational Boarding and Day 8–19
*Special needs:* **ADD ADHD ASD ASP BESD CB DYP DYS** MLD SP&LD **TOU**
*Wheelchair access:* WA3
*Independent Special*

# WREXHAM

### PROSPECTS CENTRE FOR YOUNG PEOPLE
Bersham Road, Wrexham LL14 4HS
*Website:* www.prospectscare.co.uk
*Type:* Co-educational Day and Boarding 11–16

### WOODLANDS CHILDREN'S DEVELOPMENT CENTRE
27 Pentrefelyn Road, Wrexham LL13 7NB
*Website:* www.woodlandslimited.com
*Type:* Boys Day Only 11–17

# 2.3

# Profiles of Independent and Non-Maintained Special Schools

## SYMBOL KEY

### Gender

- Girls
- Boys
- Coed

### CReSTeD

◆ Crested Registered

### Accommodation

🏠 Boarding only
🏠 Boarding and Day
🏠 Day and Boarding
🏠 Day only

### Has 6th Form

▲ Has 6th Form

## Action for Children

## Action for Children Headlands School ● ♠

2 St Augustines Road, Penarth, Vale of Glamorgan CF64 1YY
**T:** 029 2070 0515 **F:** 029 2070 0515
**E:** headlands.school@actionforchildren.org.uk
**W:** www.actionforchildren.org.uk/headlands

**Principal** Mr M Burns
**Founded** 1918
**School Status** Co-ed Independent (special)
   Boarding and Day
**Religious denomination** Non-Denominational
**Membership** NAS, NASEN

**Special needs provision**
**ADD, ADHD, ASD, ASP,**
**BESD, CB, DYP, DYS,**
MLD, SP&LD, **TOU**, WA3
**Age range** 8–19; boarders from 8;
   *(boarding)* 10; *(weekly boarding)* 10
**Average class size** 7

We believe 'expectation is everything' so; we hold high expectations of our learners and staff and what they can achieve. We base our approach on attachment theories; as building positive and trusting relationships with learners is critical to their success. Action for Children Headlands School helps children and young people who are having difficulty learning as a result of challenging behaviour, including those with behavioural, emotional and social difficulties (BESD), Autistic Spectrum Disorder (ASD) and Asperger's Syndrome. Education, activities and residential care are provided on-site and children may attend as boarders or day students. We have a comprehensive wellbeing curriculum which is designed to support pupils' social; emotional and behavioural needs. Residential care packages are flexible.

## Action for Children Parklands Campus ● ♠

Action for Children, Near Appleton, Abingdon, Oxfordshire OX13 5QB
**T:** 01865 390436 **F:** 01865 390688
**E:** parklands.campus@actionforchildren.org.uk
**W:** www.actionforchildren.org.uk/parklands

**Principal** Mr Raymond Wilson
**School Status** Co-ed Non-maintained
   (special) Boarding and Day
**Religious denomination** Non-Denominational

**Membership** NASS
**Special needs provision** ADHD, ASD, **BESD**
**Age range** 11–19; boarders from 11

Action for Children Parklands Campus provides an integrated and holistic approach to education and care through day, residential, fostering and outreach services. We help young people with Behavioural, Emotional and Social Difficulties, Autistic Spectrum Disorder, Asperger's Syndrome and Complex Needs to build positive relationships in a safe environment. Our programmes of study are created and tailored for the individual to help engage and motivate within a structured pathway. Positive outcomes are achieved through appropriate leadership in the provision of a partnership approach through flexible package options; transition support (and other specialist support) and by careful reintegration into the parental home. The innovative approach to teaching and learning at Parklands makes use of the latest ICT.

# Breckenbrough School   ●🏠

Breckenbrough, Sandhutton, Thirsk, North Yorkshire YO7 4EN
**T:** 01845 587238 **F:** 01845 587385
**E:** office@breckenbrough.org.uk
**W:** www.breckenbrough.org.uk

**Headmaster** Mr G Brookes
**Founded** 1937
**School Status** Boys Non-maintained (special)
   Boarding and Day
**Religious denomination** Quaker
**Special needs provision** ADD, ADHD, ASD,
   **ASP**, **BESD**, TOU, WA3

**Age range** 9–19; boarders from 9
**No of Pupils** 48; *(boarding)* 37;
   *(full boarding)* 7; *(weekly boarding)* 30;
   *Senior* 40; *Sixth form* 8; *Boys* 48
**Average class size** 5

Breckenbrough in brief:

- Over 70 years of experience in educating boys with complex needs.
- A unique special school with a Quaker ethos.
- Educates boys aged 9 to 19 with academic potential.
- Accommodates both day and boarding pupils on a 38 week basis.
- Has expertise and success with boys with Asperger Syndrome and ADHD.
- Has high educational expectations and offers a wide range of GCSE's, vocational programmes and A levels.
- Provides individualized learning and programmes of study.
- Offers a relaxed atmosphere, within a holistic and therapeutic environment.
- Operates an effective ethos of conflict resolution.
- Encourages pupils to understand and take responsibility for their own actions.
- Employs a full-time registered psychologist and counsellor.
- Enjoys and encourages strong partnerships with families.
- Offers a wide range of activities and opportunities.
- Provides post-16 provision for working in partnership with other local providers.
- Operates a unique After Care service to provide contact and support for pupils once they have left school and in later life.
- The vast majority of boys go on to full-time further education, training and work.
- Has good access from the motorway and rail networks.

The school is a non-profit making charity, whose governors are appointed by Quakers in Yorkshire. Housed in a Victorian country house with 10 acres of land in the heart of North Yorkshire, Breckenbrough is located a few miles from Thirsk, close to the Yorkshire Dales and North York Moors National Parks.

Outdoor Education and PHSE programmes are integral to the work of the school. Life skills are developed and pupils are offered a wide and varied range of activities which provide emotional, physical and social challenge. The experiences include motorbike riding and maintenance on site, kayaking, climbing and mountain biking. Work experience and regular opportunities to integrate with the local community are a vital part of our provision.

The school has an experienced staff skilled in conflict resolution, who understand Asperger Syndrome and young people experiencing emotional problems. Students are continually encouraged through the powerful ethos of the school where external pressure is reduced and individuality encouraged.

# Centre Academy ● ♠

Centre Academy, 92 St John's Hill, Battersea,
London, SW11 1SH
**T:** 0207 7382344
**F:** 0207 7389862
**E:** info@centreacademy.net
**W:** www.centreacademy.net

**Headmaster** Dr D J Rollo BA, MA, PhD
**Head of School** Natalia Ambridge
**Founded** 1974
**School Status** Co-ed Independent
  (special) Day only
**Religious denomination**
  Non-Denominational
**Membership** BDA, CIS, LISA
**Special needs provision ADD, ADHD,**
  **ASD, ASP, DYP, DYS, MLD,** SP&LD, WA1
**Age range** 7–19
**No of Pupils** 60; *Nursery to Pre-prep* 10;
  *Prep* 23; *Senior* 22; *Sixth form* 15;
  *Girls* 30; *Boys* 30
**Teacher:pupil ratio** 1:3
**Average class size** 5

# Centre Academy East Anglia
● ♠ ◆

Church Road, Brettenham, Ipswich, Suffolk IP7 7QR
**T:** 01449 736404
**F:** 01449 737881
**E:** admin@centreacademy.net
**W:** www.centreacademy.net
The school is adjacent to the church in the rural
village of Brettenham.

**Principal** Mr Duncan Rollo BA, MA, PhD
**Head of School** Mrs Kim Salthouse BA, Med
**Founded** 1981
**School Status** Co-ed Independent (special)
  Day and Boarding
**Religious denomination** Church of England
**Membership** BDA, CReSTeD, NASEN
**Special needs provision ADD, ADHD, ASD,**
  **ASP, DYC, DYP, DYS, MLD,** SP&LD
**Age range** 8–19; boarders from 8
**No of Pupils** 40; *Nursery to Pre-prep* 5;
  *Prep* 25; *Senior* 10; *Girls* 20; *Boys* 20
**Teacher:pupil ratio** 1:3
**Average class size** 5

The Centre Academy Schools enable students with a variety of learning difficulties to reclaim their futures. We do so by teaching the skills and coping strategies that students with Dyslexia, ADD, ADHD, Dyspraxia and other learning challenges require in order to succeed. With exceptionally small classes, significant one-on-one instruction and experienced faculty members, Centre Academy Schools make it possible for their students to work to their fullest potential. Following testing and evaluation, we design a programme of instruction tailored to meet the student's individual needs. We cater to individual strengths by offering both the British National Curriculum through GCSE and the American High School Diploma. The Diploma, seen as the gateway to university, involves a system of continual assessment; thus reducing pressure and anxiety that so frequently accompany exams. At both schools English and maths form the core of a student's studies. Other key areas involve: history; science; ICT; music; drama; art; PSHE; geography; religious studies; and a modern foreign language. Students have a wide variety of choices for GCSE studies, and Centre Academy students frequently earn A*–C in seven or eight subjects (including English and Maths). The efforts of our teaching staff are complemented by a coterie of specialists: speech and language; operational therapy; reading; counselling. At CA London we use the capital's cultural, artistic and historic possibilities as our own personal classroom. The Houses of Parliament, National Gallery, Natural History Museum, Science Museum and many other sites are easily accessible. Choices are as broad as the imagination – and our students are the richer for it. We are well served by public transport, and Clapham Junction is only a five-minute walk. Offering both boarding and day programmes, CA East Anglia is located on the edge of a small, rural village, 40 minutes from Cambridge by car, and one hour by train from London. Our ten-acre campus comprises a variety of elegant classroom buildings and excellent boarding facilities for boys and girls. There are excellent sport, art and drama facilities and a range of activities including riding, sailing and karate. All boarders are supported by highly trained staff and an experienced Head of Care. The family atmosphere at both schools reflects our ethos of care and nurturing. Parents are invited to ring either school for a prospectus and to arrange a visit.

# Chailey Heritage Foundation

Haywards Heath Road, North Chailey, Lewes, East Sussex BN8 4EF
**T:** 01825 724444 **F:** 01825 723773
**E:** schooloffice@chs.org.uk **W:** www.chs.org.uk
We welcome visits to the school – please contact the School Office to arrange
an appointment

**Principal** Mrs Sylvia Lamb BA Hons, PGCE, MA
**Headteacher** Mr Simon Yates BA Hons, PGCE, NPQH
**Founded** 1903
**School Status** Co-ed Non-maintained (special)
　Day and Boarding
**Religious denomination** Non-Denominational
**Special needs provision** ASD, **CP**, EPI, **HEA**, HI, **IM**,

MLD, PMLD, SLD, SP&LD, VI, WA1
**Age range** 3–19
**No of Pupils** 73; *(boarding)* 19; *(full boarding)* 10;
　*(weekly boarding)* 9; *Nursery* 2;
　*Nursery to Pre-prep* 26; *Senior* 25; *Sixth form* 22;
　*Girls* 34; *Boys* 39
**Average class size** 6

Nationally recognized charity which educates and cares for children / young people aged 3–25 with complex disabilities & health needs. The charity encompasses Chailey Heritage School, The Children's Home and Futures@Chailey Heritage. Our aim is to offer a stimulating and inclusive environment for every child / young adult, to ensure their full potential is reached. The Children's Home offers flexible residential packages of up to 52 weeks per year. The school, judged 'Outstanding' at the last Ofsted inspection in 2009, offers a broad and balanced curriculum, bespoke for each pupil. Chailey Heritage School shares its location with Chailey Heritage Clinical Services (CHCS), part of the Sussex Community NHS Trust, and pupils' clinical needs are overseen, on-site, by medical specialists, minimizing disruption to education. Futures@Chailey Heritage is a transition service for young adults with physical disabilities, aged 19–25, where they are empowered to make choices and decisions about all areas of their lives.
　Registered Charity number 1075837

---

# Cotswold Chine School

Box, Stroud, Gloucestershire GL6 9AG
**T:** 01453 837550 **F:** 01453 834970
**E:** info@novalis-trust.org.uk **W:** www.cotswold-chine.org.uk

**Headteacher** Ms M Smith
**Founded** 1954
**School Status** Co-ed Independent (special)
　Boarding and Day
**Religious denomination** Christian
**Membership** BILD
**Special needs provision** ADD, **ADHD**, ASD, **ASP**,

BESD, CB, DYP,
EPI, **MLD**, SLD, SP&LD, TOU, WA3
**Age range** 9–19; boarders from 9
**No of Pupils** 60; *(boarding)* 42; *(full boarding)* 42;
　*Girls* 18; *Boys* 30
**Teacher:pupil ratio** 1:2
**Average class size** 7

Cotswold Chine School is an independent day and residential therapeutic special school (DfE Registered). The school offers outstanding education and care for vulnerable students with a range of complex learning needs. The school's holistic approach to education and care provides an environment in which young people can make progress and achieve both socially and academically. Facilities include therapy and psychology support from a range of in-house professionals. There is a high staff to student ratio and health promotion supported by our dedicated school nurse.
　Registration is for co-educational provision for students aged 7 to 19 years. Students board from 39 to 52 weeks of the year. A number of day places are also available. The school has seven housegroups including a few semi-independent living units. 'Cotswold Chine School provides an outstanding quality of education that fully meets its aims, maintaining its high standards for the previous inspection. Students make outstanding progress because the quality of the curriculum, teaching and assessment is outstanding.' (Ofsted 2010)
　The school offers full access to the National Curriculum and students leave school with a wide range of externally accredited qualifications including Unit Awards, Entry Level Certificates, Duke of Edinburgh, ASDAN, COPE, Work Related Learning, and GCSEs, with some students gaining a Grade C and above, and proceeding to A levels. Students have access to an extensive craft and vocational curriculum which enables them to develop a wide range of practical and artistic skills.
　Cotswold Chine was founded in 1954 and is administered by Novalis Trust, a charitable organization based on the principles of care and education of Rudolf Steiner.
　Head Teacher: Maureen Smith MA(Ed) Admissions: Rebecca Benson 01453 837550

# Doncaster School for the Deaf

Leger Way, Doncaster, South Yorkshire DN2 6AY
**T:** 01302 386710 **F:** 01302 361808
**E:** principal@ddt-deaf.org.uk **W:** www.deaf-school.co.uk
Enrolment throughtout the year. Please contact us to arrange an informal visit.

**Executive Principal** Mr A W Robinson
**Deputy Head** Jane Goodman
**School Status** Co-ed Independent (special)
   Boarding and Day
**Religious denomination** Non-Denominational
**Membership** NASS

**Special needs provision**
   ADHD, BESD, CP, DYS, **HI**, MLD, PMLD,
   SLD, SP&LD, WA1
**Age range** 3–19
**No of Pupils** 26; *(boarding)* 3; *(full boarding)* 3;
   *Sixth form* 1; *Girls* 8; *Boys* 18
**Average class size** 5

We offer a broad and balanced curriculum accessible to all our pupils; providing smooth progression and continuity through all Key Stages. Pupils are admitted with a range of preferred needs. Our goal is to provide a pupil centred approach based on their method of communication. The School aims to meet communication needs through English and British Sign Language. On-site there is an Audiologist; Speech Therapist; Nurse and Mental Health Nurse as well as a visiting Doctor. A core national curriculum is offered leading to a range of qualifications including GCSE and Entry Level Certificate. Deaf Studies and BSL are also taught. The School is registered to 19 years. Key Stage 4 and 5 pupils are given choices and opportunities to access courses provided by Communication Specialist College Doncaster.

---

# Fairley House School

30 Causton Street, London, SW1P 4AU
**T:** 020 7976 5456 **F:** 020 7976 5905
**E:** ps@fairleyhouse.org.uk **W:** www.fairleyhouse.org.uk
The Junior Department is located at 218–220 Lambeth Road;
SE1 7YJ

**Head** Michael Taylor
**Principal Educational Psychologist** Miss
   J Murray BA (Hons) MEd DipPsychol MSc
   Dip RSA (SpLD) HCPC Reg
**Founded** 1982
**School Status** Co-ed Independent Day only
**Religious denomination** Non-Denominational
**Membership** BDA, CReSTeD, ISA

**Special needs provision** DYC, DYP, DYS,
   HEA, SP&LD, WA1
**Age range** 5–14
**No of Pupils** 194; *Junior dept* 92;
   *Senior dept* 102; *Girls* 44; *Boys* 150
**Teacher:pupil ratio** 1:3
**Average class size** 12

The primary aim is to transform the lives of children with specific learning difficulties. We do this by improving their literacy, numeracy and self-confidence via a full and rich curriculum. We bring out any talents a child might have. There is a structured, multi-sensory approach. Speech and language and occupational therapy are integrated with education. The National Curriculum is followed with emphasis on ICT, Science, Art and DT. Most children remain for two to three years and are carefully prepared for a return to mainstream education. Nearly 99 per cent achieve this. The trans-disciplinary team includes full-time speech and language and occupational therapists. All class teachers and special provision staff are experienced in SPLD.

# Frederick Hugh House

48 Old Church Street, London, SW3 5BY
**T:** 0207 3498833
**F:** 0207 3526821
**E:** info@frederickhughhouse.com
**W:** www.frederickhughhouse.com

**Headmistress** Ms Tanya Jamil
**Founded** 2010
**School Status** Co-ed Independent (special) Day only
**Religious denomination** Christian
**Special needs provision ADD, ADHD, ASD, ASP, CP, DOW, DYC, DYP, DYS, EPI, IM,**

**MLD**, SP&LD, TOU, WA1
**Age range** 4–16
**No of Pupils** 7; *Nursery to Pre-prep* 6; *Prep* 1; *Girls* 4; *Boys* 3
**Teacher:pupil ratio** 1:4
**Average class size** 8

An exciting Special Needs Primary School in Chelsea. Frederick Hugh House is an innovative and unique special needs primary school in the Royal Borough of Kensington and Chelsea, serving children with learning difficulties. At Frederick Hugh House every child benefits from a tailor-made therapeutic programme. This includes in-house speech, occupational and physiotherapists who work closely with our teaching staff; integrating each child's targets into all aspects of the school day. As well as 1:1 sessions, our therapists are involved in all aspects of the school day; taking lessons and joining play-times. It is our practice to differentiate between children's needs so that they may access the curriculum individually whilst working in group and classroom settings. Lessons are multi-sensory with tactile materials; visuals, songs and hands-on activities, in order to meet the needs of all children. Frederick Hugh House's curriculum includes not only the formal requirements of the National Curriculum but also a range of intra-curricular activities organized in order to enrich the experience of the children. We are proud of the breadth of our curriculum; with a wide range of subjects and activities all taught on a weekly basis. All facets of teaching and learning are supported by multi-sensory state-of-the-art facilities, including an interactive multi-sensory theatre, enabling each child to access the curriculum whatever their learning style. In addition to our stimulating, holistic curriculum, we are proud of the exciting experiences we are able to share with our children, including horse riding, pottery classes and dance and drama workshops. Our regular shopping, park and community trips all contribute to making learning fun and meaningful. Our ethos is to discover and nurture the talents or passion of every child, so that they may fulfil their potential. An important strength is the impact made by the various therapists employed by the school. The full-time speech therapist develops pupils' speaking and language skills effectively both in individual therapy sessions and when working alongside subject teachers. (Ofsted; 2011) Arrangements for the welfare, health and safety of pupils are outstanding. Staff care exceptionally well for pupils and pay very good attention to their well-being. (Ofsted; 2011) For more information please visit www.frederickhughhouse.com

# The key to finding the right place is having the right choice.

**WILSIC HALL SCHOOL**

**FULLERTON HOUSE SCHOOL**

Everyone at Hesley Group is here to enable people with complex needs achieve their full potential.

To do this we believe in creating stable placements in safe environments. In places where care and education plans can be built around the individual, focused on their needs and goals. We also believe in offering children and young adults with autism, a learning disability and associated complex needs the choice of where they want to live, learn and grow in confidence.
After all, finding a place that's right for them is everything.

We offer a choice of two schools. Both offer a wealth of experience and specialist expertise on hand together with high-quality therapeutic environments and resources. Which one is right is often a personal thing. So why not visit both?

**Fullerton House School**
The school supports 8 to 19 year olds. Situated in the village of Denaby Main, near Doncaster, it has a real 'heart of the community' feel.

**Wilsic Hall School**
Situated in its own picturesque 14 acre countryside setting five miles south of Doncaster, Wilsic Hall School supports young people from 11 to 19 years of age.

**SEE OUR NEW WEBSITE**

We've made it easier for families, carers, professionals, and the people we can support, find all the information they need to know about our services.

**www.hesleygroup.co.uk**

Referral enquiries freephone
## 0800 055 6789

# Hillcrest

**Positive Actions
Positive Outcomes**

## Hillcrest Schools provide full National Curriculum, Vocational Qualifications and Social and Independent Living Skills.

**We have particular expertise with students identified as having social, emotional and behavioural difficulties and other complex needs and disorders**

### Hillcrest schools provide:

- Full national curriculum and GCSE programmes;
- Vocational qualifications which can lead to ASDAN, COPE and BTEC qualifications including Sports Leadership, Catering, Horticulture, Painting & Decorating, Carpentry & Joinery and Bricklaying;
- Regular contact with parents and carers (where appropriate), ensuring that they are kept fully informed of progress and all matters concerning their child's education;
- Social and independent living skills;
- Particular expertise with students identified as having social, emotional and behavioural difficulties and other complex needs and disorders;
- Verbal progress reports on request; written reports are produced annually and for reviews.

Hillcrest schools have an excellent adult to pupil ratio with class sizes of up to a maximum of 5 students, enabling us to give our children high levels of support at all times.

### Assessment

On entry all students are given a "B-squared" baseline assessment in Literacy, Numeracy and ICT which forms the basis of their programme of study. Student progress is monitored as part of an ongoing process and is assessed at the end of each half term against National Curriculum levels.

### Individually Tailored Programmes

Hillcrest delivers a structured programme of education, tailored to each student's individual needs and taking into account their Statement of Special Educational Needs. Students are taught in small cohorts and individually, by fully qualified teachers. All of our Head Teachers hold an NPQH qualification.

# I CAN

## I CAN's Dawn House School

Helmsley Road, Rainworth, Mansfield, Nottinghamshire NG21 0DQ
**T:** 01623 795361 **F:** 01623 491173
**E:** dawnhouse@ican.org.uk **W:** www.dawnhouseschool.org.uk

**Headteacher** Mrs Angela Child MA
**Founded** 1974
**School Status** Co-ed Non-maintained
   (special) Day and Boarding
**Membership** BDA, NAS, NASEN, NASS,
   NATSPEC
**Special needs provision** ASP, SP&LD, WA1

**Age range** 5–19
**No of Pupils** 76; *(boarding)* 40;
   *(full boarding)* 20; *(weekly boarding)* 20;
   *Sixth form* 27; *Girls* 16; *Boys* 60
**Average class size** 10

Dawn House School provides intensive, specialist support for pupils aged 5–19 with severe and complex communication difficulties or Asperger's Syndrome.

The school supports pupils' development in speech and language, thinking and reasoning, self-confidence and independence. Education, therapy and care programmes are tailored to meet individual needs.

Teaching and therapy are supported by up-to-date technology and Paget Gorman / Makaton Signed Speech. Joint planning by highly qualified, experienced staff ensures a fully integrated language environment.

Dawn House School was rated a 'Good' school by Ofsted in April 2011. Highly valued Independent living skills are fostered through curriculum and care programmes.

The FE Dept provides a highly inclusive programme for students aged 16–19.

---

## I CAN Centre with Meath School

Brox Road, Ottershaw, Chertsey, Surrey KT16 0LF
**T:** 01932 872302 **F:** 01932 875180
**E:** meath@meath-ican.org.uk **W:** www.meathschool.org.uk

**Headteacher** Ms Janet Dunn
**Founded** 1982
**School Status** Co-ed Non-maintained
   (special) Day and Boarding
**Religious denomination** Non-Denominational
**Membership** NASS

**Special needs provision** ADD, **ASP**, DYP, EPI,
   HEA, HI, IM, **SP&LD**, VI, WA1
**Age range** 4–11; boarders from 5

Meath School provides a multi-professional, integrated and collaborative approach to the teaching, therapy and care of children (and families) whose primary difficulty is speech, language and communication, including Asperger's Syndrome. Children with additional or associated difficulties – including some degree of learning difficulty, attention control, motor coordination problems, mild visual or hearing impairments, and social interaction problems – can also benefit. Specialist practice and programmes enable full access to the National Curriculum teaching. Classes have a teacher, speech and language therapist and a teaching assistant. An OT department provides individual and group sessions. A life skills programme is offered in the residential setting; this reinforces a 24-hour curriculum.

# Ingfield Manor School  ● ⌂

Ingfield Manor Drive, Five Oaks, Billingshurst, West Sussex RH14 9AX
**T:** 01403 782294/784241 **F:** 01403 785066
**E:** ingfield.manor@scope.org.uk **W:** www.scope.org.uk

**Headteacher** Mrs Catherine Allison
**Founded** 1961
**School Status** Co-ed Independent (special)
  Day and Boarding

**Special needs provision CP**, IM, SP&LD, WA2
**Age range** 3–19; *(boarding)* 16;
  *(full boarding)* 8; *(weekly boarding)* 8

Ingfield Manor is acknowledged as one of the leading centres for Conductive Education in the UK. It has a national reputation for the development of communication work with pupils. The school is a day and weekly boarding school for children with cerebral palsy. It has established a new Pre-School and Assessment Service for children with physical disabilities and associated learning difficulties. The main school has recently expanded to include pupils past the age of 16. Ofsted have concluded that: 'The work in Conductive Education by pupils and staff is outstanding'. This is a centre of excellence for an alternative approach to the education of children with cerebral palsy. The Dame Vera Lynn Trust School for Parents is a unique free service for families of young children with cerebral palsy and other disabilities. Parents and children learn daily living skills together using the principles of Conductive Education. The School for Parents is run in partnership with The Dame Vera Lynn Trust for Children with Cerebral Palsy. Ofsted described it as 'outstanding provision' and a 'centre of excellence'.

## Kisimul

# Kisimul School – Woodstock House  ● ⌂

Woodstock House, Woodstock Lane North, Long Ditton, Surbiton,
Surrey KT6 5HN
**T:** 0208 3352570 **F:** 0208 3352571
**E:** admissions@kisimul.co.uk **W:** www.kisimul.co.uk

**Director of Education** Mr Danny Carter
**Head Teacher** Mr Chris Owen
**School Status** Co-ed Independent (special)
  Day and Boarding
**Religious denomination** Non-Denominational
**Membership** BILD, EQUALS

**Special needs provision** ASD, **CB**, DOW,
  **EPI**, **SLD**, SP&LD, WA1
**Age range** 8–19; boarders from 8
**No of Pupils** 60; *Girls* 30; *Boys* 30
**Teacher:pupil ratio** 1:1
**Average class size** 6

Woodstock House specializes in providing high quality care and education for children and young people with severe learning difficulties and challenging behaviour, for up to 52 weeks per year. We provide a caring, consistent, safe and supportive environment in which our pupils can flourish and develop their skills, in order to fully realize their individual potential. Our 24-hour approach enables pupils to progress in their personal development and promotes their confidence, self-esteem and independence. Classes are small, with a staffing ratio of at least 1:1. Alongside the National Curriculum, Adult Pre-Entry Curriculum Framework (Post-16) and Foundation Learning, we also offer a wide range of therapeutic and developmental programmes; collectively designed to meet the diverse sensory needs of our pupils.

# Kisimul School – Old Vicarage

61 High Street, Swinderby, Lincoln, Lincolnshire LN6 9LU
**T:** 01522 868279
**F:** 01522 866001
**E:** admissions@kisimul.co.uk
**W:** www.kisimul.co.uk

**Director of Education** Mr Danny Carter
**Founded** 1977
**School Status** Co-ed Independent (special)
   Boarding and Day
**Religious denomination** Non-Denominational
**Membership** BILD, EQUALS

**Special needs provision** ASD, **CB**, DOW, EPI,
   HI, **SLD**, SP&LD, WA1
**Age range** 8–19; boarders from 8
**No of Pupils** 70; *Girls* 35; *Boys* 35
**Average class size** 6

Kisimul School specializes in providing high quality care and education for children and young people with severe learning difficulties and challenging behaviour; for up to 52 weeks per year. We provide a caring, consistent, safe and supportive environment in which our pupils can flourish and develop their skills; in order to fully realize their individual potential. Our 24-hour approach enables pupils to progress in their personal development and promotes their confidence, self-esteem and independence. Classes are small, with a staffing ratio of at least 1:1. Alongside the National Curriculum, Adult Pre-Entry Curriculum Framework (Post-16) and Foundation Learning, we also offer a wide range of therapeutic and developmental programmes; collectively designed to meet the diverse sensory needs of our pupils.

# Cruckton Hall

Cruckton, Shrewsbury, Shropshire SY5 8PR
**T:** 01743 860206
**F:** 01743 860941
**E:** admissions@kisimul.co.uk
**W:** www.cruckton.com

**Head Master** Mr P D Mayhew
**School Status** Boys Independent (special)
   Boarding and Day
**Religious denomination** Inter-Denominational
**Membership** NAS, NASEN

**Special needs provision** ADD, ADHD, ASD,
   **ASP, BESD**, CB, DYC, DYP, DYS, EPI, HI,
   MLD, WA3
**Age range** 7–19
**No of Pupils** 92; *(boarding)* 84;
   *(full boarding)* 84; *Boys* 92

Cruckton Hall School offers an integrated residential education for boys aged 8–19 years of age who have been diagnosed with Autism Spectrum Disorders. Placements are offered from day up to 52 weeks of the year. Structured individual programmes are devised to meet students' specific needs and these are met in small group settings with a high staffing ratio. A broad and balanced waking day curriculum is provided that enables students to acquire the knowledge and skills to sit GCSE examinations. In addition; the school offers ECDL, AQA Skills for Life Awards and a variety of Entry Level Certificates. The whole experience provides outstanding outcomes and opportunities for the young people to lead a meaningful adult life within society.

# Marchant Holliday School ●♠

North Cheriton, Templecombe, Somerset BA8 0AH
**T:** 01963 33234 **F:** 01963 33432
**E:** office@marchant-holliday.co.uk
**W:** www.marchantholliday.co.uk

**Headteacher** Mr T Kitts M.Ed, B.Ed (Hons),
DPSE SEN
**Assistant Headteacher** D Kitts
**Founded** 1950
**School Status** Boys Independent (special)
Boarding and Day
**Religious denomination** Non-Denominational
**Membership** NASEN, NASS

**Special needs provision ADD, ADHD, ASD,
ASP, BESD, CB,** DYC, DYP, DYS, IM, MLD,
SLD, SP&LD, TOU, W
**Age range** 5–13; boarders from 5
**No of Pupils** 36; *(boarding)* 19;
*(full boarding)* 19
**Teacher:pupil ratio** 1:3
**Average class size** 6

The school provides a 'unique, highly specialized and therapeutic level of care to children who present a range of educational and behavioural challenges' (Ofsted). It is situated in beautiful countryside surroundings and consists of a large country house in 13 acres of woodland, field and gardens. It is readily accessible from London, Bristol, Southampton, the South and West and all areas of the home counties. The school offers positive learning experiences within a secure and caring environment which will enable each child to develop his full potential for social, emotional, physical and intellectual growth. There are a wide range of facilities and residential accommodation is modern with single and double rooms, the majority being en suite.

# Mulberry Bush School ●♠

Abingdon Road, Standlake, Witney, Oxfordshire OX29 7RW
**T:** 01865 300202 **F:** 01865 300084
**E:** aburnett@mulberrybush.org.uk **W:** www.mulberrybush.org.uk

**Director** Mr John Turberville
**Headteacher** Andy Lole
**Founded** 1948
**School Status** Co-ed Non-maintained
(special) Boarding only
**Religious denomination** Non-Denominational
**Membership** NASS

**Special needs provision**
ADD, **ADHD, BESD,** DYP,
DYS, WA2
**Age range** 5–13
**No of Pupils** 31; *(boarding)* 31;
*(full boarding)* 31; *Girls* 11; *Boys* 20
**Teacher:pupil ratio** 1:3
**Average class size** 8

The Mulberry Bush School is an early intervention for 'at risk' children aged 5–13 and their families, who display severe social and emotional difficulties. The aim of our work, evidenced by excellent outcomes, is to break the cycle of disadvantage they have suffered due to early year's trauma. Such an early intervention provides the children with a safe and nurturing environment in which they can build a positive future. Without such an intervention these problematic behaviours make it very difficult for the child to live within mainstream family, school and community settings. Our core values apply to all aspects of our specialist residential provision, and to our new outreach services from Mulberry Bush Training. Outcomes: 93 per cent of children placed are successfully re-integrated into a suitable family and 100 per cent can be placed in an appropriate school on departure. Ofsted 'outstanding' 2007–2013.

## NAS National Autistic Society Schools

# Anderson School ● 🏠

Rookery Lane, Pilning,
Bristol BS35 4JN
**T:** 01454 632 532
**F:** 01454 634 907
**E:** nasanderson@nas.org.uk
**W:** www.andersonschool.org.uk

**Head of School** Mark Helstrip
**Founded** 2012
**School Status** Co-ed Independent (special)
   Day and Boarding
**Religious denomination** Non-Denominational

**Membership** NAS, NASS
**Special needs provision ASD, ASP**, CB
**Age range** 10–19; boarders from 10
**No of Pupils** 20; *Girls* 10; *Boys* 10

### Anderson School

Anderson School in Bristol provides a new generation of specialist autism education for the local area, as well as welcoming students from other parts such as South Wales and South West England. Our provision is innovative: our students may attend the school full time, or spend some of their time in a community school. Some may take up year round residential placements, others come as part-time boarders or day pupils.

### Our Approach

School days are clearly structured, and the curriculum builds on students' skills and talents and addresses the particular challenges they face. This model allows young people with autism to thrive. Students also participate in a wide variety of enrichment activities and our high staff to student ratio allows them to take advantage of the activities that are available in, and our tranquil location on, the outskirts of Bristol.

We have an ethos of family and community engagement in all our schools; research confirms that this leads to better outcomes for pupils. Parents know their child the best and are an invaluable source of knowledge. We also recognize that approaches and strategies used with young people with autism, profound learning difficulties and challenging behaviour, need to be consistent across all settings, especially home and school.

### Our Facilities

On site the homely, friendly and relaxed atmosphere and appropriate autism-specific environment enables pupils to learn. Living and learning areas are separate, fixtures and furnishings autism-friendly and assistive technology installed throughout.

At the school, we treat every child as an individual. We listen to and respect their values and views. And we put their needs and well-being before anything else. The curriculum is geared to the needs of individual pupils and our facilities which include: multi-sensory room, music and recording facilities, outdoor horticultural and forest school areas and teaching kitchens enable us to cater for a wide range of abilities.

# Daldorch House School

Sorn Road, Catrine,
East Ayrshire KA5 6NA
**T:** 01290 551 666
**F:** 01290 553 399
**E:** daldorch@nas.org.uk
**W:** www.daldorchhouseschool.org.uk

**Principal** Mrs Shona Pinkerton
**Founded** 1998
**School Status** Co-ed Independent (special)
  Boarding only

**Religious denomination** Non-Denominational
**Membership** NAS, NASS
**Special needs provision ASD**, **ASP**, CB
**Age range** 5–21; boarders from 5

## Daldorch House School

At Daldorch House developing communication, health and well-being, social and life skills is at the core of our 24-hour curriculum. All our pupils also have access to a broad and balanced programme of study personalized to reflect their abilities and meet their needs. Our high staff to pupil ratio and extensive support for learning allows us to enrich each pupil's education by capitalizing on their interests and expanding their understanding of the world. We offer primary and secondary day and residential education for pupils up to the age of 21.

## Our Approach

Learning is an ongoing process at Daldorch House, and our unique fusion of care and education runs throughout the school day, evenings and weekends within classrooms, the wider school campus and in community settings. Through developing breadth, depth and coherence in the learning opportunities we are strengthening pupils' ability to generalize their learning.

Using this approach we embrace the concept of a 'Curriculum for Excellence' and we are committed to enabling the children and young people to become successful learners, confident individuals, responsible citizens and effective contributors.

The curriculum is also designed to offer challenge and enjoyment, as well as relevance to the modern world. Expressive Arts, Social Studies, Technologies and Science, as well as Religious and Moral Education, equally extend the learning of our pupils.

Our staff team continually build on their strong understanding of autism and increase their expertise – we are passionate about what we do, and together we've created an exciting, caring environment for each child. Parents are an essential part of this programme and we keep in constant contact with them, and provide parental accommodation within our grounds.

'Staff know young people very well and provide a caring, secure and nurturing environment for them.' (Education Scotland, Care Inspectorate 2012)

## Our Facilities

Daldorch House provides rich and rewarding educational opportunities within our beautiful 11 acres of grounds; the campus consists of a Grade B listed building, built around 1806 which houses classrooms, a sensory room and soft play, life skills kitchen, a medical room, meeting room and office accommodation. We also have excellent sports and leisure facilities.

There is exceptionally wide use of community leisure and recreational facilities such as local swimming pools, library, community resource/leisure centres, shops and cinemas. Pupils are encouraged to enjoy walking in the countryside and to visit places of historical interest. In addition road safety programmes, supported use of public transport, shopping for food, clothes and household items, provide meaningful experiences in the wider community.

All of these facilities are used to maximize learning opportunities and develop greater independence in our pupils.

# Helen Allison School

Longfield Road, Meopham,
Gravesend, Kent DA13 0EW
**T:** 01474 814878
**F:** 01474 812033
**E:** helen.allison@nas.org.uk
**W:** www.helenallisonschool.org.uk

| | |
|---|---|
| **Executive Principal** Dr Jacqui Ashton-Smith | **Religious denomination** Non-Denominational |
| **Head of School** Susan Conway | **Membership** NAS, NASS |
| **Founded** 1968 | **Special needs provision ASD**, ASP, CB, WA3 |
| **School Status** Co-ed Independent | **Age range** 5–19; boarders from 5 |
|    Boarding and Day | **No of Pupils** 70; *Girls* 35; *Boys* 35 |

## Helen Allison School

At Helen Allison school we have over 40 years' experience delivering a high quality, relevant and enjoyable education that meets the needs of children and young adults with autism within a structured and safe environment. We believe that education is fun, are ambitious for each child and focus on their strengths.

## Our Approach

Helen Allison School provides high quality education and care in a safe and stimulating environment for children and young people with autism.

Our pupils and students are supported and encouraged to achieve their full potential, and equipped with skills for life. We run small classes with a high student to teacher ratio that maximize the benefits of our expert teaching and individual programmes, and reflect each student's needs and abilities – enabling them to reach their potential.

Our enthusiastic and caring staff take the time to really get to know each child or young person who comes here. They have an excellent understanding and awareness of autism and Asperger's Syndrome. Using this personal and specialist knowledge we design a curriculum that meets the specific learning needs of each individual child.

Our goal is to create a safe and structured environment so that each child or young person can be happy and progress. Staff have a warm and supportive relationship with the children and young people. This enables staff to work closely with them as part of a group and individually. Finding out their likes and dislikes is often the key to how they will learn best.

'The quality of the curriculum is outstanding as is the quality of teaching and assessment. As a result, the students make outstanding progress in their learning and the outcomes for boarders are outstanding.' (Ofsted, 2012 – www.ofsted.gov.uk)

## Our Facilities

We supplement our main curriculum with a wide range of community-based learning and activities including: regular swimming sessions at the local pool, expressive arts, drama lessons and rock climbing for our secondary students. We also have an allotment where students grow and sell their own produce; our conservation area and social activities enable every student to enjoy their childhood to the full and ultimately to become active and equal members of adult society.

Our primary and secondary departments are on one site in the village of Meopham and offer excellent facilities. Further education (Post-16) department and residential units are in nearby Gravesend, giving students easy access to a range of shops, amenities and public transport. We also provide senior student accommodation.

# Radlett Lodge School

Harper Lane, Radlett,
Hertfordshire WD7 9HW
**T:** 01923 854 922
**F:** 01293 859 922
**E:** radlett.lodge@nas.org.uk
**W:** www.radlettlodgeschool.org.uk

| | |
|---|---|
| **Principal** Jo Galloway | **Membership** NAS, NASS |
| **Founded** 1974 | **Special needs provision ASD, ASP**, CB, WA2 |
| **School Status** Co-ed Independent (special) | **Age range** 4–19 |
| Day and Boarding | **No of Pupils** 55; *Girls* 28; *Boys* 27 |
| **Religious denomination** Non-Denominational | |

### Radlett Lodge School

At Radlett Lodge School, we look beyond autism to the individual needs of every pupil and we put these needs first. Our ultimate aim is to enable every one of our students to become as independent as possible. We emphasize developing communication and social skills through a curriculum which meets the specific needs of students with autism. Our pupils receive consistent education and care thanks to a close working relationship between school, home and other professionals. Radlett Lodge is a very successful school and since 2009 has consistently been rated 'outstanding' by Ofsted.

We recognize that many of our pupils have very special needs but believe that compassion, tolerance and positive intervention can bring about positive change. We offer primary, secondary and further education to children and young people aged 4 to 19.

### Our Approach

We have a high staff to student ratio which enables students to access all areas of the National Curriculum at the right level. Some students are encouraged to visit other local schools for specific sessions. We prepare students for adult life by supporting them to enjoy activities in the wider community and learn life and independent living skills, by making everything we teach relevant to the real world. We are a friendly and approachable school, where children are nurtured and treated as one of the family. We work closely with parents, friends and professionals to provide a caring and positive environment where our students thrive.

'Students' achievements are outstanding because teachers find ways of making the learning both meaningful and memorable for pupils so that all pupils make extremely good progress from their starting points.' (Ofsted, 2013 – www.ofsted.gov.uk)

### Our Facilities

Our facilities include a sensory room, an art and design area, a soft play area, purpose built gymnasium, outdoor play area and a teaching kitchen. Through a structured and supportive learning environment and friendly, approachable staff, students develop social relationships and receive a broad and balanced education. Beyond the classroom, we offer a wide range of activities including sports, youth club, Scouts and lunchtime clubs.

Pupils with a residential place stay in the warm and caring environment of the Lodge. Bedrooms are for one or two pupils, depending on their compatibility. The Lodge team reinforce everything pupils learn in school and help them to become more independent.

'The provision is outstanding. The school continues to provide excellent high quality 24-hour care and education. Students receive outstanding support enabling them to progress at school.' (Ofsted, 2011 – www.ofsted.gov.uk)

# Robert Ogden School

Clayton Lane, Thurnscoe, Rotherham,
South Yorkshire S63 0BG
**T:** 01709 874 443
**F:** 01709 870 701
**E:** robert.ogden@nas.org.uk
**W:** www.robertogdenschool.org.uk

**Executive Principal** Dr Jaqui Ashton-Smith
**Head of School** Dr Khursh Khan
**Founded** 1977
**School Status** Co-ed Independent (special)
 Day and Boarding
**Religious denomination** Non-Denominational

**Membership** NAS, NASS
**Special needs provision ASD**, **ASP**, CB, WA2
**Age range** 5–19
**Teacher:pupil ratio** 1:1
**Average class size** 6

## Robert Ogden School

The Robert Ogden School is one of the largest schools in the UK for children and young people with autism. Our stable, structured and nurturing environment helps children to see school as a comfortable, positive place where they are welcome.

We offer full-time day places, term-time and 52-week residential care to children and young people aged 5 to 19 from across the autism spectrum. Our 200 specialist staff are a dedicated close-knit team. They work together to create a stable and structured environment where our children can learn and be nurtured.

## Our Approach

Our curriculum takes into account the specific challenges that our children face in the areas of language, communication and social awareness: we help the whole child develop from primary through to further education, creating an individual plan for each child that allows them to develop the skills necessary for adulthood. We delight in all our children's achievements, whether this is exam success or a smaller but no less significant step forward, such as wanting to be part of a social group. Our communication methods include speech, symbols, photographs, objects and signing, and are targeted according to each child's level of understanding.

In the Primary Department children are taught in their class group by their class teacher. In the Secondary Department children have a class tutor for English, Mathematics and Personal, Social, Health and Citizenship Education (PSHCE) and subject specialists for other areas. Our high staff to child ratio enables us to give our children high quality care and, where appropriate, one-to-one teaching. All children at Key Stage 4 can take externally accredited courses including ASDAN (a range of work-related courses) and GCSEs. Our most recent Ofsted inspection resulted in an Outstanding rating.

'The quality of education at the Robert Ogden School is outstanding. The school successfully meets its aims, providing an environment in which young people feel at ease and are enabled to make outstanding progress in their learning.' (Ofsted, 2011)

## Our Facilities

Each child at Robert Ogden School accesses the National Curriculum in a way that is specifically geared to their educational needs and abilities. We provide specialist academic and leisure amenities that motivate our pupils and help them to build social confidence. Our modern ICT facilities, teaching kitchen and café, sensory gardens, pottery studio and training flat allow our pupils to learn new skills and enjoy the benefits of a broad and balanced education.

# Sybil Elgar School  ● 🏠

The National Autistic Society, Havelock
Road, Southall, Middlesex UB2 4NY
**T:** 020 8813 9168
**F:** 020 8571 7332
**E:** sybil.elgar@nas.org.uk
**W:** www.sybilelgarschool.org.uk

**Principal** Chloe Phillips
**Founded** 1965
**School Status** Co-ed Independent (special)
   Day and Boarding
**Religious denomination** Non-Denominational

**Membership** NAS, NASS
**Special needs provision ASD, ASP,** CB, WA1
**Age range** 14–19
**No of Pupils** 100; *Girls* 50; *Boys* 50

## Sybil Elgar School

At Sybil Elgar School we treat every child as an individual and listen to and respect their values and views. We put their needs and well-being before anything else. We have created a warm and welcoming place where our students feel happy and safe, and where they can focus on learning through interesting and exciting lessons and activities.

### Our Approach

Our curriculum covers a breadth of academic subjects, as well as social and life skills, and we use our expertise in autism to make the curriculum accessible to every student. We cater for a wide range of abilities and needs through individual educational programmes and our high staff to student ratio. Every student receives a broad, balanced and relevant education based on the National Curriculum and, where appropriate, an extended curriculum of activities. Our students especially enjoy our creative and expressive arts programme.

We are committed to providing the very highest quality of care and education for young people with autism. We have an international reputation for being leaders in the education of young people with autism and work closely with our colleagues in The National Autistic Society.

We are known for being an innovative and progressive school and are always looking for fresh, new approaches. This makes our school an exciting and dynamic place for our young people on their pathway to adulthood.

### Our Facilities

We have three sites in West London which offer secondary school provision for ages 11 to 16, further education provision for ages 16 to 19, and weekly boarding and short break provision for ages 11 to 19.

Our purpose-built upper years primary and secondary school (9 to 16 years) near Southall is surrounded by spacious playgrounds. Its specialist classrooms and teaching areas provide the ideal environment for children with autism to learn.

From 16 years students move into our specialist further education department. We are known for being creative, innovative and progressive, and our school is a dynamic place for young people on their way to adulthood, enabling them to access their wider community.

Our multi-disciplinary team, which includes a speech and language therapist, occupational therapist, social worker, behaviour co-ordinators and a psychologist, is based on-site – providing support to all our students.

We understand the needs beyond school and offer a short break service during weekends and holidays for young people with autism, including those not attending Sybil Elgar. We are also able to run an outreach service and transition service for children and mainstream schools in the area.

'Students thrive within a nurturing environment which centres on their uniqueness.' (Ofsted, 2011)

# Thames Valley School

Conwy Close, Tilehurst,
Reading, Berkshire RG30
**T:** 0117 9748 430
**E:** thames.valley@nas.org.uk
**W:** www.thamesvalleyschool.org.uk

| | |
|---|---|
| **Principal Designate** Fiona Veitch | **Special needs provision ASD**, **ASP**, CB |
| **School Status** Co-ed Independent (special) | **Age range** 4–16 |
| Day only | **No of Pupils** 50; *Girls* 25; *Boys* 25 |
| **Membership** NAS, NASS | **Average class size** 6 |

## Thames Valley School

Thames Valley School represents a new chapter in the provision of high quality education for children and young people with autism and Asperger's Syndrome aged 4 to 16 years.

The school is a collaboration between The National Autistic Society (NAS), local authorities, voluntary groups, schools and parents. These groups have come together from Reading, West Berkshire, Wokingham and Windsor & Maidenhead to establish the school. The school also benefits from The National Autistic Society's nearly 50 years' experience in the autism sector and is the first school owned and operated by the newly formed NAS Academies Trust.

## Our Approach

We provide truly personalized teaching that capitalizes on an individual's strengths and removes barriers to learning. The curriculum develops a core foundation of knowledge and skills for each student to prepare them for the transition into further study or employment. We also support all of our students to increase inclusion in their community.

At Thames Valley, each child has an inclusion plan to develop their ability to thrive in a range of environments. Inclusion opportunities may involve joining certain classes at a mainstream school, or going to after-school clubs and other social occasions. IT is utilized to offer a range of learning opportunities and approaches.

Thames Valley School is able to offer short to medium placements for some pupils to equip them with the skills they need to be able to return to mainstream education. The school also has assessment places for children who do not yet have a Statement of Educational Need.

## Our Facilities

Thames Valley School is housed in a new purpose-built building located in Tilehurst, Reading. The building features the most up-to-date design and facilities for our pupils, helping to make sure that they feel comfortable and secure.

Primary provision can be found on the ground floor with secondary on the first floor. Both floors have a central learning area, designed to be as flexible as possible to meet the changing needs of the pupils. There are chill-out spaces and calm rooms to help reduce anxiety, and individual work stations to maximize learning opportunities.

Specialist classrooms for art, science, food technology and design technology are also available.

For the smaller numbers of pupils who have extremely challenging behaviour and complex needs, provision includes individual tutor rooms, soft play and sensory rooms, and a skills base where pupils will learn independent living skills.

Parents and carers are also catered for with their own room for meetings and training events. Outdoors, there are landscaped areas for primary, secondary and enhanced provisions where activities such as horticulture and sport support the enrichment curriculum.

# New College Worcester   ● ♠

Whittington Road, Worcester, Worcestershire WR5 2JX
**T:** 01905 763933 **F:** 01905 763277
**E:** astanton@newcollegeworcester.co.uk **W:** www.newcollegeworcester.co.uk

**Principal** Mrs Mardy Smith
**Assistant Principal** Dr Chris Stonehouse
**School Status** Co-ed Independent (special)
 Boarding and Day
**Religious denomination** Non-Denominational
**Membership** NASEN, NASS, NATSPEC

**Special needs provision** ASP, DYP, DYS, HEA, HI, IM, **VI**, W
**Age range** 11–19
**No of Pupils** 88; *(boarding)* 88; *(full boarding)* 88;
 Girls 41; Boys 47
**Average class size** 5

NCW is a residential school and college for students aged 11 to 19 who are blind or partially sighted.

Every student has a tailored programme, carefully planned to meet their individual needs in three key areas; academic achievement, independent living skills and involvement in extracurricular activities.

We offer the full National Curriculum to our students and a wide range of GCSE, AS and A2 options. Alternatively, Sixth Form students can also follow vocational programmes such as ASDAN or BTEC courses, or programmes at a local college supported by NCW staff. Students have Independent Living Skills, ICT and Mobility lessons as part of their timetable and Braille lessons are also provided if required. All of our teachers are subject specialists, as well as qualified teachers for the visually impaired.

Outside of lessons we offer our students a wonderfully varied choice of challenging activities after school and at weekends which, together with their academic achievements, further develops their self-esteem and confidence.

---

# Nugent House School   ● ♠

Carr Mill Road, Billinge, Wigan, Lancashire WN5 7TT
**T:** 01744 892551 **F:** 01744 895697
**E:** HEAD@NugentWiganSch.uk **W:** www.nugenthouse.co.uk

**Principal** John Gilfillan
**School Status** Boys Independent (special)
 Boarding and Day
**Religious denomination** Roman Catholic
**Membership** NASEN, NASS, SEBDA
**Special needs provision** ADD, ADHD, **ASD**, ASP,

BESD, **CB**, DYP, **DYS**, TOU, WA1
**Age range** 7–19
**No of Pupils** 65; *(boarding)* 36; *(full boarding)* 36;
 Boys 65

Nugent House School offers students the National Curriculum; with exemption and modification where necessary. The school prides itself on providing a holistic approach to education by preparing pupils for all the opportunities; responsibilities and experiences of adult life. Through this supportive environment, children can begin to develop self-respect and self-confidence; which is an important step towards re-integration into mainstream schooling. Each class has access to a Teaching Assistant who aids the class teacher in the delivery of the curriculum. Those who require additional support are allocated a Personal Support Assistant to accompany them. A specialist Literacy Support Department assists children with specific learning difficulties and the school's Ed Psych advises staff on assessment and testing methods. The therapeutic needs of the boys are met in a variety of ways. The current school therapy team, under the direction of a Consultant Child and Adolescent Psychiatrist, includes a play therapist and two counsellors; a full-time horticultural therapist; a speech and language therapist; a clinical psychologist and mental health practitioners. As far as possible, close liaison is maintained with professionals already involved with the pupils in their referring authority to provide consistency and continuity of care. The school grounds allow pupils and staff to experience both open space and where preferred, tranquil spaces. Our residential houses are situated in a cul-de-sac called Hope Lane. The spacious accommodation affords the opportunity for both privacy and shared living. Each house accommodates six pupils who enjoy their own room with en-suite shower facilities. Pupils are placed in one of six houses based on a combination of age and individual need. Visits by relatives are encouraged with prior notification to ensure there is no clash with scheduled school activities. Pupils are also actively encouraged to keep in contact with home by telephone. Each student house is equipped with a pay phone, available for pupils' use and a Night Child Care Worker is on duty. 38- and 52-week care are available. Referrals to the school are made through the Local Education Authority, Social Services Department or Local Health Authority. All prospective pupils along with their parents' carers and interested representative from the Local Authority are invited to visit the school, where they have the opportunity to talk with our staff and pupils.

## Options Group

# Barton School ●🏠

Barrow Road, Barton-Upon-Humber,
North Lincolnshire DN18 6DA
**T:** 01652 631280 **F:** 01652 637419
**E:** info@bartonschool.co.uk **W:** www.optionsgroup.co.uk

**Options Group**

*making a difference*

| | |
|---|---|
| **Head of service** Mr Ian Thorsteinsson | **ASP, CB, EPI,** HEA, |
| **Registered Manager** Andrea McKeown | MLD, PMLD, SP&LD, |
| **Founded** 2006 | WA1 |
| **School Status** Co-ed Independent (special) | **Age range** 8–19 |
| Boarding and Day | **No of Pupils** 36; *(boarding)* 26; |
| **Special needs provision** ADD, ADHD, **ASD,** | *(full boarding)* 26; *Girls* 18; *Boys* 18 |

Barton School is a specialist school providing integrated programmes of care, education and therapy for children and young people aged 8–19 with autism, Asperger's Syndrome, learning disabilities and associated complex needs including challenging behaviours. Specifically designed to support children with a diverse range of needs and abilities, Barton School offers day, respite, outreach and up to 52-week residential placements. Using proven approaches, teaching frameworks and communication tools, Barton School provides high quality education including access to an adapted and differentiated National Curriculum and life skills programmes. Barton School provides consistency both in and out of school; ensuring that learning takes place throughout the waking day – not just in the classroom!

---

# Higford School ●🏠

Higford Hall, Higford, Shifnal, Shropshire TF11 9ET
**T:** 01952 630600 **F:** 01952 630605
**E:** info@higfordschool.co.uk
**W:** www.optionsgroup.co.uk

**Options Group**

*making a difference*

| | |
|---|---|
| **Head of Service** Mr Graham Norris | |
| **Head Teacher** Anne Adams | |
| **School Status** Co-ed Independent (special) | SLD, **SP&LD,** VI, W |
| Boarding and Day | **Age range** 8–19 |
| **Special needs provision** ADD, ADHD, **ASD,** | **No of Pupils** 25; *Girls* 12; *Boys* 13 |
| **ASP, CB, EPI, HEA,** HI, IM, MLD, PMLD, | **Average class size** 5 |

Higford School provides integrated programmes of care, education and professional/clinical services for children and young people aged 8–19 with autism, Asperger's Syndrome, learning disabilities and associated complex needs including challenging behaviours.

Set in 28 acres of rolling Shropshire countryside, Higford School is an NAS accredited service offering day, short breaks, outreach and residential placements. Up to 52-week residential care is provided within specifically adapted accommodation, with dedicated short breaks provision also available on-site.

Higford School delivers a person-centred and outcomes-focused approach to providing care and education that is designed to enable each student to exercise choice and control, increase their confidence and prepare for adulthood.

# Kinsale School  ● 🏠

Kinsale Hall, Llanerach-y-mor, Holywell,
Flintshire CH8 9DX
**T:** 01745 562500 **F:** 01745 562501
**E:** info@kinsaleschool.co.uk **W:** www.optionsgroup.co.uk

**Options Group**
*making a difference*

**Head of Service** Mr Mark Williams
**Headteacher** Emma Keyworth
**School Status** Co-ed Independent (special)
   Boarding and Day
**Religious denomination** Non-Denominational
**Membership** EQUALS, NAS

**Special needs provision** ADD, ADHD, **ASD**,
   **ASP**, **CB**, **EPI**, HEA, **MLD**, PMLD, SLD,
   SP&LD, WA1
**Age range** 8–19
**No of Pupils** 30; *Girls* 15; *Boys* 15
**Teacher:pupil ratio** 1:1
**Average class size** 3

Kinsale School is an Estyn 'Excellent' rated and NAS accredited specialist residential school providing integrated programmes of care, education and professional/clinical services for children and young people aged 8–19 with autism, Asperger's Syndrome, learning disabilities and complex needs.

Overlooking the Dee Estuary in North Wales, Kinsale School offers day, short breaks, outreach and up to 52-week residential placements.

Kinsale School adopts a person-centred and outcomes-focused approach to learning and believes that education should be individually tailored and delivered in a variety of environments.

Kinsale School adopts a person-centred and outcomes-focused approach to learning and believes that education should be individually tailored and delivered in a variety of environments, enabling each student to exercise choice and control, increase their confidence and prepare for adulthood.

# Young Options College  ● 🏠

Lamledge Lane, Shifnal, Shropshire TF11 8SD
**T:** 01952 468220
**F:** 019524 468221
**E:** info@youngoptions.co.uk
**W:** www.optionsgroup.co.uk

**Options Group**
*making a difference*

**Head of service** Mr Richard Jones
**Head Teacher** Louise De-Hayes
**School Status** Co-ed Independent (special)
   Boarding and Day
**Religious denomination** Non-Denominational
**Membership** SEBDA

**Special needs provision** ADD, ADHD, ASP,
   **BESD**, CB, HEA, WA1
**Age range** 7–19
**No of Pupils** 50; *(boarding)* 50;
   *(full boarding)* 50; *Girls* 25; *Boys* 25

Young Options College is an Ofsted 'Outstanding' rated specialist school providing care, education and therapy for children and young people aged 7–19 with behavioural, emotional and social difficulties (BESD).

Set in 28 acres of beautiful Shropshire countryside, Young Options College offers up to 52-week residential care in small group homes, rated as either 'Good' or 'Outstanding' by Ofsted, located in the communities surrounding the school.

Attendance at Young Options College is often the first step of a longer journey through the Young Options Pathway, which includes Transitions, Fostering and Supported Housing Services. The Young Options Pathway prepares students for leaving care and the transition to independent living.

# Young Options Pathway College Stoke ● 🏠

**Options Group**

*making a difference*

Phoenix House, Marlborough Road, Longton,
Stoke-On-Trent, Staffordshire ST13 1EJ
**T:** 01782 377270 **F:** 01782 313667
**E:** info@pathwaystoke.co.uk **W:** www.optionsgroup.co.uk

**Head of service** Mr Richard Jones
**Head Teacher** Mel Callaghan
**School Status** Co-ed Independent (special)
  Boarding and Day
**Religious denomination** Inter-Denominational

**Membership** SEBDA
**Special needs provision** ADD, ADHD, **BESD**,
  CB, **HEA**, MLD
**Age range** 11–19
**No of Pupils** 15; *Girls* 7; *Boys* 8

Young Options Pathway College Stoke provides integrated programmes of care, education and professional/clinical services for young people aged 11–19 with behavioural, emotional and social difficulties (BESD).

Young Options Pathway College Stoke offers both day and up to 52-week residential care, provided within small group homes located in the communities surrounding the school.

Students are supported to access the National Curriculum and Vocational Curriculum as well as work placements in their local communities, promoting the development of life skills, and increased confidence alongside academic achievement.

Young Options Pathway College Stoke is part of the Young Options Pathway. The Young Options Pathway prepares students for leaving care and the transition to independent living.

# Philpots Manor School

West Hoathly, East Grinstead, West Sussex RH19 4PR
**T:** 01342 810268
**F:** 01342 811363
**E:** jill.roberts@philpotsmanorschool.co.uk
**W:** www.philpotsmanorschool.co.uk

**Education Co-ordinator** Ms Linda Churnside
**Care Co-ordinator** Lauren Simms
**Founded** 1959
**School Status** Co-ed Independent (special)
Boarding and Day
**Religious denomination** Christian
**Special needs provision** ADD, ADHD, ASD,
ASP, **BESD**, CB, DOW, DYC, DYP, DYS, EPI,

MLD, SP&LD, TOU, WA3
**Age range** 7–19
**No of Pupils** 37; *(boarding)* 25;
*(full boarding)* 25; *Prep* 16; *Senior* 7;
*Sixth form* 14; *Girls* 12; *Boys* 25
**Teacher:pupil ratio** 1:2
**Average class size** 5

Philpots Manor School is based on the education principles of Rudolf Steiner. The school admits children who present a broad range of emotional and behavioural difficulties. The academic ability of the children ranges from high average to moderate learning difficulties. Children are eligible providing they have the capacity to function in a classroom situation where children are helped to reach their full potential within the Steiner curriculum. GCSEs, Entry Level and OCN qualifications are taken.

# Potterspury Lodge School ● ♠

Potterspury Lodge, Towcester, Northamptonshire NN12 7LL
**T:** 01908 542912
**F:** 01908 543399
**E:** mail@potterspurylodge.co.uk
**W:** www.potterspurylodge.co.uk

**Principal** Mr J W D Brown
**Deputy Principal/Bursar** Clive Laidler
**Founded** 1956
**School Status** Boys Independent (special)
 Day and Boarding
**Religious denomination** Non-Denominational
**Membership** NASEN, NASS, SEBDA

**Special needs provision** ADD, ADHD, **ASD**,
 **ASP**, **BESD**, WA2
**Age range** 8–18
**No of Pupils** 45; *(boarding)* 13;
 *(full boarding)* 3; *(weekly boarding)* 10;
 *Prep* 1; *Senior* 37; *Sixth form* 7; *Boys* 45
**Teacher:pupil ratio** 1:3
**Average class size** 8

Potterspury Lodge is a charitable trust, which offers high quality education for boys aged between 8 to 18 years who have autistic spectrum disorders and a variety of emotional, social and behavioural difficulties and associated learning difficulties.

We teach the full National Curriculum, with the exception of a modern foreign language. Class sizes are kept to around eight or nine students and in addition to the subject teachers there are also learning support assistants in every class.

For boarders, the accommodation is organized so that they live in small groups of five or six in self contained houses, with them all enjoying the benefit of their own care staff and sharing in the day-to-day living arrangements, as one would in a family.

From year 10, pupils follow a life skills programme, in year 11, some students are able to take part in work based training and all year 10 and year 11 students undertake two week-long periods of work experience.

We have provision for students in years 12 and 13 in The Stables Further Education Centre. Education and Residential support managers enable students to follow programmes of education and training according to their individual needs, using our own resources and those of local colleges, amenities and workplace training providers.

The School enables children to develop and grow in a caring and supportive atmosphere, and gives them the perfect opportunity to socialize and enjoy life. We organize trips for the pupils on a regular basis, including skiing holidays in Italy and outdoor pursuits expeditions in the UK and France. All pupils are given the opportunity to be fully included in activities.

The grounds are wonderful for sports and outdoor games, particularly when the weather is nice. The children are also encouraged to join in the wide number of after school clubs, which include such diverse activities as Badminton, Pottery, Football, Computers and Technology as well as our own Scout Group. We make full use of local recreational and Leisure facilities and some students are members of the local Sea Cadets Corps.

# Prior's Court School   ● ♠

Hermitage, Thatcham, Berkshire RG18 9NU
**T:** 01635 247202
**F:** 01635 247203
**E:** mail@priorscourt.org.uk
**W:** www.priorscourt.org.uk

**Principal** Stephen Bajdala-Brown
**Director of Education and Lifelong Learning**
   Sue Piper
**School Status** Co-ed Independent (special)
   Boarding and Day
**Religious denomination** Inter-Denominational
**Membership** EQUALS, NAS, NASEN, NASS

**Special needs provision ASD**, CB, EPI, MLD,
   SLD, SP&LD, WA2
**Age range** 5–19
**No of Pupils** 62; *Girls* 12; *Boys* 50
**Teacher:pupil ratio** 1:1
**Average class size** 6

Prior's Court offers specialist education and care for young people with autism, learning difficulties and complex needs. The school is set in 50 acres with outstanding facilities. Experienced staff and a large on-site therapeutic team work in partnership with parents to help students develop communication, independent living and social skills, choice-making, advocacy and self-managed behaviour. Each pupil has an individual learning programme with Waking Day curriculum adapted to ensure it is meaningful, functional and built around each student's interests and abilities. Skills are extended with a rich and varied range of activities at school and in the community. Vocational development is encouraged by projects such as horticulture and animal husbandry with on-site and off-site work placements.

## RNIB Royal National Institute for the Blind

### RNIB Pears Centre for Specialist Learning ●🏠

Wheelwright Lane, Ash Green, Coventry, Warwickshire CV7 9RA
**T:** 024 7636 9500
**F:** 024 7636 9501
**E:** pearscentre@rnib.org.uk
**W:** www.rnib.org.uk/pearscentre
We welcome visits from parents, carers, children, other family members and professionals. Get in touch to discuss places or arrange an informal visit.

**Headteacher** Mr Andy Moran
**Principal Manager Care & Wellbeing**
  Virginia Tyler
**Founded** 1957
**School Status** Co-ed Non-maintained (special)
  Boarding and Day
**Religious denomination** Non-Denominational

**Membership** NASS
**Special needs provision** ASD, BESD, CB, CP, DOW, EPI, HEA, HI, **IM**, **PMLD**, **SLD**, SP&LD, **VI**, WA1
**Age range** 4–19
**Average class size** 7

RNIB Pears Centre for Specialist Learning (formerly RNIB Rushton School and Children's Home) in Coventry offers individually-tailored education, care, health care and therapies to children and young people with multiple disabilities and complex health needs who are blind or partially sighted, from pre-school up to the age of 19.

Building on over 50 years' experience, we offer a stimulating, creative, supportive and purpose-built environment for young people, enabling them to reach their full potential for learning, independence and fulfilment.

Our school and children's home are both graded 'Outstanding' by Ofsted.

Education: Our specialist school offers a highly personalized and multi-sensory approach to learning. Our broad, balanced and relevant curriculum is differentiated to meet individual needs and learning styles. Lessons are varied, with students taking part in one-to-one work, small group sessions and whole class activities.

Teachers, teaching assistants, therapists and social care professionals work with parents and carers to continue a consistent approach outside of the school day. Our developing outreach service called 'Periscope' provides educational advice, guidance and practical support to pupils, parents and service providers locally and nationally.

Care: We offer up to 52-week specialized residential care from new purpose-built bungalows with gardens and outdoor play areas. This is available to children and young people from pre-school age whether or not they attend our school.

Young people are actively encouraged to make their own everyday choices and develop independence skills. We work closely with parents, carers and families to ensure that they are involved at each step of their child's journey.

Therapies and health care: our multi-disciplinary team includes in-house therapists and health-care consultants, such as behaviour specialists trained in the care of people with learning disabilities, a mobility/habilitation specialist, nurses, physiotherapists, and speech and language therapists.

All young people receive the highest level of health care. We can also support young people with high health needs during transition periods from hospital to their home environment.

Visit us! We welcome visits from parents, carers, children, other family members and professionals. Call us on 024 7636 9500 or email pearscentre@rnib.org.uk.

# RNIB Sunshine House School ● ♠

33 Dene Road, Northwood, Middlesex HA6 2DD
**T:** 01923 822538
**F:** 01923 826227
**E:** shsadmin@rnib.org.uk
**W:** www.rnib.org.uk/sunshinehouse

**Executive Head Teacher** Mr John Ayres
   National Leader of Education (NLE)
**Head of School** Jackie Seaman
**Founded** 1948
**School Status** Co-ed Non-maintained
   (special) Day and Boarding
**Religious denomination** Non-Denominational
**Membership** NASEN, NASS

**Special needs provision** CP, EPI, HEA, HI, IM,
   **PMLD**, **SLD**, SP&LD, **VI**, WA1
**Age range** 2–11; boarders from 2
**No of Pupils** 31; *(boarding)* 6;
   *(full boarding)* 6; *Nursery* 1; *Girls* 14;
   *Boys* 17
**Teacher:pupil ratio** 1:2
**Average class size** 6

## RNIB Sunshine House School and Residence

RNIB Sunshine House School and Residence in Northwood, Middlesex, is a specialist primary school and residence for blind and partially sighted children with significant learning difficulties and disabilities. We also offer a support services for parents, carers, siblings and other family members.

Boasting a range of specialist indoor and outdoor facilities, Sunshine House provides a safe and supportive environment for children to meet their full potential.

Everyone at Sunshine House is treated as an individual with their own set of needs and learning goals. Working together with parents and specialists we ensure that achievements go beyond the classroom into everyday life.

Our specialist primary school educates children from 2 to 11 years old who have a range of physical, learning and sensory needs. From September 2014 we will support children aged 2 to 14. Children follow an individually tailored curriculum supporting their special education needs. Most children are working between P levels 1 and 8. Each class has no more than seven children with a minimum support ratio of two adults for every three children.

Our team of in-house therapists combine their work with a child's learning, making therapies a part of everyday school life. We also have a paediatric community nurse who visits daily to ensure that all medical needs are met.

Our residence offers a range of flexible day care, overnight and short stay options including an after school club, play days, theme days, sleepovers and overnight stays where children aged between 2 and 14 years can stay up to four nights per week (Monday to Thursday) for up to 50 weeks per year during the school term and holidays. We welcome children who attend school elsewhere, providing we can meet their needs.

Find out more online at rnib.org.uk/sunshinehouse or call 01923 82 25 38.

# Royal School for the Deaf Derby

180 Ashbourne Road, Derby, Derbyshire DE22 3BH
**T:** 01332 362512 **F:** 01332 299708
**E:** principal@rsdd.org.uk **W:** www.rsd-derby.org.uk

**Principal** Ms C Ford
**Bursar** T Quipp
**Founded** 1893
**School Status** Co-ed Non-maintained
  (special) Day and Boarding
**Religious denomination** Non-Denominational
**Membership** NASS
**Special needs provision HI**, WA1

**Age range** 3–19; boarders from 5
**No of Pupils** 140; *(boarding)* 45;
  *(weekly boarding)* 45; *Nursery* 6;
  *Nursery to Pre-prep* 8; *Prep* 37; *Senior* 31;
  *Sixth form* 58; *Girls* 46; *Boys* 94
**Teacher:pupil ratio** 1:6
**Average class size** 6

RSD Derby values British Sign Language and English equally. The curriculum is delivered through English and BSL and progress is monitored through formal assessment and external examinations. The School promotes a positive sense of identity for pupils, preparing them for the opportunities of adult life.

The National Curriculum is followed and is adapted to suit the needs of the individual through personalized learning programmes. It is taught by phase or subject specialist teachers of the deaf to small class groups. Examinations offered include GCSE, DIDA and Entry Levels.

Post-16 students follow individual programmes of study at mainstream colleges and are supported by Transition Support Communicators. Key Skills, Wider Key Skills and Skills for Life are delivered by teachers of the deaf at base.

---

# St Elizabeth's School

South End, Much Hadham, Hertfordshire SG10 6EW
**T:** 01279 844270 **F:** 01279 843903
**E:** school@stelizabeths.org.uk **W:** www.stelizabeths.org.uk

**Principal** Sharon Wallin
**Founded** 1903
**School Status** Co-ed Non-maintained
  (special) Boarding and Day
**Religious denomination** Roman Catholic
**Membership** NASS
**Special needs provision** ADD, ADHD, **ASD**,
  ASP, BESD, **CB**, CP, DOW, DYP, DYS, **EPI**,

HEA, IM, **MLD**, **PMLD**, **SLD**, SP&LD, TOU,
WA1
**Age range** 5–19
**No of Pupils** 45; *(boarding)* 34; *(full boarding)*
  30; *(weekly boarding)* 4; *Girls* 18; *Boys* 27
**Teacher:pupil ratio** 1:1
**Average class size** 6

St Elizabeth's School is a specialist residential school for children and young people aged 5–19 with Epilepsy and other associated disabilities. Our multi-disciplinary teams, in partnership with Great Ormond Street Hospital, also equip the School to serve a wider range of complex needs such as autistic spectrum conditions and associated ADHD with language and communication needs or difficult to manage behaviours. Every young person we welcome to our School is different and special. Our integrated care, therapeutic and academic provision is planned around the individual and delivered through a coordinated and consistent waking day curriculum. The centre is situated in 65 acres of safe, spacious parkland. We offer a warm, welcoming, safe and secure environment for children from throughout the UK.

## St John's Catholic School for the Deaf ●♠

Church Street, Boston Spa, Wetherby, West Yorkshire LS23 6DF
**T:** 01937 842144 **F:** 01937 541471
**E:** info@stjohns.org.uk **W:** www.stjohns.org.uk
St John's is a SEN Specialist School.

**Head Teacher** Mrs A M Bradbury
**Founded** 1870
**School Status** Co-ed Non-maintained
  (special) Boarding and Day
**Religious denomination** Roman Catholic

**Special needs provision** ADHD, ASD, ASP,
  CP, DYP, DYS, EPI, **HI**, IM, MLD, SP&LD, VI,
  WA2
**Age range** 4–19
**No of Pupils** 79; *Girls* 31; *Boys* 48
**Average class size** 6

St John's is a residential and day school offering an excellent oral education to children aged from 4 to 19 years. A strong Christian ethos permeates all aspects of school life and children of all denominations are welcomed. The curriculum is broad and balanced and provides the opportunity for pupils to take GCSEs, Entry Level qualifications and a wide range of vocational courses. In addition to 20+ qualified Teachers of the Deaf, support is available from speech and language therapists, an audiologist, highly qualified care staff and a school nurse. St John's is a SEN Specialist School in the field of sensory and physical impairment.

## St Joseph's Specialist School & College ●♠

Amlets Lane, Cranleigh, Surrey GU6 7DH
**T:** 01483 272449 **F:** 01483 276003
**E:** office@st-josephscranleigh.surrey.sch.uk
**W:** www.st-josephscranleigh.surrey.sch.uk

**Principal** Mrs M E Fawcett
**Founded** 1951
**School Status** Co-ed Non-maintained (special)
  Boarding and Day
**Religious denomination** Roman Catholic
**Membership** BILD, NASEN, NASS

**Special needs provision** ADD, **ADHD**, **ASD**,
  ASP, **CB**, **DOW**, **MLD**, **SLD**, SP&LD, WA1
**Age range** 5–19
**No of Pupils** 77; *(boarding)* 31; *(full boarding)* 9;
  *(weekly boarding)* 22; *Girls* 22; *Boys* 55
**Teacher:pupil ratio** 1:3
**Average class size** 6

St Josephs Specialist School & College provides outstanding education and care for learners aged from 5 to 19 years with Autism, moderate, complex and severe learning difficulties. With Specialist Schools status (Communication and Interaction) our well equipped therapies department is staffed by a team of HPC registered professionals who help meet learners' needs through speech and language, occupational therapy, art and music psychotherapy. Our Post-16 department focuses on learning which promotes personal, social and adult independence, as well as opportunities to undertake nationally accredited courses and work experience placements. Our residential department staff deliver a consistent 24-hour approach in a safe and caring environment with flexible boarding, available for up to 52 weeks of the year.

# St Mary's School and 6th Form College (part of The Talking Trust) ●♠◆

Wrestwood Road, Bexhill-On-Sea, East Sussex, TN40 2LU England
**T:** 01424 730740
**F:** 01424 733575
**E:** admin@stmarysbexhill.org
**W:** www.stmarysbexhill.org

**Principal** CEO Dr Sharon Menghini
**Head of School** Mrs Joanna Whiteman
**Founded** 1922
**School Status** Co-ed Non-maintained
 (special) Boarding and Day
**Accomodation Type** Boarding and Day
**Religious denomination** Non-Denominational
**Membership** NAS, NASEN, NASS, NATSPEC
**Special needs provision** ADD, ADHD, **ASD**,
 ASP, CP, DOW, DYC, DYP, DYS, EPI, HEA,
HI, IM, **MLD**, SLD, SP&LD, TOU, VI,
WA2, W
**Age range** 7–19
**Boarders from** 7
**No of Pupils** 130; *(boarding)* 106;
 *(full boarding)* 106; *(weekly boarding)* 0;
 *Nursery* 0; *Nursery to Pre-prep* 0; *Prep* 3;
 *Senior* 55; *Sixth form* 68; *Girls* 46; *Boys* 84
**Teacher:pupil ratio** 1 : 7
**Average class size** 8

"We follow the national curriculum, differentiated for individuals, and a comprehensive life skills programme. Children receive individual therapy programmes which may include specialist support from Speech and Language Therapists, Physiotherapists, and Occupational Therapists. Other specialist professionals include an audiologist, social worker, on-site nursing team, educational psychologist and children and family support worker.

Enquiries are always welcome. Entry is by formal assessment.

St Mary's is a non-maintained SEN school, situated near the East Sussex coast. The Talking Trust is a registered charity that exists to provide high quality education, therapy and care in a residential setting."

# Sunfield School ● 🏠

Clent Grove, Woodman Lane, Stourbridge, West Midlands DY9 9PB
**T:** 01562 882253
**F:** 01562 883856
**E:** referrals@sunfield.org.uk
**W:** www.sunfield.org.uk

**Chief Executive Officer** Michael Frosch Cmgr
  FCMI
**Founded** 1930
**School Status** Co-ed Independent (special)
  Boarding and Day
**Religious denomination** Non-Denominational
**Membership** BILD, EQUALS, NAHT, NASEN,
  NASS, SCA

**Special needs provision**
  ADD, **ADHD**, **ASD**,
  ASP, **CB**, DOW, EPI, HEA, **MLD**, PDA, PMLD,
  **SLD**, SP&LD, TOU
**Age range** 6–19; boarders from 6
**Teacher:pupil ratio** 1:6
**Average class size** 4

Sunfield is an independent residential special school and registered charity. We offer **education, care, psychology, therapies and family services** to children and young people (6–19 years) with **severe and complex learning needs including Autism Spectrum Disorder**. We offer:

- 52 week residential placements
- 38 week (with or without additional short breaks) placements
- Education day provision

At Sunfield we adopt a **total communication approach** that underpins our students' learning and development. **A structured waking day curriculum** offers routine and a learning environment in which students truly flourish and achieve. This is supported by an **onsite Psychology and Therapies team** offering integrated therapies which include: occupational, music, play and sensory integration therapy.

On admission to Sunfield every student undergoes a comprehensive three-month assessment led by our Psychology and Therapies Team. Following this assessment a personalized plan is put in place that spans learning, care, therapy and health targets. We meet regularly with families to celebrate achievement and outcomes and review plans and targets.

**Our strengths include: small group houses with single bedrooms; personalized development programmes and outstanding resources.** Sunfield has ten residential houses; each accommodating four to six students on the basis of their age and needs. Houses are fully self-contained with their own garden. Each house also has a dedicated team of qualified and experienced staff led by a Team Leader and every child has their own Key Worker. Sunfield has numerous facilities within its 58 acre parkland site including: a purpose built school, a farm and horticultural areas, nature trails, an adventure playground, a superb sensory integration suite, sensory rooms and outdoor specialist sensory play equipment and trampolines. Our fleet of vehicles enables our students to access a wide range of community based leisure activities which promotes community integration and independence.

Sunfield has a **Family Services** team that monitors contact and offers support, training and advice, including a sibling support programme. Our two family centres offer fully equipped flats where families can stay overnight enabling them to have meaningful, family focussed time with their child in a supported environment. We also have a visiting suite for those families who do not require overnight accommodation.

*"Any family lucky enough to get their child into Sunfield will enjoy excellent communication both for themselves and their child. You won't find a better Special School who will take care of their child and really try and give them a sense of purpose and education. This is a really great place with great people who can help your child and the whole family."* Sunfield parent

*"Professionalism, commitment, integrated holistic approach, happy atmosphere. Nothing is too much trouble and my child's needs are always met."* Sunfield parent

# Swalcliffe Park School Trust ● ♠

Swalcliffe, Banbury, Oxfordshire OX15 5EP
**T:** 01295 780302 **F:** 01295 780006
**E:** admin@swalcliffepark.co.uk **W:** www.swalcliffepark.co.uk

**Principal** Mr Kiran Hingorani B.Ed
**Vice Principal** Robert Piner
**Founded** 1965
**School Status** Boys Non-maintained (special)
   Boarding and Day
**Religious denomination** Non-Denominational
**Membership** NAS, NASEN, NASS
**Special needs provision** ADD, ADHD, **ASD**, **ASP**,
   BESD, DYC, DYP, DYS, SP&LD, TOU, WA2

**Age range** 11–19
**No of Pupils** 42; *(boarding)* 34; *(full boarding)* 6;
   *(weekly boarding)* 28; *Senior* 31; *Sixth form* 11;
   *Boys* 42
**Teacher:pupil ratio** 1:3
**Average class size** 6

Swalcliffe Park is a non-maintained charitable trust providing specialist residential education and care for up to 57 boys aged 11–19. All students have a diagnosis of Autistic Spectrum Disorder – mainly Asperger's Syndrome; many also have additional needs including ADHD, Dyslexia, Dyspraxia and language impairment. Placements are funded by LAs from across the UK for a 38-week school year, on a two weekly boarding basis. The school offers a wide range of learning opportunities during the school day, evenings and weekends. These promote academic achievement (through GCSE and other recognized qualifications), social inclusion, independence and personal well-being. The school has well qualified and trained Teachers, Learning Support Assistants and Residential Care Staff who collaborate with a specialist therapeutic team including professionals from Speech and Language Therapy, Educational Psychology, Nursing, Psychiatry, Occupational Therapy and Massage Therapy.

# The School for Profound Education ● ♠

The School for Profound Education,
Tadworth Court, Tadworth, Surrey KT20 5RU
**T:** 01737 365810 **F:** 01737 365819
**E:** profoundeducation@thechildrenstrust.org.uk
**W:** www.thechildrenstrust.org.uk/profoundeducation

**Head Teacher** Sylvia Kerambrum
**Deputy Head** Maz Smith
**Founded** 1985
**School Status** Co-ed Non-maintained (special)
   Boarding and Day
**Religious denomination** Non-Denominational
**Membership** NASEN

**Special needs provision** CP, EPI, HEA, HI, IM,
   **PMLD**, VI, WA1
**Age range** 5–25
**No of Pupils** 43; *(boarding)* 30;
   *(full boarding)* 30; *Girls* 16; *Boys* 27
**Average class size** 6

The School for Profound Education (formerly known as St Margaret's School) is one of the few special schools in the UK that works exclusively with learners with profound and multiple learning difficulties (PMLD) and complex health needs. We are a non-maintained residential special school providing education, care and therapy in a safe, caring and happy environment in which each learner's needs can be met. The school has its own doctor, nurses and therapy team. The Profound Education Curriculum has been specially developed by the school and is used by dozens of other schools around the UK. Residential provision has now been extended to young adults aged 19 to 25 at our further education college. Both the school and college offer residential placements of up to 52 weeks a year. The school is part of The Children's Trust, Tadworth, a national charity that provides education, rehabilitation and care to children with acquired brain injury, multiple disabilities and complex health needs.

# The Unicorn School ● ♠

Berkeley House, 20 Marcham Road, Abingdon,
Oxfordshire OX14 1AA
**T:** 01235 530222
**F:** 01235 536889
**E:** info@unicorndyslexia.co.uk
**W:** www.unicorndyslexia.co.uk

**Principal** Mrs Jackie Vaux
**Founded** 1991
**School Status** Co-ed Independent (special)
  Day only
**Religious denomination** Non-Denominational
**Membership** BDA

**Special needs provision** ADD, ADHD, **DYC**,
  **DYP**, **DYS**, SP&LD
**Age range** 6–13
**No of Pupils** 67; *Girls* 10; *Boys* 57
**Teacher:pupil ratio** 1:1
**Average class size** 10

The aims and philosophy of the Unicorn School are to provide specialist education for dyslexic children; from both the independent and the maintained sector; and to teach strategies and skills to enable them to return to mainstream education as soon as possible. A structured, multi-sensory programme, including an appropriately differentiated National Curriculum, is followed with extensive use of word processors and encouragement to develop creative talents. Educational and emotional needs are met on an individual basis as well as through a friendly atmosphere and community spirit. Close liaison is maintained with the local education authority; parents are supported throughout the time they are associated with the Unicorn and are helped to find suitable schools for their children to move on to.

# SYMBOL KEY

## Gender

● Girls
● Boys
● Coed

## CReSTeD

◆ Crested Registered

## Accommodation

♠ Boarding only
♠ Boarding and Day
♠ Day and Boarding
♠ Day only

## Has 6th Form

▲ Has 6th Form

# Treloar School and College  ● ♠

London Road, Holybourne,
Alton, Hampshire GU34 4GL
**T:** 01420 547425
**F:** 01420 542708
**E:** admissions@treloar.org.uk
**W:** www.treloar.org.uk

**Treloar's Principal** Mr John Stone BSc, MSc, MBA, PGC,E Cphys, MinstP
**School Status** Co-ed Non-maintained (special) Boarding and Day
**Religious denomination** Non-Denominational
**Membership** NASS
**Special needs provision CP**, DYP, DYS, EPI, HEA, HI, IM, MLD, **PMLD**, SLD, SP&LD, VI, WA1

**Age range** 5–25; boarders from 7
**No of Pupils** 166; *(boarding)* 137; *(full boarding)* 137; *Girls* 71; *Boys* 95
**Teacher:pupil ratio** 1:6
**Average class size** 6

For over 100 years, Treloar's has offered education, independence training, medical support, therapy and first-class care to young people (aged 7 through to 25) with physical disabilities. Many students have sensory impairments, communication difficulties and additional learning disabilities. Treloar's offers a curriculum which is carefully differentiated according to need.

In addition to individual therapy sessions, physiotherapists, speech and language therapists, occupational therapists, assistive technology engineers and technicians work with teachers and care staff to achieve a truly multidisciplinary approach. Students study a range of courses with accredited courses available from entry to level 3. The College has facilities for sport, photography, music, art and design. Students are encouraged to develop personal interests, independent living skills and there is an extensive enrichment programme.

From September 2013, Treloar's will offer Key Stage One provision, catering for pupils working between P1i and P8.

The Post-16 provision at Treloar School will offer three pathways for students: Pathway to Further Education; Post-16 Life and Living Skills and Post-16 Linked Provision. Pathway to Further Education offers an opportunity to work as part of a small and discrete group. The curriculum is based on ASDAN's 'Personal Progress' qualification for students working in the P Levels up to Entry Level 1.

Post-16 Life and Living Skills builds a personalized learning programme focused on developing students' skills and the confidence for moving on to further education. The curriculum is based on OCR's 'Life and Living' qualification and is available at Entry Level 1, 2 and 3.

Post-16 Linked Provision allows students to follow nationally recognized A Level and BTEC qualifications, delivered at the local tertiary provider. In addition, the curriculum enhances core skills and enables students to pursue their individual interests.

Students at Treloar College have a wide spectrum of physical, learning, communication, language and sensory difficulties. Each student has a bespoke and individual programme of study. Their Individual Learning Plan is developed from an assessment undertaken at the start of each term and is based on student's likes, dislikes, needs, interests and the Aim of Placement.

All learning requirements will be assessed across the six domains of need, ie Transition and Work experience needs, Health and Wellbeing needs, Accredited and Non-Accredited Learning needs, Communication needs, Independent Living needs and Access to the Community needs. With student needs in mind, Treloar College offers a good range of courses to cater for a wide range of academic abilities. Courses are therefore offered from pre-entry level to courses at Level 3. Learning may not always be classroom based and may take place in the community or in the residential settings.

# Directory of Colleges and Other Special Provision at 16+

# England

## BERKSHIRE

**PRIOR'S COURT COTTAGES***
Prior's Court Foundation,
Hermitage, Thatcham,
Berkshire RG18 9NU
*Website:* www.priorscourt.org.uk
*Type:* Mixed Residential and
Day 19–25
*Special needs:* **ASD** CB EPI
MLD SLD SP&LD
*Wheelchair access:* W
*Independent Special
52-week care*

## BRISTOL

**CINTRE COMMUNITY**
54 St John's Road, Clifton,
Bristol BS8 2HG
*Type:* Mixed Residential Only
16–35
*Special needs:* ASD BESD DOW
DYS EPI MLD

# CAMBRIDGESHIRE

**SENSE EAST**
72 Church Street, Market
Deeping, Peterborough,
Cambridgeshire PE6 8AL
*Type:* Mixed Residential Only
*Special needs:* **HI** MLD PMLD
SLD **VI**
*Wheelchair access:* W

# CHESHIRE

**BRIDGE COLLEGE**
Curzon Road, Offerton,
Stockport, Cheshire SK2 5DG
*Website:* www.bgws.org.uk
*Type:* Mixed Day Only 16–23
*Special needs:* ADD ADHD
**ASD ASP** BESD CB CP DOW
EPI HEA HI IM MLD PMLD **SLD**
SP&LD VI
*Wheelchair access:* WA2

# CUMBRIA

**LINDETH COLLEGE OF
FURTHER EDUCATION**
The Oaks, Lindeth,
Bowness-on-Windermere,
Cumbria LA23 3NH
*Type:* Mixed Residential and
Day 16–25
*Special needs:* ADD ADHD ASD
ASP DOW DYS EPI HI **MLD** SLD
SP&LD VI
*Wheelchair access:* WA2
*Independent Special*

# DEVON

### EXETER COLLEGE
Hele Road, Exeter,
Devon EX4 4JS
*Website:* www.exe-coll.ac.uk
*Type:* Mixed Day Only
*Special needs:* ADD ADHD ASD
ASP BESD CP DOW DYC DYP
DYS EPI HI MLD SLD SP&LD
TOU VI
*Wheelchair access:* W

### EXETER ROYAL ACADEMY
### FOR DEAF EDUCATION
50 Topsham Road, Exeter,
Devon EX2 4NF
*Website:* www.
exeterdeafacademy.ac.uk
*Type:* Mixed Residential and
Day 5–23
*Special needs:* ADHD ASD ASP
BESD CP DYS EPI **HI** IM MLD
SLD SP&LD VI
*Wheelchair access:* WA2
*Non-maintained*

### EXETER ROYAL ACADEMY
### FOR DEAF EDUCATION
College, 50 Topsham Road,
Exeter, Devon EX2 4NF
*Website:* www.
exeterdeafacademy.ac.uk
*Type:* Mixed Day and
Residential 16–25
*Special needs:* ADHD ASD
BESD EPI **HI** SLD SP&LD VI
*Wheelchair access:* WA2
*Independent Special*

### OAKWOOD COURT
7–9 Oak Park Villas, Dawlish,
Devon EX7 0DE
*Website:* www.
oakwoodcourtcollege.co.uk
*Type:* Mixed Residential Only
16–25
*Special needs:* ADHD ASD ASP
BESD CP DOW DYP DYS EPI
MLD SLD SP&LD TOU
*Wheelchair access:* W

### RNIB MANOR HOUSE
Middle Lincombe Road,
Torquay, Devon TQ1 2NG
*Type:* Mixed Residential and
Day
*Special needs:* CP DYS EPI
HI **VI**
*Wheelchair access:* W

### THE WEST OF ENGLAND
### COLLEGE FOR STUDENTS
### WITH LITTLE OR NO SIGHT
Countess Wear, Exeter,
Devon EX2 6HA
*Type:* Mixed Residential and
Day 16–22
*Special needs:* MLD **VI**
*Wheelchair access:* W

# DORSET

### FORTUNE CENTRE OF
### RIDING THERAPY
Avon Tyrrell, Bransgore,
Christchurch, Dorset BH23 8EE
*Website:* www.fortunecentre.org
*Type:* Mixed Residential Only
16–25
*Special needs:* ADD ADHD ASP
BESD CB CP DOW DYP EPI HI
**MLD** SP&LD VI
*Wheelchair access:* W

### IVERS INCLUSIVE LEARNING
### PROJECT
Hains Lane, Marnhull,
Sturminster Newton, Dorset
DT10 1JU
*Type:* Mixed Day and
Residential 18–40
*Special needs:* ASD BESD CB
**DOW** EPI **MLD** SLD SP&LD
*Wheelchair access:* WA2
*52-week care*

### THE WING CENTRE
126 Richmond Park Road,
Bournemouth, Dorset BH8 8TH
*Website:* www.cambiangroup.com
*Type:* Boys Residential and Day
16–19
*Special needs:* **ASP** CB DYC
DYP DYS EPI HEA SP&LD
*Wheelchair access:* W
*Independent Special*

# COUNTY DURHAM

### FINCHALE TRAINING
### COLLEGE
Durham, County Durham
DH1 5RX
*Website:*
www.finchalecollege.co.uk
*Type:* Mixed Residential and Day
*Special needs:* ASP CP DYC
DYP DYS EPI HEA HI MLD VI
*Wheelchair access:* WA1

# ESSEX

### HOPEWELL SCHOOL
Harmony House, Baden Powell Close, Dagenham, Essex RM9 6XN
*Type:* 11–16
*Special needs:* BESD MLD
*Independent Special*

# GLOUCESTERSHIRE

### NATIONAL STAR COLLEGE
Ullenwood Manor, Cheltenham, Gloucestershire GL53 9QU
*Website:* www.natstar.ac.uk
*Type:* Mixed Residential and Day 16–25
*Special needs:* ASP **CP** DYP EPI HEA PMLD SP&LD VI
*Wheelchair access:* WA1

# HAMPSHIRE

### ENHAM
Enham Place, Enham Alamein, Andover, Hampshire SP11 6JS
*Website:* www.enham.org.uk
*Type:* Mixed Residential and Day
*Special needs:* ASD CP DYP DYS EPI MLD SP&LD
*Wheelchair access:* WA1
*52-week care*

### TRELOAR COLLEGE
London Road, Holybourne, Alton, Hampshire GU34 4EN
*Website:* www.treloar.org.uk
*Type:* Mixed Residential and Day 16–25
*Special needs:* **CP** DYP DYS EPI HEA HI IM MLD PMLD SLD SP&LD VI
*Wheelchair access:* WA1
*Non-maintained*

# HEREFORDSHIRE

### THE ROYAL NATIONAL COLLEGE FOR THE BLIND (RNC)
College Road, Hereford, Herefordshire HR1 1EB
*Website:* www.rncb.ac.uk
*Type:* Mixed Residential and Day 16–65
*Special needs:* ASP BESD CP DYC DYP DYS EPI HEA HI IM MLD SP&LD TOU VI
*Wheelchair access:* WA1

# KENT

### DORTON COLLEGE OF FURTHER EDUCATION
Royal London Society for the Blind, Seal Drive, Seal, Sevenoaks, Kent TN15 0AH
*Website:* www.rlsb.org.uk
*Type:* Mixed Residential and Day
*Special needs:* MLD **VI**
*Wheelchair access:* WA1
*Independent Special*

### NASH COLLEGE OF FURTHER EDUCATION
Croydon Road, Hayes, Bromley, Kent BR2 7AG
*Website:* www.nash.ac.uk
*Type:* Mixed Residential and Day 16–25
*Special needs:* **CP** DOW DYP DYS EPI HEA HI IM **PMLD** SLD SP&LD VI
*Wheelchair access:* W

### THE NEW SCHOOL AT WEST HEATH*
Ashgrove Road, Sevenoaks, Kent TN13 1SR
*Website:* www.westheathschool.com
*Type:* Mixed Residential and Day 11–19
*Special needs:* ADD **ADHD ASP BESD HEA** SP&LD **TOU**
*Independent Special*

### THE ROYAL SCHOOL FOR DEAF CHILDREN MARGATE*
Victoria Road, Margate, Kent CT9 1NB
*Website:* www.townsendtrust.com
*Type:* Mixed Residential and Day 4–16
*Special needs:* ADD ADHD ASD ASP BESD CB CP DOW DYP DYS EPI HEA **HI** IM MLD PMLD SLD SP&LD TOU VI
*Wheelchair access:* WA2
*Non-maintained*

### SHALOM PLACE
Hawthorne Farm, Knatts Lane, Knatts Valley, West Kingsdown, Kent TN15 6YA
*Website:* www.shalomplace.co.uk
*Type:* Mixed 8–16
*Special needs:* ASD **ASP**
*Independent Special*

### WESTGATE COLLEGE FOR DEAF PEOPLE
Westcliff House, 37 Sea Road, Westgate, Kent CT8 8QP
*Website:* www.westgate-college.org.uk
*Type:* Mixed Residential and Day 16–25
*Special needs:* ADD ASD ASP BESD CB DOW DYC DYP DYS EPI HEA **HI** IM MLD PMLD SLD SP&LD TOU VI
*Wheelchair access:* WA2
*52-week care*

# LANCASHIRE

### BEAUMONT COLLEGE OF FURTHER EDUCATION
Slyne Road, Lancaster, Lancashire LA2 6AP
*Type:* Mixed Residential and Day
*Special needs:* CP EPI MLD SLD SP&LD

# LEICESTERSHIRE

**HOMEFIELD RESIDENTIAL COLLEGE**
42 St Mary's Road, Sileby,
Loughborough, Leicestershire
LE12 7TL
*Type:* Mixed Residential and
Day
*Special needs:* ASD HI MLD
SLD

**RNIB COLLEGE LOUGHBOROUGH***
Radmoor Road, Loughborough,
Leicestershire LE11 3BS
*Website:* www.rnibcollege.ac.uk
*Type:* Mixed Residential and
Day 16–63
*Special needs:* ADD ADHD ASD
ASP CB CP DOW EPI HEA HI
IM MLD SLD SP&LD TOU **VI**
*Wheelchair access:* WA1
*Independent Special*

# LINCOLNSHIRE

**BROUGHTON HOUSE**
Brant Broughton, Lincolnshire
LN5 0SL
*Website:*
www.cambiangroup.com
*Type:* Mixed Residential
Only 16–25
*Special needs:* **ASD CB EPI
MLD SLD** SP&LD
*Wheelchair access:* W
*Independent Special*
*52-week care*

**LINKAGE COLLEGE**
Toynton Campus, Toynton All
Saints, Spilsby, Lincolnshire
PE23 5AE
*Website:* www.linkage.org.uk
*Type:* Mixed Residential and
Day 16–25
*Special needs:* **ADD ADHD
ASD ASP CP DOW** DYP DYS
**EPI** HEA **HI MLD SLD** SP&LD
**TOU** VI
*Wheelchair access:* WA3

# NORTH EAST LINCOLNSHIRE

**LINKAGE COLLEGE**
Weelsby Campus, Weelsby
Road, Grimsby, North East
Lincolnshire DN32 9RU
*Type:* Mixed Residential and
Day 16–25
*Special needs:* ADD ADHD ASD
**ASP** CP **DOW** DYP DYS EPI HEA
HI **MLD SLD** SP&LD TOU VI
*Wheelchair access:* W
*Independent Special*

# NORTH LINCOLNSHIRE

**AALPS NORTH***
Winterton Road, Roxby,
Nr Scunthorpe, North
Lincolnshire DN15 0BJ
*Website:* www.optionsgroup.co.uk
*Type:* Mixed Residential Only
16+
*Special needs:* ADD ADHD
**ASD ASP** CB **EPI HEA** HI IM
MLD PMLD SLD SP&LD TOU VI
*Wheelchair access:* WA1
*52-week care*

# LONDON

**THE PRIORY LODGE SCHOOL**
Priory Lane, Roehampton,
London SW15 5JJ
*Website:* www.priorygroup.com/
priorylodge
*Type:* Mixed Day Only 7–19
*Special needs:* ADHD **ASD ASP**
*Independent Special*

# GREATER MANCHESTER

**FOURWAYS ASSESSMENT
UNIT**
Cleworth Hall Lane, off
Manchester Road, Tyldesley,
Greater Manchester M29 8NT
*Type:* Mixed Residential and
Day 18–25
*Wheelchair access:* W

# NORFOLK

**EAGLE LIFE COLLEGE**
Andrew's Furlong, Mill Road,
Banham, Norfolk NR16 2HH
*Website:*
www.eaglelifecollege.co.uk
*Type:* Mixed Residential and
Day 19–25
*Special needs:* ADD ADHD ASD
**ASP** CB DYP EPI MLD SLD
SP&LD
*Wheelchair access:* WA2

# NORTHAMPTONSHIRE

**HILL FARM COLLEGE**
CastleCare Education Ltd, The
Manor House, Squires Hill,
Rothwell, Northamptonshire
NN14 6BQ
*Website:*
www.castlecaregroup.co.uk
*Type:* Boys
*52-week care*

**HINWICK HALL COLLEGE**
Hinwick, Wellingborough,
Northamptonshire NN29 7JD
*Website:*
www.hinwick.demon.co.uk
*Type:* Mixed Residential and
Day 16–25
*Special needs:* ASD CP **DOW** HI
MLD **PMLD SLD** SP&LD
*Wheelchair access:* WA1

**SOLDEN HILL HOUSE**
Banbury Road, Byfield,
Daventry, Northamptonshire
NN11 6UA
*Type:* Mixed Residential Only
*Special needs:* **MLD**

# NORTHUMBERLAND

**DILSTON COLLEGE OF
FURTHER EDUCATION**
Dilston Hall, Corbridge,
Northumberland NE45 5RJ
*Type:* Mixed Residential and
Day 16–25
*Special needs:* ASD ASP DOW
EPI HI MLD SLD SP&LD

# NOTTINGHAMSHIRE

**PORTLAND COLLEGE**
Nottingham Road, Mansfield,
Nottinghamshire NG18 4TJ
*Type:* Mixed Residential and
Day 16–25
*Special needs:* CP DYC DYP
DYS EPI HI MLD SP&LD
*Wheelchair access:* W

# SHROPSHIRE

**DERWEN COLLEGE**
Oswestry, Shropshire SY11 3JA
*Website:*
Derwen@enterprise.net
*Type:* Mixed Residential Only
*Special needs:* ASP CP DOW
DYS EPI HI MLD SLD SP&LD VI
*Wheelchair access:* W

**LOPPINGTON HOUSE
FURTHER EDUCATION &
ADULT CENTRE**
Loppington, Wem, Shropshire
SY4 5NF
*Website:*
www.loppingtonhouse.co.uk
*Type:* Mixed Residential Only
18–25
*Special needs:* ASD BESD
CP DOW EPI HI MLD SLD
SP&LD VI
*Wheelchair access:* WA2
*52-week care*

# SOMERSET

**LUFTON COLLEGE OF
FURTHER EDUCATION**
Lufton, Yeovil, Somerset
BA22 8ST
*Type:* Mixed Residential and
Day 16–25
*Special needs:* MLD SLD
*Wheelchair access:* WA2

**NORTH HILL HOUSE**
Fromefield, Frome, Somerset
BA11 2HB
*Website:* www.nhh4as.co.uk
*Type:* Boys Residential and Day
7–18
*Special needs:* **ASD ASP**
*Wheelchair access:* W
*Independent Special*

# BATH & NORTH EAST SOMERSET

**RNID CARE SERVICES**
Watery Lane, Twerton on Avon,
Bath, Bath & North East
Somerset BA2 1RN
*Website:* www.rnid.org.uk
*Type:* Mixed Residential Only
*Special needs:* HI SP&LD VI
*Wheelchair access:* W

**ROOKERY RADSTOCK**
Rookery House, Wells Road,
Radstock, Bath & North East
Somerset BA3 3RS
*Website:* www.priorygroup.com
*Type:* Mixed Residential Only
18–30
*Special needs:* ADD ADHD
**ASD ASP** BESD CB
*Wheelchair access:* WA3
*Independent Special*
*52-week care*

# STAFFORDSHIRE

### STRATHMORE COLLEGE
38/40 Dimsdale Parade,
Wolstanton, Newcastle-under-
Lyme, Staffordshire ST5 8BU
*Website:*
www.strathmoresupportservices.
co.uk
*Type:* Mixed Residential and
Day
*Special needs:* ADD ADHD ASD
**ASP BESD DOW** DYP EPI **MLD
SLD** SP&LD
*Wheelchair access:* WA2
*52-week care*

# SURREY

### THE GRANGE CENTRE FOR PEOPLE WITH DISABILITIES
Rectory Lane, Bookham, Surrey
KT23 4DZ
*Website:*
www.grangecentre.org.uk
*Type:* Mixed Residential and
Day
*Special needs:* ASD ASP BESD
CP DOW EPI HI MLD SP&LD VI
*Wheelchair access:* W

### QUEEN ELIZABETH'S FOUNDATION
Leatherhead Court, Woodlands
Road, Leatherhead, Surrey
KT22 0BN
*Website:* www.qef.org.uk
*Type:* Mixed Residential Only
16–35
*Special needs:* BESD EPI MLD
SP&LD VI
*Wheelchair access:* W

### SEEABILITY (FORMERLY ROYAL SCHOOL FOR THE BLIND)
SeeABILITY House, Hook Road,
Epsom, Surrey KT19 8SQ
*Website:* www.seeability.org
*Type:* Mixed Residential and
Day
*Special needs:* BESD CP EPI HI
MLD PMLD SLD **VI**
*Wheelchair access:* W

# EAST SUSSEX

### THE MOUNT CAMPHILL COMMUNITY
Faircrouch Lane, Wadhurst,
East Sussex TN5 6PT
*Type:* Mixed Residential and
Day 16–25
*Special needs:* ASD ASP BESD
DOW MLD SLD
*Wheelchair access:* WA3

### ROOKERY HOVE
22–24 Sackville Gardens, Hove,
East Sussex BN3 4GH
*Type:* Mixed Residential Only
18–35
*Special needs:* ADD ADHD
**ASD ASP** BESD CB
*Wheelchair access:* WA1
*Independent Special*
*52-week care*

# TYNE AND WEAR

**THORNBECK COLLEGE**
14 Thornhill Park, Sunderland,
Tyne and Wear SR2 7LA
*Website:* www.tawas.org.uk
*Special needs:* ASD ASP

# WEST MIDLANDS

**HEREWARD COLLEGE**
Bramston Crescent, Tile Hill
Lane, Coventry, West Midlands
CV4 9SW
*Website:* www.hereward.ac.uk
*Type:* Mixed Residential and
Day
*Special needs:* **ASD** ASP CP
DOW DYC DYP DYS EPI HEA HI
**MLD** SLD SP&LD TOU VI

**QUEEN ALEXANDRA
COLLEGE**
Court Oak Road, Harborne,
Birmingham, West Midlands
B17 9TG
*Website:* www.qac.ac.uk
*Type:* Mixed Residential and
Day 16+
*Special needs:* **ASD ASP** CP
DOW DYP DYS EPI HEA HI IM
**MLD** SP&LD **VI**
*Wheelchair access:* W

# WILTSHIRE

**FAIRFIELD FARM COLLEGE**
Dilton Marsh, Westbury,
Wiltshire BA13 4DL
*Type:* Mixed Residential and
Day 16–23
*Special needs:* ASD ASP DOW
DYP EPI MLD SLD SP&LD

# WORCESTERSHIRE

**AALPS MIDLANDS***
Rhydd, Hanley Castle,
Worcestershire WR8 0AD
*Website:*
www.optionsgroup.co.uk
*Type:* Mixed Residential and
Day 15+
*Special needs:* ADD ADHD
**ASD ASP** CB **EPI HEA** HI IM
MLD PMLD SLD SP&LD TOU VI
*Wheelchair access:* WA1
*52-week care*

# NORTH YORKSHIRE

**HENSHAWS COLLEGE**
Bogs Lane, Harrogate,
North Yorkshire HG1 4ED
*Website:* www.henshaws.ac.uk
*Type:* Mixed Residential and
Day
*Special needs:* CP DOW DYP
EPI HI IM **MLD SLD** SP&LD VI
*Wheelchair access:* WA1
*Independent Special*

# SOUTH YORKSHIRE

**COMMUNICATION
SPECIALIST COLLEGE
DONCASTER (FORMERLY
DONCASTER COLLEGE FOR
THE DEAF)\***
Leger Way, Doncaster,
South Yorkshire DN2 6AY
*Website:*
www.deaf-college.co.uk
*Type:* Mixed Residential and
Day 16–60
*Special needs:* ADHD ASD ASP
**BESD** CP DYP DYS **HI** MLD
SLD SP&LD VI
*Wheelchair access:* WA2

# WEST YORKSHIRE

**PENNINE CAMPHILL
COMMUNITY**
Wood Lane, Chapelthorpe,
Wakefield, West Yorkshire
WF4 3JL
*Website:* www.pennine.org.uk
*Type:* Mixed Residential and
Day 16–25
*Special needs:* ADD ADHD ASD
ASP BESD CB CP DOW DYC
DYP DYS EPI HEA HI MLD SLD
SP&LD VI
*Wheelchair access:* WA2

# Scotland

## ABERDEENSHIRE

**EASTER AUGUSTON
TRAINING FARM**
Peterculter, Aberdeen,
Aberdeenshire AB14 0PJ
*Website:*
www.easteranguston.org
*Type:* Mixed Residential Only
*Special needs:* **DOW MLD**
SP&LD

## LOTHIAN

**RNIB SCOTLAND**
Employment and Learning
Centre, 24D Milton Road East,
Edinburgh, Lothian EH15 2NJ
*Website:* www.rnib.org.uk
*Type:* Mixed Residential and
Day 16–65
*Special needs:* BESD CB DYS
MLD VI
*Wheelchair access:* W

## STIRLING

**CAMPHILL BLAIR
DRUMMOND TRUST**
Blair Drummond House, Cuthil
Brae, Stirling, Stirling FK9 4UT
*Website:* www.camphill.org.uk
*Type:* Mixed Residential and
Day 16–30
*Special needs:* ASD **ASP** BESD
CB **DOW** EPI HEA HI MLD
PMLD **SLD** SP&LD
*Wheelchair access:* W
*52-week care*

# Wales

## BRIDGEND

**BRIDGEND COLLEGE**
Cowbridge Road, Bridgend,
Bridgend CF31 3DH
*Website:* www.bridgend.ac.uk
*Type:* Mixed Residential Only
16–25
*Special needs:* ADD ASP CP
DOW DYP DYS EPI HI MLD VI
*Wheelchair access:* W

**YSGOL BRYN CASTELL**
Llangewydd Road, Cefn Glas,
Bridgend, Bridgend CF31 4JP
*Type:* Mixed Day Only 8–19
*Special needs:* ADHD ASD ASP
**BESD** DOW DYS EPI HI **MLD**
SLD SP&LD TOU
*Wheelchair access:* WA3

## CARMARTHENSHIRE

**COLEG ELIDYR**
Rhandirmwyn, Llandovery,
Carmarthenshire SA20 0NL
*Website:* www.colegelidyr.com
*Type:* Mixed Residential Only
18–25
*Special needs:* ADD ASD BESD
**DOW** EPI **MLD SLD**
*Wheelchair access:* W
*Independent Special*

## DENBIGHSHIRE

**PENGWERN COLLEGE**
Sarn Lane, Rhuddlan,
Denbighshire LL18 5UH
*Website:* www.mencap.org.uk/
pengwern
*Type:* Mixed Day and
Residential 16–25
*Special needs:* **ADD ADHD**
**ASD ASP** BESD **CB CP DOW**
**DYP EPI** HEA **HI IM MLD PMLD**
**SLD** SP&LD **TOU** VI
*Wheelchair access:* WA2
*Independent Special*

# FLINTSHIRE

**AALPS CYMRU***
Llanerch-y-mor, Holywell,
Flintshire CH8 9DX
*Website:*
www.optionsgroup.co.uk
*Type:* Mixed Residential Only
18+
*Special needs:* ADD ADHD
**ASD ASP** CB **EPI HEA** MLD
PMLD SLD SP&LD
*52-week care*

# GWYNEDD

**ARAN HALL SCHOOL**
Rhydymain, Dolgellau,
Gwynedd LL40 2AR
*Website:*
www.senadgroup.com/aran
*Type:* Mixed Residential Only
11–19 (38 to 52 week
residential care available)
*Special needs:* **ADD ADHD**
ASD **ASP BESD CB CP DOW**
**DYC DYP EPI HEA HI IM MLD**
**PMLD SLD** SP&LD **TOU**
*Wheelchair access:* W
*Independent Special*
*52-week care*

**BRYN MELYN GROUP**
Llandderfel, Bala, Gwynedd
LL23 7RA
*Website:* www.brynmelyngroup.
com/foundation/
*Type:* Mixed Residential Only
12–19
*Special needs:* ADD BESD DYP
EPI MLD

# 2.5

# Profiles of Colleges and Other Special Provision at 16+

## SYMBOL KEY

### Gender
● Girls
● Boys
● Coed

### CReSTeD
◆ Crested Registered

### Accommodation

🏠 Boarding only
🏠 Boarding and Day
🏠 Day and Boarding
🏠 Day only

### Has 6th Form

▲ Has 6th Form

# Communication Specialist College Doncaster ●🏠

Leger Way, Doncaster, South Yorkshire DN2 6AY
**T:** 01302 386700 **F:** 01302 361808
**E:** enquiries@ddt-deaf.org.uk **W:** www.deaf-college.co.uk
Entry thoughout the year. Please contact us to make an informal visit

**Executive Principal** Mr A W Robinson
**Assistant Principal** Mr Jon Smith
**School Status** Co-ed Independent (special) Boarding and Day
**Religious denomination** Non-Denominational

**Membership** NATSPEC
**Special needs provision** ADHD, ASD, ASP, **BESD**, CP, DYP, DYS, **HI**, MLD, SLD, SP&LD, VI, WA2
**Age range** 16–60

A Residential, National Specialist College, providing learning and training opportunities for the deaf, hearing impaired and those with specialist communication needs. The Total Communication (TC) policy allows students to use their favoured method of communication – British Sign Language (BSL), Signed Supported English (SSE) or a mixture of speech and lip-reading. A wide range of personal and vocational courses are available through life, work and living pathways using realistic environments supported by our on-site specialist team. Learning Programmes include: Media and Office Technology; Catering and Hospitality; Construction; Design and Technology; Hair and Beauty; Health Education and Social Studies; Motor Vehicle Engineering; Sport; Recreation and Leisure Studies; Independence and life skills.

## Options Group

# AALPS Cymru ●🏠

Llanerach-y-mor, Holywell, Flintshire CH8 9DX
**T:** 01745 562570 **F:** 01745 562572
**E:** info@aalpscymru.co.uk
**W:** www.optionsgroup.co.uk

**Options Group**
*making a difference*

**Head of Service** Mr Russell Leese
**Registered Manager** Shian Thomas
**Founded** 2011
**School Status** Co-ed Boarding only
**Religious denomination** Inter-Denominational

**Membership** NAS
**Special needs provision** ADD, ADHD, **ASD**, **ASP**, CB, **EPI**, **HEA**, MLD, PMLD, SLD, SP&LD, W
**Age range** 18+; *(boarding)* 5; *(full boarding)* 5

Set in a stunning rural location overlooking the Dee Estuary, North Wales AALPS (Adolescent to Adult Life Preparation Service) Cymru is a specialist Transitions Service for people aged 18+ with autism, Asperger's Syndrome, learning disabilities and complex needs.

AALPS Cymru offers flexible person-centred placements including up to 52-week residential care and 'Options For You' outreach services.

AALPS Cymru provides flexible and person-centred support that enables people with complex needs to prepare for adulthood.

Every person at AALPS Cymru is supported to develop their individualized programme, ensuring that their needs are met 24 hours a day and that their individual choices are respected. AALPS Cymru aims to make the sometimes difficult transition to adulthood both fulfilling and rewarding.

# AALPS Midlands ● ♠

Rhydd, Hanley Castle, Worcester,
Worcestershire WR8 0AD
**T:** 01684 312610 **F:** 01684 312612
**E:** info@aalpsmids.co.uk
**W:** www.optionsgroup.co.uk

**Options Group**
*making a difference*

**Head of Service** Mr Darren Goodwin
**Registered Manager** Laura Smith
**School Status** Co-ed Boarding and Day
**Religious denomination** Non-Denominational
**Special needs provision** ADD, ADHD, **ASD**,

**ASP**, CB, **EPI**, **HEA**, HI, IM, MLD, PMLD,
SLD, SP&LD, TOU, VI, WA1
**Age range** 15+; *(boarding)* 32;
*(full boarding)* 32

AALPS (Adolescent to Adult Life Preparation Service) Midlands is an NAS accredited Transitions Service for people aged 15+ with autism, Asperger's Syndrome, learning disabilities and complex needs.

Located in the heart of Worcestershire, AALPS Midlands offers flexible person-centred placements including up to 52-week residential care, 'Options For Life' day services, short breaks and 'Options For You' outreach services.

AALPS Midlands supports people to develop individualized person-centred programmes, ensuring that their needs are met 24 hours a day and that their individual choices are respected. Outcomes-focused programmes enable people to successfully transition from higher dependency residential services into inclusive community living.

---

# AALPS North ● ♠

Winterton Road, Roxby, Nr Scunthorpe,
North Lincolnshire DN15 0BJ
**T:** 01724 733777 **F:** 01724 733666
**E:** info@aalpsnorth.co.uk
**W:** www.optionsgroup.co.uk

**Options Group**
*making a difference*

**Head of Service** Mr Russell Leese
**Registered Manager** Lesley Fisher
**School Status** Co-ed Boarding only
**Religious denomination** Non-Denominational
**Membership** NAS, NATSPEC

**Special needs provision** ADD, ADHD, **ASD**,
**ASP**, CB, **EPI**, **HEA**, HI, IM, MLD, PMLD,
SLD, SP&LD, TOU, VI, WA1
**Age range** 16+; *(boarding)* 56;
*(full boarding)* 56

AALPS (Adolescent to Adult Life Preparation Service) North is an NAS accredited specialist Transitions Service supporting people aged 16+ with autism, Asperger's Syndrome, learning disabilities and complex needs.

Situated in Scunthorpe, North Lincolnshire, AALPS North provides up to 52-week residential and 'Options For You' outreach services.

AALPS North supports people to develop individualized person-centred programmes, ensuring that their needs are met 24 hours a day and that their individual choices are respected. Outcomes-focused programmes enable people to successfully transition from higher dependency residential services into inclusive community living.

# Prior's Court Cottages

Priors Court Foundation, Hermitage, Thatcham,
Berkshire RG18 9NU
**T:** 01635 247202
**F:** 01635 247203
**E:** mail@priorscourt.org.uk
**W:** www.priorscourt.org.uk

**Manager** Ms R Over
**Founded** 1999
**School Status** Co-ed Independent (special)
Boarding and Day
**Religious denomination** Inter-Denominational

**Membership** EQUALS, NAS, NASEN, NASS
**Special needs provision ASD**, CB, EPI, MLD,
SLD, SP&LD, W
**Age range** 19–25; *(boarding)* 18;
*(full boarding)* 18

Prior's Court Cottages provide an autism-specific living and learning environment to support young adults in developing skills for a fulfilling and purposeful life with greater inclusion in their local community. Three cottages offer a mix of small group homes and flats with an on-site Learning Centre set in 50 acres. Leisure facilities support exercise, horticulture, animal husbandry and vocational work. Highly trained staff are supported by on-site therapy, medical therapists, medical professionals and other specialists to provide individual, person-centred support in developing self care, daily living and leisure skills, communication, choice-making and self-managed behaviour. A strong emphasis is placed on developing vocational skills with opportunities for work placements.

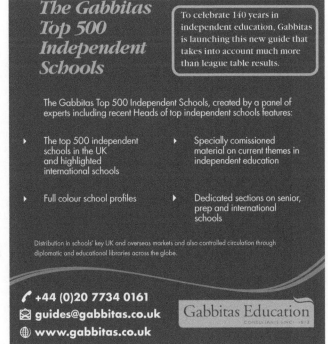

# RNIB College Loughborough  ● ♠

Radmoor Road, Loughborough, Leicestershire LE11 3BS
**T:** 01509 611077 **F:** 01509 232013
**E:** enquiries@rnibcollege.ac.uk **W:** www.rnibcollege.ac.uk

| | |
|---|---|
| **Principal** Mr Tony Warren | SLD, SP&LD, TOU, **VI**, |
| **Founded** 1989 | WA1 |
| **School Status** Co-ed Independent FE College | **Age range** 16–63; |
|    Day and Boarding |    boarders from 16 |
| **Membership** NATSPEC | **No of Pupils** 65; *(boarding)* 35; |
| **Special needs provision** ADD, ADHD, ASD, |    *(full boarding)* 35; *Girls* 33; *Boys* 32 |
|    ASP, CB, CP, DOW, EPI, HEA, HI, IM, MLD, | **Average class size** 6 |

RNIB College Loughborough is about helping you to reach your goals. We support people with a wide range of disabilities, medical and health conditions, in learning to access fulfilling adult lives. Our programmes are planned and organized to develop independence skills for involvement in work and community life. Our bespoke programmes and active learning environment create a vibrant community in which young people flourish.

We are experts at what we do. We are a friendly and safe college with purpose-built facilities. We are well regarded by students and families, and Ofsted rate us as one of the top specialist colleges in the country.

### In-house programmes

The College's enterprise curriculum forms the foundation of our in-house programmes. The four enterprises give students the opportunity to put skills into practice and develop new skills in a realistic setting. The enterprises are:

- Bell Bar – the College's catering facility
- Sell4U – the College's ebay enterprise and college shop
- Arts Centre – the College's creative hub, including performing arts, music and drama
- College Office – The College's main administrative centre

### Mainstream programmes

RNIB College has worked in partnership with mainstream Loughborough College for over 20 years. We share a campus and this unique relationship allows our students to access mainstream programmes such as A Levels and National Diplomas in a range of subjects. In addition to gaining an academic qualification, students also receive specialist RNIB learning support and a full timetable including the development of essential life skills such as cooking, shopping and travel.

### Therapies

The College has its own therapies team that work across all areas of the college and residential accommodation to support students including physiotherapy, speech and language therapy, counselling, ASD consultants and low vision specialists.

### Transition

Our aim is to support you in the future you want. Transition is important to us and we work with young people and families from their initial assessment throughout the programme to ensure smooth progression to adult life. Work placements are an important part of this and help to develop confidence, communication and social skills; all students complete a work placement as part of their programme.

### Visit

The best way to find out more about the College is to come and have a look around. During a visit you will be able to view the facilities, go into classes, meet staff and students and discuss a suitable course.

# The New School at West Heath

Ashgrove Road, Sevenoaks, Kent TN13 1SR
**T:** 01732 460553 **F:** 01732 456734
**E:** principal@westheathschool.com **W:** www.westheathschool.com

**Principal** Ms Christina Wells BA Hons
**Founded** 1998
**School Status** Co-ed Independent (special)
 Boarding and Day
**Special needs provision** ADD, **ADHD**, **ASP**,
 **BESD**, **HEA**, SP&LD, **TOU**
**Age range** 11–19; boarders from 11

**No of Pupils** 112; *(boarding)* 36;
 *(weekly boarding)* 36; *Girls* 36; *Boys* 76
**Average class size** 8

We offer an exciting broad and balanced curriculum with specialist subjects tailored to the individual. The most recent Ofsted inspection found that 'The outstanding curriculum provides a very wide range of experiences and is matched closely to the specific learning needs of students.' The school motto; 'rebuilding lives through education'; is reflected in the approach of nurturing and educating young people in a safe and highly supportive environment. Teaching is supported by in-house communication, speech and language programmes, and an emotional literacy curriculum. Our students often respond very well to the additional support provided, achieving good GCSE and A level grades. 'We believe in our students until they believe in themselves.'

# The Royal School for Deaf Children Margate

Victoria Road, Margate, Kent CT9 1NB
**T:** 01843 227561 **F:** 01843 227637
**E:** enquiries@royalschoolfordeaf.kent.sch.uk
**W:** www.johntownsendtrust.org.uk

**Principal** Mrs W Eadsforth
**School Status** Co-ed Non-maintained (special)
 Boarding and Day
**Religious denomination** Non-Denominational
**Membership** EQUALS, NASS, NATSPEC
**Special needs provision** ADD, ADHD, ASD,
 ASP, BESD, CB, CP, DOW, DYP, DYS, EPI,

HEA, **HI**, IM, MLD, PMLD, SLD, SP&LD, TOU,
VI
**Age range** 4–16; 16–19 6th Form
**No of Pupils** 69; *(boarding)* 33;
 *(weekly boarding)* 33; *Nursery to Pre-prep* 3;
 *Prep* 3; *Senior* 38; *Girls* 14; *Boys* 30
**Teacher:pupil ratio** 1:2
**Average class size** 7

We educate and care for deaf children and young people with communication difficulties who may have additional needs, for a positive future within work and their communities. The Royal School for Deaf Children Margate is a non-maintained school offering residential and day provision for pupils from 4–16 years (School) and 16–19 years (6th Form). Pupils and students attending the school are deaf or have communication difficulties. Many have additional learning and physical disabilities, mental health and associated challenging behaviours. Communication modes include speech, BSL, SSE, PECS symbols and objects of reference.

## 2.6

# Index of Independent and Non-Maintained Special Schools and Colleges Classified by Special Need

## ASPERGER'S SYNDROME

AALPS Cymru, Holywell
AALPS Midlands, Hanley Castle
AALPS North, Roxby
Action for Children Headlands School, Penarth
Alderwasley Hall School and Callow Park College, Belper
Annie Lawson School, Crowthorne
Aran Hall School, Dolgellau
Ballikinrain Residential School, Stirlingshire
Barnardo's Lecropt, Camelon
Barton School, Barton-Upon-Humber
Baston House School, Bromley
Belgrave School, Clifton
Birtenshaw School, Bolton
Bladon House School, Burton upon Trent
Blossom House School, London
Brantridge School, Haywards Heath
Breckenbrough School, Thirsk
Brewood Secondary School, Deal
Bridge College, Stockport
Bridgend College, Bridgend
Camphill Blair Drummond Trust, Stirling
Camphill School Aberdeen, Aberdeen
Cedar House School, Bentham
Centre Academy, London
Centre Academy East Anglia
Chartwell House School, Wisbech
Chelfham Mill School, Barnstaple
Chelfham Senior School, Yelverton

Chilworth House School, Wheatley
Chilworth House Upper School, Wheatley
Clarence High School, Formby
Communication Specialist College, Doncaster
Cornerstones, Warrington
Cotswold Chine School, Near Stroud
Cotswold Community, Swindon
Coxlease School, Lyndhurst
Crookhey Hall School, Lancaster
Cruckton Hall, Shrewsbury
Delamere Forest School, Warrington
Derwen College, Oswestry
Dilston College of Further Education, Corbridge
Donaldson's College for the Deaf, Edinburgh
Doucecroft School, Colchester
Eagle House – Norfolk School, Norwich
Eagle House School Mitcham, Mitcham
Eagle Life College, Banham
East Park School, Glasgow
Eden Grove School, Appleby
Ellesmere College, Thatcham
Exeter College, Exeter
Exeter Royal Academy for Deaf Education, Exeter
Fairfield Farm College, Westbury
Falkland House School, Cupar
Farleigh College Mells
Farleigh Further Education College Condover, Shrewsbury
Farney Close School, Haywards Heath

The New School, Dunkeld
The New School at West Heath, Sevenoaks
The Priory Lodge School, Roehampton
The Quest School for Autistic Children, West Malling
The Royal Blind School, Edinburgh, Edinburgh
The Royal National College for the Blind (RNC), Hereford
The Royal School for Deaf Children Margate, Margate
The Ryes College & Community, Sudbury
The Speech, Language & Hearing Centre, London
The St John Vianney School, Stockport
The Wing Centre, Bournemouth
Thornbeck College, Sunderland
Thornhill Park School, Sunderland
Tree House, London
Trinity School, Rochester

Underley Garden School, Carnforth
Underley Hall School, Carnforth
Unsted Park School, Godalming
Walton Progressive School, Liverpool
Wargrave House School, Newton-le-Willows
West Kirby Residential School, Wirral
Westgate College for Deaf People, Westgate
Westmorland School, Chorley
Westwood School, Broadstairs
Whinfell Care, Kendal
Whitstone Head School, Holsworthy
William Morris House Camphill Community, Stonehouse
Wilsic Hall School, Doncaster
Wings School, Milnthorpe
Witherslack Hall, Grange-over-Sands
Woodcroft School, Loughton
Young Options College, Shifnal
Ysgol Bryn Castell, Bridgend

# ATTENTION DEFICIT DISORDER

AALPS Cymru, Holywell
AALPS Midlands, Hanley Castle
AALPS North, Roxby
Abingdon House School, London
Action for Children Headlands School, Penarth
Alderwasley Hall School and Callow Park College, Belper
Appleford School, Salisbury
Appletree School, Kendal
Aran Hall School, Dolgellau
Ballikinrain Residential School, Stirlingshire
Barnardo's Lecropt, Camelon
Barton School, Barton-Upon-Humber
Belgrave School, Clifton
Birtenshaw School, Bolton
Bladon House School, Burton upon Trent
Brantridge School, Haywards Heath
Breckenbrough School, Thirsk
Brewood Secondary School, Deal
Bridge College, Stockport
Bridgend College, Bridgend
Bryn Melyn Group, Bala
Camphill School Aberdeen, Aberdeen
Cedar House School, Bentham
Centre Academy, London
Centre Academy East Anglia
Chaigeley School, Warrington
Chartwell House School, Wisbech
Chelfham Mill School, Barnstaple
Chelfham Senior School, Yelverton
Chilworth House School, Wheatley
Chilworth House Upper School, Wheatley
Clarence High School, Formby
Coleg Elidyr, Llandovery
Cotswold Chine School, Near Stroud
Cotswold Community, Swindon
Coxlease School, Lyndhurst
Crookhey Hall School, Lancaster

Cruckton Hall, Shrewsbury
Delamere Forest School, Warrington
Denby Grange School, Wakefield
Eagle House – Norfolk School, Norwich
Eagle House School Mitcham, Mitcham
Eagle Life College, Banham
Eastwood Grange School, Nr Chesterfield
Exeter College, Exeter
Farleigh Further Education College Condover, Shrewsbury
Farleigh College Mells
Farney Close School, Haywards Heath
Fortune Centre of Riding Therapy, Christchurch
Frederick Hugh House, London
Grafham Grange School, Guildford
Great Oaks Small School, Minster
Halton School, Runcorn
Harmeny School, Balerno
Higford School, Shifnal
High Close School (Barnardo's), Wokingham
Hillcrest Park School, Chipping Norton
Hillcrest Pentwyn School, Hereford
Hillcrest Slinfold, Nr Horsham
Hillside School, Aberdour
Jacques Hall, Manningtree
Kestrel House School, London
Kibble Centre, Paisley
Kings Manor Community College, Shoreham-by-Sea
Kinsale School, Holywell
Lakeside School, Liverpool
Learning Opportunities Centre Primary, Canterbury
Lindeth College of Further Education, Bowness-on-Windermere
Linkage College, Grimsby
Linkage College, Spilsby
Little Acorns School, Tenterden

# ATTENTION DEFICIT HYPERACTIVITY DISORDER

The Sheiling School Ringwood, Ringwood
The Speech, Language & Hearing Centre,
    London
The St John Vianney School, Stockport
The Unicorn School, Abingdon
Underley Garden School, Carnforth
Underley Hall School, Carnforth
Walton Progressive School, Liverpool
Waterloo Lodge School, Chorley
West Kirby Residential School, Wirral
Westmorland School, Chorley
Westwood School, Broadstairs

Whinfell Care, Kendal
Whitstone Head School, Holsworthy
William Henry Smith School, Brighouse
Wings East School, Newark
Wings School, Milnthorpe
Witherslack Hall, Grange-over-Sands
Woodcroft School, Loughton
Woodlands School, Wigtownshire
Young Options College, Shifnal
Young Options Pathway College Stoke,
    Stoke-on-Trent
Ysgol Bryn Castell, Bridgend

# AUTISTIC SPECTRUM DISORDER

AALPS Cymru, Holywell
AALPS Midlands, Hanley Castle
AALPS North, Roxby
Abingdon House School, London
Action for Children Headlands School, Penarth
Action for Children Parklands Campus, Abingdon
Alderwasley Hall School and Callow Park College,
    Belper
Annie Lawson School, Crowthorne
Aran Hall School, Dolgellau
Ballikinrain Residential School, Stirlingshire
Barnardo's Lecropt, Camelon
Barton School, Barton-Upon-Humber
Baston House School, Bromley
Belgrave School, Clifton
Birtenshaw School, Bolton
Bladon House School, Burton upon Trent
Blossom House School, London
Brantridge School, Haywards Heath
Breckenbrough School, Thirsk
Bridge College, Stockport
Broughton House, Brant Broughton
Burton Hill School, Malmesbury
Camphill Blair Drummond Trust, Stirling
Camphill School Aberdeen, Aberdeen
Cedar House School, Bentham
Centre Academy, London
Centre Academy East Anglia
Chailey Heritage Foundation, Nr Lewes
Chelfham Mill School, Barnstaple
Chelfham Senior School, Yelverton
Chilworth House School, Wheatley
Chilworth House Upper School, Wheatley
Cintre Community
Coleg Elidyr, Llandovery
Communication Specialist College Doncaster,
    Doncaster
Cornerstones, Warrington
Cotswold Chine School, Near Stroud
Coxlease School, Lyndhurst
Crookhey Hall School, Lancaster
Cruckton Hall, Shrewsbury
Delamere Forest School, Warrington
Dilston College of Further Education, Corbridge
Donaldson's College for the Deaf, Edinburgh

Doucecroft School, Colchester
Eagle House – Norfolk School, Norwich
Eagle House School Mitcham, Mitcham
Eagle Life College, Banham
East Park School, Glasgow
Eden Grove School, Appleby
Ellesmere College, Thatcham
Enham, Andover
Exeter College, Exeter
Exeter Royal Academy for Deaf Education, Exeter
Exeter Royal Academy for Deaf Education,
    Exeter
Fairfield Farm College, Westbury
Farleigh College Mells
Farleigh Further Education College Condover,
    Shrewsbury
Frederick Hugh House, London
Fullerton House School, Doncaster
Grafham Grange School, Guildford
Great Oaks Small School, Minster
Heathermount School, Ascot
Hereward College, Coventry
Hesley Village College, Doncaster
Higford School, Shifnal
High Close School (Barnardo's), Wokingham
Hill House School, Lymington
Hillingdon Manor School, Uxbridge
Hinwick Hall College, Wellingborough
Homefield Residential College, Loughborough
Hope House School, Newark
Hope Lodge School, Southampton
Ivers Inclusive Learning Project, Sturminster
    Newton
Jacques Hall, Manningtree
Kestrel House School, London
Kibble Centre, Paisley
Kinsale School, Holywell
Kisharon Day School, London
Kisimul School – Old Vicarage, Swinderby
Kisimul School – Woodstock House, Long Ditton
Lakeside School, Liverpool
Lambs Grange Residential and Day Education
    and Care, Cuddington
Lindeth College of Further Education,
    Bowness-on-Windermere

# BEHAVIOURAL, EMOTIONAL & SOCIAL DISORDERS

# CEREBRAL PALSY

Cedar House School, Bentham
Chailey Heritage Foundation, Nr Lewes
Communication Specialist College, Doncaster
Craig-y-Parc School, Pentyrch
Dame Hannah Rogers School, Ivybridge
Derwen College, Oswestry
Doncaster School for the Deaf, Doncaster
East Park School, Glasgow
Enham, Andover
Exeter College, Exeter
Exeter Royal Academy for Deaf Education, Exeter
Finchale Training College, Durham
Fortune Centre of Riding Therapy, Christchurch
Frederick Hugh House
Henshaws College, Harrogate
Hereward College, Coventry
Hinwick Hall College, Wellingborough
Holly Bank School, Mirfield
Hornsey Conductive Education Centre, London
Ingfield Manor School, Billingshurst
Kisharon Day School, London
Langside School, Poole
Linkage College, Grimsby
Linkage College, Spilsby
Loppington House Further Education & Adult Centre, Wem
MacIntyre School Womaston, Presteigne
Meldreth Manor, Nr Royston
Nash College, Bromley
Nash College of Further Education, Bromley
National Institute of Conductive Education, Birmingham
National Star College, Cheltenham
Oakwood Court, Dawlish
Paces Conductive Education, Sheffield
Pengwern College, Rhuddlan
Pennine Camphill Community, Wakefield
Percy Hedley School, Newcastle-upon-Tyne
Pield Heath School, Uxbridge
Portland College, Mansfield
Queen Alexandra College, Birmingham
RNIB College Loughborough, Loughborough
RNIB Manor House, Torquay

RNIB Pears Centre for Specialist Learning
RNIB Sunshine House School, Northwood
Rosewood School, Southampton
Royal School Manchester, Cheadle
Royal West of England School for the Deaf, Exeter
Rutherford School, South Croydon
Rutland House School, Nottingham
seeABILITY (formerly Royal School for the Blind), Epsom
Sheiling School, Camphill Community Thornbury, Thornbury
St Christopher's School, Westbury Park
St Elizabeth's School, Much Hadham
St John's Catholic School for the Deaf, Boston Spa
St Mary's Wrestwood Children's Trust, Bexhill-on-Sea
St Rose's School, Stroud
St Vincent's School, A Specialist School for Sensory Impairment and Other Needs, Liverpool
Stanmore House Residential School, Lanark
The David Lewis School, Nr Alderley Edge
The Grange Centre for People with Disabilities, Bookham
The London Centre for Children with Cerebral Palsy, London
The Royal Blind School, Edinburgh, Edinburgh
The Royal National College for the Blind (RNC), Hereford
The Royal School for Deaf Children Margate, Margate
The Ryes College & Community, Sudbury
The School for Profound Education, Tadworth
The Sheiling School Ringwood, Ringwood
The St John Vianney School, Stockport
The Trust Centre, Belper
Treloar College, Alton
Treloar School and College, Alton
Victoria Education Centre, Poole
Vranch House School, Exeter
Young Options College, Shifnal

# CHALLENGING BEHAVIOUR

AALPS Cymru, Holywell
AALPS Midlands, Hanley Castle
AALPS North, Roxby
Action for Children Headlands School, Penarth
Aidenswood, Stoke
Alderwasley Hall School and Callow Park College, Belper
Annie Lawson School, Crowthorne
Applegate, Colne
Appletree School, Kendal
Aran Hall School, Dolgellau
Ballikinrain Residential School, Stirlingshire
Barnardo's Lecropt, Camelon
Barton School, Barton-Upon-Humber

Birtenshaw School, Bolton
Bladon House School, Burton upon Trent
Brantridge School, Haywards Heath
Bridge College, Stockport
Broughton House, Brant Broughton
Camphill Blair Drummond Trust, Stirling
Cedar House School, Bentham
Chartwell House School, Wisbech
Chelfham Mill School, Barnstaple
Chelfham Senior School, Yelverton
Chilworth House School, Wheatley
Chilworth House Upper School, Wheatley
Clarence High School, Formby
Cornerstones, Warrington

Whinfell Care, Kendal
William Henry Smith School, Brighouse
Wilsic Hall School, Doncaster
Witherslack Hall, Grange-over-Sands

Woodcroft School, Loughton
Young Options College, Shifnal
Young Options Pathway College Stoke,
    Stoke-on-Trent

# DOWN'S SYNDROME

Aran Hall School, Dolgellau
Birtenshaw School, Bolton
Bladon House School, Burton upon Trent
Bridge College, Stockport
Bridgend College, Bridgend
Camphill Blair Drummond Trust, Stirling
Camphill School Aberdeen, Aberdeen
Cintre Community
Coleg Elidyr, Llandovery
Delamere Forest School, Warrington
Derwen College, Oswestry
Dilston College of Further Education,
    Corbridge
Easter Auguston Training Farm, Aberdeen
Exeter College, Exeter
Fairfield Farm College, Westbury
Fortune Centre of Riding Therapy, Christchurch
Frederick Hugh House
Henshaws College, Harrogate
Hereward College, Coventry
Hinwick Hall College, Wellingborough
Ivers Inclusive Learning Project, Sturminster
    Newton
Kisharon Day School, London
Kisimul School – Old Vicarage, Swinderby
Kisimul School – Woodstock House,
    Long Ditton
Lakeside School, Liverpool
Lindeth College of Further Education,
    Bowness-on-Windermere
Linkage College, Grimsby
Linkage College, Spilsby
Loddon School, Hook
Loppington House Further Education & Adult
    Centre, Wem
MacIntyre School Womaston, Presteigne
Nash College of Further Education, Bromley
Oakwood Court, Dawlish

Overley Hall School, Wellington
Parayhouse School, London
Pegasus School, Caldwell
Pengwern College, Rhuddlan
Pennine Camphill Community, Wakefield
Philip Green Memorial School, Wimborne
Pield Heath School, Uxbridge
Queen Alexandra College, Birmingham
RNIB College Loughborough, Loughborough
RNIB Pears Centre for Specialist Learning
Royal School Manchester, Cheadle
Sheiling School, Camphill Community Thornbury,
    Thornbury
Southern England Psychological Services,
    Eastleigh
Spring Hill School (Barnardo's), Ripon
St Elizabeth's School, Much Hadham
St John's School & College, Seaford
St Joseph's Specialist School & College,
    Cranleigh
St Piers School, Young Epilepsy, Lingfield
St Rose's School, Stroud
Strathmore College, Staffordshire
Sunfield School, Stourbridge
The Grange Centre for People with Disabilities,
    Bookham
The Link Primary School, Croydon
The Mount Camphill Community, Wadhurst
The Royal Blind School, Edinburgh,
    Edinburgh
The Royal School for Deaf Children Margate,
    Margate
The Sheiling School Ringwood, Ringwood
The St John Vianney School, Stockport
Underley Garden School, Carnforth
William Morris House Camphill Community,
    Stonehouse
Ysgol Bryn Castell, Bridgend

# DYSCALCULIA

Abingdon House School, London
Alderwasley Hall School and Callow Park College,
    Belper
Appleford School, Salisbury
Aran Hall School, Dolgellau
Ballikinrain Residential School, Stirlingshire
Barnardo's Lecropt, Camelon
Belgrave School, Clifton
Bladon House School, Burton upon Trent
Brewood Secondary School, Deal

Calder House School, Chippenham
Cedar House School, Bentham
Centre Academy East Anglia
Chartwell House School, Wisbech
East Court School, Ramsgate
Edington and Shapwick School, Shapwick
Exeter College, Exeter
Fairley House School, London
Farleigh College Mells
Finchale Training College, Durham

Frederick Hugh House
Frewen College, Rye
Grateley House School, Andover
Halton School, Runcorn
Harmeny School, Balerno
Hereward College, Coventry
High Close School (Barnardo's), Wokingham
Hillcrest Pentwyn School, Hereford
Knowl Hill School, Pirbright
Lakeside School, Liverpool
Mark College, Highbridge
Moon Hall School, Dorking
Moor House School, Oxted
More House School, Farnham
Northease Manor, Lewes
Oliver House, Chorley
Pennine Camphill Community, Wakefield
Philpots Manor School, East Grinstead
Portland College, Mansfield
Red Rose School, Lytham St Annes

Ripplevale School, Deal
Southern England Psychological Services,
   Eastleigh
Southlands School, Lymington
St Catherine's School, Ventnor
St Dominic's School, Godalming
Stanbridge Earls School, Romsey
Swalcliffe Park School Trust, Banbury
The Chelsea Group of Children, London
The Marchant-Holliday School, Templecombe
The Moat School, London
The New School, Dunkeld
The Royal National College for the Blind (RNC),
   Hereford
The Unicorn School, Abingdon
The Wing Centre, Bournemouth
Trinity School, Rochester
Underley Garden School, Carnforth
Westgate College for Deaf People,
   Westgate

# DYSLEXIA

Abingdon House School, London
Action for Children Headlands School, Penarth
Alderwasley Hall School and Callow Park College,
   Belper
Appleford School, Salisbury
Appletree School, Kendal
Ballikinrain Residential School, Stirlingshire
Barnardo's Lecropt, Camelon
Belgrave School, Clifton
Blossom House School, London
Brewood Secondary School, Deal
Bridgend College, Bridgend
Brown's School, Chelsfield
Caldecott Community, Ashford
Calder House School, Chippenham
Camphill School Aberdeen, Aberdeen
Cedar House School, Bentham
Centre Academy, London
Centre Academy East Anglia
Chartwell House School, Wisbech
Chelfham Mill School, Barnstaple
Chilworth House School, Wheatley
Cintre Community
Clarence High School, Formby
Communication Specialist College, Doncaster
Cotswold Community, Swindon
Crookhey Hall School, Lancaster
Cruckton Hall, Shrewsbury
Delamere Forest School, Warrington
Derwen College, Oswestry
Doncaster School for the Deaf, Doncaster
East Court School, Ramsgate
Edington and Shapwick School, Shapwick
Enham, Andover
Exeter College, Exeter
Exeter Royal Academy for Deaf Education, Exeter
Fairley House School, London

Farleigh College Mells
Finchale Training College, Durham
Frederick Hugh House
Frewen College, Rye
Grafham Grange School, Guildford
Grateley House School, Andover
Halton School, Runcorn
Harmeny School, Balerno
Hereward College, Coventry
High Close School (Barnardo's), Wokingham
Hillcrest Pentwyn School, Hereford
Hillside School, Aberdour
Kibble Centre, Paisley
Kings Manor Community College,
   Shoreham-by-Sea
Knowl Hill School, Pirbright
Lakeside School, Liverpool
Learning Opportunities Centre Primary,
   Canterbury
Lindeth College of Further Education,
   Bowness-on-Windermere
Linkage College, Grimsby
Linkage College, Spilsby
Little Acorns School, Tenterden
Little David's School, Croydon
Maple Hayes School, Lichfield
Mark College, Highbridge
Merryhay Academy, Ilminster
Moon Hall College and Burys Court, Reigate
Moon Hall School, Dorking
Moor House School, Oxted
More House School, Farnham
MRCS Educational Unit, Croydon
Mulberry Bush School, Witney
Nash College of Further Education, Bromley
New College Worcester, Worcester
Northease Manor, Lewes

Nugent House School, St Helens
Nunnykirk Centre for Dyslexia, Morpeth
Oakwood Court, Dawlish
Oliver House, Chorley
Orchard School, Retford
Owlswick School, Lewes
Parayhouse School, London
Pennine Camphill Community, Wakefield
Philpots Manor School, East Grinstead
Portland College, Mansfield
Queen Alexandra College, Birmingham
Red Rose School, Lytham St Annes
Ripplevale School, Deal
RNIB Manor House, Torquay
RNIB Scotland, Edinburgh
Rossendale School, Ramsbottom
Seafield School, Ardrossan
Sheridan School, Thetford
Snowdon School, Stirling
Southern England Psychological Services,
    Eastleigh
Southlands School, Lymington
Spring Hill School (Barnardo's), Ripon
St Catherine's School, Ventnor
St Dominic's School, Godalming
St Edward's School, Romsey
St Elizabeth's School, Much Hadham
St John's Catholic School for the Deaf, Boston Spa
St Vincent's School, A Specialist School for
    Sensory Impairment and Other Needs,
    Liverpool
Stanbridge Earls School, Romsey
Swalcliffe Park School Trust, Banbury

The Chelsea Group of Children, London
The Link Primary School, Croydon
The Lioncare School, Hove
The Marchant-Holliday School, Templecombe
The Moat School, London
The New School, Dunkeld
The Royal Blind School, Edinburgh, Edinburgh
The Royal National College for the Blind (RNC),
    Hereford
The Royal School for Deaf Children Margate,
    Margate
The Royal Wolverhampton School, Wolverhampton
The Ryes College & Community, Sudbury
The Unicorn School, Abingdon
The Wing Centre, Bournemouth
Treloar College, Alton
Treloar School and College, Alton
Trinity School, Rochester
Underley Garden School, Carnforth
Underley Hall School, Carnforth
Victoria Education Centre, Poole
Waterloo Lodge School, Chorley
West Kirby Residential School, Wirral
Westgate College for Deaf People, Westgate
Westmorland School, Chorley
Whinfell Care, Kendal
Whitstone Head School, Holsworthy
William Henry Smith School, Brighouse
Wings East School, Newark
Wings School, Milnthorpe
Witherslack Hall, Grange-over-Sands
Woodcroft School, Loughton
Ysgol Bryn Castell, Bridgend

# DYSPRAXIA

Abingdon House School, London
Action for Children Headlands School, Penarth
Alderwasley Hall School and Callow Park College,
    Belper
Appleford School, Salisbury
Appletree School, Kendal
Aran Hall School, Dolgellau
Ballikinrain Residential School, Stirlingshire
Barnardo's Lecropt, Camelon
Belgrave School, Clifton
Bladon House School, Burton upon Trent
Blossom House School, London
Brewood Secondary School, Deal
Bridgend College, Bridgend
Brown's School, Chelsfield
Bryn Melyn Group, Bala
Calder House School, Chippenham
Camphill School Aberdeen, Aberdeen
Cedar House School, Bentham
Centre Academy, London
Centre Academy East Anglia
Chartwell House School, Wisbech
Communication Specialist College, Doncaster
Cotswold Chine School, Near Stroud

Cruckton Hall, Shrewsbury
Delamere Forest School, Warrington
Eagle House School Mitcham, Mitcham
Eagle Life College, Banham
East Court School, Ramsgate
Edington and Shapwick School, Shapwick
Enham, Andover
Exeter College, Exeter
Fairfield Farm College, Westbury
Fairley House School, London
Farleigh College Mells
Finchale Training College, Durham
Fortune Centre of Riding Therapy, Christchurch
Frederick Hugh House
Frewen College, Rye
Grateley House School, Andover
Halton School, Runcorn
Henshaws College, Harrogate
Hereward College, Coventry
High Close School (Barnardo's), Wokingham
Hillcrest Pentwyn School, Hereford
Home School of Stoke Newington, London
Kestrel House School, London
Kibble Centre, Paisley

# EPILEPSY

# HEALTH PROBLEMS

AALPS Cymru, Holywell
AALPS Midlands, Hanley Castle
AALPS North, Roxby
Alderwasley Hall School and Callow Park College, Belper
Annie Lawson School, Crowthorne
Aran Hall School, Dolgellau
Barton School, Barton-Upon-Humber
Birtenshaw School, Bolton
Bladon House School, Burton upon Trent
Bridge College, Stockport
Burton Hill School, Malmesbury
Calder House School, Chippenham
Camphill Blair Drummond Trust, Stirling
Camphill School Aberdeen, Aberdeen
Cedar House School, Bentham
Chailey Heritage Foundation, Nr Lewes
Dame Hannah Rogers School, Ivybridge
Delamere Forest School, Warrington
East Park School, Glasgow
Ellesmere College, Thatcham
Fairley House School, London
Finchale Training College, Durham
Hereward College, Coventry
Higford School, Shifnal
High Close School (Barnardo's), Wokingham
Hill House School, Lymington
Kings Manor Community College, Shoreham-by-Sea
Kinsale School, Holywell
Lakeside School, Liverpool
Langside School, Poole
Linkage College, Grimsby
Linkage College, Spilsby
MRCS Educational Unit, Croydon
Nash College of Further Education, Bromley
National Institute of Conductive Education, Birmingham
National Star College, Cheltenham
New College Worcester, Worcester
Paces Conductive Education, Sheffield
Parayhouse School, London
Pegasus School, Caldwell
Pengwern College, Rhuddlan
Pennine Camphill Community, Wakefield
Philip Green Memorial School, Wimborne
Pield Heath School, Uxbridge
Pontville School, Ormskirk
Purbeck View School, Swanage
Queen Alexandra College, Birmingham
Ripplevale School, Deal
RNIB College Loughborough, Loughborough
RNIB Pears Centre for Specialist Learning
RNIB Sunshine House School, Northwood
Rosewood School, Southampton
Royal School Manchester, Cheadle
Rutherford School, South Croydon
Sheiling School, Camphill Community Thornbury, Thornbury
Southlands School, Lymington
Spring Hill School (Barnardo's), Ripon
St Catherine's School, Ventnor
St Dominic's School, Godalming
St Elizabeth's School, Much Hadham
St Joseph's Specialist School & College, Cranleigh
St Rose's School, Stroud
Sunfield School, Stourbridge
The Forum School, Shillingstone
The Lioncare School, Hove
The New School, Dunkeld
The New School at West Heath, Sevenoaks
The Royal Blind School, Edinburgh, Edinburgh
The Royal National College for the Blind (RNC), Hereford
The Royal School for Deaf Children Margate, Margate
The Ryes College & Community, Sudbury
The School for Profound Education, Tadworth
The Sheiling School Ringwood, Ringwood
The Trust Centre, Belper
The Wing Centre, Bournemouth
Treloar College, Alton
Treloar School and College, Alton
Underley Garden School, Carnforth
Victoria Education Centre, Poole
Westgate College for Deaf People, Westgate
Whitstone Head School, Holsworthy
Woodcroft School, Loughton
Young Options College, Shifnal
Young Options Pathway College Stoke, Stoke-on-Trent

# HEARING IMPAIRMENT

AALPS Midlands, Hanley Castle
AALPS North, Roxby
Action for Children Penhurst School, Chipping Norton
Alderwasley Hall School and Callow Park College, Belper
Annie Lawson School, Crowthorne
Aran Hall School, Dolgellau
Birtenshaw School, Bolton
Bladon House School, Burton upon Trent
Brewood Secondary School, Deal
Bridge College, Stockport
Bridgend College, Bridgend
Burton Hill School, Malmesbury
Camphill Blair Drummond Trust, Stirling
Camphill School Aberdeen, Aberdeen
Chailey Heritage Foundation, Nr Lewes
Communication Specialist College, Doncaster
Cotswold Community, Swindon
Cruckton Hall, Shrewsbury

## IMPAIRED MOBILITY

Pengwern College, Rhuddlan
Percy Hedley School, Newcastle-upon-Tyne
Queen Alexandra College, Birmingham
RNIB College Loughborough, Loughborough
RNIB Pears Centre for Specialist Learning
RNIB Sunshine House School, Northwood
Rosewood School, Southampton
Royal School Manchester, Cheadle
Rutherford School, South Croydon
Rutland House School, Nottingham
St Elizabeth's School, Much Hadham
St John's Catholic School for the Deaf, Boston Spa
St Joseph's Specialist School & College, Cranleigh
St Rose's School, Stroud

The London Centre for Children with Cerebral Palsy, London
The Marchant-Holliday School, Templecombe
The Royal Blind School, Edinburgh, Edinburgh
The Royal National College for the Blind (RNC), Hereford
The Royal School for Deaf Children Margate, Margate
The School for Profound Education, Tadworth
The Sheiling School Ringwood, Ringwood
The Trust Centre, Belper
Treloar College, Alton
Treloar School and College, Alton
Walton Progressive School, Liverpool
Westgate College for Deaf People, Westgate

# MODERATE LEARNING DIFFICULTIES

AALPS Cymru, Holywell
AALPS Midlands, Hanley Castle
AALPS North, Roxby
Action for Children Headlands School, Penarth
Appleford School, Salisbury
Appletree School, Kendal
Aran Hall School, Dolgellau
Ballikinrain Residential School, Stirlingshire
Barton School, Barton-Upon-Humber
Beaumont College of Further Education, Lancaster
Bladon House School, Burton upon Trent
Bramfield House, Halesworth
Brantridge School, Haywards Heath
Brewood Secondary School, Deal
Bridge College, Stockport
Bridgend College, Bridgend
Broughton House, Brant Broughton
Bryn Melyn Group, Bala
Burton Hill School, Malmesbury
Caldecott Community, Ashford
Camphill Blair Drummond Trust, Stirling
Camphill School Aberdeen, Aberdeen
Cedar House School, Bentham
Centre Academy, London
Centre Academy East Anglia
Chailey Heritage Foundation, Nr Lewes
Chartwell House School, Wisbech
Chelfham Mill School, Barnstaple
Chelfham Senior School, Yelverton
Chilworth House School, Wheatley
Cintre Community
Coleg Elidyr, Llandovery
Communication Specialist College, Doncaster
Coombe House, Crediton
Cotswold Chine School, Near Stroud
Cotswold Community, Swindon
Coxlease School, Lyndhurst
Crookhey Hall School, Lancaster
Cruckton Hall, Shrewsbury
Dame Hannah Rogers School, Ivybridge
Delamere Forest School, Warrington

Denby Grange School, Wakefield
Derwen College, Oswestry
Didsbury School, Manchester
Dilston College of Further Education, Corbridge
Doncaster School for the Deaf, Doncaster
Dorton College of Further Education, Sevenoaks
Eagle House – Norfolk School, Norwich
Eagle House School Mitcham, Mitcham
Eagle Life College, Banham
Easter Auguston Training Farm, Aberdeen
Eden Grove School, Appleby
Ellesmere College, Thatcham
Enham, Andover
Exeter College, Exeter
Exeter Royal Academy for Deaf Education, Exeter
Fairfield Farm College, Westbury
Farleigh Further Education College Condover, Shrewsbury
Farney Close School, Haywards Heath
Finchale Training College, Durham
Fortune Centre of Riding Therapy, Christchurch
Frederick Hugh House
Geilsland School, Beith
Good Shepherd Centre, Bishopton
Grafham Grange School, Guildford
Grateley House School, Andover
Halton School, Runcorn
Harmeny School, Balerno
Henshaws College, Harrogate
Hereward College, Coventry
Higford School, Shifnal
High Close School (Barnardo's), Wokingham
Hill House School, Lymington
Hillcrest Park School, Chipping Norton
Hillside School, Aberdour
Hinwick Hall College, Wellingborough
Holly Bank School, Mirfield
Homefield Residential College, Loughborough
Hopewell School, Dagenham
Ivers Inclusive Learning Project, Sturminster Newton
Jacques Hall, Manningtree

# PROFOUND & MULTIPLE LEARNING DIFFICULTIES

AALPS Cymru, Holywell
AALPS Midlands, Hanley Castle
AALPS North, Roxby
Action for Children Penhurst School, Chipping
   Norton
Annie Lawson School, Crowthorne
Aran Hall School, Dolgellau
Barrs Court School, Hereford
Barton School, Barton-Upon-Humber
Birtenshaw School, Bolton
Bladon House School, Burton upon Trent
Bridge College, Stockport
Burton Hill School, Malmesbury
Camphill Blair Drummond Trust, Stirling
Camphill School Aberdeen, Aberdeen
Chailey Heritage Foundation, Nr Lewes
Craig-y-Parc School, Pentyrch
Crookhey Hall School, Lancaster
Dame Hannah Rogers School, Ivybridge
Doncaster School for the Deaf, Doncaster
East Park School, Glasgow
Higford School, Shifnal
Hinwick Hall College, Wellingborough
Holly Bank School, Mirfield
Kinsale School, Holywell
Lambs Grange Residential and Day Education
   and Care, Cuddington
Langside School, Poole
Linn Moor Residential School, Aberdeen
Little David's School, Croydon
MacIntyre School Wingrave, Aylesbury
MacIntyre School Womaston, Presteigne
Meldreth Manor, Nr Royston
Nash College, Bromley
Nash College of Further Education, Bromley
National Star College, Cheltenham
Northern Counties School,
   Newcastle-Upon-Tyne
Overley Hall School, Wellington
Pegasus School, Caldwell
Pengwern College, Rhuddlan
Pield Heath School, Uxbridge
RNIB Pears Centre for Specialist Learning
RNIB Sunshine House School, Northwood
Rosewood School, Southampton
Royal School for the Blind, Liverpool
Royal School Manchester, Cheadle
Rutherford School, South Croydon
Rutland House School, Nottingham
seeABILITY (formerly Royal School for the Blind),
   Epsom
Sense East, Peterborough
St Christopher's School, Westbury Park
St Elizabeth's School, Much Hadham
St Piers School, Young Epilepsy, Lingfield
St Rose's School, Stroud
Stanmore House Residential School, Lanark
Sunfield School, Stourbridge
The David Lewis School, Nr Alderley Edge
The Lioncare School, Hove
The Royal Blind School, Edinburgh, Edinburgh
The Royal School for Deaf Children Margate,
   Margate
The Ryes College & Community, Sudbury
The School for Profound Education, Tadworth
Treloar College, Alton
Treloar School and College, Alton
Vranch House School, Exeter
Walton Progressive School, Liverpool
Westgate College for Deaf People, Westgate

# SEVERE LEARNING DIFFICULTIES

AALPS Cymru, Holywell
AALPS Midlands, Hanley Castle
AALPS North, Roxby
Action for Children Penhurst School, Chipping
   Norton
Aim Habonim
Annie Lawson School, Crowthorne
Aran Hall School, Dolgellau
Barrs Court School, Hereford
Barton School, Barton-Upon-Humber
Beaumont College of Further Education,
   Lancaster
Birtenshaw School, Bolton
Bladon House School, Burton upon Trent
Bridge College, Stockport
Broughton House, Brant Broughton
Burton Hill School, Malmesbury
Camphill Blair Drummond Trust, Stirling
Camphill School Aberdeen, Aberdeen
Chailey Heritage Foundation, Nr Lewes
Coleg Elidyr, Llandovery
Communication Specialist College Doncaster,
   Doncaster
Cornerstones, Warrington
Cotswold Chine School, Near Stroud
Crookhey Hall School, Lancaster
Dame Hannah Rogers School, Ivybridge
Derwen College, Oswestry
Dilston College of Further Education, Corbridge
Doncaster School for the Deaf, Doncaster
Eagle House – Norfolk School, Norwich
Eagle House School Mitcham, Mitcham
Eagle Life College, Banham
East Park School, Glasgow
Ellesmere College, Thatcham
Exeter College, Exeter
Exeter Royal Academy for Deaf Education,
   Exeter

# SPEECH & LANGUAGE DIFFICULTIES

St Dominic's School, Godalming
St Edward's School, Romsey
St Elizabeth's School, Much Hadham
St John's Catholic School for the Deaf, Boston Spa
St John's RC School, Woodford Bridge
St Joseph's Specialist School & College, Cranleigh
St Piers School, Young Epilepsy, Lingfield
St Rose's School, Stroud
St Vincent's School, A Specialist School for Sensory Impairment and Other Needs, Liverpool
Stanbridge Earls School, Romsey
Strathmore College, Staffordshire
Sunfield School, Stourbridge
Swalcliffe Park School Trust, Banbury
Tadley Horizon, Basingstoke
The Chelsea Group of Children, London
The David Lewis School, Nr Alderley Edge
The Forum School, Shillingstone
The Grange Centre for People with Disabilities, Bookham
The Link Primary School, Croydon
The Link Secondary School, Beddington
The Lioncare School, Hove
The Marchant-Holliday School, Templecombe
The New School at West Heath, Sevenoaks
The Royal Blind School, Edinburgh, Edinburgh

The Royal National College for the Blind (RNC), Hereford
The Royal School for Deaf Children Margate, Margate
The Ryes College & Community, Sudbury
The Sheiling School Ringwood, Ringwood
The Speech, Language & Hearing Centre, London
The St John Vianney School, Stockport
The Trust Centre, Belper
The Unicorn School, Abingdon
The Wing Centre, Bournemouth
Tregynon Hall School, Newtown
Treloar College, Alton
Treloar School and College, Alton
Trinity School, Rochester
Underley Garden School, Carnforth
Underley Hall School, Carnforth
Victoria Education Centre, Poole
Vranch House School, Exeter
Walton Progressive School, Liverpool
Waterloo Lodge School, Chorley
West Kirby Residential School, Wirral
Westgate College for Deaf People, Westgate
Westmorland School, Chorley
Whinfell Care, Kendal
Wilsic Hall School, Doncaster
Witherslack Hall, Grange-over-Sands
Woodcroft School, Loughton
Woodlands School, Wigtownshire
Ysgol Bryn Castell, Bridgend

# TOURETTE'S SYNDROME

AALPS Midlands, Hanley Castle
AALPS North, Roxby
Action for Children Headlands School, Penarth
Aran Hall School, Dolgellau
Barnardo's Lecropt, Camelon
Bladon House School, Burton upon Trent
Breckenbrough School, Thirsk
Brewood Secondary School, Deal
Camphill School Aberdeen, Aberdeen
Cedar House School, Bentham
Chartwell House School, Wisbech
Chelfham Mill School, Barnstaple
Chelfham Senior School, Yelverton
Clarence High School, Formby
Cotswold Chine School, Near Stroud
Coxlease School, Lyndhurst
Delamere Forest School, Warrington
Eden Grove School, Appleby
Exeter College, Exeter
Falkland House School, Cupar
Frederick Hugh House
Grateley House School, Andover
Hereward College, Coventry
Jacques Hall, Manningtree
Kibble Centre, Paisley
Lakeside School, Liverpool

Linkage College, Grimsby
Linkage College, Spilsby
Little Acorns School, Tenterden
MRCS Educational Unit, Croydon
NAS Radlett Lodge School, Radlett
Nugent House School, St Helens
Oakwood Court, Dawlish
Parayhouse School, London
Pegasus School, Caldwell
Pengwern College, Rhuddlan
Philpots Manor School, East Grinstead
Red Rose School, Lytham St Annes
Ripplevale School, Deal
RNIB College Loughborough, Loughborough
Rossendale School, Ramsbottom
Southlands School, Lymington
Spring Hill School (Barnardo's), Ripon
St Elizabeth's School, Much Hadham
St John's School & College, Seaford
St Mary's Wrestwood Children's Trust, Bexhill-on-Sea
St Piers School, Young Epilepsy, Lingfield
Sunfield School, Stourbridge
Swalcliffe Park School Trust, Banbury
Talbot House Special School, Newcastle Upon Tyne
The Marchant-Holliday School, Templecombe

The New School, Dunkeld
The New School at West Heath, Sevenoaks
The Royal National College for the Blind (RNC), Hereford
The Royal School for Deaf Children Margate, Margate
The Ryes College & Community, Sudbury

Underley Garden School, Carnforth
West Kirby Residential School, Wirral
Westgate College for Deaf People, Westgate
Whinfell Care, Kendal
Whitstone Head School, Holsworthy
Woodcroft School, Loughton
Ysgol Bryn Castell, Bridgend

# VISUAL IMPAIRMENT

AALPS Midlands, Hanley Castle
AALPS North, Roxby
Action for Children Penhurst School, Chipping Norton
Alderwasley Hall School and Callow Park College, Belper
Annie Lawson School, Crowthorne
Birtenshaw School, Bolton
Brewood Secondary School, Deal
Bridge College, Stockport
Bridgend College, Bridgend
Burton Hill School, Malmesbury
Camphill School Aberdeen, Aberdeen
Chailey Heritage Foundation, Nr Lewes
Communication Specialist College, Doncaster
Dame Hannah Rogers School, Ivybridge
Derwen College, Oswestry
Dorton College of Further Education, Sevenoaks
Dorton House School, Sevenoaks
East Park School, Glasgow
Exeter College, Exeter
Exeter Royal Academy for Deaf Education, Exeter
Exeter Royal Academy for Deaf Education, Exeter
Finchale Training College, Durham
Fortune Centre of Riding Therapy, Christchurch
Henshaws College, Harrogate
Hereward College, Coventry
Higford School, Shifnal
Holly Bank School, Mirfield
I CAN Centre with Meath School, Ottershaw
Lakeside School, Liverpool
Langside School, Poole
Lindeth College of Further Education, Bowness-on-Windermere
Linkage College, Grimsby
Linkage College, Spilsby
Little Acorns School, Tenterden
Loddon School, Hook
Loppington House Further Education & Adult Centre, Wem
Meldreth Manor, Nr Royston
Nash College, Bromley
Nash College of Further Education, Bromley
National Star College, Cheltenham
New College Worcester, Worcester
Northern Counties School, Newcastle-Upon-Tyne
Paces Conductive Education, Sheffield
Pegasus School, Caldwell
Pengwern College, Rhuddlan

Pennine Camphill Community, Wakefield
Percy Hedley School, Newcastle-upon-Tyne
Pield Heath School, Uxbridge
Queen Alexandra College, Birmingham
Queen Elizabeth's Foundation, Leatherhead
RNIB College Loughborough, Loughborough
RNIB Manor House, Torquay
RNIB Pears Centre for Specialist Learning
RNIB Scotland, Edinburgh
RNIB Sunshine House School, Northwood
RNID Care Services, Bath
Rosewood School, Southampton
Royal School for the Blind, Liverpool
Royal School Manchester, Cheadle
Royal West of England School for the Deaf, Exeter
Rutherford School, South Croydon
Rutland House School, Nottingham
seeABILITY (formerly Royal School for the Blind), Epsom
Sense East, Peterborough
Spring Hill School (Barnardo's), Ripon
St Catherine's School, Ventnor
St John's Catholic School for the Deaf, Boston Spa
St Mary's Wrestwood Children's Trust, Bexhill-on-Sea
St Rose's School, Stroud
St Vincent's School, A Specialist School for Sensory Impairment and Other Needs, Liverpool
The Grange Centre for People with Disabilities, Bookham
The Lioncare School, Hove
The Royal Blind School, Edinburgh, Edinburgh
The Royal National College for the Blind (RNC), Hereford
The Royal School for Deaf Children Margate, Margate
The School for Profound Education, Tadworth
The Trust Centre, Belper
The West of England College for Students with Little or No Sight, Exeter
The West of England School and College for Pupils with Little or no Sight, Exeter
Treloar College, Alton
Treloar School and College, Alton
Underley Garden School, Carnforth
Walton Progressive School, Liverpool
West Kirby Residential School, Wirral
Westgate College for Deaf People, Westgate

# WHEELCHAIR ACCESS

| | | | |
|---|---|---|---|
| AALPS Midlands, Hanley Castle | WA1 | Eastwood Grange School, Nr Chesterfield | W |
| AALPS North, Roxby | WA1 | Eden Grove School, Appleby | W |
| Abingdon House School, London | W | Edington and Shapwick School, Shapwick | WA3 |
| Action for Children Headlands School, | | Ellesmere College, Thatcham | WA2 |
| Penarth | WA3 | Enham, Andover | WA1 |
| Alderwasley Hall School and Callow | | Exeter College, Exeter | W |
| Park College, Belper | WA2 | Exeter Royal Academy for Deaf Education, | |
| Annie Lawson School, Crowthorne | W | Exeter | WA2 |
| Appleford School, Salisbury | WA3 | Exeter Royal Academy for Deaf Education, | |
| Appletree School, Kendal | WA2 | Exeter | WA2 |
| Aran Hall School, Dolgellau | W | Fairley House School, London | WA1 |
| Ballikinrain Residential School, Stirlingshire | WA3 | Farleigh College Mells | WA1 |
| Barnardo's Lecropt, Camelon | WA1 | Farleigh Further Education College | |
| Barrs Court School, Hereford | W | Condover, Shrewsbury | WA1 |
| Barton School, Barton-Upon-Humber | WA1 | Finchale Training College, Durham | WA1 |
| Belgrave School, Clifton | WA3 | Fortune Centre of Riding Therapy, | |
| Belmont School, Salisbury | WA3 | Christchurch | W |
| Birtenshaw School, Bolton | WA2 | Fourways Assessment Unit, Tyldesley | W |
| Bladon House School, Burton upon Trent | WA3 | Frederick Hugh House, London | WA1 |
| Blossom House School, London | WA2 | Frewen College, Rye | W |
| Brantridge School, Haywards Heath | W | Good Shepherd Centre, Bishopton | W |
| Breckenbrough School, Thirsk | WA3 | Grafham Grange School, Guildford | W |
| Brewood Secondary School, Deal | WA2 | Great Oaks Small School, Minster | W |
| Bridgend College, Bridgend | W | Halton School, Runcorn | W |
| Broughton House, Brant Broughton | W | Hamilton Lodge School for Deaf Children, | |
| Burton Hill School, Malmesbury | WA1 | Brighton | WA2 |
| Calder House School, Chippenham | WA3 | Harmeny School, Balerno | WA3 |
| Camphill Blair Drummond Trust, Stirling | W | Heathermount School, Ascot | W |
| Camphill School Aberdeen, Aberdeen | WA2 | Henshaws College, Harrogate | WA1 |
| Cedar House School, Bentham | WA2 | Higford School, Shifnal | W |
| Centre Academy, London | WA1 | High Close School (Barnardo's), Wokingham | WA1 |
| Chaigeley School, Warrington | W | Hillcrest Park School, Chipping Norton | W |
| Chailey Heritage Foundation, Nr Lewes | WA1 | Hillcrest Pentwyn School, Hereford | WA2 |
| Chartwell House School, Wisbech | WA2 | Hillcrest Slinford, Nr Horsham | WA3 |
| Chelfham Mill School, Barnstaple | W | Hillside School, Aberdour | WA3 |
| Chelfham Senior School, Yelverton | W | Hinwick Hall College, Wellingborough | WA1 |
| Clarence High School, Formby | W | Holly Bank School, Mirfield | WA2 |
| Coleg Elidyr, Llandovery | W | Hope Lodge School, Southampton | WA2 |
| Communication Specialist College, Doncaster | WA2 | Hornsey Conductive Education Centre, | |
| Cornerstones, Warrington | WA3 | London | WA1 |
| Cornfield School, Redhill | WA1 | Hythe House Education, Sheerness | WA2 |
| Cotswold Chine School, Near Stroud | WA3 | I CAN Centre with Meath School, Ottershaw | WA1 |
| Cotswold Community, Swindon | WA1 | I CAN's Dawn House School, Mansfield | WA1 |
| Coxlease School, Lyndhurst | W | Ingfield Manor School, Billingshurst | WA2 |
| Craig-y-Parc School, Pentyrch | WA1 | Ivers Inclusive Learning Project, | |
| Crookhey Hall School, Lancaster | WA3 | Sturminster Newton | WA2 |
| Cruckton Hall, Shrewsbury | WA3 | Jacques Hall, Manningtree | W |
| Denby Grange School, Wakefield | WA1 | Kestrel House School, London | WA3 |
| Derwen College, Oswestry | W | Kibble Centre, Paisley | WA2 |
| Donaldson's College for the Deaf, Edinburgh | W | Kinsale School, Holywell | W |
| Doncaster School for the Deaf, Doncaster | WA1 | Kisimul School – Old Vicarage, Swinderby | WA1 |
| Dorton College of Further Education, | | Kisimul School – Woodstock House, | |
| Sevenoaks | WA1 | Long Ditton | WA1 |
| Doucecroft School, Colchester | W | Knowl Hill School, Pirbright | WA1 |
| Eagle House – Norfolk School, Norwich | WA3 | Lakeside School, Liverpool | WA1 |
| Eagle House School Mitcham, Mitcham | WA3 | Lambs Grange Residential and Day | |
| Eagle Life College, Banham | WA2 | Education and Care, Cuddington | W |
| East Court School, Ramsgate | WA3 | Langside School, Poole | WA1 |
| East Park School, Glasgow | WA1 | Lewis Charlton School, Ashby-de-la-Zouch | WA2 |

## PART THREE

# SPECIAL SCHOOLS AND COLLEGES – MAINTAINED

www.schoolsforspecialneeds.co.uk

# 3.1

# Index of Education Authorities

State maintained schools are listed by Local Authority. Since 1996 a number of new unitary authorities have been created in addition to existing two-tier structures. The index below (for England) lists each local authority under the county of which it is deemed a part, and is designed to help you identify the local authorities responsible for schools in your area. Turn to the page number shown against each to find the schools within the authority. Schools in Northern Ireland, Scotland and Wales are listed by Local Authority only.

## ENGLAND

Special Schools and Colleges – Maintained

Special Schools and Colleges – Maintained

# NORTHERN IRELAND

# SCOTLAND

## WALES

## 3.2

# Notes on the Directory

## Maintained schools by Local Authority

Maintained schools are listed by Local Authority. An index of Local Authorities and their corresponding page entries appears on pages 291–296.

Every effort has been made to compile a comprehensive list of schools. Each entry includes the school name, address, and where available, the web address, age range and sex of students accepted.

The types of need for which a school or college makes provision are shown in abbreviated form. A key to the abbreviations used is given below. The principal types of special needs catered for, where known, are shown in bold (in addition to catering for the special needs specified, all schools and colleges recognize their responsibilities under the Disability Discrimination Act 1995 to consider the needs of all disabled children and to make reasonable adjustments to facilitate the admission of such children to the school). Please note that this information is intended as a guide only. For further information and details of auxiliary aids and services contact schools direct.

## Key to abbreviations used in the directory

### Special needs provision

| | | | |
|------|---------------------------------|-------|-------------------------------------|
| ADD  | Attention Deficit Disorder      | EPI   | Epilepsy                            |
| ADHD | Attention Deficit Hyperactivity Disorder | HEA | Health Problems (eg heart defect, asthma) |
| ASD  | Autistic Spectrum Disorder      | HI    | Hearing Impairment                  |
| ASP  | Asperger's Syndrome             | IM    | Impaired Mobility                   |
| BESD | Behavioural, Emotional and Social Disorders | MLD | Moderate Learning Difficulties |
| CB   | Challenging Behaviour           | PMLD  | Profound and Multiple Learning Difficulties |
| CP   | Cerebral Palsy                  | SLD   | Severe Learning Difficulties        |
| DOW  | Down's Syndrome                 | SP&LD | Speech and Language Difficulties    |
| DYC  | Dyscalculia                     |       |                                     |
| DYP  | Dyspraxia                       | TOU   | Tourette's Syndrome                 |
| DYS  | Dyslexia                        | VI    | Visual Impairment                   |

## *Wheelchair access*

W        Wheelchair access (unspecified)
WA1    School is fully wheelchair accessible in all areas
WA2    Main teaching areas are wheelchair accessible
WA3    No permanent access for wheelchairs; temporary ramps available

## *Symbol*

+        Registered with CReSTeD (see Part 5.1)

# Directory of Maintained Schools by Local Authority

# England

## BEDFORDSHIRE

**Bedfordshire Education Offices**

**County Hall**
**Cauldwell Street**
**Bedford**
**Bedfordshire**
**MK42 9AP**

**GLENWOOD SCHOOL**
Beech Road, Dunstable, Bedfordshire LU6 3LY
*Type:* Co-educational Day Only 2–11
*Special needs:* ASD **ASP PMLD SLD**
*Wheelchair access:* WA1

**GRANGE SCHOOL**
Halsey Road, Kempston, Bedfordshire MK42 8AU
*Type:* Co-educational Day Only 7–16
*Special needs:* ASD **MLD**
*Wheelchair access:* WA2

**HILLCREST SCHOOL**
Regis Education Centre, Regis, Bedfordshire LU5 5PX
*Type:* Co-educational Day Only 11–19
*Special needs:* ASD PMLD **SLD**
*Wheelchair access:* W

**HITCHMEAD SCHOOL**
Hitchmead Road, Biggleswade, Bedfordshire SG18 0NL
*Type:* Co-educational Day Only 7–16

**OAK BANK SCHOOL**
Sandy Lane, Leighton Buzzard, Bedfordshire LU7 8BE
*Type:* Boys Boarding Only 11–16
*Special needs:* **BESD**

**RAINBOW SCHOOL**
Chestnut Avenue, Bedford, Bedfordshire MK43 8HP
*Type:* Co-educational Day Only 5–13
*Special needs:* ASD **ASP** SLD
*Wheelchair access:* W

**RIDGEWAY SCHOOL**
Hill Rise, Bedford, Bedfordshire MK42 7EB
*Type:* Co-educational Day Only 2–19
*Special needs:* VI
*Wheelchair access:* WA1

**ST JOHNS SCHOOL**
Austin Canons, Bedford, Bedfordshire MK42 8AA
*Website:*
www.st-johns-school.co.uk
*Type:* Co-educational Day Only 2–19
*Special needs:* ASD **ASP HI** PMLD SLD VI
*Wheelchair access:* WA1

**SUNNYSIDE SCHOOL**
The Baulk, Biggleswade, Bedfordshire SG18 0PT
*Type:* Co-educational Day Only 2–19
*Special needs:* ASD **ASP PMLD SLD**
*Wheelchair access:* WA1

**WEATHERFIELD SCHOOL**
Brewers Hill Road, Dunstable,
Bedfordshire LU6 1AF
*Website:*
www.weatherfield.beds.sch.uk
*Type:* Co-educational Day Only
7–16
*Special needs:* **ADD ADHD
ASD ASP BESD CB CP DOW
DYP DYS EPI HEA HI IM MLD
SLD** SP&LD **TOU** VI
*Wheelchair access:* WA3

## Luton Borough Council

**Town Hall**
**George Street**
**Luton**
**LU1 2BQ**

**LADY ZIA WERNER SCHOOL**
Ashcroft Road, Luton,
Bedfordshire LU2 9AY
*Type:* Co-educational Day Only
2–11
*Special needs:* CP DOW **HEA
PMLD SLD** SP&LD
*Wheelchair access:* WA1

**RICHMOND HILL SCHOOL**
Sunridge Avenue, Luton,
Bedfordshire LU2 7JL
*Type:* Co-educational Day Only
5–11
*Special needs:* ASD **ASP** HI
**PMLD SLD**

**WOODLANDS SECONDARY
SCHOOL**
Northwell Drive, Luton,
Bedfordshire LU3 3SP
*Type:* Co-educational Day Only
11–19
*Special needs:* ASD ASP HI
PMLD SLD VI

# BERKSHIRE

## Bracknell Forest Education Department

**Seymour House**
**38 Broadway**
**Bracknell**
**Berkshire**
**RG12 1AU**

**KENNEL LANE SCHOOL**
Kennel Lane, Bracknell,
Berkshire RG42 2EX
*Website:*
www.kennellaneschool.com
*Type:* Co-educational Day Only
2–19
*Special needs:* ASD MLD PMLD
SLD

## Reading Borough Council

**Civic Centre**
**Reading**
**Berkshire**
**RG1 7TD**

**THE AVENUE SCHOOL**
Basingstoke Road, Reading,
Berkshire RG2 0EN
*Type:* Co-educational Day Only
2–19
*Special needs:* BESD CP EPI
HEA MLD PMLD SP&LD VI
*Wheelchair access:* W

**HOLY BROOK SCHOOL**
145 Ashampstead Road,
Reading, Berkshire RG30 3LT
*Type:* Co-educational Day Only
5–11
*Special needs:* ADD ADHD **BESD**

## Slough Borough Council

**Town Hall**
**Bath Road**
**Slough**
**Berkshire**
**SL1 3UQ**

**ARBOUR VALE SCHOOL**
Farnham Road, Slough,
Berkshire SL2 3AE
*Website:*
www.arbourvale.slough.sch.uk
*Type:* Co-educational Day Only
2–19
*Special needs:* ASD **ASP** HI
**MLD PMLD SLD** VI
*Wheelchair access:* WA1

**LITTLEDOWN SCHOOL**
Queen's Road, Slough,
Berkshire SL1 3QW
*Type:* Co-educational 5–11
*Special needs:* BESD

## West Berkshire Council

Avonbank House
West Street
Newbury
Berkshire
RG14 1BZ

**BROOKFIELDS SCHOOL**
Sage Road, Reading, Berkshire
RG31 6SW
*Type:* Co-educational Day Only
*Special needs:* ASD **MLD PMLD
SLD**
*Wheelchair access:* W

**THE CASTLE SCHOOL**
Love Lane, Newbury, Berkshire
RG14 2JG
*Website:*
www.castle.westberks.org
*Type:* Co-educational Day Only
2–19
*Special needs:* **ASD ASP DOW
MLD PMLD SLD**
*Wheelchair access:* WA2

## Windsor & Maidenhead Education Authority

Town Hall
St Ives Road
Maidenhead
Berkshire
SL6 1RF

**MANOR GREEN SCHOOL**
Elizabeth Hawkes Way,
Maidenhead, Berkshire
SL6 3EQ
*Website:*
www.manorgreenschool.org
*Type:* Co-educational Day and
Boarding 2–19
*Special needs:* ADD ADHD
**ASD ASP** BESD CB **CP DOW**
DYC DYP DYS **EPI** HEA HI IM
**MLD PMLD SLD** SP&LD TOU VI
*Wheelchair access:* WA1

## Wokingham Education Department

PO Box 150
Shute End
Wokingham
Berkshire
RG40 1WQ

**ADDINGTON SCHOOL**
Loddon Bridge Road, Reading,
Berkshire RG5 4BS
*Type:* Co-educational Day Only
2–19
*Special needs:* ASD **ASP MLD
PMLD SLD**
*Wheelchair access:* WA1

**SOUTHFIELD SCHOOL**
Gipsy Lane, Wokingham,
Berkshire RG40 2HR
*Website:* www.southfield.
wokingham.sch.uk
*Type:* Co-educational Day and
Boarding 11–16
*Special needs:* **BESD**
*Wheelchair access:* WA2

# BRISTOL

## Bristol Education and Lifelong Learning

PO Box 57
Council House
College Green
Bristol
BS99 7EB

**BRIARWOOD SCHOOL**
Briar Way, Bristol BS16 4EA
*Type:* Co-educational Day Only
3–19
*Special needs:* ASD **ASP
PMLD SLD**
*Wheelchair access:* W

**THE BRISTOL GATEWAY
SCHOOL**
Stafford Road, St Werburghs,
Bristol BS2 9UR
*Type:* Boys Day Only 11–14
*Special needs:* **BESD**

**CLAREMONT SCHOOL**
Henleaze Park, Bristol BS9 4LR
*Website:*
www.claremontspecial.ik.org
*Type:* Co-educational Day Only
2–19
*Special needs:* **PMLD**
*Wheelchair access:* WA1

**ELMFIELD SCHOOL**
Greystoke Avenue, Bristol
BS10 6AY
*Type:* Co-educational Day Only
3–16
*Special needs:* **HI**
*Wheelchair access:* WA1

**FLORENCE BROWN
COMMUNITY SCHOOL**
Leinster Avenue, Bristol
BS4 1NN
*Type:* Co-educational Day Only
7–19
*Special needs:* ADHD **BESD** IM
**MLD** SP&LD
*Wheelchair access:* WA1

**KINGSDON MANOR SCHOOL**
Kingsdon, Somerton, Bristol
TA11 7JZ
*Type:* Boys Boarding Only 10–16
*Special needs:* **BESD** MLD

**NEW FOSSEWAY SCHOOL**
New Fosseway Road, Bristol
BS14 9LN
*Type:* Co-educational Day Only
3–19
*Special needs:* PMLD SLD
*Wheelchair access:* W

**NOTTON HOUSE**
28 Notton, Lacock Nr
Chippenham, Wiltshire
SN15 2NP
*Type:* Boys Boarding Only 9–16
*Special needs:* ADD ADHD ASP
**BESD** DYP DYS

**WOODSTOCK SCHOOL**
Courtney Road, Bristol BS15 9RL
*Type:* Co-educational Day Only
7–11
*Special needs:* **BESD**

# BUCKINGHAMSHIRE

## Buckinghamshire County Council

**County Hall
Aylesbury
Buckinghamshire
HP20 1UA**

### ALFRISTON SCHOOL
Penn Road, Beaconsfield,
Buckinghamshire HP9 2TS
*Type:* Girls Day and Boarding
11–18
*Special needs:* **MLD**
*Wheelchair access:* WA2

### BOOKER PARK SCHOOL
Booker Park, Aylesbury,
Buckinghamshire HP21 9ET
*Type:* Co-educational Day Only
2–11
*Special needs:* ADD ADHD ASD
**ASP BESD** CP DOW DYC DYP
DYS EPI **MLD PMLD SLD**
SP&LD VI
*Wheelchair access:* WA1

### CHILTERN GATE SCHOOL
Verney Avenue, High Wycombe,
Buckinghamshire HP12 3NE
*Type:* Co-educational Day Only
*Special needs:* ADD ADHD ASD
**ASP BESD** CP DOW DYP EPI
HEA HI IM **MLD** SP&LD TOU VI
*Wheelchair access:* WA2

### FURZE DOWN SCHOOL
Verney Road, Winslow,
Buckinghamshire MK18 3BL
*Type:* Co-educational Day Only
5–18
*Special needs:* ADHD ASD ASP
DYC DYP DYS EPI HI **MLD** SLD
SP&LD

### HERITAGE HOUSE SCHOOL
Cameron Road, Chesham,
Buckinghamshire HP5 3BP
*Website:*
www.heritagehouseschool.co.uk
*Type:* Co-educational Day Only
2–19
*Special needs:* ASD **ASP** CP
EPI HEA IM **PMLD SLD** VI W
*Wheelchair access:* WA1

### KYNASTON SCHOOL
Stoke Leys Close, Aylesbury,
Buckinghamshire HP21 9ET
*Type:* Co-educational Day Only
5–11
*Special needs:* **BESD**

### THE LADY ADRIAN SCHOOL
Courtney Way, Cambridge,
Cambridgeshire CB4 2EE
*Type:* Co-educational 7–16
*Special needs:* ADHD ASP
BESD EPI **MLD** SLD TOU
*Wheelchair access:* W

### MAPLEWOOD SCHOOL
Faulkner Way, High Wycombe,
Buckinghamshire HP13 5HB
*Type:* Co-educational Day Only
3–19
*Special needs:* **PMLD SLD**
*Wheelchair access:* WA1

### MEADOWGATE SCHOOL
Meadowgate Lane, Wisbech,
Cambridgeshire PE13 2JH
*Website:* www.meadowgate.
cambs.sch.uk
*Type:* Co-educational Day Only
2–19
*Special needs:* ASD **ASP MLD
PMLD SLD**
*Wheelchair access:* WA1

### PEBBLE BROOK SCHOOL
Churchill Avenue, Aylesbury,
Buckinghamshire HP21 8LZ
*Type:* Co-educational Day and
Boarding 11–18
*Special needs:* **MLD**

### PRESTWOOD LODGE SCHOOL FOR BOYS
Nairdwood Lane, Great
Missenden, Buckinghamshire
HP16 0QQ
*Type:* Boys Boarding and Day
11–16
*Special needs:* **BESD**

### ROMANS FIELD SCHOOL
Shenley Road, Bletchley,
Buckinghamshire MK3 7AW
*Type:* Co-educational Day and
Boarding 5–11
*Special needs:* **BESD**
*Wheelchair access:* WA2

### SAMUEL PEPYS SCHOOL
Cromwell Road, St Neots,
Cambridgeshire PE19 2EZ
*Type:* Co-educational Day Only
3–19
*Special needs:* ASD **ASP
PMLD SLD**
*Wheelchair access:* WA1

### STOCKLAKE PARK SCHOOL
Stocklake, Aylesbury,
Buckinghamshire HP20 1DP
*Type:* Co-educational Day Only
11–19
*Special needs:* ASD **ASP** CP
DOW **MLD PMLD SLD** VI
*Wheelchair access:* WA1

**STONY DEAN SCHOOL**
Orchard End Avenue,
Amersham, Buckinghamshire
HP7 9JW
*Website:*
www.stonydean.bucks.sch.uk
*Type:* Co-educational Day Only
11–18
*Special needs:* **ASD ASP** DYS
**MLD** SP&LD
*Wheelchair access:* WA3

**WENDOVER HOUSE SCHOOL**
Church Lane, Aylesbury,
Buckinghamshire HP22 6NL
*Type:* Boys Boarding and Day
*Special needs:* **BESD**

**WESTFIELD SCHOOL**
Highfield Road, High Wycombe,
Buckinghamshire SL8 5BE
*Type:* Co-educational
*Special needs:* **BESD**
*Wheelchair access:* W

**WHITE SPIRE SCHOOL**
Rickley Lane, Milton Keynes,
Buckinghamshire MK3 6EW
*Website:* www.whitespire.
milton-keynes.sch.uk
*Type:* Co-educational 5–18
*Special needs:* **MLD**
*Wheelchair access:* WA2

## Milton Keynes Council

**Saxon Court**
**502 Avebury Boulevard**
**Milton Keynes**
**MK9 3HS**

**THE GATEHOUSE SCHOOL**
Crosslands, Milton Keynes,
Buckinghamshire MK14 6AX
*Type:* Boys Boarding and Day
12–16
*Special needs:* **BESD**
*Wheelchair access:* W

**THE REDWAY SCHOOL**
Farmborough, Milton Keynes,
Buckinghamshire MK6 4HG
*Website:* www.theredway.net
*Type:* Co-educational Day Only
2–19
*Special needs:* ASD **PMLD SLD**
*Wheelchair access:* WA1

**SLATED ROW SCHOOL**
Old Wolverton Road, Milton
Keynes, Buckinghamshire
MK12 5NJ
*Type:* Co-educational Day Only
4–19
*Special needs:* **MLD**
*Wheelchair access:* WA1

**THE WALNUTS SCHOOL**
Admiral Drive, Milton Keynes,
Buckinghamshire MK8 0PU
*Website:* www.walnuts.
milton-keynes.sch.uk
*Type:* Co-educational Boarding
and Day 4–19
*Wheelchair access:* WA1
*52-week care*

# CAMBRIDGESHIRE

## Cambridgeshire LEA

**Shire Hall**
**Castle Hill**
**Cambridge**
**CB3 0AP**

**THE HARBOUR SCHOOL**
Station Road, Ely,
Cambridgeshire CB6 3RR
*Type:* Co-educational Boarding
and Day 5–14
*Special needs:* **BESD**

**HIGHFIELD SCHOOL**
Downham Road, Ely,
Cambridgeshire CB6 1BD
*Type:* Co-educational Day Only
2–19
*Special needs:* ADD ASD ASP
CP DOW DYP EPI HI MLD
PMLD SLD SP&LD TOU VI
*Wheelchair access:* WA1

## Peterborough City Council

**Town Hall**
**Bridge Street**
**Peterborough**
**PE1 1QT**

**THE CAUSEWAY SCHOOL**
Park Lane, Peterborough,
Cambridgeshire PE1 5GZ
*Type:* Co-educational Day Only
*Special needs:* ADD ADHD
**BESD**

**HELTWATE SCHOOL**
North Bretton, Peterborough,
Cambridgeshire PE3 8RL
*Type:* Co-educational Day Only
5–16
*Special needs:* ASD HI **MLD**
**SLD** SP&LD
*Wheelchair access:* WA2

**MARSHFIELDS SCHOOL**
Eastern Close, Peterborough,
Cambridgeshire PE1 4PP
*Type:* Co-educational Day Only
9–18
*Special needs:* BESD **MLD**
SP&LD
*Wheelchair access:* W

**THE PHOENIX SCHOOL**
Orton Goldhay, Peterborough,
Cambridgeshire PE2 5SD
*Type:* Co-educational Day Only
2–19
*Special needs:* ASD DOW EPI
HI **PMLD SLD** SP&LD VI
*Wheelchair access:* WA1

# CHANNEL ISLANDS

## Guernsey Education Department

**Grange Road**
**St Peter Port**
**Guernsey**
**Channel Islands**
**GY1 3AU**

**LONGFIELD CENTRE**
Maurepas Road, Guernsey,
Channel Islands GY1 2DS
*Type:* Co-educational Day Only
3–7
*Special needs:* ADHD ASD EPI
HI **MLD** SP&LD
*Wheelchair access:* W

**MONT VAROUF SCHOOL**
Le Neuf Chemin, Guernsey,
Channel Islands GY7 9FG
*Type:* Co-educational Day Only
3–19
*Special needs:* ASD DOW EPI
**PMLD SLD** SP&LD VI

**OAKVALE SCHOOL**
Collings Road, Guernsey,
Channel Islands GY1 1FW
*Type:* Co-educational Day Only
11–19
*Special needs:* **MLD**
*Wheelchair access:* WA1

## States of Jersey

**PO Box 142**
**Jersey**
**Channel Islands**
**JE4 8QJ**

**D'HAUTREE HOUSE SCHOOL**
St Saviour, Jersey, Channel
Islands JE2 4QP
*Type:* Co-educational Day Only
11–16
*Special needs:* ADHD **BESD**
MLD

**MONT A L'ABBE SCHOOL**
Jersey, Channel Islands
JE2 3FN
*Type:* Co-educational Day Only
3–18
*Special needs:* ASD CB MLD
**PMLD SLD**
*Wheelchair access:* WA1

**ST JAMES' SCHOOL**
Le Breton Lane, Jersey,
Channel Islands JE2 4QN
*Type:* Co-educational
*Special needs:* **BESD**

# CHESHIRE

## Cheshire Education and Community Education Department

**County Hall**
**Chester**
**Cheshire**
**CH1 1SF**

**ADELAIDE SCHOOL**
Adelaide Street, Crewe,
Cheshire CW1 3DT
*Type:* Co-educational Day Only
*Special needs:* **BESD**

**CAPENHURST GRANGE SCHOOL**
Chester Road, Great Sutton,
Cheshire CH66 2NA
*Type:* Co-educational Boarding
Only 11–16
*Special needs:* ADHD **BESD**
MLD

**CLOUGHWOOD SCHOOL**
Stones Manor Lane, Northwich,
Cheshire CW8 1NU
*Type:* Boys Boarding Only
*Special needs:* **BESD**

**DEE BANKS SCHOOL**
Sandy Lane, Chester, Cheshire
CH3 5UX
*Type:* Co-educational Day Only
2–19
*Special needs:* ASD PMLD **SLD**
*Wheelchair access:* WA1

**DORIN PARK SCHOOL**
Wealstone Lane, Upton-by-
Chester, Cheshire CH2 1HD
*Website:* www.dorinpark.org.uk
*Type:* Co-educational Day Only
*Special needs:* PMLD

**GREENBANK SCHOOL**
off Green Bank Lane, Northwich,
Cheshire CW8 1LD
*Type:* Co-educational Boarding
Only 6–18
*Special needs:* ASD **MLD SLD**
*Wheelchair access:* WA2

**HEBDEN GREEN SCHOOL**
Woodford Lane West, Winsford,
Cheshire CW7 4EJ
*Type:* Co-educational Day and
Boarding 2–19
*Special needs:* CP EPI HEA HI
PMLD SP&LD VI
*Wheelchair access:* WA1

**HINDERTON SCHOOL**
Capenhurst Lane, Ellesmere
Port, Cheshire CH65 7AQ
*Type:* Co-educational Day Only
3–11
*Special needs:* ASD SP&LD

**OAKLANDS SCHOOL**
Cheviot Square, Winsford,
Cheshire CW7 1NU
*Type:* Co-educational Day Only
11–16
*Special needs:* **MLD**

**PARK LANE SCHOOL**
Park Lane, Macclesfield,
Cheshire SK11 8JR
*Website:* www.parklane.school.
cheshire.org.uk
*Type:* Co-educational Day Only
2–19
*Special needs:* PMLD SLD
*Wheelchair access:* WA1

**ROSEBANK SCHOOL**
Townfield Lane, Northwich,
Cheshire CW8 4QP
*Type:* Co-educational Day Only
3–11
*Special needs:* ASD **ASP MLD**
SP&LD
*Wheelchair access:* WA2

**THE RUSSETT SCHOOL**
Middlehurst Avenue, Northwich,
Cheshire CW8 3BW
*Type:* Co-educational Day Only
2–19
*Special needs:* ASD DOW EPI
HI **PMLD SLD** VI
*Wheelchair access:* W

**ST JOHN'S WOOD
COMMUNITY SCHOOL**
Knutsford, Cheshire WA16 8PA
*Website:*
www.st-johns-school.co.uk
*Type:* Co-educational Day Only
11–16
*Special needs:* BESD
*Wheelchair access:* WA2

**SPRINGFIELD SCHOOL**
Crewe Green Road, Crewe,
Cheshire CW1 5HS
*Website:* www.springfield.
cheshire.sch.uk
*Type:* Co-educational Day Only
3–19
*Special needs:* ASD DOW
**PMLD SLD**
*Wheelchair access:* WA1

## Halton Borough Council

**Municipal Building
Kingsway
Widnes
Cheshire
WA8 7QF**

**ASHLEY SCHOOL**
Cawfield Avenue, Widnes,
Halton WA8 7HG
*Type:* Co-educational Day Only
11–16
*Special needs:* **MLD**

**BROOKFIELDS SCHOOL**
Moorfield Road, Widnes,
Halton WA8 3JA
*Type:* Co-educational Day Only
3–11
*Special needs:* ASD PMLD SLD
*Wheelchair access:* WA1

**CAVENDISH SCHOOL**
Lincoln Close, Runcorn,
Cheshire WA7 4YX
*Type:* Co-educational Day Only
2–19
*Special needs:* ADHD ASD CP
EPI **PMLD SLD**
*Wheelchair access:* W

**CHESNUT LODGE SCHOOL**
Green Lane, Widnes, Cheshire
WA8 7HF
*Website:*
www.chesnutlodgeschool.co.uk
*Type:* Co-educational Day Only
2–16
*Special needs:* CP DYP EPI
MLD SP&LD VI
*Wheelchair access:* W

## Warrington Education and Lifelong Learning Department

**New Town House
Buttermarket Street
Warrington
Cheshire
WA1 2NJ**

**FOX WOOD SCHOOL**
Chatfield Drive, Warrington,
Cheshire WA3 6QW
*Type:* Co-educational Day Only
4–19
*Special needs:* ASD **ASP
PMLD SLD**

**GRAPPENHALL RESIDENTIAL
SCHOOL**
Church Lane, Warrington,
Cheshire WA4 3EU
*Type:* Boys Boarding and Day
*Special needs:* ADD ADHD ASD
ASP **BESD** CB MLD SP&LD
TOU

**GREEN LANE SCHOOL**
Green Lane, Warrington,
Cheshire WA1 4JL
*Type:* Co-educational Day Only
4–16
*Special needs:* ASD **MLD** SLD
*Wheelchair access:* WA2

# CORNWALL

## Cornwall Education Department

**Treyew Road**
**Truro**
**Cornwall**
**TR1 3AY**

### CURNOW SCHOOL
Drump Road, Redruth,
Cornwall TR15 1LU
*Website:*
www.curnow.cornwall.sch.uk
*Type:* Co-educational Day Only
*Special needs:* **PMLD SLD**
*Wheelchair access:* WA2

### NANCEALVERNE SCHOOL
Madron Road, Penzance,
Cornwall TR20 8TP
*Type:* Co-educational Day Only
2–19
*Special needs:* PMLD SLD
*Wheelchair access:* WA2

### PENCALENICK SCHOOL
Truro, Cornwall TR1 1TE
*Type:* Co-educational Day Only
11–16
*Special needs:* **SLD**

# CUMBRIA

## Cumbria Education Service

**5 Portland Square**
**Carlisle**
**CA1 1PU**

### GEORGE HASTWELL SCHOOL
Moor Tarn Lane, Barrow in
Furness, Cumbria LA14 3LW
*Type:* Co-educational Day Only
2–19
*Special needs:* PMLD SLD
*Wheelchair access:* WA1

### MAYFIELD SCHOOL
Moresby, Whitehaven,
Cumbria CA28 8TU
*Website:*
www.mayfieldcumbria.org
*Type:* Co-educational Day Only
*Special needs:* PMLD **SLD**
*Wheelchair access:* WA1

### SANDGATE SCHOOL
Sandylands Road, Kendal,
Cumbria LA9 6JG
*Type:* Co-educational Day Only
2–19
*Special needs:* ASD **ASP** BESD
CP EPI HI MLD **PMLD SLD** VI
*Wheelchair access:* WA1

### SANDSIDE LODGE SCHOOL
Sandside Road, Ulverston,
Cumbria LA12 9EF
*Type:* Co-educational Day Only
2–19
*Special needs:* ASD **ASP** EPI HI
**PMLD SLD** SP&LD
*Wheelchair access:* WA1

# DERBYSHIRE

## Derby City Council

**Corporation Street
Derby
DE1 2FS**

**IVY HOUSE SCHOOL**
Moorway Lane, Derby,
Derbyshire DE23 7FS
*Type:* Co-educational Day Only
2–19
*Special needs:* PMLD SLD
*Wheelchair access:* WA1

**ST ANDREW'S SCHOOL**
St Andrew's View, Derby,
Derbyshire DE2 4EW
*Website:*
www.standrewschool.co.uk
*Type:* Co-educational Day and
Boarding 11–19
*Special needs:* ASD **SLD**
*Wheelchair access:* WA1

**ST CLARE'S SCHOOL**
Rough Heanor Road, Derby,
Derbyshire DE3 5AZ
*Type:* Co-educational Day Only
11–16
*Special needs:* ASD **BESD** HI
**MLD** SLD SP&LD

**ST GILES SCHOOL**
Hampshire Road, Derby,
Derbyshire DE21 6BT
*Website:*
www.stgiles.derby.sch.uk
*Type:* Co-educational Day Only
4–11
*Special needs:* **ADHD** ASD **ASP
BESD CB CP DOW DYS EPI** HI
IM **MLD PMLD SLD** SP&LD VI W
*Wheelchair access:* WA1

**ST MARTIN'S SCHOOL**
Wisgreaves Road, Derby,
Derbyshire DE2 8RQ
*Type:* Co-educational Day Only
11–16
*Special needs:* ADD ASD ASP
BESD DOW DYP DYS **MLD**
*Wheelchair access:* WA2

## Derbyshire Education Offices

**County Hall
Matlock
Derbyshire
DE4 3AG**

**ALFRETON PARK
COMMUNITY SPECIAL
SCHOOL**
Wingfield Road, Alfreton,
Derbyshire DE55 7AL
*Type:* Co-educational Day Only
2–19
*Special needs:* ASD PMLD **SLD**
*Wheelchair access:* W

**ASHGATE CROFT SCHOOL**
Ashgate Road, Chesterfield,
Derbyshire S40 4BN
*Type:* Co-educational Day Only
2–19
*Special needs:* ASD BESD CP
DYS EPI HEA HI **MLD PMLD
SLD** SP&LD VI
*Wheelchair access:* WA1

**BARNSTAPLE TUTORIAL
UNIT (PRU)**
St Johns Lane, Barnstaple,
Devon EX32 9DD
*Type:* Co-educational Day Only
*Special needs:* **BESD**

**BENNERLEY FIELDS
SCHOOL**
Stratford Street, Ilkeston,
Derbyshire DE7 8QZ
*Type:* Co-educational Day Only
3–16
*Special needs:* ASD **ASP** BESD
DOW DYP DYS HI **MLD SLD**
SP&LD
*Wheelchair access:* W

**BRACKENFIELD SCHOOL**
Bracken Road, Nottingham,
Nottinghamshire NG10 4DA
*Website:* www.brackenfield.
derbyshire.sch.uk
*Type:* Co-educational Day Only
5–16
*Special needs:* BESD MLD
*Wheelchair access:* WA1

**THE DELVES SCHOOL**
Hayes Lane, Swanwick,
Derbyshire DE55 1AR
*Type:* Co-educational 5–16
*Special needs:* ASD BESD MLD
SLD SP&LD

**HOLBROOK CENTRE FOR
AUTISM**
Holbrook, Belper, Derbyshire
DE56 0TE
*Type:* Co-educational Day and
Boarding 5–19
*Special needs:* ASD **ASP** CB
SLD

**HOLLY HOUSE SCHOOL**
Church Street North,
Chesterfield, Derbyshire
S41 9QR
*Type:* Co-educational Day Only
4–11
*Special needs:* **BESD**

**PEAK SCHOOL**
Buxton Road, High Peak,
Derbyshire SK23 6ES
*Type:* Co-educational Boarding
and Day 2–19
*Special needs:* ASD **ASP** CP
EPI **PMLD SLD**
*Wheelchair access:* W

**STANTON VALE**
Thoresby Road, Nottingham,
Nottinghamshire NG10 3NP
*Type:* Co-educational Boarding
and Day 2–16
*Special needs:* CP
*Wheelchair access:* W

**STUBBIN WOOD SCHOOL**
Burlington Avenue, Mansfield,
Derbyshire NG20 9AD
*Type:* Co-educational Day Only
2–16
*Special needs:* ASD **ASP** BESD
MLD PMLD SLD SP&LD
*Wheelchair access:* WA1

# DEVON

## Devon County Council

**County Hall**
**Topsham Road**
**Exeter**
**Devon**
**EX2 4QD**

**BARLEY LANE SCHOOL**
Barley Lane, Exeter, Devon
EX4 1TA
*Type:* Co-educational Day Only
8–14
*Special needs:* **BESD**

**BIDWELL BROOK SCHOOL**
Shinner's Bridge, Dartington,
Devon TQ9 6JU
*Website:* www.bidwellbrook.
devon.sch.uk
*Type:* Co-educational Day Only
3–19
*Special needs:* ASD MLD
**PMLD SLD**
*Wheelchair access:* WA2

**COURTLANDS SCHOOL**
Widey Court, Plymouth, Devon
PL6 5JS
*Type:* Co-educational Day Only
*Special needs:* ADD ADHD ASP
**MLD** SP&LD

**ELLEN TINKHAM SCHOOL**
Hollow Lane, Exeter,
Devon EX1 3RW
*Type:* Co-educational Day Only
3–19
*Special needs:* ASD CP EPI HI
MLD **PMLD SLD** VI
*Wheelchair access:* WA1

**HILL CREST SCHOOL**
St John's Road, Exmouth,
Devon EX8 4ED
*Type:* Boys Boarding and Day
10–16
*Special needs:* **BESD**

**THE LAMPARD COMMUNITY
COLLEGE**
St John's Lane, Barnstaple,
Devon EX32 9DD
*Website:*
www.lampardschool.co.uk
*Type:* Co-educational Day Only
7–16
*Special needs:* ASD **ASP
DOW MLD**
*Wheelchair access:* WA1

**MARLAND SCHOOL**
Torrington, Devon EX3 8QQ
*Type:* Boys Boarding Only
11–16
*Special needs:* ADD ADHD
**BESD**

**MILL FORD SCHOOL**
Rochford Crescent, Plymouth,
Devon PL5 2PY
*Type:* Co-educational Day Only
3–19
*Special needs:* ASD **PMLD SLD**
*Wheelchair access:* WA1

**MILL WATER SCHOOL**
Honiton Bottom Road, Honiton,
Devon EX14 2ER
*Type:* Co-educational Day Only
4–18

**OAKLANDS PARK SCHOOL**
John Nash Drive, Dawlish,
Devon EX7 9SF
*Website:* www.oaklandspark.
devon.sch.uk
*Type:* Co-educational Boarding
and Day 3–19
*Special needs:* ASD **ASP** CP
EPI PMLD **SLD**
*Wheelchair access:* W

**PATHFIELD SCHOOL**
Abbey Road, Barnstaple,
Devon EX31 1JU
*Website:*
www.pathfield.devon.sch.uk
*Type:* Co-educational Day Only
3–19
*Special needs:* ASD **ASP
PMLD SLD**
*Wheelchair access:* WA1

**RATCLIFFE SCHOOL**
John Nash Drive, Dawlish,
Devon EX7 9RZ
*Website:* www.dawlish-ratcliffe.
devon.sch.uk
*Type:* Co-educational Day and
Boarding 8–16
*Special needs:* ASD **ASP BESD**
*Wheelchair access:* WA3

**SOUTHBROOK COLLEGE**
Bishop Westall Road, Exeter,
Devon EX2 6JB
*Website:* www.southbrook.
devon.sch.uk
*Type:* Co-educational Day Only
7–16
*Special needs:* ASD **MLD**
*Wheelchair access:* WA1

## Plymouth City Council

**Civic Centre**
**Plymouth**
**PL1 2EW**

**BROOK GREEN CENTRE
FOR LEARNING**
Bodmin Road, Plymouth, Devon
PL5 4DZ
*Type:* Co-educational Day Only
11–16
*Special needs:* BESD **MLD**
*Wheelchair access:* WA1

**DOWNHAM SCHOOL**
Horn Lane, Plymouth, Devon
PL9 9BR
*Type:* Co-educational 3–16
*Special needs:* **SLD**
*Wheelchair access:* WA1

**LONGCAUSE SCHOOL**
Plympton, Plymouth,
Devon PL7 3JB
*Type:* Co-educational
*Special needs:* ASD **ASP MLD**

**MOUNT TAMAR SCHOOL**
Row Lane, Plymouth, Devon
PL5 2EF
*Type:* Co-educational Day Only
5–16
*Special needs:* **BESD**

**WOODLANDS SCHOOL**
Wood View Learning
Community, Devon PL6 5ES
*Website:* www.woodlands.
plymouth.sch.uk
*Type:* Co-educational Day Only
2–16 (Post-16 consultation
currently under way)
*Wheelchair access:* WA1
*52-week care*

**Torbay Lifelong
Learning and Culture
Services Directorate**

**Oldway Mansion
Torquay Road
Paignton
Devon
TQ3 2TE**

**THE BICKNELL SCHOOL**
Petersfield Road, Bournemouth,
Dorset BH7 6QP
*Type:* Boys Day and Boarding
7–16
*Special needs:* ADD ADHD
ASP **BESD** DYC DYP DYS
SP&LD TOU

**LINWOOD SCHOOL**
Alma Road, Bournemouth,
Dorset BH9 1AJ
*Type:* Co-educational Day Only
3–19
*Special needs:* ASD **ASP MLD
PMLD SLD**

# DORSET

## Borough of Poole

**Room 159
Civic Centre
Poole
Dorset
BH15 2RU**

**LONGSPEE SCHOOL**
Learoyd Road, Poole, Dorset
BH17 8PJ
*Type:* Co-educational Day Only
4–11
*Special needs:* ADD ADHD ASP
**BESD** CB

**MONTACUTE SCHOOL**
3 Canford Heath Road, Poole,
Dorset BH17 9NG
*Website:*
www.montacute.poole.sch.uk
*Type:* Co-educational Day Only
3–19
*Special needs:* ASD PMLD **SLD**
*Wheelchair access:* WA1

**WINCHELSEA SCHOOL**
Guernsey Road, Poole, Dorset
BH12 4LL
*Type:* Co-educational Day Only
3–16
*Special needs:* ASD **ASP MLD**
*Wheelchair access:* WA1

## Dorset Education
## Offices

**County Hall
Colliton Park
Dorchester
Dorset
DT1 1XJ**

**BEAUCROFT SCHOOL**
Wimborne Road, Wimborne,
Dorset BH21 2SS
*Type:* Co-educational Day Only
4–16
*Special needs:* ASD ASP BESD
DOW EPI MLD SLD SP&LD VI
*Wheelchair access:* WA2

**MOUNTJOY SCHOOL**
Flood Lane, Bridport, Dorset
DT6 3QG
*Website:*
www.mountjoy.dorset.sch.uk
*Type:* Co-educational Day Only
2–19
*Special needs:* ASD **ASP** CP
**DOW** EPI HEA HI **PMLD** SLD
SP&LD VI
*Wheelchair access:* W

**PENWITHEN SCHOOL**
Winterborne Monkton,
Dorchester, Dorset DT2 9PS
*Type:* Co-educational Boarding
and Day 7–16
*Special needs:* **BESD**

**WYVERN SCHOOL**
Dorchester Road, Weymouth,
Dorset DT3 5AL
*Website:* www.wyvern.sch.uk
*Type:* Co-educational Day Only
2–19
*Special needs:* ASD PMLD SLD
*Wheelchair access:* WA1

**YEWSTOCK SCHOOL**
Honeymead Lane, Sturminster
Newton, Dorset DT10 1EW
*Website:* www.yewstock.sch.uk
*Type:* Co-educational Day Only
2–19
*Special needs:* ASD MLD
PMLD SLD
*Wheelchair access:* WA2

# COUNTY DURHAM

## Darlington Education Offices

2nd Floor
Town Hall
Darlington
County Durham
DL1 5QT

### BEAUMONT HILL TECHNOLOGY COLLEGE & PRIMARY SCHOOL
Darlington Education Village,
Darlington, County Durham
DL1 2AN
*Type:* Co-educational Day Only
2–19
*Special needs:* ADHD ASD **ASP BESD** CP MLD **PMLD** SLD
*Wheelchair access:* WA1

## Durham County Council

County Hall
County Durham
DH1 5UL

### DENE VIEW SCHOOL
Cotsford Park, Peterlee, County
Durham SR8 4SZ
*Type:* Co-educational Day Only
5–16
*Special needs:* **MLD**
*Wheelchair access:* W

### DURHAM TRINITY SCHOOL
Flambard and Kirkham
Premises, Durham, County
Durham DH1 5TS
*Type:* Co-educational Day Only
2–19
*Special needs:* ASD **ASP MLD PMLD** SLD

### ELEMORE HALL SCHOOL
Littletown, Sherburn, County
Durham DH6 1QD
*Website:* www.elemore.co.uk
*Type:* Co-educational Boarding
and Day
*Special needs:* **BESD**

### GLEN DENE SCHOOL
Crawlaw Road, Peterlee, County
Durham SR8 3BQ
*Type:* Co-educational Day Only
2–19
*Special needs:* ASD MLD PMLD
SLD
*Wheelchair access:* W

### HARE LAW SCHOOL
Catchgate, Stanley, County
Durham DH9 8DT
*Website:* www.Harelaw.School@
durham.gov.uk
*Type:* Co-educational Day Only
4–16
*Special needs:* ASD MLD SLD
*Wheelchair access:* W

### THE MEADOWS SCHOOL
Whitworth, Spennymoor, County
Durham DL16 7QW
*Type:* Co-educational Day Only
11–16

### VILLA REAL SCHOOL
Villa Real Road, Consett, County
Durham DH8 6BH
*Website:*
www.villareal.durham.sch.uk
*Type:* Co-educational Day Only
2–19
*Special needs:* ADD ADHD ASD
**ASP** BESD **CB** CP DOW EPI
HEA IM **PMLD SLD** SP&LD VI
*Wheelchair access:* WA1

### WALWORTH SCHOOL
Bluebell Way, Newton Aycliffe,
County Durham DL5 7LP
*Type:* Co-educational Day and
Boarding 5–11
*Special needs:* **ADD ADHD** ASP
**BESD** MLD SP&LD

### WARWICK ROAD SCHOOL
Warwick Road, Bishop
Auckland, County Durham
DL14 6LS
*Type:* Co-educational Day Only
*Special needs:* DYP DYS **MLD**

### WINDLESTONE SCHOOL
Ferryhill, County Durham
DL17 0HP
*Website:*
www.windlestoneschool.com
*Type:* Co-educational Boarding
and Day 11–16
*Special needs:* **BESD**
*Wheelchair access:* WA1

## Hartlepool Borough Council

Civic Centre
Victoria Road
Hartlepool
Cleveland
TS24 8AY

### CATCOTE SCHOOL
Catcote Road, Hartlepool
TS25 4EZ
*Type:* Co-educational Day Only
11–19
*Special needs:* ASD **MLD PMLD** SLD
*Wheelchair access:* WA1

### SPRINGWELL SCHOOL
Wiltshire Way, Hartlepool
TS26 0TB
*Website:*
www.oaveryspecialschool.com
*Type:* Co-educational Day Only
3–11
*Special needs:* ASD CP
PMLD SLD

# ESSEX

## Essex County Council

**County Hall**
**Market Road**
**Chelmsford**
**Essex**
**CM1 1LX**

### CASTLEDON SCHOOL
Bromfords Drive, Wickford,
Essex SS12 0PW
*Type:* Co-educational Day Only
5–16
*Special needs:* ASD **MLD**

### CEDAR HALL SCHOOL
Hart Road, Benfleet,
Essex SS7 3UQ
*Type:* Co-educational Day Only
4–16
*Special needs:* **HI MLD** SP&LD
*Wheelchair access:* WA2

### THE EDITH BORTHWICK SCHOOL
Fennes Road, Braintree,
Essex CM7 5LA
*Website:* www.edithborthwick.
essex.sch.uk
*Type:* Co-educational Day Only
3–19
*Special needs:* ASD **ASP MLD PMLD SLD** SP&LD
*Wheelchair access:* WA1

### THE ENDEAVOUR SCHOOL
Hogarth Avenue, Brentwood,
Essex CM15 8BE
*Website:*
www.endeavour.essex.sch.uk
*Type:* Co-educational Day Only
5–16
*Special needs:* ADHD ASD ASP
DOW **MLD** SP&LD
*Wheelchair access:* WA2

### GLENWOOD SCHOOL
Rushbottom Lane, Benfleet,
Essex SS7 4LW
*Type:* Co-educational Day Only
3–19
*Special needs:* ASD PMLD SLD
*Wheelchair access:* WA1

### HARLOW FIELDS SCHOOL
Tendring Road, Harlow, Essex
CM18 6RN
*Type:* Co-educational Day Only
3–19
*Special needs:* ASD **ASP MLD PMLD SLD**

### THE HAYWARD SCHOOL
Maltese Road, Chelmsford,
Essex CM1 2PA
*Type:* Co-educational Day Only
5–16
*Special needs:* ADD ADHD ASD
**ASP** DOW DYP DYS **MLD**
SP&LD

### THE HEATH SCHOOL
Winstree Road, Colchester,
Essex CO3 5GE
*Type:* Boys Day and Boarding
11–16
*Special needs:* **BESD**
*Wheelchair access:* W

### HOMESTEAD SCHOOL
School Road, Colchester,
Essex CO4 5PA
*Type:* Boys Boarding Only
14–19
*Special needs:* **BESD**

### KINGSWODE HOE SCHOOL
Sussex Road, Colchester,
Essex CO3 3QJ
*Type:* Co-educational Day Only
5–16
*Special needs:* ADD ADHD ASD
BESD DOW DYC DYS EPI **MLD**
SP&LD
*Wheelchair access:* WA3

### LEXDEN SPRINGS SCHOOL
Halstead Road, Colchester,
Essex CO3 9AB
*Type:* Co-educational Day Only
3–19
*Special needs:* ASD **ASP PMLD SLD**
*Wheelchair access:* WA1

### MARKET FIELD SCHOOL
School Road, Colchester,
Essex CO7 7ET
*Type:* Co-educational Day Only
5–16
*Special needs:* ASD **ASP** DOW
EPI **MLD** SLD SP&LD
*Wheelchair access:* WA1

### OAKVIEW SCHOOL
Whitehills Road, Loughton,
Essex IG10 1TS
*Type:* Co-educational Day Only
3–19
*Special needs:* ASD **MLD SLD**
*Wheelchair access:* WA1

### THE RAMSDEN HALL SCHOOL
Ramsden Heath, Billericay,
Essex CM11 1HN
*Type:* Boys Boarding Only
*Special needs:* **BESD**

### SHOREFIELDS SCHOOL
Ogilvie House, Clacton,
Essex CO15 6HF
*Type:* Co-educational Day Only
3–19
*Special needs:* PMLD SLD
*Wheelchair access:* WA1

### THRIFTWOOD SCHOOL
Slades Lane, Chelmsford,
Essex CM2 8RW
*Type:* Co-educational Day Only
5–16
*Special needs:* ADHD ASD ASP
CP DOW DYS **MLD** SP&LD
*Wheelchair access:* W

### WELLS PARK SCHOOL
Lambourne Road, Chigwell,
Essex IG7 6NN
*Type:* Co-educational Boarding
Only 5–12
*Special needs:* **BESD**
*Wheelchair access:* W

### WOODLANDS CAMPUS, CNMSS
Patching Hall Lane, Chelmsford,
Essex CM1 4BX
*Type:* Co-educational Day Only
3–19
*Special needs:* ASD **ASP** PMLD **SLD**
*Wheelchair access:* WA1

## Southend-on-Sea Borough Council

**5th Floor**
**Civic Centre**
**Victoria Avenue**
**Southend-on-Sea**
**SS2 6ER**

### KINGSDOWN SCHOOL
Snakes Lane, Southend-on-Sea, Essex SS2 6XT
*Type:* Co-educational Day Only
*Special needs:* CP DOW EPI HEA HI IM PMLD SLD VI
*Wheelchair access:* WA1

### LANCASTER SCHOOL
Prittlewell Chase, Westcliff-on-Sea, Essex SS0 0RT
*Website:* www.lancaster-school-southend.co.uk
*Type:* Co-educational Day Only 14–19
*Special needs:* ASD CP HEA IM **PMLD SLD**
*Wheelchair access:* WA1

### PRIORY SCHOOL
Burr Hill Chase, Southend-on-Sea, Essex SS2 6PE
*Type:* Co-educational Day Only 11–16
*Special needs:* **BESD**

### THE ST CHRISTOPHER SCHOOL
Mountdale Gardens, Leigh-on-Sea, Essex SS9 4AW
*Website:* www.tscs.southend.sch.uk
*Type:* Co-educational Day Only 3–19
*Special needs:* **ADHD** ASD **ASP** BESD DOW DYP DYS EPI HI **MLD** SLD SP&LD
*Wheelchair access:* WA2
52-week care

### ST NICHOLAS SCHOOL
Philpott Avenue, Southend-on-Sea, Essex SS2 4RL
*Type:* Co-educational Day Only 11–16
*Special needs:* **ADD ADHD ASD ASP BESD CB DOW DYC DYP DYS EPI HEA HI** IM **MLD** SP&LD **TOU** VI
*Wheelchair access:* WA3

## Thurrock Council

**New Road**
**Grays**
**Essex**
**RM17 6GF**

### KNIGHTSMEAD SCHOOL
Fortin Close, South Ockendon, Essex RM15 5NH
*Website:* www.knightsmead.thurrock.sch.uk
*Type:* Co-educational Day Only 3–19
*Special needs:* ASD **ASP PMLD SLD**
*Wheelchair access:* W

### TREETOPS SCHOOL
Buxton Road, Grays, Essex RM16 2XN
*Website:* www.treetopsschool.org
*Type:* Co-educational Day Only 3–16
*Special needs:* ADHD ASD MLD SP&LD
*Wheelchair access:* WA1

### WOODACRE SCHOOL
Erriff Drive, South Ockendon, Essex RM15 5AY
*Type:* Co-educational Day Only 3–16
*Special needs:* CP DYP EPI MLD PMLD SLD SP&LD
*Wheelchair access:* W

# GLOUCESTERSHIRE

### Gloucestershire LEA

**Shire Hall**
**Westgate Street**
**Gloucester**
**Gloucestershire**
**GL1 2TG**

### ALDERMAN KNIGHT SCHOOL
Ashchurch Road, Tewkesbury, Gloucestershire GL20 8JJ
*Type:* Co-educational Day Only 5–16
*Special needs:* **ASD** ASP BESD DYS **EPI** HEA MLD SLD SP&LD
*Wheelchair access:* WA1

### AMBERLEY RIDGE SCHOOL
Amberley, Stroud, Gloucestershire GL5 5DB
*Type:* Co-educational Day and Boarding
*Special needs:* **BESD**
*Wheelchair access:* W

### BATTLEDOWN CENTRE FOR CHILDREN AND FAMILIES
Harp Hill, Cheltenham, Gloucestershire GL52 6PZ
*Website:* www.battledown.gloucs.sch.uk
*Type:* Co-educational Day Only
*Special needs:* ASD **ASP** BESD CB CP DOW EPI HEA HI IM **PMLD SLD** SP&LD VI
*Wheelchair access:* WA2

### BELMONT SCHOOL
Warden Hill Road, Cheltenham, Gloucestershire GL51 3AT
*Website:* www.belmont.gloucs.sch.uk
*Type:* Co-educational Day Only 5–16
*Special needs:* ADD ADHD ASP **BESD MLD** SP&LD
*Wheelchair access:* WA2

### BETTRIDGE SCHOOL
Warden Hill Road, Cheltenham, Gloucestershire GL51 3AT
*Website:* www.bettridge.org.uk
*Type:* Co-educational Day Only 2–19
*Special needs:* ASD DOW EPI PMLD **SLD** VI
*Wheelchair access:* W

**CAM HOUSE SCHOOL**
Drake Lane, Dursley,
Gloucestershire GL11 5HD
*Website:*
www.camhouseschool.ik.org
*Type:* Boys Boarding and Day
11–16
*Special needs:* **BESD**

**COLN HOUSE SCHOOL**
Horcott Road, Fairford,
Gloucestershire GL7 4DB
*Type:* Co-educational Boarding
and Day 9–16
*Special needs:* **BESD**

**HEART OF THE FOREST
COMMUNITY SPECIAL
SCHOOL**
Speech House, Coleford,
Gloucestershire GL16 7EJ
*Type:* Co-educational Day Only
3–19
*Special needs:* ASD **DOW
PMLD SLD**
*Wheelchair access:* WA1

**THE MILESTONE SCHOOL**
Longford Lane, Gloucestershire
GL2 9EU
*Type:* Co-educational Day Only
2–16
*Special needs:* ADHD ASD **ASP**
BESD CP DOW EPI **MLD PMLD
SLD** VI
*Wheelchair access:* WA1

**PATERNOSTER SCHOOL**
Watermoor Road, Cirencester,
Gloucestershire GL7 1JS
*Website:* www.paternoster.
gloucs.ik.org
*Type:* Co-educational Day Only
2–16
*Special needs:* PMLD **SLD**
*Wheelchair access:* WA1

**SANDFORD SCHOOL**
Seven Springs, Cheltenham,
Gloucestershire GL53 9NG
*Type:* Co-educational Day Only
6–16
*Special needs:* **BESD**

**THE SHRUBBERIES SCHOOL**
Oldends Lane, Stonehouse,
Gloucestershire GL10 2DG
*Website:* www.shrubberies.
gloucs.sch.uk
*Type:* Co-educational Day Only
2–19
*Special needs:* ASD **ASP PMLD
SLD**
*Wheelchair access:* WA1

# SOUTH GLOUCESTERSHIRE

**South Gloucestershire
Council Education
Service**

**Bowling Hill
Chipping Sodbury
Bristol
BS37 6JX**

**CULVERHILL SCHOOL**
Kelston Close, Yate, South
Gloucestershire BS37 4SZ
*Website:*
www.culverhillschool.ik.org
*Type:* Co-educational Day Only
7–16
*Special needs:* ADD ADHD ASD
ASP BESD CP DOW DYP EPI HI
**MLD** SP&LD VI
*Wheelchair access:* WA1

**NEW SIBLANDS SCHOOL**
Easton Hill Road, Thornbury,
South Gloucestershire
BS35 2JU
*Type:* Co-educational Day Only
2–19
*Special needs:* ASD **PMLD SLD**

**WARMLEY PARK SCHOOL**
Tower Road North, Bristol
BS30 8XL
*Website:*
www.warmleypark.org.uk
*Type:* Co-educational Day Only
*Special needs:* ASD **PMLD SLD**
*Wheelchair access:* WA1

# HAMPSHIRE

## Hampshire County Council

**The Castle**
Winchester
Hampshire
SO23 8UG

### BASINGSTOKE SCHOOL PLUS
Pack Lane, Basingstoke,
Hampshire RG22 5TH
*Type:* Co-educational Day and
Boarding 10–16
*Special needs:* **BESD**

### BAYCROFT SCHOOL
Gosport Road, Fareham,
Hampshire PO14 2AE
*Type:* Co-educational Day Only
11–16
*Special needs:* ASD **ASP MLD**

### DOVE HOUSE SPECIAL SCHOOL
Sutton Road, Basingstoke,
Hampshire RG21 5SU
*Type:* Co-educational Day Only
11–16
*Special needs:* ASD **ASP MLD**

### FOREST EDGE SPECIAL SCHOOL
Lydlynch Road, Southampton,
Hampshire SO40 3DW
*Type:* Co-educational Day Only
4–11
*Special needs:* ASD MLD
SP&LD
*Wheelchair access:* WA1

### GLENWOOD SPECIAL SCHOOL
Washington Road, Emsworth,
Hampshire PO10 7NN
*Website:*
www.glenwood.hants.sch.uk
*Type:* Co-educational Day Only
11–16
*Special needs:* **MLD**
*Wheelchair access:* WA2

### HEATHFIELD SPECIAL SCHOOL
Oldbury Way, Fareham,
Hampshire PO14 3BN
*Type:* Co-educational Day Only
3–11
*Special needs:* ADHD ASD **ASP**
BESD CP DOW DYP EPI HEA HI
**MLD** SP&LD VI
*Wheelchair access:* WA1

### HENRY TYNDALE SPECIAL SCHOOL
Ship Lane, Farnborough,
Hampshire GU14 8BX
*Type:* Co-educational Day Only
2–19
*Special needs:* ASD **ASP MLD
PMLD SLD**
*Wheelchair access:* WA1

### HOLLYWATER SCHOOL
Mill Chase Road, Bordon,
Hampshire GU35 0HA
*Type:* Co-educational Day Only
2–19
*Special needs:* ADD ADHD ASD
**ASP** DOW EPI **MLD** PMLD **SLD**
TOU
*Wheelchair access:* WA1

### ICKNIELD SPECIAL SCHOOL
River Way, Andover, Hampshire
SP11 6LT
*Type:* Co-educational Day Only
2–19
*Special needs:* ASD **ASP PMLD
SLD**
*Wheelchair access:* WA1

### LAKESIDE SPECIAL SCHOOL
Winchester Road, Eastleigh,
Hampshire SO53 2DW
*Type:* Boarding and Day
*Special needs:* ADHD ASP
**BESD** SP&LD

### LIMINGTON HOUSE SPECIAL SCHOOL
St Andrew's Road, Basingstoke,
Hampshire RG22 6PS
*Type:* Co-educational Day Only
2–19
*Special needs:* PMLD **SLD**

### LORD WILSON SPECIAL SCHOOL
Coldeast Way, Southampton,
Hampshire SO31 7AT
*Type:* Boys 11–16

### MAPLE RIDGE SPECIAL SCHOOL
Maple Crescent, Basingstoke,
Hampshire RG21 5SX
*Type:* Co-educational Day Only
4–11
*Special needs:* ASD **MLD**
*Wheelchair access:* W

### THE MARK WAY SCHOOL
Bachelors Barn Road, Andover,
Hampshire SP10 1HR
*Website:*
www.markway.hants.sch.uk
*Type:* Co-educational Day Only
11–16
*Special needs:* **ADHD** ASD **ASP**
DYS HI **MLD** SP&LD
*Wheelchair access:* WA1

### NORMAN GATE SPECIAL SCHOOL
Vigo Road, Andover,
Hampshire SP10 1JZ
*Website:*
www.newnormangate.ik.org
*Type:* Co-educational Day Only
2–11
*Special needs:* ASD MLD
*Wheelchair access:* W

### OAK LODGE SCHOOL
Roman Road, Southampton,
Hampshire SO4 5RQ
*Type:* Co-educational Day Only
11–16
*Special needs:* ASD **MLD**
*Wheelchair access:* WA3

### OSBORNE SPECIAL SCHOOL
Andover Road, Winchester,
Hampshire SO23 7BU
*Type:* Co-educational Boarding
and Day 11–19
*Special needs:* ADD ADHD ASD
ASP BESD CP DOW EPI HEA HI
MLD PMLD SLD SP&LD TOU
*Wheelchair access:* W

## RACHEL MADOCKS
Eagle Avenue, Portsmouth,
Hampshire PO8 9XP
*Type:* Co-educational Day Only
2–19
*Special needs:* **PMLD SLD**
*Wheelchair access:* WA1

## RIVERSIDE COMMUNITY SPECIAL SCHOOL
Scratchface Lane, Waterlooville,
Hampshire PO7 5QD
*Website:*
www.riverside.hants.sch.uk
*Type:* Co-educational 3–11
*Special needs:* VI
*Wheelchair access:* W

## ST FRANCIS SPECIAL SCHOOL
Oldbury Way, Fareham,
Hampshire PO14 3BN
*Type:* Co-educational Day Only
2–19
*Special needs:* ASD **ASP** CP
EPI **PMLD SLD**
*Wheelchair access:* WA1

## SALTERNS SPECIAL SCHOOL
Commercial Road,
Southampton, Hampshire
SO40 3AF
*Type:* Co-educational Day Only
2–19
*Special needs:* ASD PMLD **SLD**
*Wheelchair access:* WA1

## SAMUEL CODY SPECIALIST SPORTS COLLEGE
Lynchford Road, Farnborough,
Hampshire GU14 6BJ
*Type:* Co-educational Day Only
11–16
*Special needs:* ASD **MLD**
*Wheelchair access:* WA3

## SAXON WOOD SPECIAL SCHOOL
Rooksdown, Basingstoke,
Hampshire RG24 9NH
*Website:* www.saxonwood.
hants.sch.uk
*Type:* Co-educational Day Only
2–11
*Special needs:* **CP EPI** HEA HI
**IM** MLD PMLD SLD VI
*Wheelchair access:* WA1

## SHEPHERDS DOWN SCHOOL
Shepherds Lane, Winchester,
Hampshire SO21 2AJ
*Type:* Co-educational Day Only
4–11
*Special needs:* ASD **MLD PMLD SLD**
*Wheelchair access:* WA1

## SUNDRIDGE SPECIAL SCHOOL
Cowplain, Hampshire PO8 8TR
*Special needs:* **BESD**

## WATERLOO SPECIAL SCHOOL
Warfield Avenue, Waterlooville,
Hampshire PO7 7JJ
*Type:* Co-educational Day Only
4–11
*Special needs:* **BESD**

## WOLVERDENE SPECIAL SCHOOL
22 Love Lane, Andover,
Hampshire SP10 2AF
*Type:* Co-educational Day and
Boarding 4–11
*Special needs:* **BESD**

## Portsmouth Education Authority

**4th Floor Civic Offices
Guildhall Square
Portsmouth
Hampshire
PO1 2BG**

## CLIFFDALE PRIMARY SCHOOL
Battenburg Avenue, Portsmouth,
Hampshire PO2 0SN
*Type:* Co-educational Day Only
4–11
*Special needs:* ASD **ASP IM MLD SLD**
*Wheelchair access:* WA1

## EAST SHORE SPECIAL SCHOOL
Eastern Road, Portsmouth,
Hampshire PO3 6EP
*Type:* Co-educational Day Only
2–19
*Special needs:* ASD DOW EPI
**PMLD SLD**
*Wheelchair access:* W

## THE FUTCHER SCHOOL
Drayton Lane, Portsmouth,
Hampshire PO6 1HG

## THE POLYGON SPECIAL SCHOOL
Handel Terrace, Southampton,
Hampshire SO1 2FH
*Website:* www.polygon.
southampton.sch.uk
*Type:* Boys Day Only 11–16
*Special needs:* ADD ADHD ASD
ASP **BESD**
*Wheelchair access:* WA2

## REDWOOD PARK SCHOOL
Wembley Grove, Portsmouth,
Hampshire PO6 2RY
*Type:* Co-educational 11–16
*Special needs:* ASD **MLD**

## VERMONT SPECIAL SCHOOL
Vermont Close, Southampton,
Hampshire SO1 7LT
*Type:* Boys Day Only 4–11
*Special needs:* ADD ADHD ASD
**BESD** MLD

## WATERSIDE SCHOOL & UNIT
Tipner Lane, Portsmouth,
Hampshire PO2 8RA
*Website:*
www.watersideschool.com
*Type:* Co-educational Boarding
and Day 11–16
*Special needs:* ADD ADHD
**BESD** TOU
*Wheelchair access:* W

## THE WILLOWS CENTRE FOR CHILDREN
Battenburg Avenue,
Portsmouth, Hampshire
PO2 0SN
*Website:* www.
willowsnurseryschool.co.uk
*Type:* Co-educational Day Only
2–5
*Special needs:* ADD ADHD ASD
**ASP** BESD CP DOW DYP DYS
EPI HEA HI **MLD** SLD SP&LD VI
*Wheelchair access:* WA1

## Southampton Lifelong Learning & Leisure Directorate

5th Floor
Frobisher House
Nelson Gate
Southampton
SO15 1BZ

**THE CEDAR SPECIAL SCHOOL**
Redbridge Lane, Southampton,
Hampshire SO16 0XN
*Type:* Co-educational 2–16
*Wheelchair access:* WA1

**GREAT OAKS SCHOOL**
Vermont Close, Southampton,
Hampshire SO16 7LT
*Website:* www.greatoaks.
southampton.sch.uk
*Type:* Co-educational Day Only
11–16
*Special needs:* ASD **ASP MLD
SLD**
*Wheelchair access:* WA1

**NETLEY COURT SPECIAL SCHOOL**
Victoria Road, Southampton,
Hampshire SO31 5DR
*Type:* Co-educational Day Only
4–11
*Special needs:* ASD **MLD SLD**
SP&LD

# HEREFORDSHIRE

## Herefordshire Council

PO Box 185
Blackfriars Street
Hereford
Herefordshire
HR4 9ZR

**BLACKMARSTON SCHOOL**
Honddu Close, Hereford,
Herefordshire HR2 7NX
*Type:* Co-educational Day Only
3–11
*Special needs:* **PMLD SLD**
*Wheelchair access:* WA1

**THE BROOKFIELD SCHOOL**
Grandstand Road,
Herefordshire HR4 9NG
*Type:* Co-educational Day Only
*Special needs:* **BESD** MLD

**WESTFIELD SCHOOL**
Westfield Walk, Leominster,
Herefordshire HR6 8HD
*Website:*
www.westfield.hereford.sch.uk
*Type:* Co-educational Day Only
4–19
*Special needs:* ASD PMLD **SLD**
*Wheelchair access:* WA1

# HERTFORDSHIRE

## Hertfordshire Children, Schools & Families

County Hall
Hertford
Hertfordshire
SG13 8DF

**AMWELL VIEW SCHOOL**
St Margarets, Stanstead
Abbotts, Hertfordshire SG12 8EH
*Type:* Co-educational Day Only
2–19
*Special needs:* ASD **ASP** CP
DOW EPI **PMLD SLD**
*Wheelchair access:* W

**BATCHWOOD SCHOOL**
Townsend Drive, St Albans,
Hertfordshire AL3 5RP
*Type:* Co-educational Day Only
11–16
*Special needs:* **BESD**

**BOXMOOR HOUSE SCHOOL**
Box Lane, Hemel Hempstead,
Hertfordshire HP3 0DF
*Type:* Boys Day and Boarding
11–16
*Special needs:* **BESD**

**BRANDLES SCHOOL**
Weston Way, Baldock,
Hertfordshire SG7 6EY
*Type:* Boys 11–16
*Special needs:* **BESD**

**BREAKSPEARE SCHOOL**
Gallows Hill Lane, Abbots
Langley, Hertfordshire WD5 0BU
*Website:* www.breakspeare.
herts.sch.uk
*Type:* Co-educational Day Only
2–19
*Wheelchair access:* WA1

## THE COLLETT SCHOOL
Lockers Park Lane, Hemel Hempstead, Hertfordshire HP1 1TQ
Website: www.thecollettschool.co.uk
Type: Co-educational Day Only 5–16
Special needs: ADHD ASD ASP CP DOW DYP EPI HI **MLD** SLD VI
Wheelchair access: WA2

## COLNBROOK SCHOOL
Hayling Road, Watford, Hertfordshire WD19 7UY
Website: www.colnbrook.herts.sch.uk
Type: Co-educational Day Only 4–11
Special needs: ASD **MLD**

## FALCONER SCHOOL
Falconer Road, Watford, Hertfordshire WD2 3AT
Type: Boys Day and Boarding 11–16
Special needs: **BESD**

## GARSTON MANOR SCHOOL
Horseshoe Lane, Watford, Hertfordshire WD25 7HR
Type: Co-educational Day Only 11–16
Special needs: **MLD**

## GREENSIDE SCHOOL
Shephall Green, Stevenage, Hertfordshire SG2 9XS
Type: Co-educational Day Only 2–19
Special needs: ASD **ASP PMLD SLD**
Wheelchair access: W

## HAILEY HALL SCHOOL
Hailey Lane, Hertford, Hertfordshire SG13 7PB
Website: www.haileyhall.herts.sch.uk
Type: Boys Boarding and Day 11–16
Special needs: **BESD**

## HAYWOOD GROVE
St Agnells Lane, Hemel Hempstead, Hertfordshire HP2 7BG
Type: Co-educational 5–11
Special needs: **BESD**

## HEATHLANDS SCHOOL
Heathlands Drive, St Albans, Hertfordshire AL3 5AY
Website: www.healthlands.herts.sch.uk
Type: Co-educational Boarding and Day 2–18
Special needs: **HI**
Wheelchair access: WA2

## KNIGHTSFIELD SCHOOL
Knightsfield, Welwyn Garden City, Hertfordshire AL8 7LW
Website: www.knightsfield.herts.sch.uk
Type: Co-educational Day and Boarding 11–18
Special needs: **HI**
Wheelchair access: WA1

## LAKESIDE SCHOOL
Lemsford Lane, Welwyn Garden City, Hertfordshire AL8 6YN
Website: www.lakeside.herts.sch.uk
Type: Co-educational Day Only
Special needs: PMLD SLD
Wheelchair access: WA1

## LARWOOD SCHOOL
Webb Rise, Stevenage, Hertfordshire SG1 5QU
Type: Co-educational Day and Boarding 4–11
Special needs: **ADD ADHD** ASD **ASP BESD**
Wheelchair access: WA2

## LONSDALE SCHOOL
Webb Rise, Stevenage, Hertfordshire SG1 5QU
Type: Co-educational Day and Boarding 3–18
Special needs: HI **IM** VI
Wheelchair access: WA1

## MEADOW WOOD SCHOOL
Coldharbour Lane, Watford, Hertfordshire WD2 3NU
Website: www.meadowwood.herts.sch.uk
Type: Co-educational Day Only 3–11
Special needs: **IM**
Wheelchair access: WA1

## MIDDLETON SCHOOL
Walnut Tree Walk, Ware, Hertfordshire SG12 9PD
Type: Co-educational Day Only 4–11
Special needs: ASD **MLD**
Wheelchair access: WA1

## PINEWOOD SCHOOL
Hoe Lane, Ware, Hertfordshire SG12 9PB
Type: Co-educational 11–16
Special needs: **MLD**
Wheelchair access: WA1

## ST GEORGE'S SCHOOL
Watergate Road, Newport, Isle of Wight PO30 1XW
Type: Co-educational Day Only 11–19
Special needs: **MLD PMLD SLD**
Wheelchair access: W

## ST LUKE'S SCHOOL
Crouch Hall Lane, Redbourn, Hertfordshire AL3 7ET
Type: Co-educational Day Only 9–16
Special needs: ASD ASP HI **MLD**
Wheelchair access: WA1

## SOUTHFIELD SCHOOL
Travellers Lane, Hatfield, Hertfordshire AL10 8TJ
Type: Co-educational Day Only 4–11
Special needs: ASD **MLD**
Wheelchair access: WA1

## THE VALLEY SCHOOL
Valley Way, Stevenage, Hertfordshire SG2 9AB
Type: Co-educational Day Only
Special needs: **MLD**

## WATLING VIEW SCHOOL
Watling View, St Albans, Hertfordshire AL1 2NU
Website: www.watlingviewschool.co.uk
Type: Co-educational 2–19
Special needs: ASD PMLD SLD
Wheelchair access: WA1

## WOODFIELD SCHOOL
Malmes Croft, Hemel Hempstead, Hertfordshire HP3 8RL
Type: Co-educational Day Only 5–19
Special needs: ASD SLD
Wheelchair access: W

## WOOLGROVE SCHOOL
Pryor Way, Letchworth, Hertfordshire SG6 2PT
Website: www.wooldgrove.org.uk
Type: Co-educational Day Only 5–11
Special needs: ASD **MLD**
Wheelchair access: WA1

# ISLE OF WIGHT

## Isle of Wight LEA

**County Hall**
**Newport**
**Isle of Wight**
**PO30 1UD**

### MEDINA HOUSE SCHOOL
School Lane, Newport,
Isle of Wight PO30 2HS
*Type:* Co-educational Day Only
2–11
*Special needs:* ASD **ASP** BESD
CB **MLD** PMLD **SLD**
*Wheelchair access:* WA1

# KENT

## Kent County Council

**Education and Learning**
**County Hall**
**Maidstone**
**Kent**
**ME14 1XQ**

### BOWER GROVE SCHOOL
Fant Lane, Maidstone, Kent
ME16 8NL
*Website:*
www.bower-grove.kent.sch.uk
*Type:* Co-educational Day Only
5–16
*Special needs:* ASD BESD DYP
MLD SP&LD
*Wheelchair access:* WA2

### BROOMHILL BANK SCHOOL
Broomhill Road, Tunbridge
Wells, Kent TN3 0TB
*Website:*
www.broomhill-bank.kent.sch.uk
*Type:* Girls Boarding and Day
8–19
*Special needs:* **MLD** SP&LD

### GRANGE PARK SCHOOL
Birling Road, Maidstone, Kent
ME19 5QA
*Type:* Co-educational Day Only
11–19
*Special needs:* **ASD ASP**
*Wheelchair access:* WA2

### HARBOUR SCHOOL
Elms Vale Road, Dover, Kent
CT17 9PS
*Website:*
www.harbour.kent.sch.uk
*Type:* Co-educational Day Only
5–16
*Special needs:* **ADD ADHD**
ASD **ASP BESD CB** DOW DYP
DYS EPI HEA HI **MLD** SP&LD
TOU VI

### HIGHVIEW SCHOOL
Moat Farm Road, Folkestone,
Kent CT19 5DJ
*Type:* Co-educational Day Only
5–16
*Special needs:* **MLD**

### IFIELD SCHOOL
Cedar Avenue, Gravesend,
Kent DA12 5JT
*Type:* Co-educational Day Only
4–19
*Special needs:* ASD DOW IM
MLD PMLD SP&LD
*Wheelchair access:* WA1

### ISP RAINHAM
Old Church, Gillingham, Kent
ME8 8AY
*Type:* Co-educational Day Only
5–11
*Special needs:* **BESD**
*Wheelchair access:* WA3

### LALEHAM GAP SCHOOL
Northdown Park Road, Margate,
Kent CT9 2TP
*Type:* Co-educational Boarding
and Day 5–16
*Special needs:* ASD **ASP** DYP
DYS SP&LD

### MEADOWFIELD SCHOOL
Swantree Avenue,
Sittingbourne, Kent ME10 4NL
*Type:* Co-educational Day Only
5–19
*Special needs:* **SLD**

### MILESTONE SCHOOL
Ash Road, Dartford,
Kent DA3 8JZ
*Website:*
www.milestone.kent.sch.uk
*Type:* Co-educational Day Only
2–19
*Special needs:* ASD **ASP PMLD
SLD** VI
*Wheelchair access:* WA1

### OAKLEY SCHOOL
Pembury Road, Tunbridge
Wells, Kent TN2 4NE
*Type:* Co-educational Day Only
5–19
*Special needs:* **PMLD**
*Wheelchair access:* WA2

**ORCHARD SCHOOL**
Cambridge Road, Canterbury,
Kent CT1 3QQ
*Website:* www.orchard.ik.org
*Type:* Co-educational Day Only
11–16
*Special needs:* **MLD**
*Wheelchair access:* W

**PORTAL HOUSE SCHOOL**
Sea Street, Dover,
Kent CT15 6AR
*Type:* Co-educational Day Only
11–16
*Special needs:* **BESD**
*Wheelchair access:* WA3

**RIDGE VIEW SCHOOL**
Cage Green Road, Tonbridge,
Kent TN10 4PT
*Website:* www.ridge-view.kent.
sch.uk
*Type:* Co-educational Day Only
2–19
*Special needs:* ASD **ASP** DOW
**PMLD SLD**
*Wheelchair access:* WA1

**ROWHILL SCHOOL**
Stock Lane, Dartford,
Kent DA2 7BZ
*Website:* www.rowhill.kent.sch.uk
*Type:* Co-educational Day Only
5–16
*Special needs:* **BESD**
*Wheelchair access:* WA1

**ST ANTHONY'S SCHOOL**
St Anthony's Way, Margate,
Kent CT9 3RA
*Website:*
www.st-anthonys.kent.sch.uk
*Type:* Co-educational Day Only
3–16
*Special needs:* BESD

**STONE BAY SCHOOL**
Stone Road, Broadstairs,
Kent CT10 1EB
*Type:* Boarding and Day
*Special needs:* ASD **ASP** CB
MLD SLD
*Wheelchair access:* WA3

**VALENCE SCHOOL**
Westerham, Kent TN16 1QN
*Type:* Co-educational Boarding
and Day 5–19
*Special needs:* CP EPI
*Wheelchair access:* WA1

**WYVERN SCHOOL**
Willesborough Site, Ashford,
Kent TN24 0QF
*Type:* Co-educational Day Only
5–19
*Special needs:* MLD SLD

## Medway Towns Education and Leisure

**Civic Centre**
**Strood**
**Rochester**
**Kent**
**ME2 4AU**

**BRADFIELDS SCHOOL**
Churchill Avenue, Chatham,
Kent ME5 0LB
*Type:* Co-educational Day Only
11–19
*Special needs:* ASD **MLD**
*Wheelchair access:* WA1

**DANECOURT SCHOOL**
Hotel Road, Gillingham,
Kent ME8 6AA
*Type:* Co-educational Day Only
4–11
*Special needs:* ADD ADHD ASD
**ASP** DOW **MLD** SLD SP&LD
*Wheelchair access:* WA1

# LANCASHIRE

## Blackburn with Darwen Council

**King William Street**
**Town Hall**
**Blackburn**
**Lancashire**
**BB1 7DY**

**BROADLANDS SCHOOL**
Roman Road, Blackburn,
Lancashire BB1 2LA
*Type:* Co-educational Day Only
3–5

**CROSSHILL SCHOOL**
Shadsworth Road, Blackburn,
Lancashire BB1 2HR
*Type:* Co-educational Day Only
11–16
*Special needs:* **MLD**
*Wheelchair access:* WA1

**FERNHURST SCHOOL**
Heys Lane, Blackburn,
Lancashire BB2 4NW

**NEWFIELD SCHOOL**
Roman Road, Blackburn,
Lancashire BB1 2LA
*Type:* Co-educational Day Only
2–19
*Special needs:* ASD **ASP**
**PMLD SLD**
*Wheelchair access:* WA1

**SUNNYHURST CENTRE**
Salisbury Road, Darwen,
Lancashire BB3 1HZ
*Type:* Co-educational Day Only
5–16

## Blackpool Borough Council

**PO Box 77**
**Town Hall**
**Blackpool**
**Lancashire**
**FY1 1AD**

**HIGHFURLONG SCHOOL**
Blackpool Old Road, Blackpool,
Lancashire FY3 7LR

**PARK SCHOOL**
Whitegate Drive, Blackpool,
Lancashire FY3 9HF
*Type:* Co-educational Day Only
*Special needs:* **MLD**
*Wheelchair access:* W

## Lancashire Education and Cultural Services Directorate

PO Box 78 County Hall
Fishergate
Preston
Lancashire
PR1 8XJ

### ASTLEY PARK SCHOOL
Harrington Road, Chorley,
Lancashire PR7 1JZ
*Type:* Co-educational Day Only
4–16
*Special needs:* **MLD**
*Wheelchair access:* W

### BEACON SCHOOL
Tanhouse Road, Skelmersdale,
Lancashire WN8 6BA
*Type:* Co-educational Day Only
5–16
*Special needs:* **BESD**

### BLEASDALE HOUSE SCHOOL
Emesgate Lane, Carnforth,
Lancashire LA5 0RG
*Type:* Co-educational Boarding
and Day 2–19
*Special needs:* CP EPI HEA
**PMLD** SLD VI
*Wheelchair access:* WA1

### BROADFIELD SCHOOL
Fielding Lane, Accrington,
Lancashire BB5 3BE
*Type:* Co-educational Day Only
*Special needs:* ASD **MLD** SLD
*Wheelchair access:* WA1

### BROOKFIELD SCHOOL
Fouldrey Avenue, Poulton-le-
Fylde, Lancashire FY6 7HT
*Type:* Co-educational Day Only
11–16
*Special needs:* **BESD**
*Wheelchair access:* WA2

### CALDER VIEW SCHOOL
March Street, Burnley,
Lancashire BB12 0BU
*Type:* Co-educational Day Only
4–16
*Special needs:* ASD ASP **MLD**
**SLD** SP&LD
*Wheelchair access:* W

### THE COPPICE SCHOOL
Ash Grove, Preston, Lancashire
PR5 6GY
*Type:* Co-educational Day Only
2–19
*Special needs:* ASD CP PMLD
SLD VI
*Wheelchair access:* WA1

### CRIBDEN HOUSE SCHOOL
Haslingden Road, Rossendale,
Lancashire BB4 6RX
*Type:* Co-educational Day Only
5–11
*Special needs:* **BESD**

### GREAT ARLEY SCHOOL
Holly Road, Blackpool,
Lancashire FY5 4HH
*Type:* Co-educational 4–16
*Special needs:* **MLD**

### HILLSIDE SPECIALIST SCHOOL
Ribchester Road, Preston,
Lancashire PR3 3XB
*Type:* Co-educational Day Only
2–16
*Special needs:* ASD **ASP**

### KINGSBURY SCHOOL
Skelmersdale, Lancashire
WN8 8EH
*Website:*
www.kingsbury.lancs.sch.uk
*Type:* Co-educational Day Only
2–11
*Special needs:* ASD MLD PMLD
SLD
*Wheelchair access:* WA2

### THE LOYNE SPECIALIST SCHOOL
Sefton Drive, Lancaster,
Lancashire LA1 2PZ
*Website:* www.loyneschool.org.uk
*Type:* Co-educational Day Only
2–19
*Special needs:* ASD **ASP BESD**
**EPI HI PMLD SLD** VI
*Wheelchair access:* WA1

### MAYFIELD SCHOOL
Gloucester Road, Chorley,
Lancashire PR7 3HN
*Website:* www.
mayfieldspecialschool.co.uk
*Type:* Co-educational Day Only
2–19
*Special needs:* ADD ADHD ASD
**ASP** BESD **CB** CP DOW DYP
EPI HEA HI IM **MLD PMLD SLD**
SP&LD TOU VI W

### MOOR HEY SCHOOL
Far Croft, Preston, Lancashire
PR5 5SU
*Type:* Co-educational Day Only
5–16
*Special needs:* **MLD**

### MOORBROOK SCHOOL
Ainslie Road, Preston,
Lancashire PR2 3DB
*Type:* Co-educational Day Only
11–16
*Special needs:* **BESD**

### MOORLANDS VIEW SCHOOL
Manchester Road, Lancashire
BB1 5PQ
*Type:* Co-educational Day Only
11–16

### MORECAMBE AND HEYSHAM ROAD SCHOOL
Morecambe Road, Morecambe,
Lancashire LA3 3AB
*Website:* www.morecombe.
lancsngfl.ac.uk
*Type:* Co-educational Day Only
3–16
*Special needs:* ASD BESD DOW
HI **MLD** VI

### NORTH CLIFFE SCHOOL
Blackburn Old Road, Blackburn,
Lancashire BB6 7UW
*Type:* Co-educational Day Only
5–16
*Special needs:* **MLD**
*Wheelchair access:* WA2

### OAKFIELD HOUSE SCHOOL
Station Road, Preston,
Lancashire PR4 0YH
*Website:*
www.oakfieldhouseschool.co.uk
*Type:* Boys Day Only 6–11

**PEAR TREE SCHOOL**
29 Station Road, Kirkham,
Lancashire PR4 2HA
*Type:* Co-educational Day Only
2–19
*Special needs:* PMLD **SLD**
*Wheelchair access:* WA1

**PENDLE COMMUNITY HIGH SCHOOL AND COLLEGE**
Gibfield Road, Colne,
Lancashire BB8 8JT
*Type:* Co-educational Day Only
11–19
*Special needs:* ADHD ASD **MLD PMLD SLD**
*Wheelchair access:* WA1

**RED MARSH SCHOOL**
Holly Road, Blackpool,
Lancashire FY5 4HH
*Website:*
www.redmarsh.lancs.sch.uk
*Type:* Co-educational Day Only
2–19
*Special needs:* ASD PMLD **SLD**
*Wheelchair access:* WA1

**ROYAL CROSS SCHOOL**
Elswick Road, Preston,
Lancashire PR2 1NT
*Website:*
www.royalcross.lancs.sch.uk
*Type:* Co-educational Day Only
4–11
*Special needs:* **HI** SP&LD
*Wheelchair access:* WA1

**TOR VIEW SCHOOL**
Clod Lane, Haslingden,
Lancashire BB4 6LR
*Website:*
www.torview.lancsngfl.ac.uk
*Type:* Co-educational Day Only
4–19
*Special needs:* ADHD ASD **ASP CB** DOW EPI **HEA** HI **MLD PMLD SLD** VI
*Wheelchair access:* WA1

**WENNINGTON HALL**
Wennington, Lancashire LA2 8NS
*Type:* Boys Boarding and Day
*Special needs:* ADHD **BESD**
*Wheelchair access:* WA3

**WEST LANCASHIRE COMMUNITY HIGH SCHOOL**
School Lane, Skelmersdale,
Lancashire WN8 8EH
*Type:* Co-educational Day Only
11–19
*Special needs:* ASD **ASP MLD PMLD SLD** SP&LD
*Wheelchair access:* WA1

**WHITE ASH SCHOOL**
Thwaites Road, Accrington,
Lancashire BB5 4QG
*Website:*
www.whiteash.lancsngfl.ac.uk
*Type:* Co-educational Day Only
3–19
*Special needs:* **ASD** ASP CP DOW EPI HI **PMLD SLD** SP&LD VI
*Wheelchair access:* WA1

# LEICESTERSHIRE

**Leicester Education Department**

**Marlborough House
38 Welford Place
Leicester
Leicestershire
LE2 7AA**

**ASH FIELD SCHOOL**
Broad Avenue, Leicester,
Leicestershire LE5 4PY
*Type:* Co-educational Day and Boarding 14–19
*Special needs:* **CP** HI SP&LD VI
*Wheelchair access:* WA1

**ELLESMERE COLLEGE**
Ellesmere Road, Leicester,
Leicestershire LE3 1BE
*Website:*
www.ellesmere.leicester.sch.uk
*Type:* Co-educational Day Only
11–19
*Special needs:* **MLD**
*Wheelchair access:* WA2

**KEYHAM LODGE SCHOOL**
Keyham Lane, Leicester,
Leicestershire LE5 1FG
*Type:* Boys Day Only 11–16
*Special needs:* **BESD**

**MILLGATE SCHOOL**
18a Scott Street, Leicester,
Leicestershire LE2 6DW
*Type:* Boys Boarding and Day
11–16
*Special needs:* ADD ADHD **BESD**
*Wheelchair access:* WA2

**NETHER HALL SCHOOL**
Netherhall Road, Leicester,
Leicestershire LE5 1DT
*Type:* Co-educational Day Only
5–19
*Special needs:* ASD **ASP PMLD SLD**
*Wheelchair access:* WA1

**OAKLANDS SCHOOL**
Whitehall Road, Leicester,
Leicestershire LE5 6GJ
*Type:* Co-educational Day Only
5–11
*Special needs:* ASD DOW EPI **MLD** SP&LD
*Wheelchair access:* W

**WEST GATE SCHOOL**
Glenfield Road, Leicester,
Leicestershire LE3 6DN
*Website:*
www.westgate.leicester.sch.uk
*Type:* Co-educational Day Only
5–19
*Special needs:* ADHD ASD **ASP** BESD CP DOW EPI HI **MLD PMLD SLD** SP&LD VI
*Wheelchair access:* WA1

**WESTERN PARK SCHOOL**
Western Park, Leicester,
Leicestershire LE3 6HX
*Type:* Co-educational Day Only
*Special needs:* ADD ASP CP
DOW DYP EPI HEA HI SP&LD
TOU VI
*Wheelchair access:* W

## Leicestershire
## Education Offices

**County Hall**
**Glenfield**
**Leicester**
**LE3 8RF**

**ASHMOUNT SCHOOL**
Ashmount, Loughborough,
Leicestershire LE11 2BG
*Type:* Co-educational Day Only
3–19
*Special needs:* ASD CP DOW
EPI PMLD **SLD**
*Wheelchair access:* WA1

**BIRKETT HOUSE SPECIAL
SCHOOL**
Launceston Road, Magna,
Leicestershire LE18 2FZ
*Type:* Co-educational 5–19
*Special needs:* ASD CP DOW
EPI HI **PMLD SLD** SP&LD VI
*Wheelchair access:* WA1

**DOROTHY GOODMAN
SCHOOL**
Stoke Road, Hinckley,
Leicestershire LE10 OEA
*Website:*
www.dorothygoodman.co.uk
*Type:* Co-educational Day Only
3–19
*Special needs:* ADHD ASD
**ASP** CB DOW EPI HEA **MLD**
**PMLD SLD**
*Wheelchair access:* WA1

**FOREST WAY AREA SPECIAL
SCHOOL**
Warren Hius Road, Leicester,
Leicestershire LE67 4UU
*Type:* Co-educational Day Only
3–19
*Special needs:* ASD BESD CP
DOW EPI HEA HI **MLD** PMLD
**SLD** SP&LD VI
*Wheelchair access:* WA1

**MAPLEWELL HALL SCHOOL**
Maplewell Road,
Loughborough, Leicestershire
LE12 8QY
*Type:* Co-educational Day Only
11–16
*Special needs:* ASD **MLD**
*Wheelchair access:* WA3

# LINCOLNSHIRE

## Lincolnshire County
## Council

**County Offices**
**Newland**
**Lincoln**
**Lincolnshire**
**LN1 1YQ**

**AMBERGATE SCHOOL**
Dysart Road, Grantham,
Lincolnshire NG31 7LP
*Website:*
www.ambergateschool.co.uk
*Type:* Co-educational 5–16
*Special needs:* **MLD**
*Wheelchair access:* W

**THE ASH VILLA SPECIAL
SCHOOL**
Rauceby Hospital, Sleaford,
Lincolnshire NG34 8QA
*Type:* Co-educational Boarding
and Day 8–18
*Special needs:* ADD ADHD ASP
BESD HEA
*Wheelchair access:* W

**THE ERESBY SCHOOL**
Eresby Avenue, Spilsby,
Lincolnshire PE23 5HU
*Type:* Co-educational Day Only
2–19
*Special needs:* PMLD SLD
*Wheelchair access:* WA1

**FORTUNA SCHOOL**
Kingsdown Road, Lincoln,
Lincolnshire LN6 0FB
*Type:* Co-educational Day Only
*Special needs:* **BESD**
*Wheelchair access:* WA1

**GARTH SCHOOL**
Pinchbeck Road, Spalding,
Lincolnshire PE11 1QF
*Website:* www.
spaldingspecialschools.co.uk
*Type:* Co-educational Day Only
2–19
*Special needs:* ASD PMLD **SLD**
*Wheelchair access:* WA1

**GOSBERTON HOUSE
SCHOOL**
Westhorpe Road, Spalding,
Lincolnshire PE11 4EW
*Type:* Co-educational Day Only
*Special needs:* ASD **ASP** MLD VI

**JOHN FIELDING SCHOOL**
Ashlawn Drive, Boston,
Lincolnshire PE21 9PX
*Website:*
www.johnfieldingschool.co.uk
*Type:* Co-educational Day Only
2–19
*Special needs:* **ASP DOW EPI**
**HEA HI IM PMLD SLD**
*Wheelchair access:* WA1

**THE LADY JANE FRANKLIN
SCHOOL**
Partney Road, Spilsby,
Lincolnshire PE23 5EJ
*Type:* Co-educational Day Only
11–16
*Special needs:* ADD **ADHD** ASD
**ASP BESD CB** HEA
*Wheelchair access:* WA1

**THE PHOENIX SCHOOL**
Great North Road, Grantham,
Lincolnshire NG31 2LH

**PRIORY SCHOOL**
Neville Avenue, Spalding,
Lincolnshire PE11 2EH
*Type:* Co-educational Day Only
11–16
*Special needs:* ADD **ADHD** ASD
**ASP** BESD DOW **MLD**
*Wheelchair access:* WA2

**QUEENS PARK SCHOOL**
South Park, Lincoln, Lincolnshire
LN5 8EW
*Website:* www.
queensparkschool.net
*Type:* Co-educational Day Only
2–19
*Special needs:* ASD ASP CP
DOW HEA **PMLD SLD**
*Wheelchair access:* W

**ST BERNARD'S SCHOOL**
Wood Lane, Louth, Lincolnshire
LN11 8RS
*Type:* Co-educational Day and
Boarding 2–19
*Special needs:* **SLD**

**ST CHRISTOPHER'S SCHOOL**
Hykeham Road, Lincoln,
Lincolnshire LN6 8AR
*Type:* Co-educational 3–16

**ST FRANCIS SPECIAL
SCHOOL**
Wickenby Crescent, Lincoln,
Lincolnshire LN1 3TJ
*Type:* Co-educational Day and
Boarding 2–19
*Special needs:* **CP** DOW EPI
HEA MLD
*Wheelchair access:* W

**ST LAWRENCE SCHOOL**
Bowl Alley Lane, Horncastle,
Lincolnshire LN9 5EJ
*Type:* Co-educational Day and
Boarding
*Special needs:* ASD DOW **MLD**
SP&LD VI
*Wheelchair access:* WA2

**SANDON SCHOOL**
Sandon Close, Grantham,
Lincolnshire NG31 9AX
*Type:* Co-educational Day Only
2–19
*Special needs:* ASD CP **DOW**
EPI **PMLD SLD**
*Wheelchair access:* W

**WILLIAM HARRISON SPECIAL
SCHOOL**
Middlefield Lane,
Gainsborough, Lincolnshire
DN21 1PU
*Type:* Co-educational Day Only
3–16
*Special needs:* ADD ADHD ASD
DOW EPI HI MLD SP&LD
*Wheelchair access:* WA1

**THE WILLOUGHBY SCHOOL**
South Road, Bourne,
Lincolnshire PE10 9JE
*Type:* Co-educational Day Only
2–19
*Special needs:* ASD **ASP** CP
DOW **PMLD SLD**
*Wheelchair access:* W

# NORTH EAST LINCOLNSHIRE

**North East Lincolnshire
County Council**

**Municipal Offices
Town Hall Square
Grimsby
North East Lincolnshire
DN31 1HU**

**CAMBRIDGE PARK SCHOOL**
Cambridge Road, Grimsby,
North East Lincolnshire DN34 5EB
*Website:* www.
cambridgepark.ne-lincs.sch.uk
*Type:* Co-educational Day Only
3–16
*Special needs:* ADD ASD **ASP**
BESD DOW DYP EPI HI **MLD**
SP&LD VI
*Wheelchair access:* WA1

**HUMBERSTON PARK
SCHOOL**
St Thomas Close, Humberston,
North East Lincolnshire DN36
4HS
*Website:*
www.humberstonpark.org.uk
*Type:* Co-educational Day Only
3–19
*Special needs:* ASD PMLD **SLD**
*Wheelchair access:* WA1

# NORTH LINCOLNSHIRE

## North Lincolnshire Education Offices

**Pittwood House**
**Ashby Road**
**Scunthorpe**
**North Lincolnshire**
**DN16 1AB**

## ST HUGH'S SCHOOL
Bushfield Road, Scunthorpe,
North Lincolnshire DN16 1NB
*Type:* Co-educational Day Only
11–19
*Special needs:* ADD ADHD ASD
ASP CP DOW EPI HEA HI **MLD**
PMLD **SLD** VI
*Wheelchair access:* WA1

## ST LUKE'S PRIMARY SCHOOL
Burghley Road, Scunthorpe,
North Lincolnshire DN16 1JD
*Type:* Co-educational Day Only
3–11
*Special needs:* ADHD ASD CB
CP DOW EPI HI **MLD PMLD**
**SLD** VI
*Wheelchair access:* WA1

# LONDON

## Barnet LEA

**The Burroughs**
**Hendon**
**London**
**NW4 4BG**

### MAPLEDOWN SCHOOL
Claremont Road, London
NW2 1TR
*Website:*
www.mapledownschool.org
*Type:* Co-educational Day Only
11–19
*Special needs:* PMLD SLD
*Wheelchair access:* WA1

### NORTHWAY SCHOOL
The Fairway, London NW7 3HS
*Type:* Co-educational Day Only
5–11
*Special needs:* ASD **ASP** DOW
DYC DYS EPI HEA HI **MLD**
TOU VI
*Wheelchair access:* W

### OAK LODGE SCHOOL
Heath View, London N2 0QY
*Type:* Co-educational Day Only
11–19
*Special needs:* ASD MLD
*Wheelchair access:* WA1

### OAKLEIGH SCHOOL
Oakleigh Road North, London
N20 0DH
*Type:* Co-educational Day Only
2–11
*Special needs:* ASD PMLD **SLD**
*Wheelchair access:* WA1

## Bexley Council

**Education Offices**
**Hill View Drive**
**Welling**
**Kent**
**DA16 3RY**

### MARLBOROUGH SCHOOL
Marlborough Park Avenue,
Sidcup, Kent DA15 9DP
*Type:* Co-educational Day Only
11–19
*Special needs:* **PMLD SLD**
*Wheelchair access:* WA1

### OAKWOOD SCHOOL
Woodside Road, Bexleyheath,
Kent DA7 6LB
*Website:*
www.oakwood.bexley.sch.uk
*Type:* Co-educational Day Only
11–16
*Special needs:* **BESD**

### SHENSTONE SCHOOL
Old Road, Crayford,
Kent DA1 4DZ
*Type:* Co-educational Day Only
2–11
*Special needs:* ASD **ASP** CP
DOW EPI HI **PMLD SLD** VI
*Wheelchair access:* WA1

### WESTBROOKE SCHOOL
South Gipsy Road, Welling,
Kent DA16 1JB
*Type:* Co-educational Day Only
5–11
*Special needs:* ASP **BESD**
*Wheelchair access:* WA2

## WOODSIDE SCHOOL
Halt Robin Road, Belvedere,
Kent DA17 6DW
*Type:* Co-educational Day Only
5–16
*Special needs:* ADHD ASD **ASP**
HI **MLD** VI
*Wheelchair access:* WA3

## Brent Council

**Chesterfield House
9 Park Lane
Wembley
Middlesex
HA9 7RW**

## GROVE PARK SCHOOL
Grove Park, London NW9 0JY
*Type:* Co-educational Day Only
2–19
*Special needs:* CP EPI **HEA**
*Wheelchair access:* WA1

## HAY LANE SCHOOL
Grove Park, London NW9 0JY
*Type:* Co-educational Day Only
2–19
*Special needs:* PMLD SLD
*Wheelchair access:* W

## MANOR SCHOOL
Chamberlayne Road, London
NW10 3NT
*Type:* Co-educational Day Only
4–11
*Special needs:* ASD **ASP**
**MLD SLD**
*Wheelchair access:* WA2

## VERNON HOUSE SCHOOL
Drury Way, London NW10 0NQ
*Type:* Co-educational 5–12
*Special needs:* **BESD**

## WOODFIELD SCHOOL
Glenwood Avenue, London
NW9 7LY
*Website:*
www.woodfield.surrey.sch.uk
*Type:* Co-educational Day Only
11–16
*Special needs:* ASD **MLD**
SP&LD
*Wheelchair access:* WA1

## Bromley Education Offices

**Civic Centre
Stockwell Close
Bromley
Kent
BR1 3UH**

## BURWOOD SCHOOL
Avalon Road, Orpington, Kent
BR6 9BD
*Type:* Boys Day Only 9–16

## GLEBE SCHOOL
Hawes Lane, West Wickham,
Kent BR4 9AE
*Website:*
www.glebe.bromley.sch.uk
*Type:* Co-educational Day Only
11–16
*Special needs:* ASD **MLD**

## MARJORIE MCCLURE SCHOOL
Hawkwood Lane, Chislehurst,
Kent BR7 5PS
*Type:* Co-educational Day Only
3–19
*Special needs:* CP EPI HEA
*Wheelchair access:* W

## RIVERSIDE SCHOOL
Main Road, Orpington, Kent
BR5 3HS
*Type:* Co-educational Day Only
4–19
*Special needs:* PMLD SLD
*Wheelchair access:* WA1

## Camden LEA

**Crowndale Centre
218–220 Eversholt Street
London
NW1 1BD**

## BECKFORD PRIMARY SCHOOL
Dornfell Street,
London NW6 1QL
*Type:* Co-educational Day Only
3–11

## CHALCOT SCHOOL
Harmood Street,
London NW1 8DP
*Website:*
www.chalcot.camden.sch.uk
*Type:* Boys Day Only
*Special needs:* **BESD**

## CHRISTOPHER HATTON PRIMARY SCHOOL
38 Laystall Street,
London EC1R 4PQ
*Type:* Co-educational Day Only
3–11
*Special needs:* SP&LD

## FRANK BARNES SCHOOL
Harley Road, London NW3 3BY
*Website:*
www.fbarnes.camden.sch.uk
*Type:* Co-educational Day Only
2–11
*Special needs:* **HI**

## JACK TAYLOR SCHOOL
Ainsworth Way, London NW8 0SR
*Type:* Co-educational Day Only
5–19

## REGENTS PARK UNDER 5S CENTRE
Augustus Street, London NW1 3TJ
*Type:* Co-educational Day Only
*Special needs:* ADD ADHD ASD
ASP BESD CB CP DOW DYC
DYP DYS EPI HEA HI IM MLD
PMLD SLD SP&LD TOU VI
*Wheelchair access:* W

## SOUTH CAMDEN COMMUNITY SECONDARY SCHOOL
Charrington Street, London
NW1 1RG
*Website:*
www.sccs.camden.sch.uk
*Type:* Co-educational Day Only
11–19
*Wheelchair access:* WA2

## SWISS COTTAGE SPECIALIST SEN SCHOOL
Avenue Road, London NW8 6HX
*Website:*
www.swisscottageschool.com
*Type:* Co-educational Day Only
2–16
*Special needs:* **MLD** SP&LD
*Wheelchair access:* WA1

## City of Westminster LEA

PO Box 240, 14th Floor
Westminster City Hall
64 Victoria St
London
SW1E 6QP

### COLLEGE PARK SCHOOL
Garway Road, London W2 4PH
*Type:* Co-educational Day Only
5–16
*Special needs:* **MLD**

### QUEEN ELIZABETH II SCHOOL
Kennet Road, London W9 3LG
*Type:* Co-educational Day Only
5–19
*Special needs:* PMLD SLD
*Wheelchair access:* W

## Croydon Education Department

Taberner House
Park Lane
Croydon
Surrey
CR9 1TP

### BECKMEAD SCHOOL
Monks Orchard Road,
Beckenham, Surrey BR3 3BZ
*Type:* Boys Day Only
*Special needs:* **BESD**

### BENSHAM MANOR SCHOOL
Ecclesbourne Road, Thornton
Heath, Surrey CR7 7BR
*Website:*
www.benshammanor.com
*Type:* Co-educational Day Only
11–16
*Special needs:* ASD **MLD**

### PRIORY SCHOOL
Tennison Road, London
SE25 5RR
*Type:* Co-educational Day Only
12–19
*Special needs:* ASD DOW **SLD**
*Wheelchair access:* W

### RED GATES SCHOOL
Farnborough Ave, South
Croydon, Surrey CR2 8HD
*Website:* www.redgates.
croydon.sch.uk
*Type:* Co-educational Day Only
4–12
*Special needs:* ASD **ASP PMLD
SLD**
*Wheelchair access:* WA1

### ST GILES' SCHOOL
Pampisford Road, Croydon,
Surrey CR2 6DF
*Type:* Co-educational Day Only
4–19
*Special needs:* CP DYP EPI
HEA HI **IM PMLD** VI
*Wheelchair access:* WA1

### ST NICHOLAS SCHOOL
Old Lodge Lane, Purley, Surrey
CR8 4DN
*Type:* Co-educational Day Only
4–11
*Special needs:* ASD **MLD**

### TUDOR LODGE SCHOOL
Teaching Annexe, Purley, Surrey
CR8 3NA
*Type:* Co-educational Day Only
11–17
*Special needs:* ADD ADHD
BESD
*Wheelchair access:* WA3

## Ealing Education Offices

Perceval House
14–16 Uxbridge Road
Ealing
London
W5 2HL

### BELVUE SCHOOL
Rowdell Road, Northolt,
Middlesex UB5 6AG
*Website:* www.belvueschool.org
*Type:* Co-educational Day Only
12–19
*Special needs:* ADD ASD BESD
CB **MLD** SLD SP&LD
*Wheelchair access:* W WA1

### CASTLEBAR SCHOOL
Hathaway Gardens, London
W13 0DH
*Website:*
www.castebar.ealing.sch.uk
*Type:* Co-educational Day Only
3–11
*Special needs:* ASD **ASP** HI
**MLD SLD**
*Wheelchair access:* W

### DURANTS SCHOOL
4 Pitfield Way, Enfield,
Middlesex EN3 5BY
*Type:* Co-educational Day Only
5–18
*Special needs:* SLD
*Wheelchair access:* WA3

### JOHN CHILTON SCHOOL
Compton Crescent, Northolt,
Middlesex UB5 5LD
*Type:* Co-educational Day Only

### MANDEVILLE SCHOOL
Eastcote Lane, Northolt,
Middlesex UB5 4HW
*Type:* Co-educational Day Only
2–11
*Special needs:* ASD **ASP
PMLD SLD**
*Wheelchair access:* WA1

### ST ANN'S SCHOOL
Springfield Road,
London W7 3JP
*Type:* Co-educational Day Only
*Special needs:* ASD **PMLD SLD**
*Wheelchair access:* WA1

### SPRINGHALLOW SCHOOL
Compton Close,
London W13 0JG
*Type:* Co-educational Day Only
3–16
*Special needs:* ASD **ASP**
*Wheelchair access:* W

## Enfield Education Services

Civic Centre
Silver Street
Enfield
EN1 3XY

**AYLANDS SCHOOL**
Keswick Drive, Enfield,
Middlesex EN3 6NY

**OAKTREE SCHOOL**
Chase Side, London N14 4HN
*Website:*
www.oaktree.enfield.sch.uk
*Type:* Co-educational Day Only
5–19
*Special needs:* **MLD**

**RUSSET HOUSE**
11 Autumn Close, Enfield,
Middlesex EN1 4JA
*Type:* Co-educational Day Only
3–11
*Special needs:* ASD **ASP**
*Wheelchair access:* WA2

**WAVERLEY SCHOOL**
105 The Ride, Enfield,
Middlesex EN3 7DL
*Website:*
www.waverley-school.com
*Type:* Co-educational Day Only
3–19
*Special needs:* PMLD **SLD**
*Wheelchair access:* WA1

**WEST LEA SCHOOL**
Haslebury Road,
London N9 9TU
*Website:*
www.westleaschool.co.uk
*Type:* Co-educational Day Only
4–17
*Special needs:* ADD ADHD
**ASD** ASP CP DYC DYP EPI
**HEA** HI SP&LD TOU VI
*Wheelchair access:* W

## Greenwich Education Service

Wellington Street
Woolwich
London
SE18 6PW

**CHARLTON SCHOOL**
Charlton Park Road, London
SE7 8HX
*Type:* Co-educational Boarding
and Day
*Special needs:* **CP** EPI **PMLD**
SLD SP&LD
*Wheelchair access:* W

**MOATBRIDGE SCHOOL**
Eltham Palace Road, London
SE9 5LX
*Type:* Boys Day Only 11–16
*Special needs:* **BESD**
*Wheelchair access:* WA1

**NEWHAVEN PRU SCHOOL**
Newhaven Annexe, London
SE2 0HY
*Type:* Co-educational Day Only
11–17
*Special needs:* BESD

**WATERSIDE SCHOOL**
Robert Street,
London SE18 7NB
*Type:* Co-educational Day Only
5–11

**WILLOW DENE SCHOOL**
Swingate Lane,
London SE18 2JD
*Website:*
www.willowdeneschool.co.uk
*Type:* Co-educational Day Only
2–11
*Special needs:* ASD MLD PMLD
SLD
*Wheelchair access:* WA2

## Hackney The Learning Trust

Reading Lane
Hackney
London
E8 1QG

**CRUSOE HOUSE SCHOOL**
Nile Street, London N1 7DR
*Type:* Boys Day Only
*Special needs:* **BESD**

**DOWNSVIEW SCHOOL**
Tiger Way, London E5 8QP
*Type:* Co-educational Day Only
5–16
*Special needs:* **MLD**

**HORIZON SCHOOL**
Wordsworth Road,
London N16 8BZ
*Website:*
www.horizonschool.co.uk
*Type:* Co-educational Day Only
11–16
*Special needs:* **MLD**

**ICKBURGH SCHOOL**
Ickburgh Road, London E5 8AD
*Type:* Co-educational Day Only
2–19
*Special needs:* PMLD SLD

**STORMONT HOUSE SCHOOL**
Downs Park Road, London
E5 8NP
*Type:* Co-educational 11–16
*Special needs:* HEA SP&LD

## Hammersmith and Fulham Council

King Street
London
W6 9JU

**CAMBRIDGE SCHOOL**
Cambridge Grove,
London W6 0LB
*Website:*
www.cambridge.lbhs.sch.uk
*Type:* Co-educational 11–16
*Special needs:* **ADHD ASD** ASP
**BESD MLD**
*Wheelchair access:* WA2

### GIBBS GREEN SCHOOL
Mund Street, London W14 9LY
*Type:* Co-educational Day Only
4–11
*Special needs:* **BESD**

### JACK TIZARD SCHOOL
South Africa Road,
London W12 7PA
*Website:*
www.jacktizard.lbhf.sch.uk
*Type:* Co-educational Day Only
2–19
*Special needs:* CP EPI HEA
**PMLD SLD** VI W

### QUEENSMILL SCHOOL
Clancarty Road, London
SW6 3AA
*Type:* Co-educational Day Only
3–11
*Special needs:* ASD **ASP**
*Wheelchair access:* WA1

### WOODLANE HIGH SCHOOL
Du Cane Road, London W12 0TN
*Website:*
www.woodlane.lbhf.sch.uk
*Type:* Co-educational Day Only
11–16
*Special needs:* **ASD** ASP **HEA**
SP&LD VI
*Wheelchair access:* WA1

## Haringey Education Offices

**Civic Centre**
**High Road**
**Wood Green**
**London**
**N22 8LE**

### BLANCHE NEVILE SCHOOL IN PARTNERSHIP WITH FORTISMERE SCHOOL
Burlington Road, London N10 1NJ
*Type:* Co-educational Day Only
*Special needs:* **HI**

### MOSELLE SPECIAL SCHOOL
Adams Road, London N17 6HW
*Website:*
www.moselle.haringey.sch.uk
*Type:* Co-educational Day Only
4–16
*Special needs:* ASD **ASP** BESD
**DOW** EPI **MLD SLD** SP&LD VI
*Wheelchair access:* WA2

### VALE SPECIAL SCHOOL
c/o Northumberland Park
Community School, London
N17 0PG
*Website:*
www.vale.haringey.sch.uk
*Type:* Co-educational Day Only
2–19
*Special needs:* CP EPI **IM**
SP&LD
*Wheelchair access:* WA1

### WILLIAM C HARVEY SPECIAL SCHOOL
Adams Road, London N17 6HW
*Website:* www.haringey.gov.uk
*Type:* Co-educational Day Only
4–16
*Special needs:* PMLD SLD
*Wheelchair access:* WA1

## Harrow Education Services

**PO Box 22**
**Civic Centre**
**Harrow**
**Middlesex**
**HA1 2XF**

### ALEXANDRA SCHOOL
Alexandra Avenue, Harrow,
Middlesex HA2 9DX
*Special needs:* MLD

### KINGSLEY HIGH SCHOOL
Whittlesea Road, Harrow Weald,
Middlesex HA3 6ND
*Type:* Co-educational Day Only
*Special needs:* **PMLD SLD**
*Wheelchair access:* WA1

### SHAFTESBURY SCHOOL
Headstone Lane, Harrow,
Middlesex HA3 6LE
*Type:* Co-educational Day Only
11–18
*Special needs:* MLD
*Wheelchair access:* WA1

### WOODLANDS SCHOOL
Whittlesea Road, Harrow,
Middlesex HA3 6LE
*Type:* Co-educational 3–11
*Special needs:* ASD **PMLD** SLD

## Havering LEA

**Town Hall**
**Main Road**
**Romford**
**Essex**
**RM1 3BB**

### CORBETS TEY SCHOOL
Harwood Hall Lane, Upminster,
Essex RM14 2YQ
*Website:*
www.corbetsteyschool.org.uk
*Type:* Co-educational Day Only
4–16
*Special needs:* ASD **MLD** SLD

### DYCORTS SCHOOL
Settle Road, Romford,
Essex RM3 9YA
*Type:* Co-educational Day Only
3–16
*Special needs:* DYS EPI MLD
SP&LD
*Wheelchair access:* W

### RAVENSBOURNE SCHOOL
Neave Crescent, Romford,
Essex RM3 8HN
*Type:* Co-educational Day Only
2–19
*Special needs:* ASD BESD CP
DOW DYS HEA **SLD** VI
*Wheelchair access:* W

## Hounslow Council

**Civic Centre**
**Lampton Road**
**Hounslow**
**Middlesex**
**TW3 4DN**

### THE CEDARS PRIMARY SCHOOL
High Street, Hounslow,
Middlesex TW5 9RU
*Website:*
www.cedars.hounslow.lgfl.net
*Type:* Co-educational Day Only
4–11
*Special needs:* **BESD**

## LINDON BENNETT SCHOOL

Main Street, Hanworth,
Middlesex TW13 6ST
*Website:*
www.lindonbennett.ik.org
*Type:* Co-educational Day Only
4–11
*Special needs:* ASD **PMLD SLD**
*Wheelchair access:* WA1

## MARJORY KINNON SPECIAL SCHOOL

Hatton Road, Bedfont,
Middlesex TW14 9QZ
*Website:* www.
marjorykinnonschool.co.uk
*Type:* Co-educational Day Only
4–19
*Special needs:* ASD **MLD**
*Wheelchair access:* WA1

## OAKLANDS SCHOOL

Woodlands Road, Isleworth,
Middlesex TW7 6HD
*Type:* Co-educational Day Only
11–19
*Special needs:* PMLD **SLD**
*Wheelchair access:* W

## SYON PARK SCHOOL

Twickenham Road, Isleworth,
Middlesex TW7 6AU
*Website:* www.syonpark.
hounslow.sch.uk
*Type:* Co-educational Day Only
11–16
*Special needs:* **BESD**

## Islington Council

**222 Upper Street**
**London**
**N1 1XR**

## THE BRIDGE SCHOOL & PROFESSIONAL TRAINING CENTRE

251 Hungerford Road, London
N7 9LD
*Website:* www.thebridge.
islington.sch.uk
*Type:* Co-educational Day Only
2–19
*Special needs:* ASD PMLD SLD
*Wheelchair access:* WA1

## RICHARD CLOUDESLEY SCHOOL

Golden Lane, London EC1Y 0TJ
*Type:* Co-educational Day Only
2–18
*Special needs:* CP EPI SP&LD
*Wheelchair access:* W

## SAMUEL RHODES SCHOOL

Richmond Avenue, London
N1 0LS
*Website:* www.islington.gov.uk
*Type:* Co-educational Day Only
5–16
*Special needs:* **MLD**

## Kingston Upon Thames Education & Leisure Services

**Guildhall 2**
**Kingston upon Thames**
**Surrey**
**KT1 1EU**

## BEDELSFORD SCHOOL

Grange Road, Kingston upon
Thames, Surrey KT1 2QZ
*Website:* www.bedelsford.
kingston.sch.uk
*Type:* Co-educational Day Only
2–16
*Special needs:* **CP** EPI HEA HI
MLD **PMLD** VI
*Wheelchair access:* WA1

## DYSART SCHOOL

190 Ewell Road, Surbiton,
Surrey KT6 6HL
*Website:*
www.dysart-school.org.uk
*Type:* Co-educational Day Only
4–19
*Special needs:* ASD **ASP**
PMLD **SLD**
*Wheelchair access:* WA1

## ST PHILIP'S SPECIAL SCHOOL

Harrow Close, Chessington,
Surrey KT9 2HP
*Type:* Co-educational Day Only
10–19
*Special needs:* ASD **ASP** DOW
**MLD**
*Wheelchair access:* WA3

## Lambeth Council

**Town Hall**
**Brixton Hill**
**London**
**SW2 1RW**

## ELM COURT SCHOOL

Elm Park, London SW2 2EF
*Type:* Co-educational Day Only
11–16
*Special needs:* ADD ADHD ASD
BESD **MLD** SP&LD
*Wheelchair access:* WA1

## LANSDOWNE SCHOOL

Argyll Close, London SW9 9QL
*Type:* Co-educational Day Only
5–16
*Special needs:* **MLD**

## THE LIVITY SCHOOL

Mandrell Road, London
SW2 5DW
*Type:* Co-educational Day Only
3–11
*Special needs:* ASD DOW
PMLD SLD
*Wheelchair access:* W

## THE MICHAEL TIPPETT SCHOOL

Oakden Street, London
SE11 4UG
*Type:* Co-educational Day Only
11–19
*Special needs:* ASD PMLD SLD
*Wheelchair access:* WA1

## TURNEY SCHOOL

Turney Road, London SE21 8LX
*Website:*
www.turneyschool.co.uk
*Type:* Co-educational 5–16
*Special needs:* ADD ADHD ASD
**ASP** DOW **MLD** SP&LD

## London Borough of Hillingdon

Civic Centre
High Street
Uxbridge
Middlesex
UB8 1UW

**CHANTRY SCHOOL**
Falling Lane, West Drayton,
Middlesex UB7 8AB
*Type:* Co-educational Day Only
*Special needs:* **ADD ADHD
BESD**

**GRANGEWOOD SCHOOL**
Fore Street, Pinner, Middlesex
HA5 2JQ
*Website:*
www.grangewoodschool.co.uk
*Type:* Co-educational 3–11

**HEDGEWOOD SCHOOL**
Weymouth Road, Hayes,
Middlesex UB4 8NF
*Type:* Co-educational Day Only
*Special needs:* ASD **ASP** DOW
DYP HI **PMLD** VI

**MEADOW HIGH SCHOOL**
Royal Lane, Uxbridge,
Middlesex UB8 3QU
*Website:*
www.meadowhigh.com
*Type:* Co-educational Day Only
11–18
*Special needs:* ASD **ASP MLD**
*Wheelchair access:* WA1

**MOORCROFT SCHOOL**
Bramble Close, Uxbridge,
Middlesex UB8 3BF
*Website:* www.moorcroft.
hillingdon.sch.uk
*Type:* Co-educational Day Only
11–19
*Special needs:* ASD PMLD **SLD**
*Wheelchair access:* WA1

**THE WILLOWS SCHOOL**
Stipularis Drive, Hayes,
Middlesex UB4 9QB
*Website:* www.hillingdon.gov.uk
*Type:* Co-educational Day Only
*Special needs:* **BESD**

## London Borough of Lewisham

Town Hall
Catford
London
SE6 4RU

**BRENT KNOLL SCHOOL**
Mayow Road, London SE23 2XH
*Type:* Co-educational Day Only
4–16

**GREENVALE SCHOOL**
69 Perry Rise, London SE23 2QU
*Type:* Co-educational Day Only
11–19
*Special needs:* PMLD SLD
*Wheelchair access:* W

**MEADOWGATE SCHOOL**
Revelon Road, London SE4 2PR
*Type:* Co-educational Day Only
4–11
*Special needs:* ASD **ASP** MLD
*Wheelchair access:* W

**NEW WOODLANDS SCHOOL
(JMI)**
49 Shroffold Road, Bromley,
Kent BR1 5PD
*Type:* Boys Day Only 5–11
(Key Stage 3   11–14)
*Special needs:* **ADD ADHD
BESD**
*Wheelchair access:* WA1

**PENDRAGON SCHOOL**
Pendragon Road, Bromley,
Kent BR1 5LD
*Website:* www.pendragon.
lewisham.sch.uk
*Type:* Co-educational Day Only
11–16
*Special needs:* **MLD**

**WATERGATE SCHOOL**
Lushington Road, London
SE6 3WG
*Website:* www.watergate.
lewisham.sch.uk
*Type:* Co-educational Day Only
2–11
*Special needs:* PMLD **SLD**
*Wheelchair access:* W

## London Borough of Merton

Merton Civic Centre
London Road
Morden
Surrey
SM4 5DX

**CRICKET GREEN SCHOOL**
Lower Green West, Mitcham,
Surrey CR4 3AF
*Type:* Co-educational Day Only
5–16
*Special needs:* ADHD ASD MLD
*Wheelchair access:* WA1

**MELROSE SCHOOL**
Church Road, Mitcham, Surrey
CR4 3BE
*Type:* Co-educational Day Only
9–16
*Special needs:* **BESD**

**ST ANN'S SCHOOL**
Bordesley Road, Morden,
Surrey SM4 5LT
*Website:*
www.st-anns.merton.sch.uk
*Type:* Co-educational Day Only
2–19
*Special needs:* ASD PMLD SLD
*Wheelchair access:* WA1

## London Borough of Newham

Broadway House
High Street
Stratford
London
E15 1AJ

**ELEANOR SMITH SCHOOL**
North Street, London E13 9HN
*Type:* Co-educational Day Only
5–11
*Special needs:* **BESD**

**JOHN F KENNEDY SCHOOL**
Pitchford Street, London
E15 4RZ
*Type:* Co-educational Day Only
2–19

## London Borough of Richmond upon Thames

**Regal House, First Floor**
**London Road**
**Twickenham**
**Middlesex**
**TW1 3QB**

### CLARENDON SCHOOL
Hanworth Road, Hampton,
Middlesex TW12 3DH
*Website:* www.clarendon.richmond.sch.uk
*Type:* Co-educational Day Only
7–16
*Special needs:* **MLD**
*Wheelchair access:* WA2

### STRATHMORE SCHOOL
Meadlands Drive, Petersham,
Surrey TW10 7ED
*Type:* Co-educational Day Only
7–19
*Special needs:* ASD **ASP PMLD SLD**
*Wheelchair access:* WA1

## Redbridge Education Services

**Lynton House**
**255–259 High Road**
**Ilford**
**IG1 1NN**

### HATTON SCHOOL
Roding Lane South, Woodford
Green, Essex IG8 8EU
*Type:* Co-educational Day Only
3–11
*Special needs:* ASD **ASP MLD** SP&LD

### LITTLE HEATH SCHOOL
Hainault Road, Romford, Essex
RM6 5RX
*Website:* www.littleheath.essex.sch.uk
*Type:* Co-educational Day Only
11–16
*Special needs:* ADD ADHD ASP **MLD** SP&LD

### NEW RUSH HALL SCHOOL
Fencepiece Road, Hainault,
Essex IG6 2LJ
*Website:* www.nrhs.redbridge.sch.uk
*Type:* Co-educational Day Only
4–16
*Special needs:* **BESD**

### NEWBRIDGE SCHOOL
Barley Lane Campus, Ilford,
Essex IG3 8XS
*Website:* www.newbridge.redbridge.sch.uk
*Type:* Co-educational Day Only
2–19
*Special needs:* ASD **ASP** CP MLD **PMLD SLD** VI
*Wheelchair access:* WA1

## Southwark Education

**John Smith House**
**144–152 Walworth Road**
**London**
**SE17 1JL**

### BEORMUND PRIMARY SCHOOL
Crosby Row, London SE1 3PS
*Website:* www.beormundschool.co.uk
*Type:* Co-educational Day Only
5–11
*Special needs:* **BESD**

### BREDINGHURST SCHOOL
Stuart Road, London SE15 3AZ
*Type:* Boys Boarding and Day
*Special needs:* ADD ADHD **BESD**

### CHERRY GARDEN SPECIAL PRIMARY SCHOOL
Macks Road, London SE16 3XU
*Website:* www.cherrygarden.suffolk.sch.uk
*Type:* Co-educational Day Only
2–11
*Special needs:* ASD **ASP** CP EPI HI PMLD **SLD** SP&LD VI
*Wheelchair access:* W

### HAYMERLE'S SCHOOL
Haymerle Road, London
SE15 6SY
*Type:* Co-educational Day Only
5–11
*Special needs:* ADD ADHD ASD BESD CP DOW DYP DYS EPI HEA MLD SP&LD
*Wheelchair access:* W

### HIGHSHORE SPECIAL SCHOOL
Bellenden Road, London
SE15 5BB
*Website:* www.highshore.southwark.sch.uk
*Type:* Co-educational Day Only
11–17
*Special needs:* ADD ADHD ASD DOW DYC DYP DYS EPI IM **MLD** SP&LD
*Wheelchair access:* WA1

### SPA SCHOOL
Monnow Road, London SE1 5RN
*Type:* Co-educational 11–16
*Special needs:* ASD **ASP** MLD

### TUKE SCHOOL
4 Woods Road,
London SE15 2PX
*Type:* Co-educational Day Only
11–19
*Special needs:* ASD IM **PMLD SLD**
*Wheelchair access:* WA2

## Sutton Education Offices

**The Grove**
**Carshalton**
**Surrey**
**SM5 3AL**

### CAREW MANOR SCHOOL
Church Road, Wallington,
Surrey SM6 7NH
*Website:* www.carewmanor.org.uk
*Type:* Co-educational Day Only
7–16
*Special needs:* ASD ASP **MLD**
*Wheelchair access:* WA3

**SHERWOOD PARK SCHOOL**
Streeters Lane, Wallington,
Surrey SM6 7NP
*Website:*
www.sherwoodpark.org.uk
*Type:* Co-educational Day Only
2–19
*Special needs:* ASD **ASP CP
DOW PMLD SLD**
*Wheelchair access:* WA1

**WANDLE VALLEY SCHOOL**
Welbeck Road, Carshalton,
Surrey SM5 1LW
*Type:* Co-educational Day Only
5–16
*Special needs:* **BESD**
*Wheelchair access:* WA2

## The Royal Borough of Kensington & Chelsea

**The Town Hall
Hornton Street
London
W8 7NX**

**PARKWOOD HALL SCHOOL**
Beechenlea Lane, Swanley,
Kent BR8 8DR
*Website:* www.parkwoodhall.
rbkc.sch.uk
*Type:* Co-educational Boarding
and Day 8–19
*Special needs:* ASD **DOW HEA
MLD** SLD SP&LD

## Tower Hamlets Borough Council

**Mulberry Place
5 Clove Crescent
London
E14 2BG**

**BEATRICE TATE SCHOOL**
St Jude's Road, London E2 9RW
*Website:* www.beatricetate.
towerhamlets.sch.uk
*Type:* Co-educational Day Only
11–19
*Special needs:* CB DOW EPI HI
PMLD **SLD** VI
*Wheelchair access:* WA1

**BOWDEN HOUSE**
Firle Road, Seaford, East
Sussex BN25 2JB
*Type:* Boys Boarding Only
10–16
*Special needs:* **BESD**

**CHERRY TREES SCHOOL**
68 Campbell Road, London
E3 4EA
*Type:* Boys 5–11
*Special needs:* **BESD**

**IAN MIKARDO HIGH SCHOOL**
60 William Guy Gardens,
London E3 3LF
*Type:* Boys 11–16

**PHOENIX SCHOOL**
49 Bow Road, London E3 2AD
*Website:* www.phoenix.
towerhamlets.sch.uk
*Type:* Co-educational Day Only
2–16
*Special needs:* ASD **ASP** MLD
SP&LD
*Wheelchair access:* W

**STEPHEN HAWKING SCHOOL**
Brunton Place, London E14 7LL
*Website:* www.stephenhawking.
towerhamlets.sch.uk
*Type:* Co-educational Day Only
2–11 (2–11 yrs)
*Special needs:* **PMLD SLD**

## Waltham Forest Council

**Town Hall
Forest Road
London
E17 4JF**

**BELMONT PARK SCHOOL**
Leyton Green Road, London
E10 6DB
*Type:* Co-educational 11–16

**BROOKFIELD HOUSE
SCHOOL**
Alders Avenue, Woodford
Green, Essex IG8 9PY
*Type:* Co-educational Day Only
2–16
*Special needs:* CP EPI **HEA**
HI **IM**
*Wheelchair access:* WA1

**ELSLEY SCHOOL**
31 Elsely Road, London
SW11 5TZ
*Type:* Co-educational Day Only
5–11
*Special needs:* ADD ADHD
**BESD** MLD
*Wheelchair access:* W

**JOSEPH CLARKE SCHOOL**
Vincent Road, London E4 9PP
*Type:* Co-educational Day Only
2–19
*Special needs:* VI
*Wheelchair access:* W

**WHITEFIELD SCHOOL AND
CENTRE**
Macdonald Road, London
E17 4AZ
*Website:* www.whitefield.org.uk
*Type:* Co-educational Day Only
3–19
*Special needs:* ASD **ASP** CP
DOW DYP EPI HI MLD **PMLD**
SLD SP&LD VI
*Wheelchair access:* WA1

**WILLIAM MORRIS SCHOOL**
Folly Lane, London E17 5NT
*Type:* Co-educational Day Only
11–19
*Special needs:* ASD **ASP CB
CP EPI HEA HI MLD PMLD
SLD** SP&LD
*Wheelchair access:* WA1

## Wandsworth LEA

**The Town Hall
Wandsworth High Street
London
SW18 2PU**

**BRADSTOW SCHOOL**
34 Dumpton Park Drive,
Broadstairs, Kent CT10 1RG
*Website:* www.bradstow.
wandsworth.sch.uk
*Type:* Co-educational Boarding
Only 5–19
*Special needs:* ASD **ASP** BESD
EPI **SLD**

**GARRATT PARK SCHOOL**
Waldron Road, London
SW18 3SY
*Website:* www.garrattpark.
wandsworth.sch.uk
*Type:* Co-educational Day Only
11–17
*Special needs:* ADHD ASD
BESD DYC DYS HI MLD
SP&LD VI
*Wheelchair access:* WA2

**GREENMEAD SCHOOL**
St Margaret's Crescent, London
SW15 6HL
*Type:* Co-educational Day Only
3–11
*Special needs:* **CP** MLD **PMLD**
SLD
*Wheelchair access:* WA1

**LINDEN LODGE SCHOOL**
61 Princes Way, London
SW19 6JB
*Type:* Co-educational Day and
Boarding 5–18
*Special needs:* VI

**NIGHTINGALE SCHOOL**
Beechcroft Road, London
SW17 7DF
*Type:* Boys Day Only
*Special needs:* **BESD**

**OAK LODGE SCHOOL**
101 Nightingale Lane, London
SW12 8NA
*Website:* www.oaklodge.
wandsworth.sch.uk
*Type:* Co-educational Boarding
and Day 11–19
*Special needs:* **HI**
*Wheelchair access:* WA3

**PADDOCK SCHOOL**
Priory Lane, London SW15 5RT
*Website:* www.
paddock.wandsworth.sch.uk
*Type:* Co-educational Day Only
3–19
*Special needs:* PMLD **SLD**
*Wheelchair access:* W

**THE VINES SCHOOL**
Forthbridge Road, London
SW11 5NX
*Website:*
www.thevinesschool.co.uk
*Type:* Co-educational Day Only
3–11
*Special needs:* ADHD ASD
BESD DOW HEA **MLD** VI
*Wheelchair access:* WA2

# GREATER MANCHESTER

**Bolton Education and
Culture**

**Town Hall**
**Victoria Square**
**Bolton**
**Greater Manchester**
**BL1 1RU**

**FIRWOOD SCHOOL**
Crompton Way, Bolton, Greater
Manchester BL2 3AF
*Type:* Co-educational Day Only
11–19
*Special needs:* ASD **PMLD SLD**
*Wheelchair access:* WA1

**GREEN FOLD SCHOOL**
Highfield Road, Farnworth,
Greater Manchester BL4 0RA
*Type:* Day Only 3–11
*Special needs:* ASD CP EPI
**PMLD SLD**
*Wheelchair access:* WA1

**LADYWOOD SCHOOL**
Masefield Road, Bolton, Greater
Manchester BL3 1NG
*Type:* Co-educational Day Only
4–11
*Special needs:* ASD MLD

**LEVER PARK SCHOOL**
Stocks Park Drive, Bolton,
Greater Manchester BL6 6DE
*Type:* Co-educational Day Only
11–16
*Special needs:* ADD ADHD
**BESD** TOU
*Wheelchair access:* WA1

**RUMWORTH SCHOOL**
Armdale Road, Bolton, Greater
Manchester BL3 4TP
*Website:* www.rumworth.sch.uk
*Type:* Co-educational Day Only
11–19
*Special needs:* ASD **MLD SLD**
*Wheelchair access:* WA1

**THOMASSON MEMORIAL
SCHOOL**
Devonshire Road, Bolton,
Greater Manchester BL1 4JP
*Website:* www.thomasson.
bolton.sch.uk
*Type:* Co-educational Day Only
3–11
*Special needs:* **HI**
*Wheelchair access:* WA2

**Bury Education &
Culture Department**

**Athenaeum House**
**Market Street**
**Bury**
**Greater Manchester**
**BL9 0BN**

**CLOUGHSIDE**
Bury New Road, Manchester,
Greater Manchester M25 3BL

**ELMS BANK SPECIALIST
ARTS COLLEGE**
Ripon Avenue, Manchester,
Greater Manchester M45 8PJ
*Website:*
www.elmsbank.bury.sch.uk
*Type:* Co-educational Day Only
11–19
*Special needs:* ASD **MLD**
**PMLD SLD**
*Wheelchair access:* WA1

**MILLWOOD PRIMARY SPECIAL SCHOOL**
Fletcher Fold Road, Bury,
Greater Manchester BL9 9RX
*Type:* Co-educational Day Only
2–11
*Special needs:* ASD MLD PMLD
SLD
*Wheelchair access:* WA1

## Manchester Education Department

**Overseas House**
**Quay Street**
**Manchester**
**M3 3BB**

**THE BIRCHES SPECIALIST SUPPORT SCHOOL**
Newholme Road, Manchester,
Greater Manchester M20 2XZ
*Type:* Co-educational Day Only
2–11
*Special needs:* BESD PMLD **SLD**
*Wheelchair access:* WA1

**BUGLAWTON HALL**
Buxton Road, Congleton,
Cheshire CW12 3PQ
*Type:* Boys Day Only 8–16
*Special needs:* BESD

**CAMBERWELL PARK SCHOOL**
Bank House Road, Manchester,
Greater Manchester M9 8LT
*Type:* Co-educational Day Only
2–11
*Special needs:* ASD BESD
PMLD **SLD**
*Wheelchair access:* WA1

**EWING SCHOOL**
Central Road, Manchester,
Greater Manchester M20 4ZA
*Type:* Co-educational Day Only
5–16
*Special needs:* SP&LD

**GRANGE SCHOOL**
77 Dickenson Road,
Manchester, Greater
Manchester M14 5AZ
*Type:* Co-educational Day Only
4–19
*Special needs:* ASD **ASP**
*Wheelchair access:* WA1

**LANCASTERIAN SCHOOL**
Elizabeth Slinger Road,
Manchester, Greater
Manchester M20 2XA
*Type:* Co-educational Day Only
2–16
*Special needs:* **CP HEA MLD**
**SLD**
*Wheelchair access:* WA1

**MEADE HILL SCHOOL**
Middleton Road, Manchester,
Greater Manchester M8 4NB
*Type:* Co-educational Day Only
*Special needs:* ADD ADHD
ASP BESD DYP DYS HI MLD
SP&LD TOU

**MEDLOCK VALLEY HIGH SCHOOL**
Palmerstone Street, Manchester,
Greater Manchester M12 6PT
*Type:* Co-educational Day Only
11–16
*Special needs:* MLD

**MELLAND HIGH SCHOOL**
Holmcroft Road, Manchester,
Greater Manchester M18 7NG
*Type:* Co-educational Day Only
11–19
*Special needs:* PMLD **SLD**
*Wheelchair access:* W

**PIPER HILL SPECIAL SCHOOL**
200 Yew Tree Lane, Manchester,
Greater Manchester M23 0FF
*Type:* Co-educational Day Only
11–19
*Special needs:* PMLD SLD
*Wheelchair access:* W

**RICHMOND PARK SCHOOL**
Cochrane Avenue, Manchester,
Greater Manchester M12 4FA
*Type:* Co-educational Day Only
*Special needs:* **MLD**

**RODNEY HOUSE SCHOOL**
388 Slade Lane, Manchester,
Greater Manchester M19 2HT
*Type:* Co-educational Day Only
2–7
*Special needs:* ASD **ASP** BESD
CP DOW EPI HEA HI MLD
PMLD **SLD** SP&LD TOU VI
*Wheelchair access:* W

**ROUNDWOOD SCHOOL**
Roundwood Road, Manchester,
Greater Manchester M22 4AB
*Type:* Day Only
*Special needs:* **MLD**

**SOUTHERN CROSS SCHOOL**
Barlow Hall Road, Manchester,
Greater Manchester M21 7JJ
*Type:* Co-educational Day Only
11–16
*Special needs:* **BESD**
*Wheelchair access:* WA2

**WOODSIDE SPECIAL SCHOOL**
Crossacres Road, Manchester,
Greater Manchester M22 5DR
*Type:* Co-educational Day Only
*Special needs:* **MLD**

## Oldham Education and Culture

**Civic Centre**
**West Street**
**Oldham**
**Greater Manchester**
**OL1 1UG**

**BROWNHILL SPECIAL SCHOOL**
Heights Lane, Rochdale,
Lancashire OL12 0PZ
*Type:* Co-educational Day Only
*Special needs:* **BESD**

**HARDMAN FOLD SCHOOL**
Dean Street, Failsworth, Greater
Manchester M35 0DQ
*Type:* Co-educational Day Only
11–16
*Special needs:* **BESD**

**HILL TOP SCHOOL**
Arncliffe Rise, Oldham, Greater
Manchester OL4 2LZ
*Type:* Co-educational Day Only
11–19
*Special needs:* ASD ASP
DOW **SLD**
*Wheelchair access:* W

**KINGFISHER COMMUNITY SPECIAL SCHOOL**
Chadderton, Oldham, Greater Manchester OL9 9QR
*Type:* Co-educational Day Only 2–11
*Special needs:* ASD BESD MLD PMLD SLD SP&LD VI
*Wheelchair access:* W

**MARLAND FOLD SCHOOL**
Rosary Road, Oldham, Greater Manchester OL8 2RP
*Special needs:* **MLD**

**PARK DEAN SCHOOL**
St Martin's Road, Oldham, Greater Manchester OL8 2PZ
*Type:* Co-educational Day Only 11–19
*Special needs:* CP EPI HEA HI VI
*Wheelchair access:* W

**SPRING BROOK SCHOOL**
Heron Street, Oldham, Greater Manchester OL8 4JD
*Type:* Co-educational Day Only 5–11
*Special needs:* **BESD**

## Rochdale Metropolitan Borough Council

**PO Box 39 Municipal Offices
Smith Street
Rochdale
Greater Manchester
OL16 1LQ**

**ALDERMAN KAY SPECIAL SCHOOL**
Tintern Road, Middleton, Greater Manchester M24 6TQ
*Type:* Co-educational Day Only 5–16
*Special needs:* **BESD** DOW DYS EPI HI **MLD SLD** SP&LD

**BIRTLE VIEW SPECIAL SCHOOL**
George Street, Heywood, Greater Manchester OL10 4PW

**HIGH BIRCH SPECIAL SCHOOL (ADLINGTON UNIT)**
Bolton Road, Rochdale, Greater Manchester OL11 4RA

**INNES SPECIAL SCHOOL**
Ings Lane, Rochdale, Greater Manchester OL12 7AL
*Website:*
www.innes.rochdale.sch.uk
*Type:* Co-educational Day Only 5–19
*Special needs:* ASD **ASP** CP DOW EPI HEA HI IM **PMLD SLD** VI
*Wheelchair access:* WA1

**RYDINGS SPECIAL SCHOOL**
Great Howarth, Rochdale, Greater Manchester OL12 9HJ
*Type:* Co-educational Day Only 3–16
*Special needs:* **BESD MLD SLD**
*Wheelchair access:* W

## Salford Education and Leisure

**Minerva House
Pendlebury Road
Salford
Greater Manchester
M27 4EQ**

**CHATSWORTH HIGH SCHOOL**
Chatsworth High School, Salford, Greater Manchester M30 9DY
*Type:* Co-educational Day Only 11–19
*Special needs:* ASD EPI **PMLD SLD** SP&LD
*Wheelchair access:* WA1

**IRWELL PARK HIGH**
Britannia Street, Lancashire, Greater Manchester M6 6JB
*Type:* Co-educational 11–16

**OAKWOOD HIGH SCHOOL**
Chatsword Road, Eccles, Greater Manchester M30 9DY
*Type:* Co-educational Day Only 11–16

**SPRINGWOOD PRIMARY SCHOOL**
Barton Road, Manchester, Greater Manchester M27 5LP
*Type:* Co-educational 2–11

## Stockport Metropolitan Borough Council

**Education Services
Stopford House
Piccadilly
Stockport
SK1 3XE**

**CASTLE HIGH SCHOOL**
Lapwing Lane, Stockport, Greater Manchester SK5 8LF
*Website:* www.castlehill.stockport.sch.uk
*Type:* Co-educational Day Only 11–16
*Special needs:* **MLD**
*Wheelchair access:* WA2

**HEATON SCHOOL**
St James Road, Stockport, Greater Manchester SK4 4RE
*Type:* Co-educational Day Only 11–19
*Special needs:* ASD **PMLD SLD**
*Wheelchair access:* WA2

**LISBURNE SCHOOL**
Half Moon Lane, Stockport, Greater Manchester SK2 5LB
*Type:* Co-educational Day Only
*Special needs:* ASD DYP MLD SLD SP&LD

**OAK GROVE SCHOOL**
Matlock Road, Stockport, Greater Manchester SK8 3BU
*Type:* Co-educational Day Only 4–11

**VALLEY SCHOOL**
Whitehaven Road, Stockport, Greater Manchester SK7 1EN
*Type:* Co-educational Day Only 2–11 (with inclusive nursery)
*Special needs:* ASD PMLD SLD
*Wheelchair access:* WA1

**WINDLEHURST SCHOOL**
Windlehurst Lane, Stockport, Cheshire SK6 7HZ
*Type:* Co-educational Day Only
*Special needs:* **BESD**

## Tameside LEA

Council Offices
Wellington Road
Ashton-under-Lyne
Lancashire
OL6 6DL

### CROMWELL HIGH SCHOOL
Yew Tree Lane, Cheshire
SK16 5BJ
*Type:* Co-educational Day Only
11–16
*Special needs:* PMLD **SLD**
*Wheelchair access:* WA1

### DALE GROVE SCHOOL
Wilshaw Lane, Ashton-under-
Lyne, Lancashire OL7 9RF
*Type:* Co-educational Day Only
5–16
*Special needs:* **BESD**

### HAWTHORNS SCHOOL
Sunnyside Moss Campus,
Audenshaw, Greater
Manchester M34 5SF
*Type:* Co-educational Day Only
4–11
*Special needs:* **MLD**
*Wheelchair access:* WA1

### OAKDALE SCHOOL & ACORN
### NURSERY
Cheetham Hill Road, Dukinfield,
Greater Manchester SK16 5LD
*Type:* Co-educational Day Only
2–11
*Special needs:* ASD **PMLD SLD**
*Wheelchair access:* W

### SAMUEL LAYCOCK SCHOOL
Mereside, Stalybridge, Cheshire
SK15 1JF
*Type:* Co-educational Day Only
11–16
*Special needs:* **MLD**

## Trafford Metropolitan Borough Council

Waterside House
Sale Waterside
Sale
M33 7ZF

### BRENTWOOD SCHOOL
Brentwood Avenue, Altrincham,
Greater Manchester WA14 1SR
*Type:* Co-educational Day Only
*Special needs:* ASD PMLD SLD
*Wheelchair access:* WA1

### DELAMERE SCHOOL
Irlam Road, Urmston, Greater
Manchester M41 6AP
*Type:* Co-educational Day Only
*Special needs:* ASD PMLD SLD
*Wheelchair access:* W

### EGERTON HIGH SCHOOL
Kingsway Park, Urmston,
Greater Manchester M41 7FZ
*Type:* Co-educational Day Only
11–16
*Special needs:* **BESD**
*Wheelchair access:* W

### LONGFORD PARK SCHOOL
Longford Park, Stretford,
Greater Manchester M32 8PR
*Website:*
www.longford.trafford.sch.uk
*Type:* Co-educational Day Only
5–11
*Special needs:* ADD ADHD
BESD **MLD**

### MANOR HIGH SCHOOL
Manor Avenue, Sale, Greater
Manchester M33 5JX
*Type:* Co-educational Day Only
11–18

### PICTOR SCHOOL
Grove Lane, Altrincham, Greater
Manchester WA15 6PH
*Type:* Co-educational Day Only
2–11 (mixed gender)
*Wheelchair access:* WA1

## Wigan Borough Council

Progress House
Westwood Park Drive
Wigan
Lancashire
WN3 4HH

### HIGHLEA SECONDARY
### SCHOOL
294 Mosley Common Road,
Worsley, Greater Manchester
M28 1DA
*Website:*
www.medinahouseschool.co.uk
*Type:* Co-educational Boarding
Only
*Special needs:* **BESD CP**

### LANDGATE SCHOOL
Landgate Lane, Wigan, Greater
Manchester WN4 0EP

### MERE OAKS SCHOOL
Boars Head, Wigan, Greater
Manchester WN1 2RF
*Type:* Co-educational Day Only
2–19
*Wheelchair access:* W

### NEW GREEN HALL SCHOOL
Green Hall Close, Atherton,
Greater Manchester M46 9HP
*Type:* Co-educational Day Only
2–14
*Special needs:* **MLD**
*Wheelchair access:* WA1

### OAKFIELD HIGH SCHOOL
Close Lane, Wigan, Greater
Manchester WN2 3SA
*Website:*
www.oakfield.wigan.sch.uk
*Type:* Co-educational Day Only
11–19
*Special needs:* **MLD**
*Wheelchair access:* WA2

### WIGAN HOPE
Kelvin Grove, Wigan, Greater
Manchester WN3 6SP
*Type:* Co-educational Day Only
*Special needs:* PMLD SLD

### WILLOW GROVE PRIMARY
Willow Grove, Wigan, Greater
Manchester WN4 9HP
*Type:* Co-educational Day Only
*Special needs:* ADHD **BESD**
DYP DYS
*Wheelchair access:* WA1

# MERSEYSIDE

## Knowsley Education Offices

**Huyton Hey Road**
**Huyton**
**Knowsley**
**Merseyside**
**L36 5YH**

### ALT BRIDGE SECONDARY SUPPORT CENTRE
Wellcroft Road, Knowsley,
Merseyside L36 7TA
*Type:* Co-educational Day Only
11–16
*Special needs:* ASP BESD HI
**MLD** SP&LD

### THE ELMS SPECIAL SCHOOL
Whitethorn Drive, Stockbridge
Village, Merseyside L28 1RX
*Type:* Co-educational Day Only
2–19
*Special needs:* ASD **ASP** DOW
**PMLD SLD**
*Wheelchair access:* W

### HIGHFIELD SCHOOL
Baileys Lane, Halewood,
Merseyside L26 0TY
*Type:* Co-educational Day Only
6–14
*Special needs:* **BESD**

### KNOWSLEY CENTRAL PRIMARY SUPPORT CENTRE
Knowsley, Merseyside L36 7SY
*Special needs:* ADD ASD DYS
MLD

### KNOWSLEY NORTHERN PRIMARY SUPPORT CENTRE
Bramcote Walk, Kirkby,
Merseyside L33 9UR
*Type:* Co-educational Day Only
*Special needs:* ASD BESD DYS
**MLD** SLD SP&LD
*Wheelchair access:* WA2

### KNOWSLEY SOUTHERN PRIMARY SUPPORT CENTRE
Arncliffe Road, Liverpool,
Merseyside L25 9QE
*Type:* Co-educational Day Only
3–11
*Special needs:* ADD ADHD ASD
ASP **BESD** CB DOW EPI HEA
**MLD** SLD SP&LD
*Wheelchair access:* WA1

### SPRINGFIELD SPECIAL SCHOOL
Cawthorne Close, Kirkby,
Merseyside L32 3XG
*Website:* www.springfield.
knowsley.sch.uk
*Type:* Co-educational Day Only
2–19
*Special needs:* PMLD SLD
*Wheelchair access:* WA1

## Liverpool Education Offices

**2nd Floor Millennium House**
**Victoria Street**
**Liverpool**
**Merseyside**
**L1 8RF**

### ABBOTS LEA SCHOOL
Beaconsfield Road, Liverpool,
Merseyside L25 6EE
*Type:* Co-educational Boarding
and Day 5–19
*Special needs:* ASD **ASP**
*Wheelchair access:* WA1

### ASHFIELD SCHOOL
Childwall Abbey Road,
Liverpool, Merseyside L16 5EY
*Type:* Co-educational Day Only
11–16
*Special needs:* ADD ADHD ASD
ASP DOW DYP DYS HEA HI
**MLD** SP&LD TOU VI
*Wheelchair access:* WA3

### BARLOWS PRIMARY SCHOOL (ASSESSMENT CENTRE)
Barlows Lane, Liverpool,
Merseyside L9 9EH
*Type:* Co-educational Day Only
3–7
*Special needs:* ASD **BESD MLD**
SLD SP&LD
*Wheelchair access:* WA1

### CLIFFORD HOLROYDE CENTRE OF EXPERTISE
Thingwall Lane, Liverpool,
Merseyside L14 7NX
*Type:* Co-educational Day Only
5–16
*Special needs:* **BESD**

### ERNEST COOKSON SPECIAL SCHOOL
Mill Lane, Liverpool, Merseyside
L12 7JA
*Type:* Boys Day Only
*Special needs:* **BESD**

### GREENWAYS SCHOOL
Dingle Lane, Liverpool,
Merseyside L8 9UB
*Type:* Co-educational Day Only
3–7
*Special needs:* ADD **ADHD**
**ASD ASP** CB DYP EPI **MLD**
**SLD** SP&LD TOU
*Wheelchair access:* WA1

### HOPE SCHOOL
Naylorsfield Drive, Liverpool,
Merseyside L27 0YD
*Type:* Boys Day Only 6–13
*Special needs:* **BESD**
*Wheelchair access:* WA2

### LOWER LEE SPECIAL SCHOOL
Beaconsfield Road, Liverpool,
Merseyside L25 6EF
*Type:* Boys Boarding Only
8–16
*Special needs:* **BESD**

## MARGARET BEAVAN SCHOOL
Almonds Green, Liverpool,
Merseyside L12 5HP
*Type:* Co-educational Day Only
5–16
*Special needs:* **MLD**

## MEADOW BANK SPECIAL SCHOOL
Sherwoods Lane, Liverpool,
Merseyside L10 1LW
*Type:* Co-educational Day Only
5–17
*Special needs:* **ADD** ASD **ASP**
EPI **MLD** SP&LD

## MERSEY VIEW SCHOOL
Minehead Road, Liverpool,
Merseyside L17 6AX
*Type:* Co-educational Day Only
5–16
*Special needs:* **MLD**

## MILLSTEAD SPECIAL NEEDS PRIMARY SCHOOL
Old Mill Lane, Liverpool,
Merseyside L15 8LW
*Type:* Co-educational Day Only
2–11
*Special needs:* ASD PMLD **SLD**
*Wheelchair access:* W

## PALMERSTON SCHOOL
Beaconsfield Road, Liverpool,
Merseyside L25 6EE
*Type:* Co-educational Day Only
11–19
*Special needs:* ADD ADHD ASD
ASP CP DOW DYP **EPI** HEA HI
**PMLD SLD** SP&LD VI
*Wheelchair access:* W

## PRINCES SCHOOL
Selborne Street, Liverpool,
Merseyside L8 1YQ
*Website:*
www.princesprimary.com
*Type:* Co-educational Day Only
2–11
*Special needs:* ASD **ASP PMLD
SLD** SP&LD VI
*Wheelchair access:* WA1

## REDBRIDGE HIGH SCHOOL
Sherwoods Lane, Liverpool,
Merseyside L10 1LW
*Type:* Co-educational Day Only
11–19
*Special needs:* ASD **ASP
PMLD SLD**
*Wheelchair access:* WA1

## SANDFIELD PARK SCHOOL
Sandfield Walk, Liverpool,
Merseyside L12 1LH
*Type:* Co-educational Day Only
11–19
*Special needs:* **CP EPI MLD**
PMLD
*Wheelchair access:* WA1

## WATERGATE SCHOOL
Upper Essex Street, Liverpool,
Merseyside L8 6QB
*Type:* Co-educational Day Only
5–16
*Special needs:* MLD SP&LD

## Sefton Council

**Oriel Road
Bootle
Merseyside
L20 7AE**

## CROSBY HIGH SPECIALIST HUMANITIES COLLEGE
De Villiers Avenue, Crosby,
Merseyside L23 2TH
*Type:* Co-educational Day Only
12–16
*Special needs:* ADHD ASD
BESD **MLD**
*Wheelchair access:* W

## MEREFIELD SPECIAL SCHOOL
Westminster Drive, Southport,
Merseyside PR8 2QZ
*Type:* Co-educational Day Only
3–19
*Special needs:* ASD **ASP PMLD
SLD**
*Wheelchair access:* WA1

## NEWFIELD SPECIAL SCHOOL
Edge Lane, Liverpool,
Merseyside L23 4TG
*Type:* Co-educational Day Only
5–16
*Special needs:* ADD ADHD ASP
**BESD** DYP DYS EPI
*Wheelchair access:* WA1

## PRESFIELD SPECIAL SCHOOL
Preston New Road, Southport,
Merseyside PR9 8PA
*Type:* Co-educational Day Only
11–19
*Special needs:* ASD **ASP MLD**
*Wheelchair access:* WA1

## ROWAN PARK SCHOOL
Sterrix Lane, Litheland,
Merseyside L21 0DB
*Type:* Co-educational Day Only
*Special needs:* ASD **ASP** DOW
**PMLD SLD** SP&LD VI
*Wheelchair access:* W

## St Helens Education and Leisure Dept

**The Rivington Centre
Rivington Road
St Helens
Merseyside
WA10 4ND**

## HURST SCHOOL
Hard Lane, St Helens,
Merseyside WA10 6PN
*Type:* Co-educational Day Only
*Special needs:* **MLD** SP&LD

## MILL GREEN SCHOOL
Mill Lane, Newton-le-Willows,
Merseyside WA12 8BG
*Type:* Co-educational Day Only
7–19
*Special needs:* ASD **PMLD SLD**
*Wheelchair access:* WA1

**PENKFORD SCHOOL**
Wharf Road, Newton-le-Willows,
Merseyside WA12 9XZ
*Type:* Co-educational Day Only
*Special needs:* **BESD MLD**
*Wheelchair access:* W

## Wirral Borough Council

**Hamilton Building
Conway Street
Birkenhead
Wirral
CH41 4FD**

**CLARE MOUNT SCHOOL**
Fender Lane, Wirral, Merseyside
CH46 9PA
*Type:* Co-educational Day Only
11–19
*Special needs:* **MLD** SLD
*Wheelchair access:* WA2

**ELLERAY PARK SCHOOL**
Elleray Park Road, Wallasey,
Merseyside CH45 0LH
*Type:* Co-educational Day Only
2–11
*Special needs:* ASD **ASP** CP
DOW DYP EPI HEA HI **PMLD**
**SLD** SP&LD VI
*Wheelchair access:* WA1

**FOXFIELD SCHOOL**
Douglas Drive, Wirral,
Merseyside CH46 6BT
*Type:* Co-educational Day Only
11–19
*Special needs:* ASD PMLD SLD
*Wheelchair access:* WA2

**GILBROOK SCHOOL**
Pilgrim Street, Birkenhead,
Merseyside CH41 5EH
*Type:* Co-educational Day Only
5–11
*Special needs:* **ADD ADHD**
**BESD**
*Wheelchair access:* W

**HAYFIELD SCHOOL**
Manor Drive, Wirral,
Merseyside CH49 4LN
*Type:* Co-educational
*Special needs:* ASD **ASP MLD**
SP&LD

**KILGARTH SCHOOL**
Cavendish Street, Birkenhead,
Merseyside CH41 8BA
*Type:* Boys Day Only 11–16
*Special needs:* **BESD**

**THE LYNDALE SCHOOL**
Wirral, Merseyside CH63 4JY

**MEADOWSIDE SCHOOL**
Pool Lane, Birkenhead,
Merseyside CH49 5LA
*Type:* Co-educational Day Only
11–19
*Special needs:* ADHD ASD CP
DOW DYP EPI HEA IM MLD
PMLD SLD SP&LD VI
*Wheelchair access:* WA1

**ORRETS MEADOW SCHOOL**
Chapelhill Road, Birkenhead,
Merseyside CH46 9QQ
*Type:* Co-educational Day Only
7–11
*Special needs:* DYS

**STANLEY SCHOOL**
Pensby Road, Heswall,
Merseyside CH61 7UG
*Type:* Co-educational Day Only
2–11
*Special needs:* ASD **SLD**

# MIDDLESBROUGH

## Middlesbrough County Council

**PO Box 99A
Town Hall
Middlesbrough
TS1 2QQ**

**BEVERLEY SCHOOL FOR
CHILDREN WITH AUTISM**
Beverley Road, Middlesbrough
TS4 3LQ
*Website:*
www.beverleyautism.ik.org
*Type:* Co-educational Day Only
3–19
*Special needs:* ASD **ASP**
*Wheelchair access:* WA2

**HOLMWOOD SCHOOL**
Saltersgill Avenue, Easterside,
Middlesbrough TS4 3PT
*Website:*
www.millenniumschools.co.uk
*Type:* Co-educational Day Only
*Special needs:* ADHD ASP
**BESD MLD**
*Wheelchair access:* WA1

**PRIORY WOODS SCHOOL**
Tothill Avenue, Middlesbrough
TS3 0RH
*Type:* Co-educational Day Only
4–19
*Special needs:* PMLD **SLD**
*Wheelchair access:* W

**TOLLESBY SCHOOL**
Saltersgill Avenue,
Middlesbrough TS4 3JS
*Type:* Co-educational Day Only
11–16
*Special needs:* **BESD** MLD

# NORFOLK

## Norfolk County Council

**County Hall**
**Martineau Lane**
**Norwich**
**Norfolk**
**NR1 2DL**

### ALDERMAN JACKSON SPECIAL SCHOOL
Marsh Lane, King's Lynn, Norfolk PE30 3AE
*Type:* Co-educational Day Only 2–19
*Special needs:* ASD **ASP CP PMLD** SLD
*Wheelchair access:* WA1

### CHAPEL ROAD SPECIAL SCHOOL
Chapel Road, Attleborough, Norfolk NR17 2DS
*Type:* Co-educational 3–19
*Special needs:* ASD CB CP DOW EPI HI **PMLD SLD** VI
*Wheelchair access:* WA1

### THE CLARE SCHOOL
South Park Avenue, Norwich, Norfolk NR4 7AU
*Type:* Co-educational Day Only
*Special needs:* HI **IM** SP&LD VI
*Wheelchair access:* WA1

### EATON HALL SPECIAL SCHOOL
Pettus Road, Norwich, Norfolk NR4 7BU
*Type:* Boys Boarding and Day 10–16
*Special needs:* **BESD**

### THE ETHEL TIPPLE SCHOOL
Winston Churchill Drive, King's Lynn, Norfolk PE30 4RP
*Type:* Co-educational 7–16
*Special needs:* **MLD**
*Wheelchair access:* WA1

### FRED NICHOLSON SPECIAL SCHOOL
Westfield Road, Dereham, Norfolk NR19 1BJ
*Type:* Co-educational Day and Boarding 7–16
*Special needs:* **MLD**
*Wheelchair access:* W

### HALL SPECIAL SCHOOL
St Faith's Road, Norwich, Norfolk NR6 7AD
*Type:* Co-educational Day Only 3–19
*Special needs:* ASD CP DOW EPI HEA HI IM **PMLD SLD** SP&LD VI
*Wheelchair access:* WA1

### HARFORD MANOR SPECIAL SCHOOL
43 Ipswich Road, Norwich, Norfolk NR2 2LN
*Website:* www.hardfordmanor. norfolk.sch.uk
*Type:* Co-educational Day Only 3–19
*Special needs:* ASD PMLD SLD
*Wheelchair access:* WA1

### JOHN GRANT SPECIAL SCHOOL
St George's Drive, Great Yarmouth, Norfolk NR30 5QW
*Type:* Co-educational Day Only 3–19
*Special needs:* PMLD **SLD**
*Wheelchair access:* W

### PARKSIDE SPECIAL SCHOOL
College Road, Norwich, Norfolk NR2 3JA
*Type:* Co-educational Day Only
*Special needs:* **ADD ADHD ASD** ASP BESD **DOW** EPI HI **MLD** SP&LD TOU
*Wheelchair access:* WA1

### SHERINGHAM WOODFIELDS SCHOOL
Holt Road, Sheringham, Norfolk NR26 8ND
*Type:* Co-educational Day Only 2–19
*Special needs:* PMLD **SLD**
*Wheelchair access:* WA1

### SIDESTRAND HALL SPECIAL SCHOOL
Cromer Road, Cromer, Norfolk NR27 0NH
*Type:* Co-educational Boarding and Day 7–16
*Special needs:* **MLD**

# NORTHAMPTONSHIRE

## Northamptonshire Education Offices

**PO Box 216**
**John Dryden House**
**Northampton**
**Northamptonshire**
**NN4 7DD**

## BILLING BROOK SCHOOL
Penistone Road, Northampton,
Northamptonshire NN3 8EZ
*Type:* Co-educational Day Only
2–16
*Special needs:* ASD **ASP MLD
SLD**

## DEGRA HOUSE
67 Queens Park Parade,
Northampton, Northamptonshire
NN2 6LR
*Type:* Co-educational Day Only
11–16

## FAIRFIELDS SCHOOL
Trinity Avenue, Northampton,
Northamptonshire NN2 6JN
*Type:* Co-educational Day Only
3–11
*Special needs:* ASD PMLD SLD
*Wheelchair access:* WA1

## FRIARS SCHOOL
Friar's Close, Wellingborough,
Northamptonshire NN8 2LA
*Website:* www.friarsschool.ik.org
*Type:* Co-educational Day Only
11–19
*Special needs:* ASD **MLD** SLD
*Wheelchair access:* WA2

## THE GATEWAY SCHOOL
St John's Road, Tiffield,
Northamptonshire NN12 8AA
*Website:*
www.thegatewayschool.ik.org
*Type:* Co-educational Day Only
11–18
*Special needs:* **ADD ADHD
ASD** ASP **BESD CB** TOU

## GREENFIELDS SCHOOL AND SPORTS COLLEGE
Harborough Road,
Northampton, Northamptonshire
NN2 8LR
*Type:* Co-educational Day Only
11–19
*Special needs:* ASD **ASP PMLD
SLD**
*Wheelchair access:* WA1

## ISEBROOK SCHOOL
Eastleigh Road, Kettering,
Northamptonshire NN15 6PT
*Website:*
www.isebrook-school.ik.org
*Type:* Co-educational Day Only
11–19
*Special needs:* ADHD ASD ASP
BESD CP DOW EPI HI **MLD** SLD
*Wheelchair access:* WA1

## KINGSLEY SCHOOL
Churchill Way, Kettering,
Northamptonshire NN15 5DP
*Website:*
www.kingsleyschool.ik.org
*Type:* Co-educational Day Only
3–11
*Special needs:* ASD ASP CP
DOW EPI HI MLD PMLD SLD
SP&LD VI
*Wheelchair access:* WA1

## MAPLEFIELDS SCHOOL
School Place, Corby,
Northamptonshire NN18 0QP
*Website:* www.maplefields.
northants.sch.uk
*Type:* Co-educational Day Only
5–16
*Special needs:* ADD ADHD
**BESD**

## NORTHGATE SCHOOL
Arts College, Northampton,
Northamptonshire NN2 6LR
*Website:* www.northgate.ik.org
*Type:* Co-educational Day Only
11–16
*Special needs:* ADD ADHD ASD
ASP CP DOW DYP DYS EPI HI
IM **MLD** SLD SP&LD VI
*Wheelchair access:* WA1

## THE ORCHARD SCHOOL
Beatrice Road, Kettering,
Northamptonshire NN16 9QR
*Type:* Co-educational Day Only
11–16
*Special needs:* **BESD**
*Wheelchair access:* W

## WREN SPINNEY SCHOOL
Westover Road, Kettering,
Northamptonshire NN16 0AP
*Type:* Co-educational Day Only
11–19
*Special needs:* ASD CB **PMLD
SLD**
*Wheelchair access:* WA1

# NORTHUMBERLAND

## Northumberland Education Directorate

County Hall
Morpeth
Northumberland
NE61 2EF

### ATKINSON HOUSE SCHOOL
North Terrace, Cramlington,
Northumberland NE23 7EB
*Type:* Day Only
*Special needs:* ADD ADHD
**BESD**

### BARNDALE HOUSE SCHOOL
Barndale House, Alnwick,
Northumberland NE66 1DQ
*Type:* Co-educational Day and
Boarding 8–19
*Special needs:* **SLD**

### CLEASWELL HILL SCHOOL
School Avenue, Choppington,
Northumberland NE62 5DJ
*Type:* Co-educational Day Only
4–18
*Special needs:* ADD ADHD ASD
ASP BESD DOW EPI HEA **MLD**
SLD SP&LD TOU
*Wheelchair access:* WA2

### COLLINGWOOD SCHOOL
Stobhillgate, Morpeth,
Northumberland NE61 2HA
*Type:* Co-educational Day Only
4–16
*Special needs:* **MLD**
*Wheelchair access:* WA1

### EAST HARTFORD SCHOOL
East Hartford, Cramlington,
Northumberland NE23 9AR
*Type:* Co-educational Day Only
4–11
*Special needs:* ADHD ASD
ASP **BESD** CB DOW DYP DYS
**MLD** SLD

### THE GROVE SCHOOL
Grove Gardens, Berwick Upon
Tweed, Northumberland
TD15 2EN
*Type:* Co-educational Day Only
3–19
*Special needs:* ASD DOW
PMLD **SLD**
*Wheelchair access:* WA1

### HILLCREST SCHOOL
East View Avenue, Cramlington,
Northumberland NE23 9DY
*Type:* Co-educational Day Only
11–16
*Wheelchair access:* WA2

### PRIORY SCHOOL
Dene Park, Hexham,
Northumberland NE46 1HN
*Type:* Co-educational Day Only
3–19
*Special needs:* ASD **PMLD SLD**
*Wheelchair access:* WA1

# NOTTINGHAMSHIRE

## Nottingham City Council

Sandfield Centre
Lenton
Nottingham
Nottinghamshire
NG7 1HQ

### ASPLEY WOOD SCHOOL
Robins Wood Road,
Nottingham, Nottinghamshire
NG8 3LD
*Website:* www.aspleywood.
nottingham.sch.uk
*Type:* Co-educational Day Only
3–16
*Special needs:* **CP IM** VI
*Wheelchair access:* WA1

### CARLTON DIGBY SCHOOL
Digby Avenue, Mapperley,
Nottinghamshire NG3 6DS
*Type:* Co-educational Day Only
3–19
*Special needs:* ASD PMLD SLD
*Wheelchair access:* WA2

### NETHERGATE SCHOOL
Swansdowne Drive,
Nottingham, Nottinghamshire
NG11 8HX
*Type:* Co-educational Day Only
5–16
*Special needs:* ADHD ASD
BESD DOW DYP DYS EPI **MLD**
SP&LD
*Wheelchair access:* W

### ROSEHILL SCHOOL
St Matthias Road, Nottingham,
Nottinghamshire NG3 2FE
*Type:* Co-educational Day Only
4–19
*Special needs:* ASD ASP

### SHEPHERD SCHOOL
Harvey Road, Nottingham,
Nottinghamshire NG8 3BB
*Type:* Co-educational Day Only
3–19
*Special needs:* ASD EPI PMLD SLD
*Wheelchair access:* W

### WESTBURY SCHOOL
Chingford Road, Nottingham,
Nottinghamshire NG8 3BT
*Website:*
www.westburyschool.co.uk
*Type:* Co-educational Day Only
7–16
*Special needs:* **BESD**
*Wheelchair access:* W

### WOODLANDS SCHOOL
Beechdale Road, Nottingham,
Nottinghamshire NG8 3EZ
*Type:* Co-educational Day Only
3–16
*Special needs:* ASD BESD
MLD SLD

## Nottinghamshire County Council

**County Hall**
**West Bridgford**
**Nottingham**
**Nottinghamshire**
**NG7 7QP**

### ASH LEA SCHOOL
Owthorpe Road, Nottingham,
Nottinghamshire NG12 3PA
*Type:* Co-educational Day Only
*Special needs:* **PMLD SLD**
*Wheelchair access:* WA1

### BEECH HILL SCHOOL
Fairholme Drive, Mansfield,
Nottinghamshire NG19 6DX
*Type:* Co-educational 11–16
*Special needs:* ASD BESD **MLD**

### BRACKEN HILL SCHOOL
Chartwell Road,
Kirkby-in-Ashfield,
Nottinghamshire NG17 7HZ
*Type:* Co-educational Day Only
3–19
*Special needs:* ADD ADHD ASD
ASP HEA MLD SLD SP&LD
*Wheelchair access:* WA2

### DERRYMOUNT SCHOOL
Churchmoor Lane, Arnold,
Nottinghamshire NG5 8HN
*Type:* Co-educational Day Only
3–16
*Special needs:* ASD **ASP** BESD
CP EPI **HI MLD** SLD SP&LD VI

### FOUNTAINDALE SCHOOL
Nottingham Road, Mansfield,
Nottinghamshire NG18 5BA
*Type:* Co-educational Boarding
and Day 3–19
*Special needs:* CP EPI HEA
SP&LD VI
*Wheelchair access:* W

### FOXWOOD SCHOOL AND TECHNOLOGY COLLEGE
Derby Road, Nottinghamshire
NG9 3GF
*Website:*
www.foxwood.sch.dccl.net
*Type:* Co-educational Day Only
3–19
*Special needs:* ASD ASP MLD
*Wheelchair access:* WA1

### FREYBURG SCHOOL
Duncanwood Lodge, Worksop,
Nottinghamshire S80 2BP
*Type:* Boys Day Only 12–15

### NEWARK ORCHARD SCHOOL
Newark, Nottinghamshire
NG24 1JR
*Website:* www.newarkorchard.
notts.sch.uk
*Type:* Co-educational Day Only
3–19
*Special needs:* ASD **ASP PMLD
SLD**
*Wheelchair access:* WA2

### REDGATE SCHOOL
Somersall Street, Mansfield,
Nottinghamshire NG19 6EL
*Type:* Co-educational Day Only
3–11
*Special needs:* **ADD ADHD**
ASD **ASP EPI IM SLD**

### ST GILES SCHOOL
Babworth Road, Retford,
Nottinghamshire DN22 7NJ
*Type:* Co-educational Day Only
3–19
*Special needs:* ADD ADHD ASD
ASP BESD CP DOW EPI HI
**MLD** PMLD **SLD** VI
*Wheelchair access:* WA1

### YEOMAN PARK SCHOOL
Park Hall Road, Mansfield,
Nottinghamshire NG19 8PS
*Type:* Co-educational Day Only
3–19
*Special needs:* ASD **ASP PMLD
SLD**
*Wheelchair access:* W

# OXFORDSHIRE

## Oxfordshire County Council

**Macclesfield House**
**New Road**
**Oxford**
**OX1 1NA**

### BARDWELL SCHOOL
Hendon Place, Bicester,
Oxfordshire OX26 4RZ
*Type:* Co-educational Day Only
2–19
*Special needs:* ASD **ASP** CP
DOW EPI HI IM **PMLD SLD**
SP&LD VI
*Wheelchair access:* WA1

### BISHOPSWOOD SCHOOL
Grove Road, Berkshire RG4 9RJ
*Website:* www.bishopswood.
oxon.sch.uk
*Type:* Co-educational Day Only
2–16
*Special needs:* ASD **ASP PMLD
SLD** SP&LD VI
*Wheelchair access:* W

### FITZWARYN SPECIAL SCHOOL
Denchworth Road, Wantage,
Oxfordshire OX12 9ET
*Type:* Co-educational Day Only
3–16
*Special needs:* ASD **ASP MLD
PMLD SLD**
*Wheelchair access:* WA2

### FRANK WISE SCHOOL
Hornbeam Close, Banbury,
Oxfordshire OX16 9RL
*Website:*
www.frankwise.oxon.sch.uk
*Type:* Co-educational Day Only
2–16
*Special needs:* PMLD **SLD**
*Wheelchair access:* WA1

### IFFLEY MEAD SPECIAL SCHOOL
Iffley Turn, Oxford, Oxfordshire
OX4 4DU
*Type:* Day Only
*Special needs:* **MLD**
*Wheelchair access:* WA2

**JOHN WATSON SPECIAL SCHOOL**
Littleworth Road, Oxford, Oxfordshire OX33 1NN
*Website:* www.johnwatsonschool.co.uk
*Type:* Co-educational Day Only
*Special needs:* PMLD **SLD**
*Wheelchair access:* W

**KINGFISHER SCHOOL**
Radley Road, Abingdon, Oxfordshire OX14 3RR
*Website:* www.kingfisherschool.co.uk
*Type:* Co-educational Day Only 2–16
*Special needs:* MLD PMLD SLD
*Wheelchair access:* WA1

**MABEL PRICHARD SPECIAL SCHOOL**
St Nicholas Road, Littlemore, Oxfordshire OX4 4PN
*Website:* www.mable-prichard.oxon-sch.uk
*Type:* Co-educational Day Only
*Special needs:* ASD CP DOW EPI HI PMLD SLD SP&LD VI
*Wheelchair access:* W

**NORTHERN HOUSE SPECIAL SCHOOL**
South Parade, Oxford, Oxfordshire OX2 7JN
*Website:* www.northernhouseschool.ik.org
*Type:* Co-educational Day Only 5–11
*Special needs:* ADD ADHD ASD ASP **BESD** DYS HI MLD SP&LD TOU VI
*Wheelchair access:* WA2

**NORTHFIELD SPECIAL SCHOOL**
Knights Road, Oxford, Oxfordshire OX4 6DQ
*Type:* Co-educational Day Only
*Special needs:* **BESD**

**ORMEROD SPECIAL SCHOOL**
Waynflete Road, Oxford, Oxfordshire OX3 8DD
*Type:* Co-educational Day Only 2–16
*Special needs:* ADHD ASD CP MLD SLD SP&LD VI
*Wheelchair access:* W

**SPRINGFIELD SPECIAL SCHOOL**
@ The Bronze Barrow, Witney, Oxfordshire OX28 1AR
*Type:* Co-educational Day Only 2–16
*Special needs:* PMLD **SLD**
*Wheelchair access:* WA1

**WOODEATON MANOR SCHOOL**
Woodeaton, Oxford, Oxfordshire OX3 9TS
*Type:* Co-educational Boarding and Day 12–16
*Special needs:* BESD EPI HI **MLD** VI

# REDCAR AND CLEVELAND

**Redcar & Cleveland**

**P O Box 83**
**Council Offices**
**Kirkleatham**
**Redcar and Cleveland**
**T510 1YA**

**KILTON THORPE SCHOOL**
Marshall Drive, Brotton, Redcar and Cleveland TS12 2UW
*Type:* Co-educational Day Only 3–19
*Special needs:* ASD **ASP MLD PMLD** SLD SP&LD
*Wheelchair access:* W

**KIRKLEATHAM HALL SCHOOL**
Kirkleatham, Redcar, Redcar and Cleveland TS10 4QR
*Type:* Co-educational Day Only 4–19
*Special needs:* ADHD ASD CP DOW EPI HEA HI **PMLD SLD** SP&LD VI
*Wheelchair access:* W

# RUTLAND

## Rutland County Council

**Catmose**
**Oakham**
**Rutland**
**LE15 6HP**

**THE PARKS SCHOOL**
Barleythorpe Road, Oakham,
Rutland LE15 6NR
*Type:* Co-educational Day Only
2–6
*Special needs:* ASD ASP BESD
CP DOW EPI HEA HI MLD
PMLD SLD SP&LD VI
*Wheelchair access:* WA2

# SHROPSHIRE

## Shropshire County Council

**Shirehall**
**Abbey Foregate**
**Shrewsbury**
**Shropshire**
**SY2 6ND**

**ACCESS SCHOOL**
Holbrrok Villa Farm, Shrewsbury,
Shropshire SY4 3EW
*Type:* Co-educational Day Only
7–16

**RUBICON**
Smallbrook Lodge, Whitchurch,
Shropshire SY5 7AH
*Type:* Co-educational Day Only
11–19

**SEVERNDALE SCHOOL**
Hearne Way, Shrewsbury,
Shropshire SY2 5SL
*Website:* www.severndale.
shropshire.sch.uk
*Type:* Co-educational Day Only
*Special needs:* ASD **ASP MLD**
**PMLD SLD**
*Wheelchair access:* WA1

**WOODLANDS SCHOOL**
Tilley Green, Shrewsbury,
Shropshire SY4 5PJ
*Type:* Co-educational Day Only
11–16

## Telford & Wrekin Education and Culture

**Civic Offices**
**PO Box 440**
**Telford**
**Shropshire**
**TF3 4WF**

**THE BRIDGE SCHOOL**
Waterloo Road, Telford,
Shropshire TF1 5NU
*Type:* Co-educational Day Only
2–19
*Special needs:* PMLD **SLD**
*Wheelchair access:* WA2

**HAUGHTON SCHOOL**
Queen Street, Telford,
Shropshire TF7 4BW
*Type:* 5–16
*Wheelchair access:* WA2

**MOUNT GILBERT SCHOOL**
Hinkshay Road, Telford,
Shropshire TF31 1DG
*Type:* Co-educational Day Only
11–15
*Special needs:* BESD

**SOUTHALL SCHOOL**
off Rowan Road, Telford,
Shropshire TF4 3PN
*Type:* Co-educational Day Only
5–16
*Special needs:* MLD

# SOMERSET

## Bath & North East Somerset Council

**Education Services**
**Riverside**
**Temple Street**
**Bristol**
**BS31 1DN**

### FOSSE WAY SCHOOL
Longfellow Road, Bath, Bath & North East Somerset BA3 3AL
*Type:* Co-educational Boarding and Day 3–19
*Special needs:* ASD **ASP MLD SLD**
*Wheelchair access:* WA2

### THE LINK SPECIAL SCHOOL
Frome Road, Bath, Bath & North East Somerset BA2 5RF
*Type:* Co-educational Day and Boarding 4–16
*Special needs:* ADD ADHD **BESD** CB DYC DYP DYS
*Wheelchair access:* WA1

### SUMMERFIELD SCHOOL
Weston Park East, Bath, Bath & North East Somerset BA1 2UY
*Type:* Co-educational Day Only 7–16
*Special needs:* BESD **MLD** SP&LD

## North Somerset County Council

**Town Hall**
**Walliscote Grove**
**Weston-Super-Mare**
**North Somerset**
**BS23 1UJ**

### BAYTREE SCHOOL
The Campus, Weston-Super-Mare, North Somerset BS24 7DX
*Website:* www. baytreespecialschool.ik.org
*Type:* Co-educational Day Only 3–19
*Special needs:* ASD **ASP PMLD SLD**
*Wheelchair access:* WA1

### ELMWOOD SPECIAL SCHOOL
Hamp Avenue, Bridgwater, Somerset TA6 6AP
*Type:* Co-educational Day Only 4–16
*Special needs:* ASD BESD **MLD** SLD
*Wheelchair access:* WA1

### ELSTAR (SEDGEMOOR)
Ashwell Park, Ilminster, Somerset TA19 9DX
*Type:* Girls Day Only 11–19

### RAVENSWOOD SCHOOL
Pound Lane, Nailsea, North Somerset BS48 2NN
*Website:* www. ravenswood.n-somerset.sch.uk
*Type:* Co-educational Day Only 3–19
*Special needs:* ASD **ASP** DYC DYP DYS **MLD SLD**
*Wheelchair access:* WA2

### WESTHAVEN SCHOOL
Ellesmere Road, Weston-Super-Mare, North Somerset BS23 4UT
*Type:* Co-educational Day Only 7–16
*Special needs:* ADHD ASD ASP BESD CP DYC DYP DYS EPI HI SP&LD VI
*Wheelchair access:* WA2

## Somerset County Council

**County Hall**
**Taunton**
**Somerset**
**TA1 4DY**

### AVALON SPECIAL SCHOOL
Brooks Road, Street, Somerset BA16 0PS
*Type:* Co-educational Day Only 2–19
*Special needs:* ASD ASP CP DOW DYP EPI **MLD PMLD SLD** SP&LD VI
*Wheelchair access:* W

### CRITCHILL SCHOOL & LEARNING SUPPORT CENTRE
Nunney Road, Frome, Somerset BA11 4LB
*Type:* Co-educational Day Only 2–16
*Special needs:* ASD **ASP BESD CB DOW EPI HEA HI IM MLD PMLD SLD** SP&LD TOU VI W
*Wheelchair access:* W WA1 WA2

### FAIRMEAD COMMUNITY SPECIAL SCHOOL
Mudford Road, Yeovil, Somerset BA21 4NZ
*Type:* Co-educational Day Only 4–16
*Special needs:* ADD ADHD ASD ASP BESD DOW DYP EPI HI IM **MLD** SP&LD TOU VI
*Wheelchair access:* WA1

### FCL SCHOOL (FAMILIES CARE LIMITED)
Norton Fitzwarren, Taunton, Somerset TA2 6RQ
*Type:* Co-educational Day Only 9–16

### FIVEWAYS SPECIAL SCHOOL
Victoria Road, Yeovil, Somerset BA21 5AZ
*Type:* Co-educational Day Only 4–19
*Special needs:* PMLD SLD
*Wheelchair access:* WA1

### NEW HORIZON CENTRE SCHOOL
Bath House Farm, Taunton, Somerset TA6 5RH
*Type:* Co-educational Day Only 11–16

### PENROSE SPECIAL SCHOOL
Albert Street, Bridgwater, Somerset TA6 7ET
*Website:* www.penrose.ik.org
*Type:* Co-educational Day Only 2–19
*Special needs:* ASD CP DOW EPI PMLD **SLD**
*Wheelchair access:* WA1

## SELWORTHY SPECIAL SCHOOL
Selworthy Road, Taunton, Somerset TA2 8HD
*Type:* Co-educational Day Only 2–19
*Special needs:* ADD ADHD ASD **ASP** CP DOW EPI HEA HI IM MLD **PMLD SLD** VI
*Wheelchair access:* WA1

## SKY COLLEGE
Pickeridge Close, Taunton, Somerset TA2 7HW
*Website:* www.skycollege.co.uk
*Type:* Boys Boarding and Day 11–16
*Special needs:* ADHD **BESD**

# STAFFORDSHIRE

## Staffordshire County Council

Tipping Street
Stafford
Staffordshire
ST16 2DH

## BLACKFRIARS SPECIAL SCHOOL
Priory Road, Newcastle under Lyme, Staffordshire ST5 2TF
*Website:*
www.sln.org/blackfriars
*Type:* Co-educational 2–19
*Special needs:* **CP** DOW DYP EPI **HEA MLD** PMLD SLD SP&LD
*Wheelchair access:* WA1

## CHASETOWN COMMUNITY SCHOOL
Church Street, Burntwood, Staffordshire WS7 3QL

## CHERRY TREES SPECIAL SCHOOL
Giggetty Lane, Wolverhampton, West Midlands WV5 0AX
*Type:* Co-educational Day Only 2–11
*Special needs:* **PMLD SLD**
*Wheelchair access:* WA1

## CICELY HAUGHTON SCHOOL
Westwood Manor, Stoke on Trent, Staffordshire ST9 0BX
*Type:* Boys Boarding and Day 5–11
*Special needs:* **BESD**

## COPPICE SPECIAL SCHOOL
Abbots Way, Newcastle under Lyme, Staffordshire ST5 2EY
*Type:* Co-educational Day Only 3–16
*Special needs:* ASP MLD

## CROWN SPECIAL SCHOOL
Bitham Lane, Burton upon Trent, Staffordshire DE13 0HB
*Type:* Co-educational Day Only 3–18
*Special needs:* ASD PMLD **SLD**
*Wheelchair access:* W

## GREENHALL NURSERY
Second Avenue, Holmcroft, Staffordshire ST16 IPS
*Type:* Co-educational Day Only 2–5
*Special needs:* **CP** DYP EPI HEA HI IM MLD PMLD SLD SP&LD VI
*Wheelchair access:* WA1

## HORTON LODGE SPECIAL SCHOOL
Rudyard, Leek, Staffordshire ST13 8RB
*Type:* Co-educational Day and Boarding 2–11
*Special needs:* CP SP&LD VI
*Wheelchair access:* W

## LOXLEY HALL SPECIAL SCHOOL
Stafford Road, Uttoxeter, Staffordshire ST14 8RS
*Type:* Boys Boarding Only 10–16
*Special needs:* **BESD**

## MARSHLANDS SPECIAL SCHOOL
Lansdowne Way, Stafford, Staffordshire ST17 4RD
*Type:* Co-educational Day Only 2–11
*Special needs:* **MLD** PMLD **SLD**
*Wheelchair access:* WA1

## MEADOWS SPECIAL SCHOOL
High Street, Stoke on Trent, Staffordshire ST5 6BX
*Type:* Co-educational Day Only 3–19
*Special needs:* ASD ASP BESD DOW EPI HI **MLD** TOU VI
*Wheelchair access:* W

## MERRYFIELDS SPECIAL SCHOOL
Hoon Avenue, Newcastle under Lyme, Staffordshire ST5 9NY
*Type:* Co-educational Day Only
*Special needs:* ASD **MLD** PMLD **SLD**

## QUEEN'S CROFT COMMUNITY SCHOOL
Birmingham Road, Lichfield, Staffordshire WS13 6PJ
*Website:* www.queenscroft. staffs.sch.uk
*Type:* Co-educational Day Only 11–18
*Wheelchair access:* WA1

## QUINCE TREE SPECIAL SCHOOL
Quince, Tamworth, Staffordshire B77 4EN
*Type:* Co-educational Day Only 2–19
*Special needs:* PMLD **SLD**
*Wheelchair access:* W

**ROCKLANDS SPECIAL SCHOOL**
Wissage Road, Lichfield,
Staffordshire WS13 6SW
*Type:* Co-educational Day Only
2–11
*Special needs:* ASD ASP
PMLD SLD

**STRETTON COMMUNITY SPECIAL SCHOOL FEDERATION**
Bitham Lane, Burton upon Trent,
Staffordshire DE13 0HB
*Type:* Co-educational Day Only
4–18
*Special needs:* ASD **ASP MLD SLD**

**SAXON HILL SPECIAL SCHOOL**
Kings Hill Road, Lichfield,
Staffordshire WS14 9DE
*Website:*
www.saxonhill.staffs.sch.uk
*Type:* Co-educational Day and
Boarding 2–19
*Special needs:* **CP DYP EPI HEA HI IM PMLD** SP&LD VI
*Wheelchair access:* WA1

**TWO RIVERS HIGH SCHOOL**
Torc Campus, Tamworth,
Staffordshire B77 2HJ
*Type:* Co-educational Day Only
11–18
*Special needs:* **MLD SLD**
*Wheelchair access:* WA1

**WIGHTWICK HALL SPECIAL SCHOOL**
Tinacre Hill, Wolverhampton,
West Midlands WV6 8DA
*Type:* Co-educational Day Only
11–19
*Special needs:* ASD MLD SP&LD
*Wheelchair access:* WA1

**WILLIAM BAXTER SPECIAL SCHOOL**
Stanley Road, Cannock,
Staffordshire WS12 4JS
*Type:* Co-educational Day Only
11–19
*Special needs:* ADD ADHD ASD
ASP BESD CP DOW DYP EPI HI
IM **MLD** PMLD SP&LD VI
*Wheelchair access:* WA1

## Stoke-on-Trent Education and Lifelong Learning

**Civic Centre**
**Glebe Street**
**Stoke-on-Trent**
**Staffordshire**
**ST4 1HH**

**ABBEY HILL SPECIAL SCHOOL**
Greasley Road, Stoke on Trent,
Staffordshire ST2 8LB
*Type:* Co-educational Day Only
2–19
*Special needs:* ASD **ASP** BESD
**MLD** SLD
*Wheelchair access:* WA1

**AYNSLEY SPECIAL SCHOOL**
Aynsley's Drive, Blythe Bridge,
Stoke ST11 9HJ
*Type:* Co-educational Day Only
*Special needs:* ADHD ASD ASP
BESD DOW **MLD**

**HEATHFIELD SPECIAL SCHOOL**
Chell Heath Road, Stoke on
Trent, Stoke ST6 6PD
*Type:* Co-educational Day Only
2–16
*Special needs:* ASD DOW EPI
PMLD **SLD** SP&LD
*Wheelchair access:* WA1

**KEMBALL SPECIAL SCHOOL**
Duke Street, Stoke ST4 3NR
*Type:* Co-educational Day Only
2–19
*Special needs:* PMLD SLD

**MIDDLEHURST SPECIAL SCHOOL**
Turnhurst Road, Stoke ST6 6NQ
*Type:* Co-educational Day Only
5–16
*Special needs:* BESD MLD
SP&LD

# STOCKTON-ON-TEES

## Stockton-on-Tees Borough Council

**PO Box 11**
**Church Road**
**Stockton-on-Tees**
**TS18 1LD**

**ABBEY HILL SCHOOL, TECHNOLOGY COLLEGE**
Ketton Road, Stockton-on-Tees
TS19 8BU
*Type:* Co-educational Day Only
11–19
*Special needs:* ADHD ASD **ASP**
CP DOW DYP DYS EPI HEA HI
**MLD PMLD SLD** SP&LD TOU VI
*Wheelchair access:* W

**WESTLANDS ANNEXE**
Mill Lane, Norton,
Stockton-on-Tees TS20 1LG

# SUFFOLK

## Suffolk County Council

**Endeavour House**
**Russell Road**
**Ipswich**
**Suffolk**
**IP1 2BX**

### THE ASHLEY SCHOOL
Ashley Downs, Lowestoft,
Suffolk NR32 4EU
*Website:*
www.ashley.suffolk.sch.uk
*Type:* Co-educational Day and
Boarding 7–16
*Special needs:* **MLD**

### BEACON HILL SCHOOL
Stone Lodge Lane West,
Ipswich, Suffolk IP2 9HW
*Type:* Co-educational Day Only
5–16
*Special needs:* ASD **MLD**
*Wheelchair access:* WA1

### BELSTEAD SCHOOL
Sprites Lane, Ipswich, Suffolk
IP8 3ND
*Type:* Co-educational Day Only
11–19
*Special needs:* ASD PMLD SLD
*Wheelchair access:* WA1

### HEATHSIDE SCHOOL
Heath Road, Ipswich, Suffolk
IP4 5SN
*Website:*
www.heathsideschool.com
*Type:* Co-educational Day Only
*Special needs:* ASD **ASP** CB
CP **EPI PMLD SLD** W
*Wheelchair access:* WA1 WA2

### HILLSIDE SCHOOL
Hitchcock Place, Sudbury,
Suffolk CO10 1NN
*Website:*
www.hillsidespecial.org.uk
*Type:* Co-educational Day Only
3–19
*Special needs:* **SLD**
*Wheelchair access:* W

### PRIORY SCHOOL
Mount Road, Bury St Edmunds,
Suffolk 1P32 7BH
*Type:* Co-educational Day Only
9–16

### THOMAS WOLSEY SCHOOL
642 Old Norwich Road, Ipswich,
Suffolk IP1 6LA
*Type:* Co-educational Day Only
3–19

### WARREN SCHOOL
Clarkes Lane, Lowestoft, Suffolk
NR33 8HT
*Type:* Co-educational 3–19
*Special needs:* PMLD SLD
*Wheelchair access:* WA2

# SURREY

## Surrey County Council

**Wood Street**
**Kingston upon Thames**
**Surrey**
**KT1 1AB**

### THE ABBEY SCHOOL
Menin Way, Farnham, Surrey
GU9 8DY
*Website:*
www.abbey.surrey.sch.uk
*Type:* Co-educational Day Only
10–16
*Special needs:* ASD **MLD**

### BROOKLANDS SCHOOL
27 Wray Park Road, Reigate,
Surrey RH2 0DF
*Type:* Co-educational Day Only
2–11
*Special needs:* ASD DOW
**PMLD SLD**
*Wheelchair access:* WA2

### CARWARDEN HOUSE
### COMMUNITY SCHOOL
118 Upper Chobham Road,
Camberley, Surrey GU15 1EJ
*Website:*
www.carwardenhouse.com
*Type:* Co-educational Day Only
11–19
*Special needs:* **MLD**
*Wheelchair access:* WA3

### CLIFTON HILL SCHOOL
Chaldon Road, Caterham,
Surrey CR3 5PH
*Website:*
www.clifton-hill.surrey.sch.uk
*Type:* Co-educational Day Only
11–19
*Special needs:* **SLD**
*Wheelchair access:* WA1

### FREEMANTLES SCHOOL
Pycroft Road, Chertsey, Surrey
KT16 9ER
*Website:* www.freemantles.
surrey.sch.uk
*Type:* Co-educational Day Only
4–14
*Special needs:* ASD **ASP**
*Wheelchair access:* WA2

### GOSDEN HOUSE SCHOOL
Bramley, Guildford, Surrey
GU5 0AH
*Website:*
www.gosdenhouse.co.uk
*Type:* Co-educational Boarding
Only 5–16
*Special needs:* **MLD** SP&LD

## LIMPSFIELD GRANGE SCHOOL
89 Blue House Lane, Oxted, Surrey RH8 0RZ
*Type:* Girls Boarding and Day 11–16
*Special needs:* ASD ASP DYP DYS HEA IM SP&LD VI
*Wheelchair access:* WA2

## LINDEN BRIDGE SCHOOL
Grafton Road, Worcester Park, Surrey KT4 7JW
*Type:* Co-educational Boarding and Day 4–19
*Special needs:* ASD **ASP**

## MANOR MEAD SCHOOL
Laleham Road, Shepperton, Surrey TW17 8EL
*Type:* Co-educational Day Only
*Special needs:* CP EPI PMLD **SLD**
*Wheelchair access:* W

## THE PARK SCHOOL
Onslow Crescent, Woking, Surrey GU22 7AT
*Type:* Co-educational Day Only 11–16
*Special needs:* **MLD** SP&LD
*Wheelchair access:* WA1

## PHILIP SOUTHCOTE SCHOOL
Addlestone, Surrey KT15 2QH
*Website:*
www.philipsouthcote.co.uk
*Type:* Co-educational Day Only 9–16
*Special needs:* HI **MLD**
*Wheelchair access:* WA1

## POND MEADOW SCHOOL
Pond Meadow, Guildford, Surrey GU2 6LG
*Type:* Co-educational Day Only 2–19
*Special needs:* PMLD SLD
*Wheelchair access:* W

## PORTESBERY SCHOOL
Portesbery Road, Camberley, Surrey GU15 3SZ
*Type:* Co-educational Day Only 2–19
*Special needs:* PMLD **SLD**

## THE RIDGEWAY SCHOOL
14 Frensham Road, Farnham, Surrey GU9 8HB
*Type:* Co-educational Day Only 2–19
*Special needs:* ASD CP DOW EPI HI **PMLD SLD** VI
*Wheelchair access:* WA1

## ST NICHOLAS SCHOOL
Taynton Drive, Redhill, Surrey RH1 3PU
*Type:* Boys Boarding and Day 11–16
*Special needs:* BESD
*Wheelchair access:* WA3

## STARHURST SCHOOL
Chart Lane South, Dorking, Surrey RH5 4DB
*Type:* Boys Boarding and Day 11–16
*Special needs:* BESD

## SIDLOW BRIDGE CENTRE
Ironsbottom Lane, Reigate, Surrey RH2 8PP
*Type:* Co-educational Day Only 14–16
*Special needs:* **BESD**

## SUNNYDOWN SCHOOL+
Portley House, Caterham, Surrey CR3 5ED
*Type:* Boys Boarding and Day 11–16
*Special needs:* **DYS**

## WALTON LEIGH SCHOOL
Queens Road, Walton-on-Thames, Surrey KT12 5AB
*Website:*
www.waltonleighschool.org
*Type:* Co-educational Day Only 12–19
*Special needs:* ASD **PMLD SLD**
*Wheelchair access:* WA1

## WEST HILL SCHOOL
Kingston Road, Leatherhead, Surrey KT22 7PW
*Type:* Co-educational Day Only 9–16
*Special needs:* ASD **ASP MLD SLD**
*Wheelchair access:* W

## WEY HOUSE SCHOOL
Bramley, Guildford, Surrey GU5 0BJ
*Type:* Boys Day and Boarding 7–11
*Special needs:* **BESD**
*Wheelchair access:* WA3

## WISHMORE CROSS SCHOOL
Alpha Road, Chobham, Surrey GU24 8NE
*Type:* Boys Boarding Only 11–16
*Special needs:* **BESD**

## WOODFIELD SCHOOL
Sunstone Grove, Redhill, Surrey RH1 3PR
*Website:*
www.woodfield.surrey.sch.uk
*Type:* Co-educational Day Only 9–16
*Special needs:* **MLD**
*Wheelchair access:* WA1

## WOODLANDS SCHOOL
Fortyfoot Road, Leatherhead, Surrey KT22 8RY
*Type:* Co-educational Day Only 2–19
*Special needs:* ASD **ASP PMLD SLD**
*Wheelchair access:* WA1

# EAST SUSSEX

## Brighton & Hove Council

**Kings House**
**Grand Avenue**
**Hove**
**East Sussex**
**BN3 2LS**

### ALTERNATIVE CENTRE FOR EDUCATION
Queensdown School Road, Brighton, East Sussex BN1 7LA
*Type:* Co-educational Day Only 11–16
*Special needs:* **BESD**

### CEDAR CENTRE
Lynchet Road, Brighton, East Sussex BN1 7FP
*Type:* Co-educational Day Only
*Special needs:* **MLD**
*Wheelchair access:* WA2

### DOWNS PARK SCHOOL
Foredown Road, Brighton, East Sussex BN41 2FU
*Type:* Co-educational Day Only 5–16
*Special needs:* ADHD ASD **ASP** DOW **MLD** SP&LD

### DOWNS VIEW SCHOOL
Warren Road, Brighton, East Sussex BN2 6BB
*Website:* www.downsview. brighton-hove.sch.uk
*Type:* Co-educational Day Only 4–19
*Special needs:* ASD MLD PMLD SLD
*Wheelchair access:* WA1

### HILLSIDE SCHOOL
Foredown Road, Brighton, East Sussex BN41 2FU
*Website:* www.hillside. brighton-hove.sch.uk
*Type:* Co-educational Day Only 4–16
*Special needs:* ASD PMLD **SLD**
*Wheelchair access:* WA1

### PATCHAM HOUSE SCHOOL
7 Old London Road, Brighton, East Sussex BN1 8XR
*Type:* Co-educational Day Only 3–16
*Special needs:* ASP **CP** DYP EPI

## East Sussex Education Department

**PO Box 4, County Hall**
**St Annes Crescent**
**Lewes**
**East Sussex**
**BN7 1SG**

### GLYNE GAP SCHOOL
School Place, Bexhill-on-Sea, East Sussex TN40 2PU
*Type:* Co-educational Day Only 2–19
*Special needs:* ASD PMLD SLD
*Wheelchair access:* WA1

### GROVE PARK SCHOOL
Church Road, Crowborough, East Sussex TN6 1BN
*Type:* Co-educational Day Only 3–19
*Special needs:* ASD MLD PMLD SLD
*Wheelchair access:* WA1

### HAZEL COURT SCHOOL
Shinewater Lane, Eastbourne, East Sussex BN23 8AT
*Type:* Co-educational Day Only 11–19
*Special needs:* MLD PMLD SLD
*Wheelchair access:* WA1

### THE LINDFIELD SCHOOL
Lindfield Road, Eastbourne, East Sussex BN22 0BQ
*Type:* Co-educational Day Only 10–16
*Special needs:* ADD ADHD ASD **ASP** DOW DYC DYS EPI HEA HI **MLD** SP&LD VI
*Wheelchair access:* WA1

### NEW HORIZONS SCHOOL
Beauchamp Road, St Leonards-on-Sea, East Sussex TN38 9JU
*Type:* Co-educational Day Only 6–16
*Special needs:* ADD **ADHD** ASD **ASP BESD CB**
*Wheelchair access:* WA2

### OAK GROVE COLLEGE
The Boulevard, Worthing, West Sussex BN13 1JX
*Type:* Co-educational Day Only 11–19
*Special needs:* ASD **ASP MLD PMLD SLD**
*Wheelchair access:* WA1

### ST MARY'S SCHOOL
Horam, Heathfield, East Sussex TN21 0BT
*Type:* Co-educational Boarding and Day 11–19
*Special needs:* BESD MLD

### SAXON MOUNT SCHOOL
Edinburgh Road, St Leonards-on-Sea, East Sussex TN38 8DA
*Type:* Co-educational Day Only 11–16
*Special needs:* ASD **MLD** SP&LD

### THE SOUTH DOWNS COMMUNITY SPECIAL SCHOOL
Beechy Avenue, Eastbourne, East Sussex BN20 8NU
*Website:* www. southdowns.e-sussex.sch.uk
*Type:* Co-educational Day Only 4–11
*Special needs:* ADHD ASD **ASP** BESD CP DOW DYP EPI **MLD PMLD SLD** SP&LD

### TORFIELD SCHOOL
Croft Road, Hastings, East Sussex TN34 3JT
*Website:* www.torfieldschool.net
*Type:* Co-educational Day Only 4–11
*Special needs:* ASD **ASP BESD CB** MLD SP&LD
*Wheelchair access:* WA2

# WEST SUSSEX

## West Sussex County Council

**County Hall
West Street
Chichester
West Sussex
PO19 1RQ**

### ABBOTSFORD COMMUNITY SCHOOL
Cuckfield Road, Burgess Hill,
West Sussex RH15 8RE
*Type:* Boys Boarding and Day
7–16
*Special needs:* ADD ADHD ASD
ASP **BESD** DYS

### CORNFIELD SCHOOL
Cornfield Close, Littlehampton,
West Sussex BN17 6HY
*Website:*
www.cornfield.w-sussex.sch.uk
*Type:* Co-educational Day Only
11–16
*Special needs:* **BESD**

### COURT MEADOW SPECIAL SCHOOL
Hanlye Lane, Haywards Heath,
West Sussex RH17 5HN
*Type:* Co-educational Day Only
2–19
*Special needs:* ASD CB PMLD
**SLD**
*Wheelchair access:* WA1

### FORDWATER SPECIAL SCHOOL
Summersdale Road, Chichester,
West Sussex PO19 6PP
*Website:*
www.fordwater.w-sussex.sch.uk
*Type:* Co-educational Day Only
2–19
*Special needs:* ASD **ASP PMLD
SLD**
*Wheelchair access:* W

### HERONS DALE SPECIAL SCHOOL
Hawkins Crescent,
Shoreham-by-Sea, West Sussex
BN43 6TN
*Type:* 4–16
*Special needs:* ASP **MLD**

### LITTLEGREEN SPECIAL SCHOOL
Compton, Chichester,
West Sussex PO18 9NW
*Website:*
www.littlegreen.w-sussex.sch.uk
*Type:* Boys Boarding and Day
7–14
*Special needs:* ADD ADHD ASP
**BESD** TOU

### MANOR GREEN COLLEGE
Lady Margaret Road, Crawley,
West Sussex RH11 0DX
*Website:*
www.manorgreen-college.
w-sussex.sch.uk
*Type:* Co-educational Day Only
11–19
*Special needs:* ASD **MLD PMLD
SLD**
*Wheelchair access:* WA1

### NEWICK HOUSE SPECIAL SCHOOL
Birchwood Grove Road,
Burgess Hill, West Sussex
RH15 0DP
*Website:*
www.newickhouse.co.uk
*Type:* Co-educational Day Only
4–16
*Special needs:* ADD ADHD
BESD DOW DYP DYS EPI HEA
HI **MLD** SLD SP&LD
*Wheelchair access:* WA1

### PALATINE SCHOOL
Palatine Road, Worthing,
West Sussex BN12 6JP
*Website:* www.palatine.org
*Type:* Co-educational Day Only
4–11
*Special needs:* ADD ADHD ASD
**ASP** CB **CP DOW** DYP EPI **HEA
IM MLD PMLD SLD** SP&LD
TOU W
*Wheelchair access:* W WA1 WA2

### QUEEN ELIZABETH II SILVER JUBILEE SCHOOL
Comptons Lane, Horsham,
West Sussex RH13 5NW
*Website:* www.queenelizabeth2.
w-sussex.sch.uk
*Type:* Co-educational Day Only
2–19
*Special needs:* PMLD **SLD**
*Wheelchair access:* WA1
*Non-maintained*

### ST ANTHONY'S SCHOOL
Woodlands Lane, Chichester,
West Sussex PO19 5PA
*Website:* www.
st-anthonys.w-sussex.sch.uk
*Type:* Co-educational Day Only
4–16
*Special needs:* ASD **ASP MLD**
SP&LD
*Wheelchair access:* WA1

# TYNE AND WEAR

## Gateshead Education Offices

**Civic Centre
Regent Street
Gateshead
Tyne and Wear
NE8 1HH**

**THE CEDARS SCHOOL
SPORTS COLLEGE**
Ivy Lane, Gateshead,
Tyne and Wear NE9 6QD
*Website:*
www.cedarssportscollege.org.uk
*Type:* Co-educational Day Only
3–16
*Special needs:* **IM** SP&LD
*Wheelchair access:* WA1

**DRYDEN SCHOOL**
Shotley Gardens, Gateshead,
Tyne and Wear NE9 5UR
*Type:* Co-educational Day Only
*Special needs:* **PMLD SLD**
*Wheelchair access:* WA1

**ESLINGTON PRIMARY
SCHOOL**
Hazel Road, Gateshead,
Tyne and Wear NE8 2EP
*Type:* Co-educational Day Only
5–11

**FURROWFIELD SCHOOL**
Senior Site, Whitehills Drive,
Gateshead, Tyne and Wear
NE10 9RZ
*Type:* Boys Day Only 11–16
*Special needs:* ADHD ASP
**BESD** DYP
*Wheelchair access:* WA1

**GIBSIDE SCHOOL**
Burnthouse Lane, Newcastle
upon Tyne, Tyne and Wear
NE16 5AT
*Website:*
www.gibsideschool.org
*Type:* Co-educational 3–11
*Special needs:* ASD **ASP CP
DOW PMLD SLD**
*Wheelchair access:* WA1

**HILL TOP SCHOOL**
Wealcroft, Gateshead, Tyne and
Wear NE10 8LT
*Type:* Co-educational Day Only
*Special needs:* IM SP&LD VI
*Wheelchair access:* WA1

## Newcastle City Council

**Civic Centre
Barras Bridge
Newcastle upon Tyne
Tyne and Wear
NE1 8PU**

**GLEBE SCHOOL**
Woodburn Drive, Whitley Bay,
Northumberland NE26 3HW
*Type:* Co-educational Day Only
4–11
*Special needs:* ASD **MLD** SP&LD
*Wheelchair access:* WA1

**HADRIAN SCHOOL**
Bertram Crescent, Newcastle
upon Tyne, Tyne and Wear
NE15 6PY
*Website:*
www.hadrian.newcastle.sch.uk
*Type:* Co-educational Day Only
2–11
*Special needs:* **PMLD SLD**
*Wheelchair access:* W

**SIR CHARLES PARSONS
SCHOOL**
Westbourne Avenue,
Newcastle Upon Tyne, Tyne
and Wear NE6 4ED
*Website:* www.sircharlesparson.
newcastle.sch.uk
*Type:* Co-educational Day Only
11–19
*Special needs:* **PMLD SLD** SP&LD
*Wheelchair access:* WA1

**THOMAS BEWICK SCHOOL**
Hillhead Parkway, Newcastle
upon Tyne, Tyne and Wear
NE5 1DS
*Type:* Co-educational Day and
Boarding 3–19
*Special needs:* ASD ASP MLD
SLD
*Wheelchair access:* WA1

**TRINITY SCHOOL**
Kenton Lodge Site,
Newcastle Upon Tyne, Tyne
and Wear NE3 4PD
*Type:* Boys Boarding and Day
7–13
*Special needs:* **BESD**

**TRINITY SCHOOL**
Deneview Site, Newcastle upon
Tyne, Tyne and Wear NE3 1SZ
*Special needs:* **BESD**

## North Tyneside Education Offices

**Quadrant, The Silverlink North
Cobalt Business Park
North Tyneside
Tyne and Wear
NE27 0BY**

**PARKSIDE SCHOOL**
Mullen Road, Wallsend,
Tyne and Wear NE28 9HA
*Type:* Co-educational Day Only
*Special needs:* ASD **SLD**

**SILVERDALE SCHOOL**
Langdale Gardens, Wallsend,
Tyne and Wear NE28 0HG
*Type:* Co-educational Day Only
*Special needs:* **BESD**
*Wheelchair access:* WA1

**SOUTHLANDS SCHOOL**
Beach Road, North Shields,
Tyne and Wear NE30 2QR
*Type:* Co-educational Day Only
11–17
*Special needs:* BESD **MLD**

**WOODLAWN SCHOOL**
Langley Avenue, Whitley Bay,
Tyne and Wear NE25 9DF
*Website:* www.woodlawn.org.uk
*Type:* Co-educational Day Only
2–16
*Special needs:* CP DYP HEA HI
IM SP&LD VI
*Wheelchair access:* WA1

## South Tyneside Lifelong Learning & Leisure Directorate

Town Hall and Civic Offices
South Shields
NE33 2RL

### BAMBURGH SCHOOL
Cautley Road, South Shields,
Tyne and Wear NE34 7TD
*Type:* Co-educational Day Only
2–17
*Special needs:* **ASD ASP HEA
HI IM** SP&LD VI
*Wheelchair access:* WA1

### EPINAY SCHOOL
Clervaux Terrace, Jarrow,
Tyne and Wear NE32 5UP
*Website:* www.epinay.org
*Type:* Co-educational Day Only
5–17
*Special needs:* BESD **MLD** SLD
*Wheelchair access:* WA2

### GREENFIELDS SCHOOL
Victoria Road East, Hebburn,
Tyne and Wear NE31 1YQ
*Type:* Co-educational Day Only
2–19
*Special needs:* ASD IM **PMLD
SLD** VI
*Wheelchair access:* WA1

### MARGARET SUTTON SCHOOL
Ashley Road, South Shields,
Tyne and Wear NE34 0PF
*Type:* Co-educational Day Only
*Special needs:* **MLD**

### OAKLEIGH GARDENS SCHOOL
Oakleigh Gardens,
Nr. Sunderland,
Tyne and Wear SR6 7PT
*Type:* Co-educational Day Only
2–19
*Special needs:* **PMLD SLD**
*Wheelchair access:* W

## Sunderland LEA

P.O Box 101, Civic Centre
Burdon Road
Sunderland
Tyne and Wear
SR2 7DN

### BARBARA PRIESTMAN SCHOOL
Meadowside, Sunderland,
Tyne and Wear SR2 7QN
*Website:*
www.barbara-priestman.org.uk
*Type:* Co-educational Day Only
*Special needs:* ASP VI

### CASTLEGREEN COMMUNITY SCHOOL
Craigshaw Road, Sunderland,
Tyne and Wear SR5 3NF
*Website:* www.
millenniumschools.co.uk/pub/
sunderland/castlegreen/a.html
*Type:* Co-educational Day Only
11–19

### COLUMBIA GRANGE SCHOOL
Oxclose Road, Washington,
Sunderland NE38 7NY
*Website:*
www.sunderlandschools.org/
columbiagrange
*Type:* Co-educational Day Only
2–11
*Special needs:* ASD **ASP** SLD
*Wheelchair access:* W
*Non-maintained*

### DAVENPORT SCHOOL
Durham Road,
Houghton-le-Spring, Tyne
and Wear DH5 8NF
*Type:* Co-educational Day Only
3–13
*Special needs:* ASD **ASP** MLD
PMLD **SLD**

### FELSTEAD SCHOOL
Fordfield Road (North Side),
Sunderland, Tyne and Wear
SR4 0DA
*Type:* Co-educational Day Only
13–25
*Special needs:* BESD MLD

### MAPLEWOOD SCHOOL
Redcar Road, Sunderland,
Tyne and Wear SR5 5PA
*Type:* Co-educational 4–11
*Special needs:* ADD ADHD ASD
ASP **BESD** TOU
*Wheelchair access:* WA1

### PORTLAND SCHOOL
Weymouth Road, Sunderland,
Tyne and Wear SR3 2NQ
*Website:*
www.portland-school.co.uk
*Type:* Co-educational Day Only
11–19
*Special needs:* **PMLD SLD**
*Wheelchair access:* WA1

### SPRINGWELL DENE SCHOOL
Swindon Road, Sunderland,
Tyne and Wear SR3 4EE
*Type:* Co-educational Day Only
*Special needs:* **BESD**

### SUNNINGDALE SCHOOL
Shaftoe Road, Sunderland,
Tyne and Wear SR3 4HA
*Type:* Co-educational Day Only
2–11
*Special needs:* PMLD SLD
*Wheelchair access:* W

### WELLBANK SCHOOL
Wellbank Road, Washington,
Tyne and Wear NE37 1NL
*Type:* Co-educational Day Only
3–13
*Special needs:* **MLD PMLD SLD**
*Wheelchair access:* W

# WARWICKSHIRE

## Warwickshire Education Offices

**22 Northgate Street**
**Warwick**
**Warwickshire**
**CV34 4SR**

### BROOKE SCHOOL
Merttens Drive, Rugby,
Warwickshire CV22 7AE
*Type:* Co-educational Day Only
2–19
*Special needs:* MLD PMLD SLD
*Wheelchair access:* W

### THE GRIFF SCHOOL
Coventry Road, Nuneaton,
Warwickshire CV10 7AX
*Type:* Co-educational Day Only
5–16
*Special needs:* **MLD**

### OAKWOODS SCHOOLS
Morris Drive, Nuneaton,
Warwickshire CV11 4QH
*Type:* Co-educational 2–19
*Special needs:* **ADD ADHD**
**ASD ASP BESD CB CP DOW**
**DYC DYP DYS EPI HEA HI IM**
**MLD PMLD SLD** SP&LD VI
*Wheelchair access:* WA1

### RIDGEWAY SCHOOL
Montague Road, Warwick,
Warwickshire CV34 5LW
*Type:* Co-educational Day Only
2–19
*Special needs:* ASD MLD PMLD
SLD
*Wheelchair access:* WA2

### THE ROUND OAK SCHOOL
Pound Lane, Leamington Spa,
Warwickshire CV32 7RT
*Type:* Co-educational Day Only
5–16
*Special needs:* ADHD ASD
BESD DOW **MLD** SLD
*Wheelchair access:* WA2

### WOODLANDS SCHOOL
Packington Lane, Coleshill,
West Midlands B46 3JE
*Type:* Co-educational Day Only
2–19
*Special needs:* ASD **ASP** BESD
MLD **PMLD SLD**
*Wheelchair access:* WA1

# WEST MIDLANDS

## Birmingham City Council

**The Council House**
**Victoria Square**
**Birmingham**
**West Midlands**
**B1 1BB**

### BAGINTON FIELDS
Sedgemoor Road, Coventry,
West Midlands CV3 4EA
*Type:* Co-educational
*Special needs:* ADD ADHD ASD
**ASP** BESD CP DOW DYP EPI
MLD **PMLD SLD** SP&LD VI
*Wheelchair access:* WA1

### BASKERVILLE SCHOOL
Fellows Lane, Birmingham,
West Midlands B17 9TS
*Type:* Co-educational Boarding
Only 11–19
*Special needs:* **ASD ASP**

### BEAUFORT SCHOOL
16 Coleshill Road, Birmingham,
West Midlands B36 8AA
*Type:* Day Only 3–11
*Special needs:* **PMLD SLD**
*Wheelchair access:* WA1

### BRAIDWOOD SCHOOL
Bromford Road, Birmingham,
West Midlands B36 8AF
*Website:*
www.braidwoodonline.org.uk
*Type:* Co-educational Day Only
11–18
*Special needs:* **HI**
*Wheelchair access:* WA1

### BRAYS SCHOOL
Brays Road, Birmingham,
West Midlands B26 1NS
*Website:* www.brays.bham.sch.uk
*Type:* Co-educational Day Only
2–11
*Special needs:* CP DOW EPI
HEA HI **IM** PMLD SLD SP&LD
VI W
*Wheelchair access:* W WA1 WA2

### BRIDGE SCHOOL
290 Reservoir Road, Birmingham,
West Midlands B23 6DE
*Type:* Co-educational 2–11
*Special needs:* PMLD SLD

### BRIDGE SCHOOL – LONGMOOR
Coppice View Road, Sutton
Coldfield, West Midlands B7 6UE
*Website:*
www.bridgespecialschool.co.uk
*Type:* Co-educational Day and
Boarding 2–11
*Special needs:* ASD PMLD **SLD**

### CALTHORPE SCHOOL AND SPORTS COLLEGE
Darwin Street, Birmingham,
West Midlands B12 0JJ
*Website:*
www.calthorpe.bham.sch.uk
*Type:* Co-educational Day Only
2–19
*Special needs:* ASD **ASP** BESD
DOW EPI HI **PMLD SLD** SP&LD
TOU VI
*Wheelchair access:* WA1

### CHERRY OAK SCHOOL
60 Frederick Road, Birmingham,
West Midlands B29 6PB
*Type:* Co-educational Day Only
2–11
*Special needs:* ASD PMLD **SLD**
*Wheelchair access:* W

### DAME ELLEN PINSENT SCHOOL
Ardencote Road, Birmingham,
West Midlands B13 0RW
*Type:* Co-educational Day Only
4–11
*Special needs:* ASD DOW **MLD**
SLD SP&LD

### FOX HOLLIES SCHOOL AND PERFORMING ARTS COLLEGE
Highbury Community Campus,
Birmingham, West Midlands
B13 8QB
*Type:* Co-educational Day Only
11–19
*Special needs:* PMLD **SLD**
*Wheelchair access:* WA1

### HALLMOOR SCHOOL
Hallmoor Road, Birmingham,
West Midlands B33 9QY
*Type:* Co-educational Day Only
4–19
*Special needs:* **MLD**

### HAMILTON SCHOOL
Hamilton Road, Birmingham,
West Midlands B21 8AH
*Type:* Co-educational Day Only
4–11
*Special needs:* ASD ASP DOW
DYP EPI HI **MLD SLD** SP&LD

### HUNTERS HILL
Spirehouse Lane, Bromsgrove,
West Midlands B60 1QD

### KINGSTANDING SCHOOL
Old Oscott Hill, Birmingham,
West Midlands B44 9SP
*Type:* Co-educational Day Only
11–19
*Special needs:* ASD **PMLD SLD**
SP&LD
*Wheelchair access:* W

### LANGLEY SCHOOL
Lindridge Road, Sutton
Coldfield, West Midlands
B75 7HU
*Website:*
www.langley.bham.sch.uk
*Type:* Co-educational Day Only
3–11
*Special needs:* ASD DOW **MLD**
SP&LD
*Wheelchair access:* WA1

### LINDSWORTH (NORTH)
Rowden Drive, Erdington,
West Midlands B23 5UL

### LINDSWORTH (SOUTH)
Monyhull Hall Road, Kings
Norton, West Midlands B30 3QA
*Type:* Co-educational 11–16
*Special needs:* **BESD**

### LONGWILL SCHOOL
Bell Hill, Birmingham, West
Midlands B31 1LD
*Website:*
www.longwill.bham.sch.uk
*Type:* Co-educational Day Only
2–11
*Special needs:* **HI**
*Wheelchair access:* WA1

### MAYFIELD SCHOOL
Finch Road, Birmingham,
West Midlands B19 1HP
*Type:* Co-educational Day Only
2–19
*Special needs:* ADHD ASD **ASP**
BESD CP DOW EPI HI **PMLD**
**SLD**
*Wheelchair access:* WA1

### PINES SCHOOL
Dreghorn Road, Birmingham,
West Midlands B36 8LL
*Website:*
www.pines.bham.sch.uk
*Type:* Co-educational Day Only
3–11
*Special needs:* ASD **ASP** SP&LD
*Wheelchair access:* W

### PRIESTLEY SMITH SCHOOL
Perry Beeches Campus,
Birmingham, West Midlands
B42 2PY
*Type:* Co-educational Day Only
2–17
*Special needs:* ASD ASP CP
DYS HEA MLD VI
*Wheelchair access:* WA1

### QUEENSBURY SCHOOL
Wood End Road, Birmingham,
West Midlands B24 8BL
*Type:* Co-educational Day Only
11–18
*Special needs:* **MLD**
*Wheelchair access:* WA2

### SELLY OAK TRUST SCHOOL
Oak Tree Lane, Selly Oak,
West Midlands B29 6HZ
*Website:*
www.sellyoak.bham.sch.uk
*Type:* Co-educational Day Only
11–19
*Special needs:* **MLD**
*Wheelchair access:* WA2

### SKILTS (RESIDENTIAL) SCHOOL
Gorcott Hill, Redditch,
West Midlands B98 9ET
*Type:* Boys Boarding and
Day 4–12
*Special needs:* ADD **ADHD**
**ASD** ASP **BESD** DYS MLD

### SPRINGFIELD HOUSE SCHOOL
Kenilworth Road, Solihull, West
Midlands B93 0AJ
*Type:* Co-educational Boarding
and Day 5–11
*Special needs:* ASD **BESD** MLD
*Wheelchair access:* WA3

### TIVERTON SPECIAL SCHOOL
Rowington Close, Coventry,
West Midlands CV6 1PS
*Type:* Co-educational 3–11
*Special needs:* **SLD**
*Wheelchair access:* W

### UFFCULME SCHOOL
Queensbridge Road,
Birmingham, West Midlands
B13 8QB
*Website:*
www.uffculme.bham.sch.uk
*Type:* Co-educational Day Only
3–13
*Special needs:* ASD ASP
*Wheelchair access:* WA3

### VICTORIA SCHOOL
Bell Hill, Birmingham,
West Midlands B31 1LD
*Type:* Co-educational Day Only
2–19
*Special needs:* CP EPI HI MLD
PMLD SLD VI
*Wheelchair access:* W

## WAINBODY WOOD SPECIAL SCHOOL
Stoneleigh Road, Coventry,
West Midlands CV4 7AB
*Type:* Co-educational Day Only
*Special needs:* **BESD**

## WILSON STUART SCHOOL
Perry Common Road,
Birmingham, West Midlands
B23 7AT
*Website:*
www.wilsonst.bham.sch.uk
*Type:* Co-educational Day Only
2–19
*Special needs:* SP&LD
*Wheelchair access:* WA1

## Coventry Education Offices

**New Council Offices**
**Earl Street**
**Coventry**
**West Midlands**
**CV1 5RR**

## ALICE STEVENS SCHOOL
Ashington Grove, Coventry,
West Midlands CV3 4DE
*Type:* Co-educational Day Only
11–18
*Special needs:* **MLD**
*Wheelchair access:* W

## CASTLE WOOD SCHOOL
Hawkesbury Fields site, Coventry,
West Midlands CV2 1PL
*Type:* Co-educational Day Only
2–11
*Special needs:* PMLD **SLD**
*Wheelchair access:* W

## CORLEY (COVENTRY) SCHOOL
Church Lane, Nr Coventry,
West Midlands CV7 8AZ
*Type:* Co-educational Day and
Boarding
*Special needs:* ASD **ASP** MLD

## DARTMOUTH SPECIAL SCHOOL
Tiverton Road, Coventry,
West Midlands CV2 3DN
*Type:* Boys Day Only 11–16
*Special needs:* ADD ADHD ASD
**BESD** TOU
*Wheelchair access:* W

## THE MEADOWS
Hawthorn Lane, Coventry,
West Midlands CV4 9PB
*Type:* Boys Day and Boarding
11–16
*Special needs:* **BESD**

## SHERBOURNE FIELDS SCHOOL
Rowington Close, Coventry,
West Midlands CV6 1PR
*Type:* Co-educational Day Only
*Special needs:* ASD CP EPI
**HEA HI IM** MLD PMLD SLD
SP&LD VI
*Wheelchair access:* WA1

## THREE SPIRES SCHOOL
Kingsbury Road, Coventry,
West Midlands CV6 1PJ
*Type:* Co-educational Day Only
3–11
*Special needs:* **MLD**

## Dudley Directorate of Education & Lifelong Learning

**Westox House**
**1 Trinity Road**
**Dudley**
**West Midlands**
**DY1 1JB**

## THE BRIER SPECIAL SCHOOL
Bromley Lane, Kingswinford,
West Midlands DY6 8QN
*Type:* Co-educational Day Only
4–16
*Special needs:* MLD SP&LD
*Wheelchair access:* WA1

## HALESBURY SPECIAL SCHOOL
Feldon Lane, Halesowen,
West Midlands B62 9DR
*Type:* Co-educational Day Only
5–16
*Special needs:* ASP **MLD**

## OLD PARK SCHOOL
Corbyn Road, Dudley,
West Midlands DY6 9AW
*Type:* Co-educational 3–19
*Special needs:* **SLD**
*Wheelchair access:* WA1

## PENS MEADOW SCHOOL
Ridge Hill, Stourbridge,
West Midlands DY8 5ST
*Type:* Co-educational Day Only
3–19
*Special needs:* ASD PMLD **SLD**
*Wheelchair access:* WA2

## ROSEWOOD SCHOOL
Overfield Road, Dudley,
West Midlands DY1 2NX
*Website:*
www.rosewood.dudley.gov.uk
*Type:* Boys Day Only 11–16
*Special needs:* **BESD**
*Wheelchair access:* W

## THE SUTTON SCHOOL
Scotts Green Close, Dudley,
West Midlands DY1 2DU
*Type:* Co-educational Day Only
11–16
*Special needs:* **MLD**

## THE WOODSETTON SPECIAL SCHOOL
Tipton Road, Dudley, West
Midlands DY3 1BY
*Type:* Co-educational Day Only
4–11
*Special needs:* ASD **MLD**
SP&LD

## Sandwell Education & Lifelong Learning

**Shaftsbury House,**
**402 High Street**
**West Bromwich**
**Sandwell**
**West Midlands**
**B70 9LT**

## THE ORCHARD SCHOOL
Causeway Green Road,
Oldbury, West Midlands
B68 8LD
*Type:* Co-educational Day Only
*Special needs:* ASD **CP PMLD**
**SLD**
*Wheelchair access:* WA1

## Solihull Education & Children's Services

PO Box 20
Council House
Solihull
West Midlands
B91 3QU

### MERSTONE SCHOOL
Winward Way, Birmingham,
West Midlands B36 0VE
*Type:* Co-educational Day Only
2–18
*Special needs:* ASD **ASP** CP
DOW EPI **PMLD SLD**
*Wheelchair access:* W

### REYNALDS CROSS SCHOOL
Kineton Green Road, Solihull,
West Midlands B92 7ER
*Type:* Co-educational Day Only
*Special needs:* PMLD SLD
*Wheelchair access:* WA1

## Walsall Metropolitan Borough Council

Civic Centre
Darwall Street
Walsall
West Midlands
WS1 1DQ

### CASTLE BUSINESS & ENTERPRISE COLLEGE
Odell Road, Walsall, West
Midlands WS3 2ED
*Website:*
www.castle.walsall.sch.uk
*Type:* Co-educational Day Only
4–19
*Special needs:* ASD **ASP** DOW
DYP **MLD** SLD SP&LD

### DAW END SPECIAL SCHOOL
Floyds Lane, Walsall, West
Midlands WS4 1LF
*Website:*
www.daw.end.walsall.sch.uk
*Type:* Co-educational Day and
Boarding 5–16
*Special needs:* **BESD**
*Wheelchair access:* WA3

### JANE LANE SCHOOL
Churchill Road, Walsall, West
Midlands WS2 0JH
*Type:* Co-educational Day Only
4–19
*Special needs:* **MLD**
*Wheelchair access:* W

### MARY ELLIOT SPECIAL SCHOOL
Leamore Lane, Walsall, West
Midlands WS2 7NR
*Website:* www.mary-elliot.
walsall.sch.uk
*Type:* Co-educational Day Only
11–19
*Special needs:* ASD **PMLD SLD**
*Wheelchair access:* WA1

### OAKWOOD SPECIAL SCHOOL
Druids Walk, Walsall, West
Midlands WS9 9JS
*Website:*
www.oakwood.walsall.sch.uk
*Type:* Co-educational Day Only
2–14
*Special needs:* ASD CP EPI HI
**PMLD SLD** VI
*Wheelchair access:* W

### OLD HALL SPECIAL SCHOOL
Bentley Lane, Walsall,
West Midlands WS2 7LU
*Website:*
www.oldhall.walsall.sch.uk
*Type:* Co-educational Day Only
2–14
*Special needs:* **PMLD SLD**
*Wheelchair access:* WA1

## Wolverhampton Lifelong Learning

Civic Centre
St Peter's Square
Wolverhampton
WV11 1RR

### BROADMEADOW SPECIAL SCHOOL
Lansdowne Road,
Wolverhampton, West Midlands
WV1 4AL
*Type:* Co-educational Day Only
2–7
*Special needs:* ASD PMLD **SLD**
*Wheelchair access:* WA1

### GREEN PARK SPECIAL SCHOOL
Green Park Avenue, Bilston,
West Midlands WV14 6EH
*Type:* Co-educational Day Only
5–19
*Special needs:* PMLD SLD
*Wheelchair access:* W

### NEW PARK SCHOOL
Valley Park Campus,
Wolverhampton, West Midlands
WV6 0UB
*Type:* Co-educational Day Only
7–14
*Special needs:* **BESD**
*Wheelchair access:* WA2

### PENN FIELDS SCHOOL
Birches Barn Road,
Wolverhampton, West Midlands
WV3 7BJ
*Type:* Co-educational Day Only
5–16
*Special needs:* ASD **BESD** HI
**MLD** SP&LD VI
*Wheelchair access:* W

### PENN HALL SCHOOL
Vicarage Road, Wolverhampton,
West Midlands WV4 5HP
*Website:* www.penhall.co.uk
*Type:* Co-educational Day Only
3–19
*Special needs:* CP HEA HI **IM**
SP&LD VI
*Wheelchair access:* WA1

### TETTENHALL WOOD SCHOOL
School Road, Wolverhampton,
West Midlands WV6 8EJ
*Type:* Co-educational Day Only
5–19
*Special needs:* ASD CP DOW
PMLD **SLD** SP&LD
*Wheelchair access:* WA2

### WESTCROFT SCHOOL AND SPORTS COLLEGE
Greenacres Avenue,
Wolverhampton, West Midlands
WV10 8NZ
*Website:* www.westcorft.
wolverhampton.sch.uk
*Type:* Co-educational Day Only
5–8
*Special needs:* **MLD**
*Wheelchair access:* W

# WILTSHIRE

## Swindon Borough Council

**Civic Offices**
**Euclid Street**
**Swindon**
**Wiltshire**
**SN1 2JH**

### BRIMBLE HILL SPECIAL SCHOOL
Tadpole Lane, Swindon,
Wiltshire SN25 2NB
*Type:* Co-educational Day Only
2–11
*Special needs:* **SLD**
*Wheelchair access:* WA1

### THE CHALET SPECIAL SCHOOL
Liden Drive, Swindon, Wiltshire
SN3 6EX
*Type:* Co-educational Day Only
3–11
*Special needs:* ADHD ASD **ASP**
*Wheelchair access:* WA2

### CROWDYS HILL SPECIAL SCHOOL
Jefferies Avenue, Swindon,
Wiltshire SN2 7HJ
*Type:* Co-educational Day Only
11–16
*Special needs:* ADD ADHD ASD
ASP HI **MLD** PMLD SLD
*Wheelchair access:* W

### NYLAND SPECIAL SCHOOL
Nyland Road, Swindon,
Wiltshire SN3 3RD
*Type:* Co-educational Day Only
5–11
*Special needs:* **ADD ADHD
ASD ASP BESD CB** DYP DYS
SP&LD TOU

### ST LUKE'S SPECIAL SCHOOL
Cricklade Road, Swindon,
Wiltshire SN2 7AS
*Type:* Co-educational Day Only
11–16
*Special needs:* **BESD**
*Wheelchair access:* W

### UPLANDS SPECIAL SCHOOL
Leigh Road, Swindon,
Wiltshire SN2 5DE
*Type:* Co-educational Day Only
11–19
*Special needs:* ASD **ASP** CP
DOW **PMLD SLD**
*Wheelchair access:* W

## Wiltshire County Council

**County Hall**
**Bythesea Road**
**Trowbridge**
**Wiltshire**
**BA14 8JN**

### DOWNLAND SCHOOL
Downlands Road, Devizes,
Wiltshire SN10 5EF
*Type:* Boys Boarding and Day
11–16
*Special needs:* ADHD ASP
**BESD** DYS
*Wheelchair access:* WA3

### EXETER HOUSE SPECIAL SCHOOL
Somerset Road, Salisbury,
Wiltshire SP1 3BL
*Type:* Co-educational Day Only
2–19
*Special needs:* ASD PMLD SLD
*Wheelchair access:* W

### LARKRISE SPECIAL SCHOOL
Ashton Street, Trowbridge,
Wiltshire BA14 7EB
*Type:* Co-educational Day Only
3–19
*Special needs:* PMLD **SLD**

### ROWDEFORD SPECIAL SCHOOL
Rowde, Devizes,
Wiltshire SN10 2QQ
*Type:* Co-educational Day and
Boarding 11–16
*Special needs:* **ADHD ASD
ASP CP DOW DYP DYS EPI
HEA HI IM MLD** SP&LD **TOU** VI
*Wheelchair access:* WA2

### ST NICHOLAS SCHOOL
Malmesbury Road,
Chippenham,
Wiltshire SN15 1QF
*Type:* Co-educational Day Only
3–19
*Special needs:* ASD PMLD SLD

### SPRINGFIELDS SPECIAL SCHOOL
Curzon Street, Calne,
Wiltshire SN11 0DS
*Type:* Co-educational Boarding
Only 10–17
*Special needs:* **BESD**

# WORCESTERSHIRE

## Worcestershire County Education Services Directorate

**County Hall**
**Spetchley Road**
**Worcester**
**Worcestershire**
**WR5 2NP**

### THE ALEXANDER PATTERSON SCHOOL
Park Gate Road, Kidderminster, Worcestershire DY10 3PU
*Type:* Co-educational Day Only
*Special needs:* ASD **ASP** BESD **MLD PMLD** SP&LD
*Wheelchair access:* W

### BLAKEBROOK SCHOOL
Bewdley Road, Kidderminster, Worcestershire DY11 6RL
*Type:* Co-educational Day Only
*Special needs:* ASD PMLD **SLD**
*Wheelchair access:* W

### CHADSGROVE SCHOOL & SPECIALIST SPORTS COLLEGE
Meadow Road, Bromsgrove, Worcestershire B61 0JL
*Website:*
www.chadsgroveschool.co.uk
*Type:* Co-educational Day Only 2–19
*Special needs:* CP EPI HEA **IM** PMLD VI
*Wheelchair access:* WA1

### MANOR PARK SCHOOL
Turnpike Close, Worcester, Worcestershire WR2 6AB
*Website:* www.
manorparkschool.worcs.sch.uk
*Type:* Co-educational Day Only 4–19
*Special needs:* PMLD **SLD**
*Wheelchair access:* WA2

### PITCHEROAK SCHOOL
Willow Way, Redditch, Worcestershire B97 6PQ
*Type:* Co-educational Day Only 2–18
*Special needs:* ASD **ASP MLD SLD**

### REDGROVE UPPER SCHOOL
Shaw Lane, Bromsgrove, Worcestershire B60 4EL
*Type:* Co-educational
*Special needs:* BESD

### REGENCY HIGH SCHOOL
Carnforth Drive, Worcester, Worcestershire WR4 9JL
*Website:*
www.regency.worcs.sch.uk
*Type:* Co-educational Day Only 11–19
*Special needs:* **BESD CB MLD** PMLD **SLD**
*Wheelchair access:* WA1

### RIVERSIDE UPPER SCHOOL
Thornloe Road, Worcester, Worcestershire WR1 3HZ
*Type:* Co-educational Day Only 11–16
*Special needs:* BESD

### STOURMINSTER SCHOOL
Comberton Road, Kidderminster, Worcestershire DY10 3DX
*Type:* Co-educational 7–16
*Special needs:* ASD **MLD**
*Wheelchair access:* W

### THORNTON HOUSE SCHOOL
Wylds Lane, Worcester, Worcestershire WR5 1DR
*Type:* Co-educational Day Only 2–11
*Special needs:* ASD **MLD**
*Wheelchair access:* WA2

### VALE OF EVESHAM SCHOOL
Four Pools Lane, Evesham, Worcestershire WR11 1BN
*Type:* Co-educational Boarding and Day 4–19
*Special needs:* ADD ADHD ASD **ASP** DOW EPI HI **MLD PMLD** SLD SP&LD
*Wheelchair access:* W

# EAST RIDING OF YORKSHIRE

## East Riding of Yorkshire

**County Hall**
**Beverley**
**East Riding of Yorkshire**
**HU17 9BA**

### RIVERSIDE SCHOOL
Ainsty Street, Goole, East Riding of Yorkshire DN14 5JS
*Type:* 4–16
*Wheelchair access:* WA1

## Hull City Council

**Guildhall**
**Hull**
**East Riding of Yorkshire**
**HU1 2AA**

### BRIDGEVIEW SCHOOL
Ferriby Road, Hessle, East Riding of Yorkshire HU13 0HR
*Type:* Co-educational Day Only 6–16
*Special needs:* BESD

### FREDERICK HOLMES SCHOOL
Inglemire Lane, Kingston upon Hull, East Riding of Yorkshire HU6 8JJ
*Website:* www.
frederickholmesschool.co.uk
*Type:* Co-educational Day Only 2–19
*Special needs:* **CP DOW IM PMLD** SP&LD
*Wheelchair access:* WA1

**GANTON SCHOOL**
Springhead Lane, Hull, East
Riding of Yorkshire HU5 6YJ
*Type:* Co-educational Day Only
*Special needs:* ASD CP DOW
EPI PMLD SLD
*Wheelchair access:* W

**KING'S MILL SCHOOL**
Victoria Road, Driffield, East
Riding of Yorkshire YO25 7UG
*Type:* Co-educational Day and
Boarding 2–16
*Special needs:* PMLD **SLD**
*Wheelchair access:* WA1

**NORTHCOTT SCHOOL**
Dulverton Close, Kingston upon
Hull, East Riding of Yorkshire
HU7 4EL
*Type:* Co-educational Day Only
*Special needs:* ASD BESD EPI
HEA SP&LD

# NORTH YORKSHIRE

## North Yorkshire County Council

**County Hall**
**Northallerton**
**North Yorkshire**
**DL7 8AE**

**APPLEFIELDS SCHOOL**
Bad Bargain Lane, York,
North Yorkshire YO31 0LW
*Website:*
www.applefields.york.sch.uk
*Type:* Co-educational Day Only
11–19
*Special needs:* ASD MLD PMLD
SLD
*Wheelchair access:* WA1

**BALIOL SCHOOL**
Sedbergh, North Yorkshire
LA10 5LQ
*Type:* Boys Boarding Only
10–16
*Special needs:* ADHD ASP
**BESD** MLD

**BROMPTON HALL SCHOOL**
Brompton-by-Sawdon,
Scarborough, North Yorkshire
YO13 9BD
*Type:* Boys Boarding and Day
8–16
*Special needs:* ADHD ASP
**BESD** MLD

**BROOKLANDS SCHOOL**
Burnside Avenue, Skipton,
North Yorkshire BD23 2LX
*Type:* Co-educational Day Only
2–19
*Special needs:* **BESD DOW EPI**
**IM PMLD** SP&LD VI
*Wheelchair access:* WA1

**DALES SCHOOL**
Moreton-on-Swale,
Northallerton, North Yorkshire
DL7 9QW
*Type:* Co-educational Day Only
2–19
*Special needs:* ASD **CP DOW**
PMLD SLD VI

**THE FOREST SCHOOL**
Park Lane, Knaresborough,
North Yorkshire HG5 0DQ
*Type:* Co-educational Day Only
2–16
*Wheelchair access:* W

**FOREST SCHOOL**
Park Lane, Knaresborough,
North Yorkshire HG5 0DG
*Website:*
www.theforestschool.org.uk
*Type:* Co-educational Day Only
*Special needs:* ADD ADHD ASD
ASP BESD DOW **MLD** SLD
SP&LD

**MOWBRAY SCHOOL**
Masham Road, Bedale,
North Yorkshire DL8 2DS
*Type:* Co-educational Day Only
2–16
*Special needs:* ADHD ASD
BESD CP DOW **MLD** SLD
SP&LD
*Wheelchair access:* WA1

**NETHERSIDE HALL SCHOOL**
Threshfield, Skipton,
North Yorkshire BD23 5PP
*Type:* Boys Boarding and Day
11–16
*Special needs:* ADD ADHD ASP
BESD DYP **DYS**

**SPRINGHEAD SCHOOL**
Barry's Lane, Scarborough,
North Yorkshire YO11 4HA
*Website:*
www.springheadschool.com
*Type:* Co-educational Day Only
2–19
*Special needs:* PMLD **SLD**
*Wheelchair access:* WA1

**SPRINGWATER SCHOOL**
High Street, Harrogate,
North Yorkshire HG2 7LW
*Type:* Co-educational Day Only
2–19
*Special needs:* ASD **ASP PMLD**
**SLD**
*Wheelchair access:* WA1

**WELBURN HALL SCHOOL**
Kirbymoorside, York, North
Yorkshire YO62 7HQ
*Website:* www.
welburn-hall.n-yorks.sch.uk
*Type:* Co-educational Boarding
and Day 8–18
*Special needs:* CP EPI HI MLD
SLD SP&LD VI
*Wheelchair access:* WA1

## York Education and Leisure

**10–12 George Hudson Street**
**York**
**North Yorkshire**
**YO1 1ZE**

**FULFORD CROSS SCHOOL**
Fulford Cross, York, North
Yorkshire YO1 4PB
*Special needs:* **MLD**

**HOB MOOR OAKS SCHOOL**
Green Lane, York, North
Yorkshire YO24 4PS
*Type:* Co-educational Day Only
2–11
*Special needs:* MLD PMLD SLD
*Wheelchair access:* WA1

**NORTHFIELD SCHOOL**
Beckfield Lane, York, North
Yorkshire YO26 5RQ
*Type:* Co-educational 5–16

# SOUTH YORKSHIRE

## Barnsley LEA

**Town Hall**
**Church Street**
**Barnsley**
**South Yorkshire**
**S70 2TA**

**GREENACRE SCHOOL**
Keresforth Hill Road, Barnsley,
South Yorkshire S70 6RG
*Type:* Co-educational Day Only
2–19
*Special needs:* ASD **ASP PMLD
SLD**
*Wheelchair access:* WA1

## Doncaster Education Offices

**The Council House**
**College Road**
**Doncaster**
**South Yorkshire**
**DN1 3AD**

**ANCHORAGE LOWER
SCHOOL**
Cusworth Lane, Doncaster,
South Yorkshire DN5 8JL
*Type:* Co-educational Day Only
4–12
*Special needs:* BESD **MLD**

**ANCHORAGE UPPER
SCHOOL**
Barnsley Road, Doncaster,
South Yorkshire DN5 7UB
*Type:* Co-educational Day Only
13–16
*Special needs:* **MLD**

**CEDAR SCHOOL**
Cedar Road, Doncaster,
South Yorkshire DN4 9HT
*Type:* Co-educational Day Only
3–19
*Special needs:* **PMLD SLD**
*Wheelchair access:* WA1

**CHASE SCHOOL**
Ash Hill, Doncaster,
South Yorkshire DN7 6JH
*Type:* Co-educational Day Only
3–19
*Special needs:* ASD PMLD **SLD**
*Wheelchair access:* W

**HEATHERWOOD SCHOOL**
Leger Way, Doncaster,
South Yorkshire DN2 6HQ
*Type:* Co-educational Day Only
3–19
*Special needs:* HEA **IM PMLD**
SLD
*Wheelchair access:* WA1

**PENNINE VIEW SCHOOL**
Old Road, Doncaster,
South Yorkshire DN12 3LR
*Type:* Co-educational Day Only
6–16
*Special needs:* ADHD BESD
**MLD** SP&LD
*Wheelchair access:* WA2

**ROSSINGTON HALL SCHOOL**
Great North Road, Doncaster,
South Yorkshire DN11 0HS

## Rotherham Education, Culture & Leisure Services

**Norfolk House**
**Walker Place**
**Rotherham**
**South Yorkshire**
**S65 1UF**

**ABBEY SCHOOL**
Little Common Lane,
Rotherham, South Yorkshire
S61 2RA
*Type:* Co-educational Day Only
5–16
*Special needs:* **MLD**

**GREEN ARBOUR SCHOOL**
Locksley Drive, Rotherham,
South Yorkshire S66 9NT
*Website:* www.greenarbour.co.uk
*Type:* Co-educational Day Only
7–16
*Special needs:* ASD MLD SP&LD

**HILLTOP SCHOOL**
Larch Road, Rotherham,
South Yorkshire S66 8AZ
*Website:*
www.hilltop.rotherham.sch.uk
*Type:* Co-educational Day Only
2–19
*Special needs:* ASD **ASP** CP
DOW **PMLD SLD** VI
*Wheelchair access:* WA1

**KELFORD SCHOOL**
Oakdale Road, Rotherham,
South Yorkshire S61 2NU
*Type:* Co-educational Day Only
2–19
*Special needs:* ASD PMLD SLD
*Wheelchair access:* WA1

## MILTON SCHOOL
Storey Street, Mexborough,
South Yorkshire S64 8QG
*Type:* Co-educational Day Only
4–16
*Special needs:* ASD **ASP MLD**
*Wheelchair access:* W

## NEWMAN SCHOOL
East Bawtry Road, Rotherham,
South Yorkshire S60 2LX
*Type:* Co-educational Day Only
2–19
*Special needs:* CP
*Wheelchair access:* W

## Sheffield City Council

**Town Hall**
**Pinstone Street**
**Sheffield**
**South Yorkshire**
**S1 2HH**

## BENTS GREEN SECONDARY SCHOOL
Ringinglow Road, Sheffield,
South Yorkshire S11 7TB
*Type:* Co-educational Day and
Boarding
*Special needs:* ASD **ASP MLD**
SP&LD

## BROAD ELMS SCHOOL
Broad Elms Lane, Sheffield,
South Yorkshire S11 9RQ
*Type:* Co-educational 4–11

## DR JOHN WORRALL SCHOOL
Maltby Street, Sheffield,
South Yorkshire S9 2QA
*Type:* 5–16

## EAST HILL SECONDARY SCHOOL
East Bank Road, Sheffield,
South Yorkshire S2 3PX
*Website:* www.easthill-sec.
sheffield.sch.uk
*Type:* Co-educational Day Only
11–16
*Special needs:* **MLD**
*Wheelchair access:* WA3

## MOSSBROOK SCHOOL
Bochum Parkway, Sheffield,
South Yorkshire S8 8JR
*Website:* www.mossbrook.
sheffield.sch.uk
*Type:* Co-educational Day and
Boarding
*Special needs:* ASD **ASP** BESD
**DOW** EPI HEA **MLD SLD** SP&LD
*Wheelchair access:* W

## NORFOLK PARK PRIMARY SCHOOL
Park Grange Road, Sheffield,
South Yorkshire S2 3QF
*Type:* Co-educational Day Only
2–11
*Special needs:* ASD **PMLD SLD**
*Wheelchair access:* W

## THE ROWAN SCHOOL
4 Durvale Court, Sheffield,
South Yorkshire S17 3PT
*Type:* Co-educational Day Only
4–11
*Special needs:* ASD ASP SP&LD

## TALBOT SECONDARY SCHOOL
Matthews Lane, Sheffield,
South Yorkshire S8 8JS
*Type:* Co-educational Day Only
11–19

## WOOLLEY WOOD SCHOOL
Oaks Fold Road, Sheffield,
South Yorkshire S5 0TG
*Type:* Co-educational Day Only
3–10
*Special needs:* ASD **ASP PMLD SLD**
*Wheelchair access:* WA1

# WEST YORKSHIRE

## Bradford Metropolitan District Council

**City Hall**
**Bradford**
**West Yorkshire**
**BD1 1HY**

## BOLLING SCHOOL
Bradford, West Yorkshire
BD4 7S4
*Type:* Co-educational Day Only
11–19
*Special needs:* ASD HEA **PMLD SLD** VI
*Wheelchair access:* WA1

## BRAITHWAITE SCHOOL
Braithwaite Road, Keighley,
West Yorkshire BD22 6PR
*Type:* Co-educational Day Only
2–19
*Special needs:* ASD ASP CP
DOW DYS EPI **MLD** SLD SP&LD

## BRANSHAW SCHOOL
Oakworth Road, Keighley, West
Yorkshire BD21 1RA
*Type:* Co-educational Day Only
2–19
*Special needs:* ASD
**ASPPMLDSLD**
*Wheelchair access:* WA2

## CHAPEL GRANGE SCHOOL
Rhodesway, Bradford, West
Yorkshire BD8 0DQ
*Type:* Co-educational Day Only
11–19
*Special needs:* ASD MLD PMLD
SLD
*Wheelchair access:* WA2

## GREENFIELD SCHOOL
Bradford, West Yorkshire
BD10 8LU
*Type:* Co-educational Day Only
3–11
*Special needs:* ADHD ASD ASP
SLD
*Wheelchair access:* WA1

### HAYCLIFFE SCHOOL
Haycliffe Lane, Bradford,
West Yorkshire BD5 9ET
*Type:* Co-educational Day Only
11–19
*Special needs:* ASD **ASP** BESD
HI **MLD** SLD SP&LD VI
*Wheelchair access:* WA2

### HEATON ROYDS SCHOOL
Redburn Drive, Shipley,
West Yorkshire BD18 3AZ
*Type:* Co-educational Day Only
2–11
*Special needs:* EPI MLD **SLD**
SP&LD

### LISTER LANE SCHOOL
Lister Lane, Bradford, West
Yorkshire BD2 4LL
*Type:* Co-educational Day Only
2–13
*Special needs:* **CP IM MLD**
PMLD **SLD**
*Wheelchair access:* WA1

### NETHERLANDS AVENUE
SCHOOL
Netherlands Avenue, Bradford,
West Yorkshire BD6 1EA
*Type:* Co-educational Day Only
2–11
*Special needs:* ASD **ASP MLD**
**SLD** SP&LD

## Calderdale Council

**Crossley Street**
**Halifax**
**West Yorkshire**
**HX1 1UJ**

### HIGHBURY SCHOOL
Lower Edge Road, Brighouse,
West Yorkshire HD6 3LD
*Type:* Co-educational Day Only
*Special needs:* ADD ADHD ASD
**ASP** BESD **CP** DOW DYC DYP
DYS **EPI** HEA **HI** MLD **PMLD**
**SLD** SP&LD TOU **VI**
*Wheelchair access:* W

### RAVENSCLIFFE HIGH
SCHOOL AND SPORTS
COLLEGE
Skircoat Green, Halifax,
West Yorkshire HX3 0RZ
*Type:* Co-educational Day Only
11–19
*Special needs:* ASD CP **DOW**
EPI HI **IM** MLD PMLD SLD
SP&LD VI
*Wheelchair access:* WA2

### WOOD BANK SPECIAL
SCHOOL
Dene View, Halifax,
West Yorkshire HX2 6PB
*Website:* www.woodbank.
calderdale.sch.uk
*Type:* Co-educational Day Only
2–11
*Special needs:* ASD **ASP** CP
**PMLD SLD**
*Wheelchair access:* WA1

## Kirklees Education
## Service

**8th Floor, Oldgate House**
**2 Oldgate**
**Huddersfield**
**West Yorkshire**
**HD1 6QW**

### FAIRFIELD SCHOOL
Dale Lane, Heckmondwike,
West Yorkshire WF16 9PA
*Type:* Co-educational Day Only
3–19
*Special needs:* **PMLD SLD**
*Wheelchair access:* WA1

### HARTSHEAD MOOR SCHOOL
Halifax Road, Cleckheaton,
West Yorkshire BD19 6LP
*Website:* www.
hartsheadmoorschool.org.uk
*Type:* Co-educational 5–16
*Special needs:* MLD
*Wheelchair access:* W

### HIGHFIELDS SCHOOL
Cemetery Road, Huddersfield,
West Yorkshire HD1 5NF
*Type:* Co-educational Day Only
3–19
*Special needs:* ASD **PMLD SLD**
*Wheelchair access:* W

### LONGLEY SCHOOL
Dog Kennel Bank, Huddersfield,
West Yorkshire HD5 8JE
*Type:* Co-educational Day Only
5–16
*Special needs:* ADD ADHD ASD
**ASP BESD** CP DOW DYP DYS
EPI HEA HI **MLD** SP&LD VI
*Wheelchair access:* W

### LYDGATE SCHOOL
Kirkroyds Lane, Huddersfield,
West Yorkshire HD7 7LS
*Type:* Co-educational Day Only
5–16
*Special needs:* **MLD**
*Wheelchair access:* WA1

### NORTONTHORPE HALL
SCHOOL
Busker Lane, Huddersfield,
West Yorkshire HD8 9JU
*Type:* Co-educational Boarding
and Day 7–16
*Special needs:* **BESD**

### RAVENSHALL SCHOOL
Ravensthorpe Road, Dewsbury,
West Yorkshire WF12 9EE
*Website:*
www.ravenshallschool.org.uk
*Type:* Co-educational Day Only
5–16
*Special needs:* ADHD BESD
DOW **MLD** SP&LD
*Wheelchair access:* WA1

### TURNSHAWS SCHOOL
Turnshaws Avenue,
Huddersfield, West Yorkshire
HD8 0TJ
*Type:* Co-educational Day Only
3–19
*Special needs:* ASD PMLD SLD
*Wheelchair access:* W

## Leeds City Council

**Civic Hall**
**Calverley Street**
**Leeds**
**West Yorkshire**
**LS1 1UR**

**BROOMFIELD SCHOOL**
Broom Place, Leeds,
West Yorkshire LS10 3JP
*Type:* Co-educational Day Only
2–19
*Special needs:* ASD CP **MLD
PMLD SLD** VI
*Wheelchair access:* WA2

**ELMETE CENTRAL BESD
SILC**
Elmete Lane, Leeds,
West Yorkshire LS8 2LJ
*Type:* Co-educational Day Only
11–16
*Special needs:* **BESD**

**GREEN MEADOWS SCHOOL**
Bradford Road, Guiseley, West
Yorkshire LS20 8PP
*Type:* Co-educational Day Only
2–19
*Special needs:* ASD **ASP** VI

**JOHN JAMIESON SCHOOL &
TECHNOLOGY COLLEGE**
Hollin Hill Drive, Leeds, West
Yorkshire LS8 2PW
*Type:* Co-educational Day Only
*Special needs:* CP HEA **MLD**
PMLD SLD SP&LD
*Wheelchair access:* WA1

**NW SPECIALIST INCLUSIVE
LEARNING CENTRE**
Tongue Lane, Leeds, West
Yorkshire LS6 4QD
*Type:* Co-educational Day Only
2–19
*Special needs:* EPI HI **PMLD** VI
*Wheelchair access:* W

**WEST OAKS SCHOOL**
Westwood Way, Leeds, West
Yorkshire LS23 6DX
*Type:* Co-educational Day Only
2–19
*Special needs:* ASD **ASP BESD
CB DOW PMLD SLD**
*Wheelchair access:* WA1

**WEST SILC – SPECIALIST
INCLUSIVE LEARNING
CENTRE**
Milestone Site, Stanningley,
West Yorkshire LS28 6HL
*Type:* Co-educational Day Only
2–19
*Special needs:* **MLD PMLD SLD**
*Wheelchair access:* WA1

## Wakefield Metropolitan District Council

**Town Hall**
**Wood Street**
**Wakefield**
**West Yorkshire**
**WF1 2HQ**

**THE FELKIRK SCHOOL**
Highwell Hill Lane, Barnsley,
South Yorkshire S72 9DF
*Type:* Co-educational Boarding
and Day 11–16
*Special needs:* **BESD**

**HIGHFIELD SCHOOL**
Gawthorpe Lane, Ossett,
West Yorkshire WF5 9BS
*Type:* Co-educational Day Only
11–16
*Special needs:* ADD ADHD ASD
ASP **MLD** SLD VI
*Wheelchair access:* W

**KINGSLAND PRIMARY
SCHOOL**
Aberford Road, Wakefield,
West Yorkshire WF3 4BA
*Website:* www.kingsland.
wakefield.sch.uk
*Type:* Co-educational Day Only
2–11
*Special needs:* ASD **PMLD SLD**
*Wheelchair access:* WA1

**OAKFIELD PARK SCHOOL**
Barnsley Road, Wakefield,
West Yorkshire WF7 7DT
*Type:* Co-educational Day Only
11–19
*Special needs:* ASD **PMLD SLD**
*Wheelchair access:* WA1

**WAKEFIELD PATHWAYS
SCHOOL**
Poplar Avenue, Wakefield,
West Yorkshire WF10 3QJ

# Northern Ireland

## COUNTY ANTRIM

### Belfast Area Education/ Library Board

**40 Academy Street**
**Belfast**
**BT1 2NQ**

### CASTLE TOWER SCHOOL
22 Old Ballymoney Road,
Ballymena, County Antrim
BT43 6LX
*Type:* Co-educational Day Only
3–19
*Special needs:* **SLD**
*Wheelchair access:* WA1

### CEDAR LODGE SPECIAL SCHOOL
Gray's Lane, Belfast, County
Antrim BT36 7EB
*Type:* Co-educational Day Only
4–16
*Special needs:* ADHD ASD **ASP EPI HEA MLD** SP&LD
*Wheelchair access:* WA1

### CLARAWOOD SCHOOL
Clarawood Park, Belfast, County
Antrim BT5 6FR
*Website:* www.niyouthinfo.org
*Type:* Co-educational Day Only
8–11
*Special needs:* ADD ADHD ASP
**BESD** DYP DYS MLD

### DUNFANE SCHOOL
91 Fry's Road, Ballymena,
County Antrim BT43 7EN
*Type:* Co-educational
*Special needs:* ADD BESD
DOW DYP EPI MLD SP&LD VI
*Wheelchair access:* W

### FLEMING FULTON SCHOOL
Upper Malone Road, Belfast,
County Antrim BT9 6TY
*Website:*
www.flemingfulton.org.uk
*Type:* Co-educational Day and
Boarding 2–19
*Special needs:* **IM** SP&LD
*Wheelchair access:* WA1

### GLENVEAGH SPECIAL SCHOOL
Harberton Park, Belfast, County
Antrim BT9 6TX
*Type:* Co-educational Day Only
*Special needs:* ASD PMLD **SLD**

### GREENWOOD HOUSE ASSESSMENT CENTRE
Greenwood Avenue, Belfast,
County Antrim BT4 3JJ
*Type:* Co-educational Day Only
4–7
*Special needs:* ADD ADHD ASD
ASP BESD DYS EPI HEA HI
**MLD SLD** SP&LD VI
*Wheelchair access:* W

### HARBERTON
Harberton Park, Belfast, County
Antrim BT9 6TX
*Special needs:* ADD ADHD
BESD DOW DYS MLD SP&LD
*Wheelchair access:* W

### LOUGHSHORE EDUCATIONAL CENTRE
889 Shore Road, Belfast,
County Antrim BT36 7DH
*Type:* Co-educational Day Only
11–17
*Special needs:* ADD ADHD ASD
ASP BESD CB CP DYC DYP
DYS EPI HI IM MLD TOU VI
*Wheelchair access:* W

### MITCHELL HOUSE SPECIAL SCHOOL
Marmont, Belfast, County Antrim
BT4 2GU
*Type:* Co-educational Day Only
3–19
*Special needs:* ASP CP EPI HEA
MLD SP&LD
*Wheelchair access:* W

### OAKWOOD SCHOOL ASSESSMENT CENTRE
Harberton Park, Belfast, County
Antrim BT9 6TX
*Type:* Co-educational 3–8
*Special needs:* ASD BESD CP
DOW EPI HEA HI PMLD SLD
SP&LD VI
*Wheelchair access:* WA1

### PARK EDUCATION RESOURCE CENTRE
145 Ravenhill Road, Belfast,
County Antrim BT6 8GH
*Type:* Co-educational Day Only
11–19
*Special needs:* **MLD**

### ST FRANCIS DE SALES SPECIAL SCHOOL
Beechmount Drive, Belfast,
County Antrim BT12 7LU
*Type:* Co-educational Day Only

### ST GERARD'S EDUCATION RESOURCE CENTRE
Upper Springfield Road, Belfast,
County Antrim BT12 7QP
*Type:* Co-educational Day Only
4–16
*Special needs:* **MLD**

### ST VINCENT'S CENTRE
6 Willowfield Drive, Belfast,
County Antrim BT6 8HN

## North Eastern Area Education & Library Board

**Board Offices, County Hall**
**182 Galgorm Road**
**Ballymena**
**Co. Antrim**
**BT42 1HN**

### CASTLE TOWER SCHOOL
Beech Road Campus,
Ballymena, County Antrim
BT43 7EN
*Type:* Co-educational Day Only
3–11
*Special needs:* CP EPI HEA
*Wheelchair access:* WA2
*52-week care*

### HILL CROFT SCHOOL
Abbot's Road, Newtownabbey,
County Antrim BT37 9RB
*Type:* Co-educational Day Only
*Special needs:* **SLD**
*Wheelchair access:* W

### KILRONAN SCHOOL
46 Ballyronan Road,
Magherafelt, County
Londonderry BT45 6EN
*Website:* www.kilronanschool.
co.uk
*Type:* Co-educational Day Only
3–19
*Special needs:* ASD CP DOW
PMLD **SLD**
*Wheelchair access:* WA1

### RIVERSIDE SCHOOL
Fennel Road, Antrim, County
Antrim BT41 4PB
*Type:* Co-educational Day Only
3–19
*Special needs:* ASD EPI PMLD
**SLD** SP&LD

### RODDENSVALE SCHOOL
The Roddens, Larne, County
Antrim BT40 1PU
*Type:* Co-educational Day Only
4–19
*Special needs:* IM **PMLD SLD**
*Wheelchair access:* WA1

### ROSSTULLA SCHOOL
2–6 Jordanstown Road,
Newtownabbey, County Antrim
BT37 0QF
*Type:* Co-educational Day Only
4–17
*Special needs:* **MLD**
*Wheelchair access:* WA1

### SANDELFORD SCHOOL
8 Rugby Avenue, Coleraine,
County Londonderry BT52 1JL
*Type:* Co-educational Day Only
*Special needs:* **SLD**

### THORNFIELD SPECIAL SCHOOL
8–12 Jordanstown Road,
Newtownabbey, County Antrim
BT37 0QF
*Type:* Co-educational Day Only
*Special needs:* SP&LD
*Wheelchair access:* WA1

## South Eastern Area Education & Library Board

**Grahamsbridge Road**
**Dundonald**
**Belfast**
**County Antrim**
**BT16 2HS**

### ARDMORE HOUSE SCHOOL & SUPPORT SERVICE
95a Saul Street, Downpatrick,
County Down BT30 6NJ
*Type:* Co-educational Day Only
11–16
*Special needs:* **BESD**

### BEECHLAWN SCHOOL
3 Dromore Road, Hillsborough,
County Down BT26 6PA
*Website:*
www.beechlawnschool.co.uk
*Type:* Co-educational Day Only
10–16
*Special needs:* ADHD ASD ASP
DYP **DYS MLD**
*Wheelchair access:* W

### BROOKFIELD SCHOOL
65 Halfpenny Gate Road,
Craigavon, County Armagh
BT67 0HP
*Website:*
www.brookfieldsch.ik.org
*Type:* Co-educational Day Only
5–11
*Special needs:* ADD ASD **MLD**
SP&LD
*Wheelchair access:* WA1

### CLIFTON SCHOOL
292A Old Belfast Road, Bangor,
County Down BT19 1RH
*Type:* Co-educational Day Only
3–19
*Special needs:* ASD **ASP** BESD
CB CP DOW EPI HI **PMLD SLD**
SP&LD VI
*Wheelchair access:* WA1

### KILLARD HOUSE SCHOOL
North Road, Newtownards,
County Down BT23 3AP
*Type:* Girls Day Only 4–16
*Special needs:* MLD SLD
SP&LD
*Wheelchair access:* WA3

### KNOCKEVIN SCHOOL
29 Racecourse Hill,
Downpatrick, County Down
BT30 6PU

### LAKEWOOD SPECIAL SCHOOL
169 Rathgael Road, Bangor,
County Down BT19 1TA
*Type:* Co-educational

### LINDSAY SPECIAL SCHOOL
Foster Green Hospital, Belfast,
County Antrim BT8 4HD
*Type:* Co-educational Day and
Boarding 3–15
*Special needs:* **ADHD ASD** ASP
**BESD** DYP DYS HEA MLD

**LONGSTONE SCHOOL**
Millar's Lane, Belfast, County
Antrim BT16 0DA
*Type:* Co-educational Day Only
4–16
*Special needs:* BESD MLD
*Wheelchair access:* W

**PARKVIEW SCHOOL**
2 Brokerstown Road, Lisburn,
County Antrim BT28 2EE
*Type:* Co-educational Day Only
3–19
*Special needs:* ASD **ASP PMLD
SLD**
*Wheelchair access:* WA1

**TOR BANK SCHOOL**
718 Upper Newtownards Road,
Belfast, County Down BT16 1RG
*Website:*
www.torbankschool.org.uk
*Type:* Co-educational Day Only
3–19
*Special needs:* ADD ADHD ASD
ASP BESD CB CP DOW EPI
HEA HI IM MLD PMLD SLD
SP&LD TOU VI
*Wheelchair access:* WA2

# COUNTY ARMAGH

**Southern Education
and Library Board**

**3 Charlemont Place
The Mall
Armagh
County Armagh
BT61 9AX**

**CEARA SCHOOL**
Sloan Street, Craigavon, County
Armagh BT61 8NY
*Website:* www.cearaschool.com
*Type:* Co-educational 4–18

**DONARD SCHOOL**
Castlewellan Road, Banbridge,
County Down BT32 4XY
*Type:* Co-educational Day Only
*Special needs:* ASD **ASP BESD**
PMLD SLD
*Wheelchair access:* WA1

**LISANALLY SPECIAL
SCHOOL**
85 Lisanally Lane, Armagh,
County Armagh BT61 7HF
*Type:* Co-educational Day Only
4–19
*Special needs:* ADD ADHD ASD
ASP BESD CP DOW DYP DYS
MLD PMLD SLD

**RATHFRILAND HILL SCHOOL**
Rathriland Road, Newry, County
Down BT34 1HU
*Type:* Co-educational Day Only
3–19
*Special needs:* ASD **ASP PMLD
SLD**

**SPERRINVIEW SPECIAL
SCHOOL**
8 Coalisland Road, Dungannon,
County Tyrone BT71 6FA
*Website:* www.sperrinview.ik.org
*Type:* Co-educational Day Only
3–19
*Special needs:* ASD **ASP** BESD
CB **CP DOW** EPI HEA HI IM
**PMLD SLD** SP&LD VI W
*Wheelchair access:* WA1

# COUNTY TYRONE

## Western Area Education and Library Board

**1 Hospital Road**
**Omagh**
**County Tyrone**
**BT79 0AW**

### BELMONT HOUSE SCHOOL
Racecourse Road, Londonderry,
County Londonderry BT48 7RE
*Website:*
www.belmonthouse.lk.org
*Type:* Co-educational Day Only
3–19
*Special needs:* BESD **MLD**
SP&LD

### CRANNY SPECIAL SCHOOL
4a Deverney Road, Cranny,
County Tyrone BT79 0JJ
*Type:* Co-educational Day Only
*Special needs:* ASD BESD CP
DOW EPI HI **PMLD SLD** VI
*Wheelchair access:* W

### ELMBROOK SCHOOL
Derrygonnelly, Enniskillen,
County Fermanagh BT7 4AY
*Type:* Co-educational Day Only
4–19
*Special needs:* ASD **ASP** BESD
CP **DOW** EPI HEA **PMLD SLD**
SP&LD
*Wheelchair access:* WA1

### ERNE SPECIAL SCHOOL
Derrygonnelly Road, Enniskillen,
County Fermanagh BT74 7EY
*Type:* Co-educational Day Only
4–16
*Special needs:* **MLD**
*Wheelchair access:* W

### FOYLE VIEW SCHOOL
15 Racecourse Road,
Londonderry, County
Londonderry BT48 7RB
*Website:* www.fofeview.com
*Type:* Co-educational Day Only
3–19
*Special needs:* ASD PMLD **SLD**
*Wheelchair access:* W

### GLASVEY SPECIAL SCHOOL
15 Loughermore Road,
Limavady, County Londonderry
BT49 9PB
*Type:* Co-educational Day Only
3–19
*Special needs:* ASD BESD CP
DYS EPI HEA HI **PMLD SLD**
SP&LD VI
*Wheelchair access:* W

### HEATHERBANK SCHOOL
17 Deverney Road, Omagh,
County Tyrone BT79 0ND
*Type:* Co-educational Day Only
3–18
*Special needs:* **MLD SLD**
*Wheelchair access:* WA1

### LIMEGROVE SCHOOL
2 Ballyquin Road, Limavady,
County Londonderry BT49 9ET
*Type:* Co-educational Day Only
3–16
*Special needs:* BESD **MLD**

# Scotland

## ABERDEENSHIRE

### Aberdeen City Council

**Summerhill Education Centre**
**Stronsay Drive**
**Aberdeen**
**AB15 6JA**

**ABERDEEN SCHOOL FOR THE DEAF**
Sunnybank School, Aberdeen,
Aberdeenshire AB24 4NJ
*Type:* Co-educational Day Only
3–12
*Special needs:* **HI**
*Wheelchair access:* WA3

**BEECHWOOD SCHOOL**
Raeden Park Road, Aberdeen,
Aberdeenshire AB15 5PD
*Type:* Co-educational Day Only
5–18
*Special needs:* MLD SLD
SP&LD
*Wheelchair access:* W

**CORDYCE SPECIAL SCHOOL**
Riverview Drive, Aberdeen,
Aberdeenshire AB21 7NF
*Type:* Co-educational Day Only
11–16
*Special needs:* **BESD**

**HAZLEWOOD SCHOOL**
Fernielea Road, Aberdeen,
Aberdeenshire AB15 6GU
*Type:* Co-educational Day Only
4–18
*Special needs:* ADHD ASD CP
DOW EPI HI MLD PMLD SLD
SP&LD VI
*Wheelchair access:* WA1

**MARLPOOL SCHOOL**
Cloverfield Gardens, Aberdeen,
Aberdeenshire AB21 9QN
*Website:* www.marlpool.ik.org
*Type:* Co-educational Day Only
*Special needs:* ADHD ASD **ASP**
CP DOW EPI IM **MLD SLD**
SP&LD VI
*Wheelchair access:* WA2

**RAEDEN CENTRE**
Mid-Stocket Road, Aberdeen,
Aberdeen City AB15 5PD
*Type:* Co-educational Day Only
3–5
*Special needs:* **ADHD** ASD **ASP**
**CP DOW MLD PMLD**
*Wheelchair access:* WA1

**VISION SUPPORT SERVICE**
Newhills School, Aberdeen,
Aberdeenshire AB21 9UB
*Type:* Co-educational Day Only
*Special needs:* VI
*Wheelchair access:* WA1

**WOODLANDS SCHOOL**
Regent Walk, Aberdeen,
Aberdeenshire AB24 1SX
*Type:* Co-educational Day Only
*Special needs:* **PMLD**
*Wheelchair access:* W

### Aberdeenshire Council

**Woodhill**
**Westburn**
**Aberdeen**
**AB16 5GB**

**THE ANNA RITCHIE SCHOOL**
Grange Gardens, Peterhead,
Aberdeenshire AB42 2AP
*Wheelchair access:* WA2

**BANKHEAD ACADEMY**
**SEN BASE**
Bankhead Avenue, Aberdeen,
Aberdeenshire AB21 9ES

**CARRONHILL SCHOOL**
Mill of Forest Road, Stonehaven,
Kincardineshire AB39 2G2
*Type:* Co-educational Day Only
3–18
*Special needs:* ASD **ASP**
**PMLD SLD**
*Wheelchair access:* WA1

**CENTRAL PRIMARY SCHOOL**
St Peter Street, Peterhead,
Aberdeenshire AB42 1QD
*Type:* Co-educational Day Only
*Special needs:* SP&LD

**ST ANDREW'S SCHOOL**
St Andrew's Gardens, Inverurie,
Aberdeenshire AB51 3XT
*Type:* Co-educational Day Only
3–16
*Special needs:* ASD BESD
CP EPI HI MLD PMLD SLD
SP&LD VI

# ARGYLL AND BUTE

## Argyll and Bute Council

**Kilmory**
**Lochgilphead**
**Argyll and Bute**
**PA31 8RT**

**DRUMMORE DEVELOPMENT CENTRE**
Soroba Road, Oban, Argyll and Bute PA34 4SB
*Special needs:* ASD DYS HI MLD PMLD SLD SP&LD

**PARKLANDS SCHOOL**
27 Charlotte Street, Helensburgh, Argyll and Bute G84 7EZ
*Type:* Co-educational Day Only
5–18
*Special needs:* ASD ASP DOW **PMLD SLD**
*Wheelchair access:* W

**WHITEGATES LEARNING CENTRE**
Lochgilphead, Argyll and Bute PA31 8SY

# NORTH AYRSHIRE

## North Ayrshire Council

**Education Department**
**Cunninghame House**
**Irvine**
**Ayrshire**
**KA12 8EE**

**HAYSHOLM SCHOOL**
Bank Street, Irvine, North Ayrshire KA12 0NE
*Type:* Co-educational Day Only
5–16

**JAMES MACFARLANE SCHOOL**
Dalry Road, Ardrossan, North Ayrshire KA22 7DQ
*Type:* Co-educational Day Only
2–18
*Special needs:* ASD **ASP** CP EPI **PMLD** SLD
*Wheelchair access:* W

**JAMES REID SCHOOL**
Primrose Place, Saltcoats, North Ayrshire KA21 6LH
*Type:* Co-educational Day Only
5–18
*Special needs:* **ADD** ADHD ASD ASP **BESD** CP DOW DYP DYS EPI HEA HI **MLD** SP&LD VI
*Wheelchair access:* W

**STANECASTLE SCHOOL**
Burns Crescent, Irvine, North Ayrshire KA11 1AQ
*Type:* Co-educational Day Only
5–18
*Special needs:* ADHD ASD BESD **MLD** SLD SP&LD VI
*Wheelchair access:* WA1

# EAST AYRSHIRE

### East Ayrshire Council

**London Road**
**Kilmarnock**
**East Ayrshire**
**KA3 7BU**

### HILLSIDE SCHOOL
Dalgleish Avenue, Cumnock,
East Ayrshire KA18 1QQ
*Type:* Co-educational Day Only
3–18
*Special needs:* ASD CP DOW
DYP PMLD SLD
*Wheelchair access:* W

### PARK SCHOOL
Grassyards Road, Kilmarnock,
East Ayrshire KA3 7BB
*Special needs:* ASD BESD CP
DOW DYP EPI MLD SP&LD
*Wheelchair access:* W

### SOUTH PARK SCHOOL
38 Belmont Avenue, Ayr,
South Ayrshire KA7 2NA
*Type:* Boys Day Only 3–16

### WITCHHILL SCHOOL
Witch Road, Kilmarnock,
East Ayrshire KA3 1JF
*Type:* Co-educational Day Only
*Special needs:* **PMLD**
*Wheelchair access:* WA1

### WOODSTOCK SCHOOL
30 North Hamilton Street,
Kilmarnock, East Ayrshire
KA1 2QJ
*Type:* Co-educational Day Only
5–19
*Special needs:* ASD **SLD**
*Wheelchair access:* W

# SOUTH AYRSHIRE

### South Ayrshire Council

**Educational Services**
**Wellington Square**
**Ayr**
**South Ayrshire**
**KA7 1DR**

### CRAIGPARK SCHOOL
Belmont Avenue, Ayr, South
Ayrshire KA7 2ND
*Type:* Co-educational Day Only
2–19
*Special needs:* CP DOW EPI
**PMLD** VI
*Wheelchair access:* WA1

### INVERGARVEN SCHOOL
Henrietta Street, Girvan, South
Ayrshire KA26 9AL
*Type:* Co-educational Day Only

# CLACKMANNANSHIRE

### Clackmannanshire Council

**Greenfield**
**Alloa**
**Clackmannanshire**
**FK10 2AD**

### FAIRFIELD SCHOOL
Pompee Road, Alloa,
Clackmannanshire FK10 3BX
*Type:* Co-educational Day Only
*Special needs:* **PMLD SLD**
*Wheelchair access:* WA1

### LOCHIES SCHOOL
Gartmorn Road, Sauchie,
Clackmannanshire FK10 3PB
*Type:* Co-educational Day Only
5–12
*Special needs:* ADHD ASD **ASP**
BESD CP DOW DYP DYS EPI
**SLD** SP&LD
*Wheelchair access:* WA1

# DUMFRIES & GALLOWAY

## Dumfries and Galloway Council

**Council Offices**
**English Street**
**Dumfries**
**Dumfries & Galloway**
**DG1 2DD**

**ELM BANK SCHOOL**
Lovers Walk, Dumfries,
Dumfries & Galloway DG1 1DP
*Type:* Co-educational Day Only
12–16
*Special needs:* **BESD**

**LANGLANDS SCHOOL**
Loreburn Park, Dumfries,
Dumfries & Galloway DG1 1LS
*Type:* Co-educational Day Only
5–18
*Special needs:* ASD CB CP
DOW EPI IM **PMLD** SLD
SP&LD **VI**
*Wheelchair access:* WA1

**STRANRAER ACADEMY**
McMaster's Road, Stranraer,
Dumfries & Galloway DG9 8BY
*Website:*
www.schools.gabbitas.co.uk
*Type:* Co-educational Day Only
*Special needs:* ADHD **ASD**
ASP BESD CP DOW DYP **DYS**
EPI HEA HI **MLD** PMLD SLD
SP&LD VI
*Wheelchair access:* W

# DUNDEE

## Dundee City Council

**Floor 8, Tayside House**
**Crichton Street**
**Dundee**
**DD1 3RZ**

**KINGSPARK SCHOOL**
5 Glenaffric Terrace, Dundee
DD3 8HF
*Type:* Co-educational Day Only
5–18
*Special needs:* ASD CP EPI
MLD PMLD SLD SP&LD
*Wheelchair access:* W

# EAST DUNBARTONSHIRE

## East Dunbartonshire LEA

**Civic Way**
**Kirkintilloch**
**East Dunbartonshire**
**G66 4TJ**

**CAMPSIE VIEW SCHOOL**
Boghead Road, Lenzie, East
Dunbartonshire G66 4DR
*Type:* Co-educational Day Only
2–19
*Special needs:* ASD **ASP** CP
DOW EPI **PMLD** SLD SP&LD VI
*Wheelchair access:* W

**MERKLAND SCHOOL**
Langmuir Road, Kirkintilloch,
East Dunbartonshire G66 2QF
*Type:* Co-educational Day Only
5–18
*Special needs:* **MLD**
*Wheelchair access:* WA1

# WEST DUNBARTONSHIRE

## West Dunbartonshire Council

**Garshake Road**
**Dumbarton**
**West Dunbartonshire**
**G82 3PU**

### CUNARD SCHOOL
Whitecrook, Clydebank, West
Dunbartonshire G81 1RQ
*Type:* Co-educational Day Only
5–12
*Special needs:* **BESD** SP&LD

### KILPATRICK SCHOOL
Mountblow Road, Clydebank,
West Dunbartonshire G81 4SW
*Type:* Co-educational Day Only
*Special needs:* MLD PMLD SLD
*Wheelchair access:* W

# FALKIRK

## Falkirk LEA

**McLaren House**
**Marchmont Avenue**
**Polmont**
**Falkirk**
**FK2 0NZ**

### CARRONGRANGE SCHOOL
Carrongrange Avenue,
Falkirk FK5 3BH
*Type:* Co-educational Day Only
11–18
*Special needs:* ASD **MLD** PMLD
SLD
*Wheelchair access:* WA1

### DUNDAS DAY UNIT
Grangemouth, Falkirk FK3 9DL
*Special needs:* BESD

### EDUCATION ASSESSMENT UNIT
Polmont, Falkirk FK2 0XS
*Type:* Co-educational Day Only
12–16
*Special needs:* **BESD**

### FALKIRK DAY UNIT
Hope Street, Central FK1 4HA

### TORWOOD SCHOOL
Stirling Road, Falkirk FK5 4SR
*Type:* Co-educational Day Only
*Special needs:* ASD CP DOW
EPI HEA SLD SP&LD
*Wheelchair access:* WA1

### WINDSOR PARK SCHOOL
Bantaskine Road,
Falkirk FK1 5HT
*Type:* Co-educational Day Only
4–18
*Special needs:* **HI** VI
*Wheelchair access:* WA1

# FIFE

## Fife Council

**Auchterderran Centre**
**Woodend Road**
**Cardenden**
**Fife**
**KY5 0NE**

**HEADWELL SCHOOL**
Headwell Avenue, Dunfermline,
Fife KY12 0JU
*Type:* Co-educational Day Only
5–18
*Special needs:* ASD **ASP EPI**

**HYNDHEAD SCHOOL**
Barncraig Street, Leven,
Fife KY8 1JE
*Type:* Co-educational Day Only
3–19
*Special needs:* ASD DOW EPI
IM PMLD SLD
*Wheelchair access:* WA2

**JOHN FERGUS SCHOOL**
Erskine Place, Glenrothes,
Fife KY7 4JB
*Type:* Co-educational Day Only
*Special needs:* ADD ASD **ASP**
BESD CP DOW EPI HI **PMLD**
SLD **VI**
*Wheelchair access:* WA1

**KILMARON SCHOOL**
Balgarvie Road, Cupar,
Fife KY15 4PE
*Type:* Co-educational
*Special needs:* ASD ASP BESD
CP DOW EPI MLD PMLD **SLD**
*Wheelchair access:* W

**LOCHGELLY NORTH SCHOOL**
Lochgelly, Fife KY5 9PE
*Type:* Co-educational Day Only
4–19
*Special needs:* MLD PMLD SLD
*Wheelchair access:* W

**ROBERT HENRYSON**
**SCHOOL**
Linburn Road, Dunfermline,
Fife KY11 4LD
*Type:* Co-educational Day Only
2–19
*Special needs:* ASD CP EPI HI
**PMLD** SLD VI
*Wheelchair access:* WA1

**ROSSLYN SCHOOL**
Viewforth Terrace, Kirkcaldy,
Fife KY1 3BP
*Type:* Co-educational Day Only
*Special needs:* ASD PMLD SLD
*Wheelchair access:* W

# GLASGOW

## East Renfrewshire
## Council

**Eastwood Park**
**Rouken Glen Road**
**Giffnock**
**Glasgow**
**G46 6UG**

**ISOBEL MAIR SCHOOL**
1a Drumby Cresent, Clarkston,
Glasgow G76 7HN

## Glasgow City Council

**Wheatley House**
**25 Cochrane Street**
**Merchant City**
**Glasgow**
**G1 1HL**

**ABERCORN SCHOOL**
195 Garscube Road,
Glasgow G4 9QH
*Type:* Co-educational Day Only
11–18
*Special needs:* **MLD**

**ASHCRAIG SCHOOL**
100 Avenue End Road,
Glasgow G33 3SW
*Type:* Co-educational Day Only
12–19
*Special needs:* CP DYP EPI VI
*Wheelchair access:* WA1

**BANNERMAN**
**COMMUNICATION**
**DISORDER UNIT**
C/o Bannerman High,
Glasgow G69 7NS
*Type:* Boys Day Only 11–16
*Special needs:* ASD ASP

**BROOMLEA SCHOOL**
168 Broomhill Drive,
Glasgow G11 7NH
*Type:* Co-educational Day Only
2–12
*Special needs:* PMLD

**CARNBOOTH SCHOOL**
Carnbooth House,
Glasgow G76 9EG
*Type:* Co-educational Boarding
and Day
*Special needs:* HI VI
*Wheelchair access:* W

**CARTVALE SCHOOL**
80 Vicarfield Street,
Glasgow G51 2DF
*Type:* Boys Day Only 11–16
*Special needs:* **BESD**

**CROFTCROIGHN SCHOOL**
290 Mossvale Road,
Glasgow G33 5NY
*Website:* www.croftcroighn-pri.
glasgow.sch.uk
*Type:* Co-educational Day Only
2–11
*Special needs:* ASD CP EPI
**PMLD SLD**
*Wheelchair access:* W

**CROOKSTON LANGUAGE
UNIT**
C/o St Monica's Primary,
Glasgow G53 5SR
*Special needs:* SP&LD

**DARNLEY VISUAL
IMPAIRMENT UNIT**
C/o Darnley Primary,
Glasgow G53 7HT
*Type:* Co-educational Day Only
*Special needs:* **VI**

**DRUMCHAPEL LEARNING
CENTRE**
77 Hecla Avenue,
Glasgow G15 8LX

**DRUMMORE SCHOOL**
129 Drummore Road,
Glasgow G15 7NH
*Type:* Co-educational Day Only
5–12
*Special needs:* **MLD**

**DUNTARVIE PRE-SCHOOL**
C/o Cadder Primary,
Glasgow G23 5AR
*Type:* Co-educational Day Only
3–5
*Special needs:* ASD **ASP**
SP&LD
*Wheelchair access:* WA3

**EASTMUIR SCHOOL**
211 Hallhill Road,
Glasgow G33 4QL
*Type:* Co-educational Day Only
4–11
*Special needs:* ASD **MLD**

**GADBURN SCHOOL**
70 Rockfield Road,
Glasgow G21 3DZ
*Type:* Co-educational Day Only
5–12
*Special needs:* **MLD**
*Wheelchair access:* W

**HAMPDEN SCHOOL**
80 Ardnahoe Avenue,
Glasgow G42 0DL
*Type:* Day Only
*Special needs:* ASD DOW EPI
PMLD SLD SP&LD
*Wheelchair access:* W

**HOLLYBROOK SCHOOL**
135 Hollybrook Street,
Glasgow G42 7HU
*Type:* Co-educational Day Only
12–19
*Special needs:* **MLD**

**HOWFORD SCHOOL**
487 Crookston Road,
Glasgow G53 7TX
*Type:* Co-educational Day Only
*Special needs:* ASD MLD
*Wheelchair access:* WA1

**KELBOURNE SCHOOL**
109 Hotspur Street,
Glasgow G20 8LH
*Type:* Co-educational Day Only
2–12
*Special needs:* **CP** EPI **HEA**
MLD SP&LD VI
*Wheelchair access:* WA1

**KELVIN SCHOOL**
69 Nairn Street, Glasgow
G3 8SE
*Type:* Co-educational Day Only
*Special needs:* ASD BESD CP
EPI HEA HI MLD PMLD SLD
SP&LD VI
*Wheelchair access:* W

**KENNYHILL SCHOOL**
375 Cumbernauld Road,
Glasgow G31 3LP
*Type:* Co-educational Day Only
*Special needs:* **MLD**

**KIRKRIGGS SCHOOL**
500 Croftfoot Road,
Glasgow G45 0NJ
*Type:* Co-educational Day Only
*Special needs:* ADHD ASD CB
**MLD** SLD
*Wheelchair access:* WA2

**LADYWELL SCHOOL**
12A Victoria Park Drive South,
Glasgow G14 9RU
*Type:* Co-educational Day Only
12–16

**LANGLANDS SCHOOL**
100 Mallaig Road, Glasgow
G51 4PE
*Type:* Co-educational Day Only
2–12

**LINBURN SCHOOL**
77 Linburn Road, Glasgow
G52 4EX
*Type:* Co-educational Day Only
12–18
*Special needs:* PMLD SLD
*Wheelchair access:* WA1

**MIDDLEFIELD SCHOOL**
26 Partickhill Road, Glasgow
G11 5BP
*Type:* Co-educational Day and
Boarding 5–16
*Special needs:* **ASD ASP**

**MILTON SCHOOL**
6 Liddesdale Terrace,
Glasgow G22 7HL
*Type:* Co-educational Day Only
12–18

**NEWHILLS SCHOOL**
Newhills Road, Glasgow
G33 4HJ
*Type:* Co-educational Day Only
12–18
*Special needs:* PMLD SLD
*Wheelchair access:* WA1

**RICHMOND PARK SCHOOL**
30 Logan Street, Glasgow
G5 0HP
*Type:* Co-educational Day Only
4–11
*Special needs:* CP EPI MLD
SP&LD

**ROSEPARK TUTORIAL CENTRE**
Floor 2, Room 9,
Glasgow G11 7QZ

**ROSEVALE SCHOOL**
48 Scalpay Street,
Glasgow G22 7DD
*Type:* Co-educational Day Only
5–12

**ROSSHALL ACADEMY**
Visual Impairment Unit,
Glasgow G52 3PD
*Type:* Co-educational Day Only
12–18
*Special needs:* VI
*Wheelchair access:* WA2

**ROYSTON LANGUAGE UNIT**
C/o Royston Primary, Glasgow
G21 2NU
*Type:* Co-educational Day Only
5–8
*Special needs:* SP&LD

**RUCHILL COMMUNICATION UNIT**
Ruchill Primary School, Glasgow
G20 9HW
*Type:* Co-educational Day Only
1–7
*Special needs:* **ASD ASP**
*Wheelchair access:* WA3

**ST AIDAN'S SCHOOL**
255 Rigby Street,
Glasgow G32 6DJ
*Type:* Co-educational Day Only
*Special needs:* MLD
*Wheelchair access:* WA1

**ST CHARLES' LANGUAGE UNIT**
C/o St Charles' Primary,
Glasgow G20 6BG

**ST JOAN OF ARC SCHOOL**
722 Balmore Road, Glasgow
G22 6QS
*Type:* Co-educational Day Only
12–19
*Special needs:* **MLD**

**ST JOSEPH'S HEARING IMPAIRED UNIT**
C/o St Joseph's Primary,
Glasgow G4 9QX
*Type:* Co-educational Day Only
5–12 (SEN)
*Special needs:* **HI**

**ST KEVIN'S SCHOOL**
25 Fountainwell Road, Glasgow
G21 1TN
*Type:* Co-educational Day Only
5–12
*Special needs:* ASD **ASP BESD MLD** SP&LD
*Wheelchair access:* W

**ST OSWALD'S SCHOOL**
83 Brunton Street,
Glasgow G44 3NF
*Type:* Co-educational Day Only
*Special needs:* ADD ASD BESD
DOW DYS EPI **MLD**

**ST RAYMOND'S SCHOOL**
384 Drakemire Drive, Glasgow
G45 9SR
*Type:* Co-educational
*Special needs:* ADD ADHD ASD
BESD DOW DYP DYS EPI HI
**MLD** SP&LD
*Wheelchair access:* W

**ST VINCENT'S (TOLLCROSS) SCHOOL**
30 Fullarton Avenue, Glasgow
G32 8NJ
*Type:* Co-educational Day Only
2–18
*Special needs:* HI
*Wheelchair access:* W

**TORYGLEN COMMUNICATION DISORDER UNIT**
6 Drummreoch Place, Glasgow
G42 0ER
*Type:* Co-educational Day Only
*Special needs:* **ASD ASP**

# HIGHLAND

**The Highland Council**

**Glenurquhart Road**
**Inverness**
**Highland**
**IV3 5NX**

**DRUMMOND SCHOOL**
Drummond Road, Inverness,
Highland IV2 4NZ
*Type:* Co-educational Day Only
2–19
*Special needs:* ADD ADHD ASD
ASP BESD CB CP DOW DYC
DYP DYS EPI HEA HI IM MLD
PMLD SLD SP&LD TOU VI
*Wheelchair access:* WA2

**ST CLEMENT'S SCHOOL**
Tulloch Street, Dingwall,
Highland IV15 9JZ
*Type:* Co-educational Day Only
3–19
*Special needs:* ASD **ASP CP
DOW PMLD SLD**
*Wheelchair access:* W

**ST DUTHUS SCHOOL**
Old Academy, Tain, Highland
IV19 1ED
*Type:* Co-educational Day Only
3–19
*Special needs:* ASD **ASP** BESD
DOW **PMLD SLD**
*Wheelchair access:* W

# INVERCLYDE

## Inverclyde Education Services

**105 Dalrymple Street**
**Greenock**
**Renfrewshire**
**Inverclyde**
**PA15 1HT**

**GARVEL SCHOOL**
Chester Road, Greenock,
Inverclyde PA16 0TT
*Type:* Co-educational Day Only
2–11
*Special needs:* **HI**
*Wheelchair access:* W

**GLENBURN SCHOOL**
Inverkip Road, Greenock,
Inverclyde PA16 0QG
*Type:* Co-educational Day Only
*Special needs:* MLD SP&LD
*Wheelchair access:* W

**LILYBANK SCHOOL**
Birkmyre Avenue, Port Glasgow,
Inverclyde PA14 5AN
*Type:* Co-educational Day Only
5–18
*Special needs:* ASD CP DOW
EPI **PMLD SLD**
*Wheelchair access:* WA1

# NORTH LANARKSHIRE

## North Lanarkshire Council

**Municipal Buildings**
**Kildonan Street**
**Coatbridge**
**North Lanarkshire**
**ML5 3BT**

**BOTHWELL PARK SCHOOL**
Annan Street, Motherwell,
North Lanarkshire ML1 2DL
*Type:* Co-educational Day Only
12–18

**CLYDEVIEW SCHOOL**
Magna Street, Motherwell,
North Lanarkshire ML1 3QZ
*Type:* Co-educational Day Only
3–19
*Special needs:* **SLD** SP&LD

**CRAIGHALBERT CENTRE**
**CUMBERNAULD**
1 Craighalbert Way,
Cumbernauld,
Glasgow G68 0LS
*Website:*
www.craighalbert.org.uk
*Type:* Co-educational Day Only
*Special needs:* **CP** EPI IM MLD
*Wheelchair access:* WA1

**DRUMPARK SCHOOL**
Coatbridge Road, Bargeddie,
North Lanarkshire G69 7TW
*Type:* Co-educational Day Only
3–18
*Special needs:* **MLD**
*Wheelchair access:* W

**FALLSIDE SCHOOL**
Sanderson Avenue, Uddington,
North Lanarkshire G71 6JZ
*Type:* Co-educational Day Only
12–18

**FIRPARK SCHOOL**
Firpark Street, Motherwell,
North Lanarkshire ML1 2PR
*Type:* Co-educational Day Only
3–18
*Special needs:* ASD BESD CP
DOW DYP DYS EPI HI MLD
**SLD** SP&LD VI
*Wheelchair access:* W

**GLENCRYAN SCHOOL**
Greenfaulds Ring Road,
Cumbernauld, North
Lanarkshire G67 2XJ
*Type:* Co-educational Day Only
3–18
*Special needs:* ADD ASP DOW
DYC DYP DYS HEA HI MLD
SP&LD TOU VI
*Wheelchair access:* W

**MAVISBANK SCHOOL**
Mitchell Street, Airdrie,
North Lanarkshire ML6 0EB
*Type:* Co-educational 2–19
*Special needs:* **PMLD**
*Wheelchair access:* WA1

**PENTLAND SCHOOL**
Tay Street, Coatbridge,
North Lanarkshire ML5 2NA
*Type:* Co-educational Day Only
*Special needs:* **BESD**

**PORTLAND HIGH SCHOOL**
31-33 Kildonan Street,
Coatbridge, North Lanarkshire
ML5 3LG
*Type:* Co-educational Day Only
12–16

**REDBURN SCHOOL**
Mossknowe Building,
Cumbernauld, North
Lanarkshire G67 2EL
*Type:* Co-educational Day Only
2–19
*Special needs:* ASD BESD CP
DOW EPI PMLD SLD SP&LD VI
*Wheelchair access:* W

**WILLOWBANK SCHOOL**
299 Bank Street, Coatbridge,
North Lanarkshire ML5 1EG
*Type:* Co-educational Day Only
11–17
*Special needs:* **BESD**

# SOUTH LANARKSHIRE

## South Lanarkshire Education

**Almada Street
Hamilton
ML3 0AA**

### CRAIGHEAD SCHOOL
Whistleberry Road, Hamilton,
South Lanarkshire ML3 0EG
*Website:*
www.craigheadschool.org
*Type:* Co-educational Day Only
5–18
*Special needs:* ASD ASP DYP
**MLD SLD**
*Wheelchair access:* WA1

### GREENBURN SCHOOL
Maxwelton Avenue,
East Kilbride,
South Lanarkshire G74 3DU
*Type:* Co-educational Day Only
1–19
*Wheelchair access:* W

### HAMILTON SCHOOL FOR THE DEAF
Wellhall Road, Hamilton,
South Lanarkshire ML3 9UE
*Type:* Co-educational Day Only
3–11
*Special needs:* **HI**
*Wheelchair access:* WA1

### KITTOCH SCHOOL
Livingstone Drive, East Kilbride,
South Lanarkshire G75 0AB
*Type:* Co-educational Day Only
3–5
*Special needs:* **BESD**

### RIDGEPARK RESIDENTIAL SCHOOL
Mousebank Road, Lanark,
South Lanarkshire ML11 7RA

### SANDERSON HIGH SCHOOL
High Common Road, East Kilbride,
South Lanarkshire G74 2LX
*Website:*
www.sanderson.s-lanark.sch.uk
*Type:* Co-educational Day Only
11–18
*Special needs:* ADHD ASD ASP
CP DOW DYP EPI HI MLD
PMLD SLD SP&LD VI
*Wheelchair access:* WA1

### VICTORIA PARK SCHOOL
Market Road, Carluke,
South Lanarkshire ML8 4BE
*Type:* Co-educational Day Only
3–18
*Special needs:* ASD BESD CP
DOW EPI PMLD SLD SP&LD VI
*Wheelchair access:* WA1

### WEST MAINS SCHOOL
Logie Park, East Kilbride,
South Lanarkshire G74 4BU
*Type:* Co-educational Day Only
5–9
*Special needs:* SP&LD

# LOTHIAN

## Midlothian Council

**Fairfield House
8 Lotham Road
Dalkeith
Midlothian
EH22 3ZG**

### CUIKEN HOUSE
150 Cuiken Terrace, Penicuik,
Lothian EH26 0AH
*Wheelchair access:* WA1

### SALTERSGATE SCHOOL
3 Cousland Road, Dalkeith,
Lothian
*Type:* Co-educational Day Only
5–18
*Special needs:* ADD ASD BESD
DOW DYS EPI HEA MLD SLD
SP&LD
*Wheelchair access:* WA2

## West Lothian LEA

**Almondvale Boulevard
Livingston
West Lothian
EH54 6QP**

### BEATLIE SPECIAL SCHOOL
The Mall, Livingston, Lothian
EH54 5EJ
*Type:* Co-educational Day Only
3–16
*Wheelchair access:* WA1

### BURNHOUSE SCHOOL
The Avenue, Whitburn,
West Lothian EH47 0BX
*Type:* Co-educational Day Only
10–16

### CEDARBANK SPECIAL SCHOOL
Cedarbank, Livingston, Lothian
EH54 6DR
*Type:* Co-educational Day Only
3–16

### PINEWOOD SPECIAL SCHOOL
Elm Grove, Bathgate,
West Lothian EH47 7OX
*Type:* Co-educational Day Only
5–18

# ORKNEY

**Orkney Department of Education & Recreational Services**

**Council Offices**
**Kirkwall**
**Orkney**
**KW15 1HP**

**GLAITNESS AURRIDA SPECIAL SCHOOL**
Pickaquoy Road, Kirkwall,
Orkney KW15 1RP
*Type:* Co-educational Day and
Boarding 2–18
*Special needs:* MLD PMLD SLD
*Wheelchair access:* W

# PERTH AND KINROSS

**Perth & Kinross Council**

**Education & Children's Service**
**Pullar House**
**35 Kinnoull Street**
**Perth**
**PH1 5GD**

**GLEBE SCHOOL**
Abbey Road, Perth, Perth and
Kinross PH2 6LW
*Type:* Co-educational Day and
Boarding 11–18
*Special needs:* **ADHD ASD
ASP CP DOW EPI IM PMLD
SLD VI**
*Wheelchair access:* WA2

**KERSLAND SCHOOL**
Ben Nevis Road, Paisley,
Renfrewshire PA2 7BU
*Website:* www.kersland.sch.uk
*Type:* Co-educational Day Only
5–18
*Special needs:* ASD **SLD**
*Wheelchair access:* WA2

# RENFREWSHIRE

**Renfrewshire LEA**

**South Building**
**Cotton Street**
**Paisley**
**Renfrewshire**
**PA1 1LE**

**CLIPPENS SCHOOL**
Brediland Road, Linwood,
Renfrewshire PA3 3RX
*Type:* Co-educational Day Only
5–19
*Special needs:* ASD CB **PMLD
SLD**
*Wheelchair access:* WA1

**HUNTERHILL TUTORIAL CENTRE**
Cartha Crescent, Paisley,
Renfrewshire PA2 7EL
*Type:* Boys Day Only 5–11
*Special needs:* ADD ADHD
**BESD** DYS

**MARY RUSSELL SCHOOL**
Hawkhead Road, Paisley,
Renfrewshire PA2 7BE
*Type:* Co-educational 5–18

# ROXBURGHSHIRE

## Scottish Borders Council

**Newtown
St Boswell's
Melrose
Roxburghshire
TD6 0SA**

**BERWICKSHIRE HIGH SCHOOL SPECIAL UNIT**
Duns, Scottish Borders TD11 3QQ
*Website:*
www.berwickshirehs.org.uk
*Type:* Co-educational Day Only
*Special needs:* ASD CP MLD SLD
*Wheelchair access:* WA2

**WILTON PRIMARY SCHOOL SPECIAL SCHOOL**
Wellfield Road, Hawick, Scottish Borders TD9 7EN
*Website:* www.wilton-pri.
scotborders.sch.uk
*Type:* Co-educational Day Only 5–13
*Special needs:* **ASD ASP** BESD CP DOW DYS EPI **MLD PMLD SLD**
*Wheelchair access:* WA1

# STIRLING

## Stirling Council

**Room 213
Viewforth
Stirling
FK8 2ET**

**CHARLES BROWN SCHOOL**
Fallin Primary School, Els Base, Fallin, Stirling FK7 7EJ
*Website:* www.fallin.primary.ik.org
*Type:* Co-educational Day Only
*Wheelchair access:* WA1

**KILDEAN SCHOOL**
Drip Road, Kildean, Stirling FK8 1RW
*Type:* Co-educational 3–12

**WHINS OF MILTON SPECIAL SCHOOL**
Fairhill Road, Stirling FK7 0LL
*Type:* Co-educational 6–12

# Wales

## ANGLESEY

**Isle of Anglesey County Council**

Fforddd Glanhfa
Llangefni
Anglesey
LL77 7TW

**YSGOL Y BONT**
The Industrial Estate, Anglesey
LL77 7JA
*Type:* Co-educational Day Only
3–19
*Special needs:* ASD ASP BESD
CP DOW DYP EPI HEA **PMLD**
**SLD** SP&LD TOU
*Wheelchair access:* WA1

## BRIDGEND

**Bridgend County Borough Council**

Civic Offices
Angel Street
Bridgend
CF31 4WB

**HERONSBRIDGE SCHOOL**
Ewenny Road,
Bridgend CF31 3HT
*Type:* Co-educational Boarding
and Day 3–19
*Special needs:* ASD ASP
CP DOW EPI HI PMLD SLD
SP&LD VI
*Wheelchair access:* WA2

## CAERPHILLY

**Caerphilly County Borough Council**

Caerphilly Road
Ystrad Mynach
Hengoed
Caerphilly
CF82 7EP

**TRINITY FIELDS SCHOOL & RESOURCE CENTRE**
Caerphilly Road, Hengoed,
Caerphilly CF82 7XW
*Website:* www.trinityfieldschool
andresourcecentre.co.uk
*Type:* Co-educational 3–19
*Special needs:* ADHD ASD **ASP**
CP DOW EPI HI **PMLD SLD** VI
*Wheelchair access:* WA1

# CARDIFF

## Cardiff County Council

**County Hall**
**Atlantic Wharf**
**Cardiff**
**CF10 4UW**

**THE COURT SCHOOL**
96a Station Road, Cardiff
CF4 5UX
*Website:* www.thecourtsp.
cardiff.sch.uk
*Type:* Co-educational Day Only
5–11
*Special needs:* **ADD ADHD**
**ASD** ASP **BESD CB** DYP **DYS**
EPI **MLD** SP&LD **TOU**
*Wheelchair access:* WA3

**GREENHILL SCHOOL**
Heol Brynglas, Cardiff CF4 6UJ
*Type:* Co-educational Day Only
11–16
*Special needs:* **BESD**
*Wheelchair access:* WA2

**THE HOLLIES SCHOOL**
Pentwyn Drive, Cardiff CF2 7XG
*Type:* Co-educational Day Only
3–11
*Special needs:* ADD ADHD ASD
**ASP** CP SP&LD
*Wheelchair access:* WA1

**MEADOWBANK SCHOOL**
Colwill Road, Cardiff CF14 2QQ
*Type:* Co-educational Day Only
4–11
*Special needs:* SP&LD
*Wheelchair access:* WA1

**RIVERBANK SCHOOL**
Vincent Road, Cardiff CF5 5AQ
*Type:* Co-educational Day Only
4–11
*Special needs:* ADHD ASD
BESD CP DOW DYP EPI HI
**MLD SLD** SP&LD

**TY GWYN SCHOOL**
Ty Gwyn Road, Cardiff CF23 5JG
*Type:* Co-educational Day Only
3–19
*Special needs:* **PMLD** SLD
*Wheelchair access:* W

**WOODLANDS SCHOOL**
Vincent Road, Cardiff CF5 5AQ
*Type:* Co-educational Day Only
11–19
*Special needs:* HI **MLD SLD**
*Wheelchair access:* W

# CARMARTHENSHIRE

## Carmarthenshire County Council

**Education Headquarters**
**County Hall**
**Carmarthen**
**SA31 1JP**

**YSGOL HEOL GOFFA**
Heol Goffa, Llanelli,
Carmarthenshire SA15 3LS
*Type:* Co-educational Day Only
3–19
*Special needs:* CP EPI **PMLD**
**SLD**
*Wheelchair access:* WA1

# CONWY

## Conwy County Borough Council

**Bodlondeb**
**Conwy**
**LL32 8DU**

**YSGOL CEDAR COURT**
65 Victoria Park, Colwyn Bay,
Conwy LL29 7AJ
*Type:* Co-educational Boarding
and Day 11–18
*Special needs:* **BESD**

**YSGOL Y GOGARTH**
Ffordd Nant y Gamar,
Llandudno, Conwy LL30 1YF
*Type:* Co-educational Boarding
and Day 3–19
*Special needs:* ADHD ASD ASP
CP DOW EPI HI PMLD **SLD**
SP&LD VI
*Wheelchair access:* WA1

# DENBIGHSHIRE

## Denbighshire Education Services

**Canol Y Dre**
**Ruthin**
**Denbighshire**
**LL15 1QA**

### TIR MORFA SCHOOL (INFANT & JUNIOR)
Rhyl Road, Rhuddlan,
Denbighshire LL18 2RN
*Type:* Co-educational Day Only
3–19
*Special needs:* ADD **BESD** DOW
EPI HI **MLD SLD** SP&LD VI
*Wheelchair access:* W

### TIR MORFA SCHOOL (SENIORS)
Derwen Road, Rhyl,
Denbighshire LL18 2RN
*Type:* Co-educational Day Only
2–19
*Special needs:* **MLD SLD**

### YSGOL PLAS BRONDYFFRYN
Park Street, Denbigh,
Denbighshire LL16 4RH
*Website:*
www.ysgolplasbrondyffryn.co.uk
*Type:* Co-educational Boarding
and Day 3–19
*Special needs:* **ASD ASP**
*Wheelchair access:* WA2

# FLINTSHIRE

## Flintshire LEA

**County Hall**
**Mold**
**Flintshire**
**CH7 6NB**

### YSGOL BELMONT
Windmill Road, Buckley,
Flintshire CH7 3HA
*Type:* Co-educational Day Only
*Special needs:* CP EPI **MLD** SLD

### YSGOL DELYN
Alexandra Road, Mold, Flintshire
CH7 1HJ
*Type:* Co-educational Day Only
2–19
*Special needs:* ADD ADHD ASD
ASP BESD CP DOW DYP DYS
EPI HEA HI MLD **PMLD SLD**
SP&LD VI
*Wheelchair access:* W

### YSGOL Y BRYN
King George Street, Shotton,
Flintshire CH5 1EA
*Type:* Co-educational Day Only
2–19
*Special needs:* ASD PMLD **SLD**
*Wheelchair access:* W

# GWENT
# GWYNEDD

## Gwynedd Council

**County Offices**
**Shirehall Street**
**Caernarfon**
**Gwynedd**
**LL55 1SH**

### YSGOL COEDMENAI
Bangor, Gwynedd LL57 2RX
*Type:* Boys Day Only 9–15
*Special needs:* **BESD**

### YSGOL HAFOD LON
Y Ffor, Pwllheli, Gwynedd
LL53 6UD
*Type:* Co-educational Day Only
4–19
*Special needs:* ADHD ASD **CP**
**DOW** EPI **PMLD** SLD SP&LD
*Wheelchair access:* W

### YSGOL PENDALAR
Ffordd Bethel, Caernarfon,
Gwynedd LL55 1DU
*Website:*
www.ysgolpendalar.org
*Type:* Co-educational Day Only
2–19
*Special needs:* ADHD ASD
**ASP CP DOW** EPI **PMLD SLD**
SP&LD
*Wheelchair access:* WA1 WA2

# MERTHYR TYDFIL

**Merthyr Tydfil County
Borough Council**

**Civic Centre
Castle Street
Avenue de Clichy
Merthyr Tydfil
CF47 8AN**

**GREENFIELD SPECIAL
SCHOOL**
Duffryn Road, Pentrebach,
Merthyr Tydfil CF48 4BJ
*Type:* Co-educational Day Only
2–19
*Special needs:* ASD **MLD PMLD
SLD** SP&LD
*Wheelchair access:* W

# MONMOUTHSHIRE

**Monmouthshire County
Council**

**County Hall
Torfaen
Cwmbran
Monmouthshire
NP44 2XH**

**MOUNTON HOUSE SCHOOL**
Pwyllmeyric, Chepstow,
Monmouthshire NP16 6LA
*Type:* Boys Day and Boarding
11–16
*Special needs:* **BESD** MLD

# NEATH PORT TALBOT

**Neath Port Talbot
Council**

**Civic Centre
Port Talbot
Neath Port Talbot
SA13 1PJ**

**YSGOL HENDRE SPECIAL
SCHOOL**
Main Road, Neath, Neath Port
Talbot SA10 7TY
*Type:* Co-educational Boarding
Only 11–16
*Special needs:* HI **MLD SLD** VI
*Wheelchair access:* WA2

# NEWPORT

**Newport LEA**

**Civic Centre
Newport
NP20 4UR**

**MAES EBBW SCHOOL**
Maesglas Road, South Wales,
Newport NP20 3DG
*Type:* Co-educational Day Only
3–19
*Special needs:* ASD PMLD SLD
*Wheelchair access:* WA1

# PEMBROKESHIRE

## Pembrokeshire County Council

**County Hall**
**Haverfordwest**
**Pembrokeshire**
**SA61 1TP**

**PORTFIELD SCHOOL**
Portfield, Haverfordwest,
Pembrokeshire SA61 1BS
*Type:* Co-educational Day Only
3–19
*Special needs:* ASD CP EPI HI
**PMLD SLD** VI
*Wheelchair access:* WA1

# POWYS

## Powys Children, Families & Lifelong Learning Directorate

**County Hall**
**Llandrindod Wells**
**Powys**
**LD1 5LG**

**BRYNLLYWARCH HALL SCHOOL**
Kerry, Newtown,
Powys SY16 4PB
*Type:* Co-educational Boarding
and Day
*Special needs:* ADD ASP **BESD**
**MLD**

**YSGOL CEDEWAIN**
Maesyrhandir, Newtown,
Powys SY16 1LH
*Website:*
www.cedewain.powys.sch.uk
*Type:* Co-educational Day Only
2–19
*Special needs:* ASD **ASP** PMLD
**SLD** SP&LD
*Wheelchair access:* WA1

**YSGOL PENMAES**
Canal Road, Brecon, Powys
LD3 7HL
*Website:*
www.penmaes.powys.sch.uk
*Type:* Co-educational Day and
Boarding 2–19
*Special needs:* ASD PMLD **SLD**
*Wheelchair access:* WA1

# SWANSEA

## Swansea Education Department

**County Hall**
**Swansea**
**SA1 3SN**

**PEN-Y-BRYN SENIOR SCHOOL**
Glasbury Road, Morriston,
Swansea SA6 7PA
*Type:* Co-educational Day and
Boarding 4–19
*Special needs:* ASD **MLD** SLD

**YSGOL CRUG GLAS**
Croft Street, Swansea SA1 1QA
*Type:* Co-educational 3–19
*Special needs:* **PMLD**
*Wheelchair access:* WA1

# TORFAEN

**Torfaen Education Offices**

**County Hall**
**Cwmbran**
**Torfaen**
**NP44 2WN**

**CROWNBRIDGE SCHOOL**
Greenhill Road, Pontypool,
Torfaen NP4 5YW
*Type:* Co-educational Day Only
3–19
*Special needs:* ASD DOW
PMLD SLD SP&LD
*Wheelchair access:* W

# VALE OF GLAMORGAN

**Vale of Glamorgan Directorate of Learning and Development**

**Civic Offices**
**Holton Road**
**Barry**
**Vale of Glamorgan**
**CF63 4RU**

**ASHGROVE SCHOOL**
Sully Road, Penarth, Vale of
Glamorgan CF64 2TP
*Website:*
www.ashgroveschool.org
*Type:* Day and Boarding
*Special needs:* ADD **ASD ASP**

**YSGOL MAES DYFAN**
Gibbonsdown Rise, Barry,
Vale of Glamorgan CF6 7QZ
*Type:* Co-educational Day Only
3–19
*Special needs:* **MLD SLD**
*Wheelchair access:* WA1

# WREXHAM

**Wrexham Education & Leisure Services Directorate**

**Ty Henblas**
**Queen's Square**
**Wrexham**
**LL13 8AZ**

**ST CHRISTOPHER SCHOOL**
Stockwell Grove, Wrexham
LL13 7BW
*Type:* Co-educational Day Only
5–19
*Special needs:* ADD ADHD ASD
ASP **BESD** CP DOW DYC DYP
DYS HEA HI **MLD** PMLD **SLD**
SP&LD TOU VI
*Wheelchair access:* WA1

## PART FOUR

# INDEPENDENT MAINSTREAM SCHOOLS WITH SPECIALIST PROVISION

www.schoolsforspecialneeds.co.uk

## 4.1

# Independent Mainstream Schools with Specialist Provision – An Introduction

As a parent, you have the best knowledge of your child's individual needs. You will want to consider whether he or she would be happy and able to thrive with appropriate help in a mainstream school, or whether a special school, with highly specialist facilities and resources, is more appropriate. You may feel that a special school will be best able to meet his or her needs. Alternatively, you may prefer your child to learn in a mainstream school environment if the right support is available.

The term 'mainstream school' is commonly used to describe any school that is not a special school. This would include schools that offer some specialist SEN provision. In fact, the Education Act 1996 states that, for the purposes of operating the statutory framework for special educational needs, a mainstream school is any school that is not a special school or an independent school. City Technology Colleges, City Colleges for the Technology of the Arts, and Academies are independent schools, but are classified as 'mainstream' under the Act. These schools do not charge fees and are regulated by agreements with the Department for Education (DfE). They cater for children with SEN in a similar way to mainstream maintained schools.

To avoid confusion, and to tie in with common usage, 'mainstream' for the purposes of this section means independent schools (fee-charging) that are not special schools. More specifically, this section deals with such independent schools that offer help for pupils with SEN. Many schools in this category offer assistance for pupils with specific learning difficulties, such as dyslexia, and are unlikely to be able to cater for children with severe emotional and behavioural difficulties. Most mainstream independent schools are not authorized to accept children with Statements of SEN, although the Secretary of State can give approval for the placement of an individual child with a Statement. This will of course vary from one school to another, as will the expertise and facilities available.

Some schools have extensive experience in providing SEN support. A few have a significant proportion of students with SEN and a dedicated unit in school staffed by qualified specialist teachers. Pupils may be withdrawn from certain lessons during the school day, during which time they receive specialist support. Some may offer differentiated work within the normal classroom. Others may be sympathetic to special needs but may not have the facilities to make any special provision. It is important to remember that in most cases schools will expect your child to meet the normal entry requirements for the school and to be able to cope in an ordinary school setting. However, where a special need amounts to a disability under the Disability Discrimination Act, the school will need to consider whether it is able to make reasonable adjustments to accommodate such needs, including the provision of extra support for which the school is entitled to charge a separate fee.

Parents should look at the individual school's admissions policy, SEN and disability policy and accessibility plan for details of the school's admission criteria and the provisions in place for children with SEN. All independent schools must now, by law, have such policies and plans in place and copies should be available on request.

If you are considering mainstream schools, it is important to find out exactly how these would meet your child's individual needs. To help you find out which schools in the directory are appropriate for your child, the support available at each school for each type of need is shown. If you are looking for schools that make provision for dyslexia, you may also find it helpful to consult the register of schools produced by CReSTeD (Council for the Registration of Schools Teaching Dyslexic Pupils) on pages 475–82.

When contacting or visiting schools that interest you, you may wish to ask about the following points to help you make an assessment of the school's suitability.

### *Academic pace*

Finding the right academic environment for your child is every bit as essential as finding a school that will provide the right level of SEN support. Ask to see examples of children's work. Where do leavers go? Is the school's overall thrust and ethos suitable for your child?

### *Experience and expertise in managing SEN*

- How much experience has the school had of teaching children with needs or a spectrum of needs similar to your child's?
- How many such students are currently enrolled? What help do these students receive?
- What proportion of pupils in the school have SEN?
- Are staff qualified in SEN teaching?

- Does the school have full-time SEN teaching specialists or is teaching done on a part-time basis?
- What have been the destinations of recent leavers with SEN?

## Meeting the needs of your child

- What strategy would the school suggest for meeting your child's needs? How many special lessons would your child have per week? How big are the groups for these lessons? Will your child have to give up another subject in order to have special lessons or will these be given outside normal lesson times? What will the lessons cover? Will there be additional support in class? If so, from whom?
- If Information Technology facilities are an important resource for your child, what can the school offer? Is there a dedicated area available? Are computers and laptops freely available for use?
- Will the school arrange for special arrangements during GCSE and/or A level examinations, if appropriate?

## Communication with teachers and parents

- How will those in school who are responsible for teaching and caring for your child be kept informed of his or her needs and progress by the special needs department?
- How, and how often, will parents be kept in touch with progress and plans?

## Wider needs

- It is equally important to check that your child's strengths and interests outside the classroom can be catered for. If he or she is good at music, sport, drama or has a special interest in, for example, outdoor pursuits or debating, will the school offer the right levels of encouragement and opportunities to develop these, either now or at a later stage?
- Similarly, what help and advice is given to senior school pupils about university entry and careers?
- Does your child have particular medical or dietary needs that must be provided for in school?
- Are there any religious considerations? If your family is of a faith different from that of the school, how will your child's faith be accommodated? Will he or she find it difficult to play a full part in school life?

- Does the school share your values as a parent? What are its policies with reference to discipline, bullying and drugs, and the extent of guidance given on Personal & Social Education (PSE)?

If you would like more personal help to find suitable mainstream schools for your child, contact Gabbitas for assistance with independent educational assessments and selection of schools.

Gabbitas Educational Consultants
Norfolk House, 30 Charles II Street, London SW1Y 4AE
Tel: 020 7734 0161, fax: 020 7437 1764, e-mail: info@gabbitas.co.uk,
website: www.gabbitas.co.uk

# 4.2

# Notes on the Directory

## Type of school

This directory comprises mainstream independent schools listed within the Department for Education Register of Independent Schools that have requested an entry in the Guide.

## School entries

Each entry includes the school's contact details and a brief description to show pupil's gender and age range, and the type of accommodation available, eg boarding and day. The information is intended as a guide only. For more details please contact schools direct.

## Special needs provision

Provision is divided into three categories, as follows:

1  Learning difficulties.

2  Behavioural disorders/emotional and behavioural difficulties/challenging behaviour.

3  Physical impairments/medical conditions.

Within each of these categories, each school has been asked to indicate: a) the type of support provided; and b) whether it currently has pupils who have been diagnosed with specific conditions, disorders or disabilities within that general category. It should be noted that the conditions, disorders and disabilities listed are not comprehensive and are offered as a guide only. To find out about provision for other types of special needs please make contact with schools.

## Charging policy

Some forms of support may be provided within the school's standard fee. Others may be provided at the parents' or Local Authority's expense. For details of individual school policies please contact them individually.

## Key to abbreviations used in the directory

### Learning difficulties

*Support provided:*

CA    Some children with special needs receive help from classroom assistants
RA    There are currently very limited facilities for pupils with learning difficulties but reasonable adjustments can be made if necessary
SC    Some children with special needs are taught in separate classes for specific subjects
SNU   School has a dedicated Special Needs Unit, which provides specialist tuition on a one-to-one or small group basis by appropriately qualified teachers
WI    There is no dedicated Special Needs Unit but some children with special needs are withdrawn individually from certain lessons for one-to-one tuition

*The school currently has pupils who have been diagnosed with:*

DOW   Down's Syndrome
DYC   Dyscalculia
DYP   Dyspraxia
DYS   Dyslexia
MLD   Moderate Learning Difficulties
PMLD  Profound and Multiple Learning Difficulties
SLD   Severe Learning Difficulties
SP&LD Speech and Language Difficulties

### Behavioural disorders/emotional and behavioural difficulties/ challenging behaviour

*Support provided:*

CA    Some children with behavioural problems receive help from classroom assistants
CO    Trained counsellors available for pupils
RA    There are currently very limited facilities for pupils with behavioural disorders but reasonable adjustments can be made if necessary

ST          Behaviour management strategies identified in school's behaviour management
            policy
TS          Staff trained in behaviour management available

*The school currently has pupils who have been diagnosed with the following disorders:*

ADD     Attention Deficit Disorder              BESD    Behavioural, Emotional and Social
ADHD    Attention Deficit Hyperactivity                 Disorders
        Disorder                                CB      Challenging Behaviour
ASD     Autism/Autistic Spectrum Disorder       TOU     Tourette's Syndrome
ASP     Asperger's Syndrome

## Physical impairments/Medical conditions

*Support provided:*

AT          Adapted timetable for children with health problems
BL          Materials can be provided in Braille
CA          Some children with behavioural problems receive help from classroom
            assistants
DS          Signing by staff and pupils
HL          Hearing loops available
IT          Specialist IT provision available
RA          There are currently very limited facilities for pupils with physical impairments or
            medical conditions but reasonable adjustments can be made if necessary
SL          Stairlifts
SM          Staff with medical training available
TW          Accessible toilet and washing facilities
W           School has wheelchair access (unspecified)
WA1         School is fully wheelchair accessible
WA2         Main teaching areas are wheelchair accessible
WA3         No permanent access for wheelchairs; temporary ramps available

*The school currently has pupils with the following impairments/medical conditions:*

CP      Cerebral Palsy                  IM      Impaired Mobility
EPI     Epilepsy                        VI      Visual Impairment
HI      Hearing Impairment              WU      Wheelchair Users
HEA     Health Problems
        (eg heart defect, asthma)

## Symbols

+           Registered with CReSTeD
*           School profile later in this section (see Part 5.1)

## 4.3

# Directory of Independent Mainstream Schools with Specialist Provision

# England

## BEDFORDSHIRE

**MOORLANDS SCHOOL**
Leagrave Hall, Luton,
Bedfordshire LU4 9LE
*Website:*
www.moorlandsschool.com
*Type:* Co-educational Day Only
2–11
*Learning difficulties:* DYS DYP
*Behavioural and emotional
disorders:* CA TS ST/ASD
*Physical and medical conditions:*
IT RA SM TW WA2/HEA

# BERKSHIRE

### THE ABBEY SCHOOL
17 Kendrick Road, Reading,
Berkshire RG1 5DZ
*Website:* www.theabbey.co.uk
*Type:* Girls Day Only 3–18
*Learning difficulties:* WI/DYS
DYP
*Behavioural and emotional
disorders:* TS ST/ADD
*Physical and medical conditions:*
SL SM TW WA2/HEA

### THE CEDARS SCHOOL
Church Road, Aldermaston,
Berkshire RG7 4LR
*Website:*
www.thecedarsschool.co.uk
*Type:* Co-educational Day Only
4–11
*Learning difficulties:* CA WI/DYS
*Physical and medical conditions:*
W

### DOLPHIN SCHOOL
Waltham Road, Hurst, Reading,
Berkshire RG10 0FR
*Website:*
www.dolphinschool.com
*Type:* Co-educational Day Only
3–13
*Learning difficulties:* WI/DYS
*Behavioural and emotional
disorders:* RA/ASP ASD
*Physical and medical conditions:*
RA

### DOWNE HOUSE
Cold Ash, Thatcham, Berkshire
RG18 9JJ
*Website:* www.downehouse.net
*Type:* Girls Boarding and Day
11–18
*Learning difficulties:* SNU/DYS
DYP
*Behavioural and emotional
disorders:* RA
*Physical and medical conditions:*
RA/HEA HI

### HERRIES SCHOOL
Dean Lane, Cookham Dean,
Maidenhead, Berkshire SL6 9BD
*Website:* www.herries.ws
*Type:* Co-educational Day Only
3–11
*Learning difficulties:* WI

### HORRIS HILL SCHOOL
Newtown, Newbury, Berkshire
RG20 9DJ
*Website:* www.horrishill.com
*Type:* Boys Boarding and Day
7–13
*Learning difficulties:* SNU/MLD
DYS DYP
*Behavioural and emotional
disorders:* ADD
*Physical and medical conditions:*
SM/HI

### HURST LODGE SCHOOL
Bagshot Road, Ascot, Berkshire
SL5 9JU
*Website:* www.hurstlodge.co.uk
*Type:* Co-educational Day and
Boarding 3–18 (Boys and Girls
3–18)
*Learning difficulties:* CA SC
WI/MLD DYC DYS DYP
*Behavioural and emotional
disorders:* RA/ADD ADHD ASP
*Physical and medical conditions:*
AT RA/EPI HEA HI IM VI

### MEADOWBROOK
### MONTESSORI SCHOOL
Malt Hill, Warfield, Bracknell,
Berkshire RG42 6JQ
*Type:* Co-educational Day Only
3–11
*Learning difficulties:* CA RA
SNU/MLD DYS
*Behavioural and emotional
disorders:* RA TS/ADHD ASP
ASD CB
*Physical and medical conditions:*
TW WA1 WA2

### THE ORATORY SCHOOL
Woodcote, Reading, Berkshire
RG8 0PJ
*Website:* www.oratory.co.uk
*Type:* Boys Day and Boarding
11–18
*Learning difficulties:* SNU/MLD
DYS DYP

### OUR LADY'S PREPARATORY
### SCHOOL
The Avenue, Crowthorne,
Berkshire RG45 6PB
*Website:*
www.ourladysprep.co.uk
*Type:* Co-educational Day Only
1–11

### PAPPLEWICK SCHOOL
Windsor Road, Ascot, Berkshire
SL5 7LH
*Website:* www.papplewick.org.uk
*Type:* Boys Boarding and Day
6–13
*Learning difficulties:* WI/MLD DYS
*Behavioural and emotional
disorders:* RA
*Physical and medical conditions:*
RA

### ST ANDREW'S SCHOOL
Buckhold, Pangbourne,
Reading, Berkshire RG8 8QA
*Website:* www.
standrewspangbourne.co.uk
*Type:* Co-educational Day and
Boarding 3–13
*Learning difficulties:* WI/DYS

### ST BERNARD'S
### PREPARATORY SCHOOL
Hawtrey Close, Slough,
Berkshire SL1 1TB
*Website:* www.st-bernards-prep.
slough.sch.uk
*Type:* Co-educational Day Only
3–11
*Learning difficulties:* CA WI/DYS
*Physical and medical conditions:*
TW WA2/HEA

### ST GABRIEL'S
Sandleford Priory, Newbury,
Berkshire RG20 9BD
*Website:* www.stgabriels.co.uk
*Type:* Girls Day Only 3–18
(Girls 3–18 Boys 3–7)
*Learning difficulties:* CA SNU/
MLD DYC DYS DYP
*Behavioural and emotional
disorders:* CA CO/ADD ASP
BESD
*Physical and medical conditions:*
AT CA RA SM TW/HEA

## ST MARY'S SCHOOL, ASCOT
St Mary's Road, Ascot,
Berkshire SL5 9JF
*Website:*
www.st-marys-ascot.co.uk
*Type:* Girls Boarding and Day
11–18
*Learning difficulties:* WI/DYS
DYP
*Physical and medical conditions:*
RA SM WA2/EPI HEA HI W

## THORNGROVE SCHOOL
The Mount, Highclere, Newbury,
Berkshire RG20 9PS
*Website:*
www.thorngroveschool.co.uk
*Type:* Co-educational Day Only
2–13
*Learning difficulties:* CA WI/DYS
DYP
*Behavioural and emotional
disorders:* RA
*Physical and medical conditions:*
RA/CP HEA

# BRISTOL

## BRISTOL CATHEDRAL SCHOOL
College Square, Bristol BS1 5TS
*Website:* www.bristolcathedral.
bristol.sch.uk
*Type:* Co-educational Day Only
10–18 (Co-ed Sixth Form)
*Learning difficulties:* CA WI/DYS
DYP
*Behavioural and emotional
disorders:* RA/ADD ADHD ASP
TOU
*Physical and medical conditions:*
RA/HEA VI

## CLIFTON COLLEGE
32 College Road, Clifton, Bristol
BS8 3JH
*Website:*
www.cliftoncollegeuk.com
*Type:* Co-educational Boarding
and Day 13–18
*Learning difficulties:* CA
SNU/DYC DYS DYP SP&LD
*Behavioural and emotional
disorders:* CO RA/ADD ASP
*Physical and medical conditions:*
RA WA3/HEA

## CLIFTON COLLEGE PREPARATORY SCHOOL+
The Avenue, Clifton, Bristol
BS8 3HE
*Website:*
www.cliftoncollegeuk.com
*Type:* Co-educational Boarding
and Day 8–13
*Learning difficulties:* SNU/MLD
DYC DYS DYP
*Behavioural and emotional
disorders:* ST/ADD ASP BESD
*Physical and medical conditions:*
CA WA3/HEA HI VI

## CLIFTON HIGH SCHOOL
College Road, Clifton, Bristol
BS8 3JD
*Website:*
www.cliftonhigh.bristol.sch.uk
*Type:* Co-educational Day and
Boarding 3–18
*Learning difficulties:* CA RA
WI/MLD DYC DYS DYP
*Behavioural and emotional
disorders:* CO
*Physical and medical conditions:*
AT BL HL IT RA SM WA3/HEA
HI VI

## GRACEFIELD PREPARATORY SCHOOL
266 Overndale Road,
Fishponds, Bristol BS16 2RG
*Website:*
www.gracefieldschool.co.uk
*Type:* Co-educational Day Only
4–11
*Learning difficulties:* WI/MLD
*Behavioural and emotional
disorders:* TS
*Physical and medical conditions:*
WA3

## OVERNDALE SCHOOL
Chapel Lane, Old Sodbury,
Bristol BS37 6NQ
*Website:*
www.overndaleschool.co.uk
*Type:* Co-educational Day Only
1–11
*Learning difficulties:* CA
*Behavioural and emotional
disorders:* TS ST

## QUEEN ELIZABETH'S HOSPITAL
Berkeley Place, Clifton, Bristol
BS8 1JX
*Website:* www.qehbristol.co.uk
*Type:* Boys Day Only 7–18
(Sixth Form International
students are welcome on a
Guardianship basis)
*Learning difficulties:* SNU/DYS
DYP
*Behavioural and emotional
disorders:* CO/ADD ADHD
*Physical and medical conditions:*
RA SM W/CP EPI HEA HI

### THE RED MAIDS' SCHOOL
Westbury-on-Trym, Bristol
BS9 3AW
*Website:* www.redmaids.co.uk
*Type:* Girls Day Only 11–18
*Learning difficulties:* CA SNU/DYS
*Physical and medical conditions:*
CA SM TW/HEA VI

### ST URSULA'S HIGH SCHOOL
Brecon Road, Westbury-on-
Trym, Bristol BS9 4DT
*Website:*
www.st-ursulas.bristol.sch.uk
*Type:* Co-educational Day Only
3–16
*Learning difficulties:* CA WI/MLD
DYS DYP
*Behavioural and emotional
disorders:* RA/ADD ADHD ASP
*Physical and medical conditions:*
CP HEA

### TOCKINGTON MANOR SCHOOL
Tockington, Bristol BS32 4NY
*Website:* www.
tockingtonmanorschool.com
*Type:* Co-educational Day and
Boarding 2–14
*Learning difficulties:* CA SC
SNU/DYC DYS DYP

# BUCKINGHAMSHIRE

### AKELEY WOOD SCHOOL
Akeley Wood, Buckingham,
Buckinghamshire MK18 5AE
*Website:* www.
akeleywoodschool.co.uk
*Type:* Co-educational Day Only
3–18
*Learning difficulties:* SNU/MLD
DYS DYP
*Behavioural and emotional
disorders:* ADD ASP
*Physical and medical conditions:*
RA/HEA HI

### DAIR HOUSE SCHOOL TRUST LTD
Bishops Blake, Beaconsfield
Road, Farnham Royal,
Buckinghamshire SL2 3BY
*Website:* www.dairhouse.co.uk
*Type:* Co-educational Day Only
3–11
*Learning difficulties:* CA WI/DYS

### GODSTOWE PREPARATORY SCHOOL
Shrubbery Road, High
Wycombe, Buckinghamshire
HP13 6PR
*Website:* www.godstowe.org
*Type:* Girls Day and Boarding
3–13 (Boys 3–8)
*Learning difficulties:* CA SC
SNU/MLD DOW DYC DYS DYP
*Behavioural and emotional
disorders:* CA CO/ADD ADHD
ASP ASD
*Physical and medical conditions:*
CA RA SM/CP EPI HEA HI

### HIGH MARCH SCHOOL
23 Ledborough Lane,
Beaconsfield, Buckinghamshire
HP9 2PZ
*Website:* www.highmarch.co.uk
*Type:* Girls Day Only 3–11
(Boys are only admitted into our
Upper Nursery class)
*Learning difficulties:* CA WI/DYC
DYS DYP
*Behavioural and emotional
disorders:* RA
*Physical and medical conditions:*
AT CA RA TW WA2/EPI HEA

### MALTMAN'S GREEN SCHOOL
Maltmans Lane, Gerrards Cross,
Buckinghamshire SL9 8RR
*Website:*
www.maltmansgreen.com
*Type:* Girls Day Only 3–11
*Learning difficulties:* CA WI/MLD
DYS DYP
*Behavioural and emotional
disorders:* CO
*Physical and medical conditions:*
CA SM/HEA VI

### ST TERESA'S CATHOLIC INDEPENDENT & NURSERY SCHOOL
Aylesbury Road, Princes
Risborough, Buckinghamshire
HP27 0JW
*Website:*
www.st-teresas.bucks.sch.uk
*Type:* Co-educational Day Only
3–11
*Learning difficulties:* CA WI/DYS
DYP
*Behavioural and emotional
disorders:* ADD ADHD ASP ASD
*Physical and medical conditions:*
CA TW WA2/HI

### WYCOMBE ABBEY SCHOOL
High Wycombe,
Buckinghamshire HP11 1PE
*Website:*
www.wycombeabbey.com
*Type:* Girls Boarding and Day
11–18
*Learning difficulties:* SNU
WI/DYC DYS DYP
*Behavioural and emotional
disorders:* CO/ADHD
*Physical and medical conditions:*
RA SM TW WA3/EPI HEA

# CAMBRIDGESHIRE

**CAMBRIDGE CENTRE FOR SIXTH-FORM STUDIES**
1 Salisbury Villas, Station Road, Cambridge, Cambridgeshire CB1 2JF
*Website:* www.ccss.co.uk
*Type:* Co-educational Day and Boarding 15–21
*Learning difficulties:* CA RA/DYS DYP
*Behavioural and emotional disorders:* CA CO RA
*Physical and medical conditions:* RA SM/HEA

**THE PERSE SCHOOL**
Hills Road, Cambridge, Cambridgeshire CB2 8QF
*Website:* www.perse.co.uk
*Type:* Co-educational Day Only 11–18
*Learning difficulties:* CA SNU/MLD DYC DYS DYP
*Behavioural and emotional disorders:* CO RA ST/ADD ADHD ASP
*Physical and medical conditions:* AT CA HL RA SM TW WA2 WA3/EPI HEA VI

**ST MARY'S JUNIOR SCHOOL**
2 Brookside, Cambridge, Cambridgeshire CB2 1JE
*Website:* www. stmaryscambridge.co.uk
*Type:* Girls Day Only 4–11
*Learning difficulties:* CA/DYC DYS
*Behavioural and emotional disorders:* CA RA
*Physical and medical conditions:* HEA HI

**SANCTON WOOD SCHOOL**
2 St Paul's Road, Cambridge, Cambridgeshire CB1 2EZ
*Website:* www.sanctonwood.co.uk
*Type:* Co-educational Day Only 1–16
*Learning difficulties:* CA WI/DYC DYS DYP
*Behavioural and emotional disorders:* ASP TOU
*Physical and medical conditions:* AT HL RA/CP HEA HI VI

# CHANNEL ISLANDS

**ORMER HOUSE PREPARATORY SCHOOL**
La Vallee, Alderney, Channel Islands GY9 3XA
*Website:* www.ormerhouse.com
*Type:* Co-educational Day Only 2–13
*Physical and medical conditions:* W/W

# CHESHIRE

### ABBEY GATE SCHOOL
Clare Avenue, Hoole, Chester, Cheshire CH2 3HR
*Website:* www.abbeygateschool.org.uk
*Type:* Co-educational Day Only 3–11
*Learning difficulties:* CA WI/MLD DYS DYP
*Behavioural and emotional disorders:* CA TS ST/ADD ASD
*Physical and medical conditions:* CA SM TW WA1 WA2/HEA HI VI

### BRABYNS SCHOOL
34–36 Arkwright Road, Marple, Stockport, Cheshire SK6 7DB
*Website:* www. brabynsprepschool.co.uk
*Type:* Co-educational Day Only 2–11
*Learning difficulties:* RA WI/DYS DYP
*Behavioural and emotional disorders:* ASP
*Physical and medical conditions:* EPI

### GREENBANK PREPARATORY SCHOOL
Heathbank Road, Cheadle Hulme, Cheadle, Cheshire SK8 6HU
*Website:* www.greenbankschool.co.uk
*Type:* Co-educational Day Only 3–11
*Learning difficulties:* CA SC SNU/MLD DYC DYS DYP
*Behavioural and emotional disorders:* RA TS
*Physical and medical conditions:* AT RA SM TW WA1 WA2/HEA

### LORETO PREPARATORY SCHOOL
Dunham Road, Altrincham, Cheshire WA14 4GZ
*Website:* www.loretoprep.co.uk
*Type:* Co-educational Day Only 3–11 (Boys 4–7)
*Learning difficulties:* CA WI/MLD DYS
*Behavioural and emotional disorders:* CA ST
*Physical and medical conditions:* CA TW WA2/CP EPI HEA HI IM W

### NORTH CESTRIAN GRAMMAR SCHOOL
Dunham Road, Altrincham, Cheshire WA14 4AJ
*Website:* www.ncgs.co.uk
*Type:* Co-educational Day Only 11–18
*Learning difficulties:* CA WI/MLD DYC DYS DYP
*Behavioural and emotional disorders:* CA ST/ADD ADHD ASP ASD BESD CB TOU
*Physical and medical conditions:* CA SL SM TW W WA2/EPI HI W

### RAMILLIES HALL SCHOOL+
Ramillies Avenue, Cheadle Hulme, Cheadle, Cheshire SK8 7AJ
*Website:* www.ramillieshall.co.uk
*Type:* Co-educational Day Only
*Learning difficulties:* CA SNU/DYC DYS DYP
*Physical and medical conditions:* CA RA/HI VI

### TERRA NOVA SCHOOL
Jodrell Bank, Holmes Chapel, Cheshire CW4 8BT
*Website:* www.terranovaschool.co.uk
*Type:* Co-educational Day and Boarding 3–13
*Learning difficulties:* CA SNU WI/DYC DYS DYP
*Behavioural and emotional disorders:* RA/ADHD ASP
*Physical and medical conditions:* RA SM W/HEA

# CORNWALL

### GEMS BOLITHO SCHOOL
Polwithen Road, Penzance,
Cornwall TR18 4JR
*Website:*
www.bolithoschool.co.uk
*Type:* Co-educational Day and
Boarding 4–18
*Learning difficulties:* CA SNU/
MLD DYC DYS DYP
*Behavioural and emotional
disorders:* CA/ADD ADHD ASP
*Physical and medical conditions:*
IT SM TW/HI

### ROSELYON
St Blazey Road, Par, Cornwall
PL24 2HZ
*Website:* www.roselyon.
cornwall.sch.uk
*Type:* Co-educational Day Only
2–11
*Learning difficulties:* CA WI/MLD
DYS DYP
*Behavioural and emotional
disorders:* RA/ADD ADHD
*Physical and medical conditions:*
RA/HEA HI

### ST IA SCHOOL
St Ives Road, Carbis Bay,
St Ives, Cornwall TR26 2SF
*Website:*
www.st-ia.cornwall.sch.uk
*Type:* Co-educational Day Only
4–11
*Learning difficulties:* RA WI
*Behavioural and emotional
disorders:* RA
*Physical and medical conditions:*
RA/HEA

### ST JOSEPH'S SCHOOL
St Stephen's Hill, Launceston,
Cornwall PL15 8HN
*Website:* www.st-josephs.
cornwall.sch.uk
*Type:* Co-educational Day Only
3–16 (Boys 3–11)
*Learning difficulties:* SNU/MLD
DYS DYP
*Behavioural and emotional
disorders:* RA
*Physical and medical conditions:*
RA/HEA

### ST PIRAN'S SCHOOL
14 Trelissick Road, Hayle,
Cornwall TR27 4HY
*Website:* www.stpirans.net
*Type:* Co-educational Day Only
3–16
*Learning difficulties:* CA WI/MLD
DYS
*Behavioural and emotional
disorders:* ST
*Physical and medical conditions:*
RA SM WA3/CP

# CUMBRIA

### LIME HOUSE SCHOOL+
Holm Hill, Dalston, Carlisle,
Cumbria CA5 7BX
*Website:* www.limehouseschool.
co.uk
*Type:* Co-educational Boarding
and Day 4–18
*Learning difficulties:* CA SC
SNU WI/MLD DYS DYP
*Behavioural and emotional
disorders:* ADD ADHD ASP
*Physical and medical conditions:*
AT/HEA

### ST BEES SCHOOL+
St Bees, Cumbria CA27 0DS
*Website:* www.st-bees-school.org
*Type:* Co-educational Boarding
and Day 4–18
*Learning difficulties:* SNU
WI/DYC DYS DYP
*Behavioural and emotional
disorders:* RA/ADD ADHD BESD
*Physical and medical conditions:*
RA SM/EPI HEA VI

### ST URSULA'S CONVENT
### SCHOOL
Burnfoot, Wigton, Cumbria
CA7 9HL
*Website:* www.stursulas.co.uk
*Type:* Co-educational Day Only
2–11
*Learning difficulties:* SNU/DYS DYP
*Behavioural and emotional
disorders:* ASP ASD
*Physical and medical conditions:*
HEA

### SEDBERGH JUNIOR SCHOOL
Danson House, Loftus Hill,
Sedbergh, Cumbria LA10 5HG
*Website:*
www.sedberghjuniorschool.org
*Type:* Co-educational Boarding
and Day 4–13
*Learning difficulties:* CA SC
SNU WI/MLD DYS DYP
*Behavioural and emotional
disorders:* TS/ASP ASD
*Physical and medical conditions:*
CA TW/HEA IM

### SEDBERGH SCHOOL
Sedbergh, Cumbria LA10 5HG
*Website:*
www.sedberghschool.org
*Type:* Co-educational Boarding
and Day 13–18
*Learning difficulties:* SNU
WI/DYC DYS DYP
*Behavioural and emotional
disorders:* TS/ADD
*Physical and medical conditions:*
RA SM/HEA HI VI

### WINDERMERE SCHOOL
Patterdale Road, Windermere,
Cumbria LA23 1NW
*Website:* www.
windermereschool.co.uk
*Type:* Co-educational Boarding
and Day 2–18
*Learning difficulties:* WI

# DERBYSHIRE

### DERBY HIGH SCHOOL
Hillsway, Littleover, Derby,
Derbyshire DE23 3DT
*Website:*
www.derbyhigh.derby.sch.uk
*Type:* Co-educational Day Only
3–18
*Learning difficulties:* CA RA
WI/DYC DYS DYP
*Behavioural and emotional
disorders:* RA/ASD
*Physical and medical conditions:*
RA/HEA

### EMMANUEL SCHOOL
Juniper Lodge, 43 Kedleston
Road, Derby, Derbyshire
DE22 1FP
*Type:* Co-educational Day Only
3–14
*Learning difficulties:* CA WI
*Behavioural and emotional
disorders:* RA/ASP
*Physical and medical conditions:*
RA WA3/HEA VI

### GATEWAY CHRISTIAN SCHOOL
Moor Lane, Dale Abbey,
Ilkeston, Derbyshire DE7 4PP
*Website:*
www.gatewayschool.org.uk
*Type:* Co-educational Day Only
3–11
*Learning difficulties:* RA WI
*Behavioural and emotional
disorders:* RA
*Physical and medical conditions:*
RA/HEA

# DEVON

### KELLY COLLEGE PREPARATORY SCHOOL
Hazeldon House, Parkwood
Road, Tavistock, Devon PL19 0JS
*Website:*
www.kellycollegeprep.com
*Type:* Co-educational Day and
Boarding 2–11
*Learning difficulties:* CA WI/DYS
DYP
*Behavioural and emotional
disorders:* ASD

### KINGSLEY SCHOOL+
Kingsley School, Northdown
Road, Bideford, Devon EX39 3LY
*Website:* www.
kingsleyschoolbideford.co.uk
*Type:* Co-educational Boarding
and Day 11–18
*Learning difficulties:* SC
SNU/DYS DYP

### THE MAYNARD SCHOOL
Denmark Road, Exeter, Devon
EX1 1SJ
*Website:* www.maynard.co.uk
*Type:* Girls Day Only 7–18
(A selective independent day
school for girls aged 7–17)
*Learning difficulties:* WI/DYS
DYP
*Behavioural and emotional
disorders:* CO
*Physical and medical conditions:*
AT SM TW WA2/EPI HEA HI

### ST CHRISTOPHER'S SCHOOL
Mount Barton, Staverton,
Totnes, Devon TQ9 6PF
*Website:* www.st-christophers.
devon.sch.uk
*Type:* Co-educational Day Only
3–11
*Learning difficulties:* CA/MLD
DYS DYP
*Behavioural and emotional
disorders:* RA/ADHD ASD BESD
*Physical and medical conditions:*
CA IT TW W WA1/HEA HI

### ST MICHAEL'S
Tawstock Court, Tawstock,
Barnstaple, Devon EX31 3HY
*Type:* Co-educational Day Only
*Learning difficulties:* CA SNU/
MLD DOW DYS
*Physical and medical conditions:*
TW/HI VI

### TRINITY SCHOOL
Buckeridge Road, Teignmouth,
Devon TQ14 8LY
*Website:* www.trinityschool.co.uk
*Type:* Co-educational Day and
Boarding 4–20
*Learning difficulties:* CA
SNU/MLD DYC DYS DYP
*Behavioural and emotional
disorders:* CA CO TS ST/ADD
ADHD ASP
*Physical and medical conditions:*
CA IT SM TW WA2/HEA

### WEST BUCKLAND PREPARATORY SCHOOL
West Buckland, Barnstaple,
Devon EX32 0SX
*Website:* www.westbuckland.
devon.sch.uk
*Type:* Co-educational Day and
Boarding 3–11
*Learning difficulties:* CA RA/
MLD DYC DYS DYP
*Behavioural and emotional
disorders:* RA/ADD ADHD
*Physical and medical conditions:*
CA SM TW W WA2/HEA VI

### WEST BUCKLAND SCHOOL
Barnstaple, Devon EX32 0SX
*Website:* www.westbuckland.
devon.sch.uk
*Type:* Co-educational Boarding
and Day 3–18
*Learning difficulties:* CA SNU
WI/DOW DYC DYS DYP
*Behavioural and emotional
disorders:* CA CO RA TS
ST/ADD ADHD ASP BESD
*Physical and medical
conditions:* CA/EPI HEA HI VI

# DORSET

## BOURNEMOUTH COLLEGIATE PREP SCHOOL
40 St Osmund's Road, Parkstone, Poole, Dorset BH14 9JY
*Website:* www.bournemouthcollegiateschool.co.uk
*Type:* Co-educational Day Only 3–11
*Physical and medical conditions:* W

## BOURNEMOUTH COLLEGIATE SCHOOL
College Road, Bournemouth, Dorset BH5 2DY
*Website:* www.bournemouthcollegiateschool.co.uk
*Type:* Co-educational Boarding and Day 11–18
*Learning difficulties:* SNU WI/DYC DYS
*Physical and medical conditions:* AT RA WA3/HEA

## DORCHESTER PREPARATORY AND INDEPENDENT SCHOOLS
25/26 Icen Way, Dorchester, Dorset DT1 1EP
*Website:* www.dorchesterprepschool.co.uk
*Type:* Co-educational Day Only 3–18
*Learning difficulties:* CA WI/DYC DYS DYP
*Behavioural and emotional disorders:* RA/ADD ADHD ASP ASD
*Physical and medical conditions:* RA/HEA

## MILTON ABBEY SCHOOL+
Blandford Forum, Dorset DT11 0BZ
*Website:* www.miltonabbey.co.uk
*Type:* Co-educational Boarding and Day 13–18
*Learning difficulties:* SNU/DYC DYS DYP SP&LD
*Behavioural and emotional disorders:* CO TS ST/ADD ADHD
*Physical and medical conditions:* RA/HEA HI

## PORT REGIS PREPARATORY SCHOOL
Motcombe Park, Shaftesbury, Dorset SP7 9QA
*Website:* www.portregis.com
*Type:* Co-educational Boarding and Day 3–13
*Learning difficulties:* SNU WI/DYC DYS DYP
*Behavioural and emotional disorders:* CO/ADD ASP
*Physical and medical conditions:* DS HL RA SM TW/HEA HI

## SHERBORNE SCHOOL
Abbey Road, Sherborne, Dorset DT9 3AP
*Website:* www.sherborne.org
*Type:* Boys Boarding and Day 13–18
*Learning difficulties:* SNU WI/MLD DYC DYS DYP
*Physical and medical conditions:* IT/EPI HEA HI VI

# COUNTY DURHAM

## POLAM HALL
Grange Road, Darlington, County Durham DL1 5PA
*Website:* www.polamhall.com
*Type:* Co-educational Boarding and Day 2–18 (Co-educational Junior School from age 2 to Year 4. Separate teaching Year 5 to Year 11. Co-educational Sixth Form)
*Learning difficulties:* CA SC SNU/MLD DYS DYP
*Behavioural and emotional disorders:* RA/ASP ASD
*Physical and medical conditions:* AT CA RA SM WA3/HEA HI

# ESSEX

### DAME BRADBURY'S SCHOOL
Ashdon Road, Saffron Walden,
Essex CB10 2AL
*Website:*
www.damebradburys.com
*Type:* Co-educational Day Only
3–11
*Learning difficulties:* CA RA/DYS
DYP
*Behavioural and emotional
disorders:* RA/ASD
*Physical and medical conditions:*
RA/W

### FELSTED SCHOOL
Felsted, Essex CM6 3LL
*Website:* www.felsted.org
*Type:* Co-educational Boarding
and Day 13–18 (Felsted Prep
School accepts day and
boarding boys and girls from
ages 4–12. Pupils are able to
board from age 8)
*Learning difficulties:* CA WI/DYS
*Behavioural and emotional
disorders:* RA
*Physical and medical conditions:*
AT CA IT RA SM TW WA2 WA3/EPI

### ILFORD URSULINE
### PREPARATORY SCHOOL
2–4 Coventry Road, Ilford,
Essex IG1 4QR
*Website:*
www.ilfordursuline-prep.org.uk
*Type:* Girls Day Only 3–11
*Learning difficulties:* SNU/MLD
DYS DYP
*Behavioural and emotional
disorders:* TS/ADHD
*Physical and medical conditions:*
TW WA2

### LITTLEGARTH SCHOOL
Horkesley Park, Nayland,
Colchester, Essex CO6 4JR
*Website:*
www.littlegarth.essex.sch.uk
*Type:* Co-educational Day Only
2–11
*Learning difficulties:* CA SNU
WI/MLD DYC DYS DYP
*Behavioural and emotional
disorders:* CA ST/ADD ADHD
*Physical and medical conditions:*
CA IT RA SM TW WA3/HEA HI VI

### RAPHAEL INDEPENDENT
### SCHOOL
Park Lane, Hornchurch, Essex
RM11 1XY
*Website:* www.raphaelschool.com
*Type:* Co-educational Day Only
4–16
*Learning difficulties:* WI/DYS
*Physical and medical conditions:*
RA

### THORPE HALL SCHOOL
Wakering Road, Southend-on-
Sea, Essex SS1 3RD
*Website:* www.thorpehall.
southend.sch.uk
*Type:* Co-educational Day Only
2–16
*Learning difficulties:* CA SC
WI/MLD DYC DYS DYP
*Behavioural and emotional
disorders:* CA TS ST/ADD
ADHD ASP ASD
*Physical and medical conditions:*
CA HL SL SM TW WA2/EPI HEA

# GLOUCESTERSHIRE

### AIRTHRIE SCHOOL
27–29 Christchurch Road,
Cheltenham, Gloucestershire
GL50 2NY
*Website:*
www.airthrie-school.co.uk
*Type:* Co-educational Day Only
3–11
*Learning difficulties:* CA
SNU/DYS DYP
*Physical and medical conditions:*
HEA HI

### BREDON SCHOOL+
Pull Court, Bushley, Tewkesbury,
Gloucestershire GL20 6AH
*Website:* www.bredonschool.org
*Type:* Co-educational Boarding
and Day 5–18
*Learning difficulties:* CA
SNU/MLD DYC DYS DYP SP&LD
*Behavioural and emotional
disorders:* CO TS/ADD
*Physical and medical conditions:*
IT SL SM TW W WA2/HEA

### CHELTENHAM COLLEGE
Bath Road, Cheltenham,
Gloucestershire GL53 7LD
*Website:*
www.cheltenhamcollege.org
*Type:* Co-educational Boarding
and Day 13–18
*Learning difficulties:* WI

### CHELTENHAM COLLEGE
### JUNIOR SCHOOL
Thirlestaine Road, Cheltenham,
Gloucestershire GL53 7AB
*Website:*
www.cheltcoll.gloucs.sch.uk
*Type:* Co-educational Boarding
and Day 3–13
*Learning difficulties:* CA
SNU/DYS DYP SP&LD
*Behavioural and emotional
disorders:* CA CO/ADD ADHD
ASP
*Physical and medical conditions:*
RA SM WA2

### CHELTENHAM LADIES'
### COLLEGE
Bayshill Road, Cheltenham,
Gloucestershire GL50 3EP
*Website:*
www.cheltladiescollege.org
*Type:* Girls Boarding and
Day 11–18
*Learning difficulties:* SNU
WI/DYS DYP
*Behavioural and emotional
disorders:* CO RA ST/ADD
ADHD
*Physical and medical conditions:*
AT IT RA SM TW W WA2 WA3/
CP EPI HEA HI IM VI W

**HATHEROP CASTLE SCHOOL**
Hatherop, Cirencester,
Gloucestershire GL7 3NB
*Website:* www.hatheropcastle.
co.uk
*Type:* Co-educational Boarding
and Day 2–13
*Learning difficulties:* SNU WI/MLD
*Behavioural and emotional
disorders:* ST

**THE RICHARD PATE SCHOOL**
Southern Road, Leckhampton,
Cheltenham, Gloucestershire
GL53 9RP
*Website:* www.richardpate.co.uk
*Type:* Co-educational Day Only
3–11
*Learning difficulties:* CA SNU
WI/MLD DYS
*Physical and medical conditions:*
CA TW WA2/CP EPI HEA VI

**WESTONBIRT SCHOOL**
Tetbury, Gloucestershire
GL8 8QG
*Website:* www.westonbirt.
gloucs.sch.uk
*Type:* Girls Boarding and Day
11–18
*Learning difficulties:* SNU/DYC
DYS DYP
*Physical and medical conditions:*
EPI HEA HI

**WYCLIFFE COLLEGE+**
Bath Road, Stonehouse,
Gloucestershire GL10 2JQ
*Website:* www.wycliffe.co.uk
*Type:* Co-educational Boarding
and Day 2–18
*Learning difficulties:* SNU
WI/DYC DYS DYP
*Physical and medical conditions:*
RA

**WYCLIFFE PREPARATORY
SCHOOL+**
Ryeford Hall, Stonehouse,
Gloucestershire GL10 2LD
*Website:* www.wycliffe.co.uk
*Type:* Co-educational Boarding
and Day 2–13
*Learning difficulties:* CA SNU
WI/DYC DYS DYP
*Behavioural and emotional
disorders:* RA/ADD
*Physical and medical conditions:*
CA RA SM/EPI HEA

# HAMPSHIRE

**DURLSTON COURT**
Becton Lane, Barton-on-Sea, New
Milton, Hampshire BH25 7AQ
*Website:*
www.durlstoncourt.co.uk
*Type:* Co-educational Day Only
2–13
*Learning difficulties:*
CA SNU/MLD DYC DYS DYP
*Behavioural and emotional
disorders:* ADHD
*Physical and medical conditions:*
HEA

**LORD WANDSWORTH
COLLEGE**
Long Sutton, Hook, Hampshire
RG29 1TB
*Website:*
www.lordwandsworth.org
*Type:* Co-educational Boarding
and Day 11–18
*Learning difficulties:* RA WI/DYS
*Behavioural and emotional
disorders:* RA/ADD ASP
*Physical and medical
conditions:* RA SM/EPI HEA

**MAYVILLE HIGH SCHOOL+**
35 St Simon's Road, Southsea,
Hampshire PO5 2PE
*Website:*
www.mayvilleschool.com
*Type:* Co-educational Day Only
*Learning difficulties:* SNU/DYS
DYP
*Behavioural and emotional
disorders:* ST/ADD ADHD ASP
ASD
*Physical and medical
conditions:* RA SM/HEA HI

**THE PORTSMOUTH
GRAMMAR SCHOOL**
High Street, Portsmouth,
Hampshire PO1 2LN
*Website:* www.pgs.org.uk
*Type:* Co-educational Day Only
2–18
*Learning difficulties:* WI

**PORTSMOUTH HIGH SCHOOL
GDST**
Kent Road, Southsea,
Hampshire PO5 3EQ
*Website:*
www.portsmouthhigh.co.uk
*Type:* Girls Day Only 3–18
*Learning difficulties:* WI/DYS DYP
*Physical and medical conditions:*
RA/HEA

**ST NICHOLAS' SCHOOL**
Redfields House, Redfields
Lane, Church Crookham, Fleet,
Hampshire GU52 0RF
*Website:*
www.st-nicholas.hants.sch.uk
*Type:* Girls Day Only 3–16
(Boys 3–7)
*Learning difficulties:* WI/DYS
*Physical and medical conditions:*
RA/HEA

### SHERBORNE HOUSE SCHOOL
Lakewood Road, Chandler's Ford, Eastleigh, Hampshire SO53 1EU
*Website:* www.sherbornehouse.co.uk
*Type:* Co-educational Day Only 3–11
*Learning difficulties:* SNU/DYS

### THE STROUD SCHOOL
Highwood House, Highwood Lane, Romsey, Hampshire SO51 9ZH
*Website:*
www.stroud-romsey.com
*Type:* Co-educational Day Only 3–13
*Learning difficulties:*
CA SNU/MLD DYS
*Physical and medical conditions:* RA

### TWYFORD SCHOOL
Twyford, Winchester, Hampshire SO21 1NW
*Website:* www.twyfordschool.com
*Type:* Co-educational Day and Boarding 3–13
*Learning difficulties:* SNU/DYS
*Physical and medical conditions:* RA SM/HEA

### WALHAMPTON SCHOOL+
Lymington, Hampshire SO41 5ZG
*Website:*
www.walhampton.com
*Type:* Co-educational Boarding and Day 2–13
*Learning difficulties:* CA SNU/MLD DYS DYP
*Behavioural and emotional disorders:* ST/ASP
*Physical and medical conditions:* CA RA SM TW WA3/HEA HI

### WINCHESTER COLLEGE
College Street, Winchester, Hampshire SO23 9NA
*Website:*
www.winchestercollege.org
*Type:* Boys Boarding and Day 13–18
*Learning difficulties:* SNU/DYC DYS DYP
*Behavioural and emotional disorders:* RA/ADD ADHD ASP
*Physical and medical conditions:* VI

# HEREFORDSHIRE

### ROWDEN HOUSE SCHOOL
Rowden, Bromyard, Herefordshire HR7 4LS
*Website:*
www.rowdenhouse.com
*Type:* Co-educational Boarding Only 11–19 (Individualized care and education programmes for children and young adults)
*Learning difficulties:* MLD SLD PMLD DOW DYC DYP SP&LD
*Behavioural and emotional disorders:* ADD ADHD ASP ASD BESD CB TOU
*Physical and medical conditions:* W/CP EPI HEA HI IM VI

# HERTFORDSHIRE

## ABBOT'S HILL SCHOOL
Bunkers Lane, Hemel
Hempstead, Hertfordshire
HP3 8RP
*Website:*
www.abbotshill.herts.sch.uk
*Type:* Girls Day Only 3–16
(Boys 3–5)
*Learning difficulties:* CA SNU
WI/DYC DYS DYP
*Behavioural and emotional
disorders:* CO/ASP BESD
*Physical and medical conditions:*
IT SM/EPI HEA HI VI

## EGERTON ROTHESAY
## SCHOOL*
Durrants Lane, Berkhamsted,
Hertfordshire HP4 3UJ
*Website:* www.eger-roth.co.uk
*Type:* Co-educational Day Only
5–16
*Learning difficulties:* CA SC
SNU/MLD DYC DYS DYP SP&LD
*Behavioural and emotional
disorders:* ST/ADD ASP ASD
*Physical and medical conditions:*
AT CA DS RA SM TW W WA2/
CP EPI HEA HI IM VI

## HABERDASHERS' ASKE'S
## BOYS' SCHOOL
Butterfly Lane, Elstree,
Hertfordshire WD6 3AF
*Website:* www.habsboys.org.uk
*Type:* Boys Day Only 5–18
*Learning difficulties:* RA/DYS DYP
*Behavioural and emotional
disorders:* ADHD

## HARESFOOT PREPARATORY
## SCHOOL
Chesham Road, Berkhamsted,
Hertfordshire HP4 2SZ
*Website:*
www.haresfoot.herts.sch.uk
*Type:* Co-educational Day Only
(Children may join from
5 months of age into our Day
Nursery)
*Learning difficulties:* CA WI/DYS
*Physical and medical conditions:*
CA RA/HEA HI IM

## HIGH ELMS MANOR SCHOOL
High Elms Lane, Watford,
Hertfordshire WD25 0JX
*Website:*
www.highelmsmanorschool.com
*Type:* Co-educational Day Only
*Learning difficulties:* CA WI/MLD
DYC DYS DYP
*Behavioural and emotional
disorders:* RA/ADD ASP ASD
*Physical and medical conditions:*
AT CA TW WA1 WA2/HEA HI W

## KINGSHOTT SCHOOL
St Ippolyts, Hitchin,
Hertfordshire SG4 7JX
*Website:*
www.kingshottschool.co.uk
*Type:* Co-educational Day Only
4–13
*Learning difficulties:* DYS DYP
*Physical and medical conditions:*
RA SM/HEA

## NORFOLK LODGE
## MONTESSORI NURSERY
Dancers Hill Road, Barnet,
Hertfordshire EN5 4RP
*Website:*
www.norfolklodgeschool.co.uk
*Type:* Co-educational Day Only
1–4
*Learning difficulties:* RA
*Behavioural and emotional
disorders:* RA
*Physical and medical conditions:*
RA

## THE PURCELL SCHOOL
Aldenham Road, Bushey,
Hertfordshire WD23 2TS
*Website:* www.purcell-school.org
*Type:* Co-educational Day and
Boarding 8–18
*Behavioural and emotional
disorders:* CO RA/ASP
*Physical and medical conditions:*
RA/VI

## RICKMANSWORTH PNEU
## SCHOOL
88 The Drive, Rickmansworth,
Hertfordshire WD3 4DU
*Website:*
www.rickmansworthpneu.co.uk
*Type:* Girls Day Only 3–11
*Learning difficulties:*
CA SNU/DYS DYP
*Behavioural and emotional
disorders:* RA
*Physical and medical conditions:*
HEA

## ST CHRISTOPHER SCHOOL
Barrington Road, Letchworth
Garden City, Hertfordshire
SG6 3JZ
*Website:* www.stchris.co.uk
*Type:* Co-educational Boarding
and Day 2–18
*Learning difficulties:* SNU/DYS
DYP
*Behavioural and emotional
disorders:* ASP
*Physical and medical conditions:*
RA/EPI

## ST HILDA'S SCHOOL
28 Douglas Road, Harpenden,
Hertfordshire AL5 2ES
*Website:*
www.sthildasharpenden.co.uk
*Type:* Girls Day Only 2–11
*Learning difficulties:* SC WI/DYC
DYS DYP
*Physical and medical conditions:*
W/HI

## ST JOSEPH'S IN THE PARK
St Mary's Lane, Hertingfordbury,
Hertford, Hertfordshire SG14 2LX
*Website:*
www.stjosephsinthepark.co.uk
*Type:* Co-educational Day Only
3–11
*Learning difficulties:* CA SC
SNU/DYC DYS DYP
*Behavioural and emotional
disorders:* ADD ADHD
*Physical and medical conditions:*
CA/HEA HI

# ISLE OF WIGHT

**PRIORY SCHOOL**
Alverstone Manor, Luccombe
Road, Shanklin, Isle of Wight
PO37 7JB
*Website:*
www.prioryschool.org.uk
*Type:* Co-educational Day Only
2–18
*Physical and medical conditions:*
W/W

**RYDE SCHOOL**
Queen's Road, Ryde, Isle of
Wight PO33 3BE
*Website:* www.rydeschool.org.uk
*Type:* Co-educational Day and
Boarding 3–18
*Learning difficulties:* SNU/DYC
DYS DYP

# KENT

**ASHFORD SCHOOL**
East Hill, Ashford, Kent
TN24 8PB
*Website:*
www.ashfordschool.co.uk
*Type:* Co-educational Day and
Boarding 3–18 (Co-ed 3–11)
*Learning difficulties:*
CA SNU/MLD DYS DYP
*Behavioural and emotional
disorders:* CO RA/ADHD ASP
ASD
*Physical and medical conditions:*
RA SM W WA3/HEA

**ASHGROVE SCHOOL**
116 Widmore Road, Bromley,
Kent BR1 3BE
*Website:* www.ashgrove.org.uk
*Type:* Co-educational Day Only
3–11
*Learning difficulties:* WI/DYS
DYP

**BABINGTON HOUSE SCHOOL**
Grange Drive, Chislehurst, Kent
BR7 5ES
*Website:*
www.babingtonhouse.com
*Type:* Girls Day Only 3–16
(Boys 3–7)
*Learning difficulties:* CA WI/DYS
DYP
*Physical and medical
conditions:* RA/HI

**BENENDEN SCHOOL**
Cranbrook, Kent TN17 4AA
*Website:*
www.benenden.kent.sch.uk
*Type:* Girls Boarding Only
11–18
*Learning difficulties:* SNU/DYS
DYP
*Behavioural and emotional
disorders:* RA
*Physical and medical conditions:*
RA SM WA2/HEA HI VI

**BRONTE SCHOOL**
7 Pelham Road, Gravesend,
Kent DA11 0HN
*Website:*
www.bronteschool.co.uk
*Type:* Co-educational Day Only
4–11
*Learning difficulties:*
CA SC/MLD DYC DYS DYP
*Behavioural and emotional
disorders:* CA/ADD ADHD ASP
*Physical and medical conditions:*
CA RA SM WA3/HEA

**DOVER COLLEGE**
Effingham Crescent, Dover,
Kent CT17 9RH
*Website:*
www.dovercollege.org.uk
*Type:* Co-educational Boarding
and Day 3–18
*Learning difficulties:* WI/DYS
DYP
*Physical and medical conditions:*
RA SM/HEA HI VI

**DULWICH PREPARATORY
SCHOOL, CRANBROOK**
Coursehorn, Cranbrook, Kent
TN17 3NP
*Website:* www.dcpskent.org
*Type:* Co-educational Day and
Boarding 3–13
*Learning difficulties:* CA SNU
WI/DYS DYP
*Behavioural and emotional
disorders:* ADHD ASP
*Physical and medical conditions:*
IT RA W/EPI HEA IM

**FARRINGTONS SCHOOL**
Perry Street, Chislehurst, Kent
BR7 6LR
*Website:* www.farringtons.org.uk
*Type:* Co-educational Day and
Boarding 3–19
*Learning difficulties:* WI/MLD
DYS DYP
*Behavioural and emotional
disorders:* RA
*Physical and medical conditions:*
RA SM WA3/EPI HEA HI VI

**HILDEN OAKS SCHOOL**
38 Dry Hill Park Road,
Tonbridge, Kent TN10 3BU
*Website:* www.hildenoaks.co.uk
*Type:* Co-educational Day Only
*Learning difficulties:* WI

## KENT COLLEGE INFANT & JUNIOR SCHOOL
Vernon Holme, Harbledown, Canterbury, Kent CT2 9AQ
*Website:*
www.kentcollege.com/junior
*Type:* Co-educational Day and Boarding 3–11
*Learning difficulties:*
SC SNU/MLD DYC DYS DYP
*Behavioural and emotional disorders:* CA CO
*Physical and medical conditions:* TW WA3/HEA

## KENT COLLEGE PEMBURY
Old Church Road, Tunbridge Wells, Kent TN2 4AX
*Website:*
www.kent-college.co.uk
*Type:* Girls Boarding and Day 3–18
*Learning difficulties:* WI/DYC DYS DYP
*Behavioural and emotional disorders:* CO/ADD BESD
*Physical and medical conditions:* SM WA3/HEA

## KING'S PREPARATORY SCHOOL
King Edward Road, Rochester, Kent ME1 1UB
*Website:* www.kings-school-rochester.co.uk
*Type:* Co-educational Day and Boarding 8–13
*Learning difficulties:* WI/DYS DYP

## NORTHBOURNE PARK SCHOOL
Betteshanger, Deal, Kent CT14 0NW
*Website:*
www.northbournepark.com
*Type:* Co-educational Day and Boarding 3–13
*Learning difficulties:*
CA SNU/DYC DYS DYP
*Behavioural and emotional disorders:* CO/ADD ADHD ASP ASD
*Physical and medical conditions:* CA RA/HEA HI VI

## RUSSELL HOUSE SCHOOL
Station Road, Otford, Sevenoaks, Kent TN14 5QU
*Website:*
www.russellhouseschool.co.uk
*Type:* Co-educational Day Only 2–11
*Learning difficulties:* WI/DYS DYP
*Physical and medical conditions:* WA1

## ST FAITH'S AT ASH SCHOOL
5 The Street, Ash, Canterbury, Kent CT3 2HH
*Type:* Co-educational Day Only 3–11
*Learning difficulties:* CA RA WI/DYS DYP
*Behavioural and emotional disorders:* CA RA ST/BESD
*Physical and medical conditions:* RA SM WA3/HEA HI

## ST LAWRENCE COLLEGE JUNIOR SCHOOL
College Road, Ramsgate, Kent CT11 7AF
*Website:* www.slcuk.com
*Type:* Co-educational Boarding and Day 3–11
*Learning difficulties:* CA WI/MLD DYS DYP
*Behavioural and emotional disorders:* CA RA TS ST/ASP ASD
*Physical and medical conditions:* RA SM WA3/HEA HI

## ST MICHAEL'S SCHOOL
Otford Court, Otford, Sevenoaks, Kent TN14 5SA
*Website:*
www.stmichaels-otford.co.uk
*Type:* Co-educational Day Only 2–13
*Learning difficulties:* WI

## STEEPHILL INDEPENDENT SCHOOL
Castle Hill, Fawkham, Longfield, Kent DA3 7BG
*Website:* www.steephill.co.uk
*Type:* Co-educational Day Only 3–11
*Learning difficulties:* CA WI/MLD DYS
*Behavioural and emotional disorders:* RA ST
*Physical and medical conditions:* RA TW WA2

## WALTHAMSTOW HALL
Hollybush Lane, Sevenoaks, Kent TN13 3UL
*Website:*
www.walthamstow-hall.co.uk
*Type:* Girls Day Only 2–18
*Learning difficulties:* WI/DYC DYS DYP
*Behavioural and emotional disorders:* CO ST/ASP
*Physical and medical conditions:* AT SL SM TW/HEA

# LANCASHIRE

### ARNOLD SCHOOL
Lytham Road, Blackpool,
Lancashire FY4 1JG
*Website:* www.arnoldschool.com
*Type:* Co-educational Day Only
2–18
*Learning difficulties:* SNU
WI/MLD DYC DYS DYP
*Behavioural and emotional
disorders:* CA CO ST/ADD
ADHD BESD
*Physical and medical conditions:*
SL SM WA2/HEA HI

### BURY GRAMMAR SCHOOL BOYS
Tenterden Street, Bury,
Lancashire BL9 0HN
*Website:* www.bgsboys.co.uk
*Type:* Boys Day Only 7–18
*Learning difficulties:* RA/DYS
*Behavioural and emotional
disorders:* RA
*Physical and medical conditions:*
RA/EPI HEA HI

### KING EDWARD VII AND QUEEN MARY SCHOOL
Clifton Drive South, Lytham St
Annes, Lancashire FY8 1DT
*Website:* www.keqms.co.uk
*Type:* Co-educational Day Only
2–18
*Learning difficulties:* CA WI/DYC
DYS DYP
*Behavioural and emotional
disorders:* RA/ADD ADHD
*Physical and medical conditions:*
SM WA2/HEA VI

### KIRKHAM GRAMMAR SCHOOL
Ribby Road, Kirkham, Preston,
Lancashire PR4 2BH
*Website:*
www.kirkhamgrammar.co.uk
*Type:* Co-educational Boarding
and Day 3–18
*Learning difficulties:* SNU/DYC
DYS
*Physical and medical conditions:*
HEA

### STONYHURST COLLEGE
Clitheroe, Lancashire BB7 9PZ
*Website:* www.stonyhurst.ac.uk
*Type:* Co-educational Boarding
and Day 13–18
*Learning difficulties:* SNU
WI/MLD DYC DYS DYP
*Behavioural and emotional
disorders:* CO ST/ADD ADHD
ASP
*Physical and medical conditions:*
SM WA3/EPI HEA HI

# LEICESTERSHIRE

### FAIRFIELD PREPARATORY SCHOOL
Leicester Road, Loughborough,
Leicestershire LE11 2AE
*Website:* www.lesfairfield.org
*Type:* Co-educational Day Only
4–11
*Learning difficulties:* WI/DYS DYP
*Behavioural and emotional
disorders:* ASP
*Physical and medical
conditions:* SM TW WA2

### LOUGHBOROUGH HIGH SCHOOL
Burton Walks, Loughborough,
Leicestershire LE11 2DU
*Website:* www.leshigh.org
*Type:* Girls Day Only 11–18
*Learning difficulties:* RA WI/DYC
DYS DYP
*Physical and medical conditions:*
RA/EPI HEA HI VI

### MANOR HOUSE SCHOOL
South Street, Ashby-de-la-
Zouch, Leicestershire LE65 1BR
*Website:*
www.manorhouseashby.co.uk
*Type:* Co-educational Day Only
4–16
*Learning difficulties:* CA SC
WI/DYC DYS DYP
*Behavioural and emotional
disorders:* RA/ADD ASP
*Physical and medical conditions:*
CA RA WA3/HEA HI VI

### ST CRISPIN'S SCHOOL+
6 St Mary's Road, Leicester,
Leicestershire LE2 1XA
*Website:* www.stcrispins.co.uk
*Type:* Co-educational Day Only
3–16
*Learning difficulties:* CA RA SC
SNU WI/MLD DYC DYS DYP
*Behavioural and emotional
disorders:* CA TS ST/ADD
ADHD ASP BESD
*Physical and medical conditions:*
AT CA IT RA SL SM TW
WA3/HEA HI VI

# LINCOLNSHIRE

### KIRKSTONE HOUSE SCHOOL
Main Street, Baston,
Peterborough, Bourne,
Lincolnshire PE6 9PA
*Website:*
www.kirkstonehouseschool.co.uk
*Type:* Co-educational Day Only
4–16
*Learning difficulties:* CA SNU
WI/MLD DYS DYP
*Behavioural and emotional
disorders:* ADHD ASP ASD

### ST HUGH'S SCHOOL
Cromwell Avenue, Woodhall
Spa, Lincolnshire LN10 6TQ
*Website:*
www.st-hughs.lincs.sch.uk
*Type:* Co-educational Boarding
and Day 2–13
*Learning difficulties:* CA SNU
WI/MLD DYC DYS
*Behavioural and emotional
disorders:* CA/ADD ADHD ASP
ASD CB
*Physical and medical conditions:*
CA IT SM TW WA2/HEA HI IM VI

### ST MARY'S PREPARATORY SCHOOL
5 Pottergate, Lincoln,
Lincolnshire LN2 1PH
*Website:*
www.stmarysprep.co.uk
*Type:* Co-educational Day Only
2–11
*Learning difficulties:*
CA SNU/MLD DYS DYP
*Behavioural and emotional
disorders:* RA/ASD
*Physical and medical conditions:*
AT IT RA SM TW/CP HEA HI IM VI

# LONDON

### ALLEYN'S SCHOOL
Townley Road, Dulwich, London
SE22 8SU
*Website:* www.alleyns.org.uk
*Type:* Co-educational Day Only
4–18
*Learning difficulties:* WI/DYC
DYS DYP
*Behavioural and emotional
disorders:* CO/ADD ASP TOU
*Physical and medical conditions:*
RA SM TW/EPI HEA HI VI

### ASTON HOUSE SCHOOL
1 Aston Road, Ealing, London
W5 2RL
*Website:* www.happychild.co.uk
*Type:* Co-educational Day Only
2–11
*Learning difficulties:* SNU/DYS
DYP
*Behavioural and emotional
disorders:* ST
*Physical and medical conditions:*
CA SM TW WA3/HEA VI

### AVENUE HOUSE SCHOOL
70 The Avenue, Ealing, London
W13 8LS
*Website:* www.avenuehouse.org
*Type:* Co-educational Day Only
3–11
*Learning difficulties:* RA WI/MLD
DYS
*Physical and medical conditions:*
RA SM WA3/HEA

### BROOMWOOD HALL SCHOOL
68–74 Nightingale Lane,
London SW12 8NR
*Website:* www.broomwood.co.uk
*Type:* Co-educational Day Only
4–13
*Learning difficulties:*
CA RA/MLD DYS
*Behavioural and emotional
disorders:* CA/ADD ASP
*Physical and medical conditions:*
IT RA SM TW/HEA HI VI

### CHANNING SCHOOL
Highgate, London N6 5HF
*Website:* www.channing.co.uk
*Type:* Girls Day Only 4–18
*Learning difficulties:* WI/MLD
DYS DYP
*Behavioural and emotional
disorders:* ADHD
*Physical and medical conditions:*
SM TW WA1 WA2/EPI HI IM

### CHARTERHOUSE SQUARE SCHOOL
40 Charterhouse Square,
London EC1M 6EA
*Website:*
www.charterhousesquareschool.
co.uk
*Type:* Co-educational Day Only
3–11
*Learning difficulties:* WI

### DALLINGTON SCHOOL
8 Dallington Street, London
EC1V 0BW
*Website:*
www.dallingtonschool.co.uk
*Type:* Co-educational Day Only
3–11
*Learning difficulties:* CA/DYS DYP
*Behavioural and emotional
disorders:* ST/ADD
*Physical and medical conditions:*
RA/HEA HI

### THE DOMINIE+
55 Warriner Gardens, Battersea,
London SW11 4DX
*Website:* www.thedominie.co.uk
*Type:* Co-educational Day Only
6–12
*Learning difficulties:* DYC DYS
DYP
*Behavioural and emotional
disorders:* ADHD
*Physical and medical conditions:*
RA/HI

### DUFF MILLER
59 Queen's Gate, London SW7 5JP
*Website:* www.duffmiller.com
*Type:* Co-educational Day Only
14–19
*Learning difficulties:* WI/MLD
DYS DYP
*Behavioural and emotional
disorders:* ADD ADHD
*Physical and medical conditions:*
RA/EPI HEA VI

### EATON HOUSE BELGRAVIA
3–5 Eaton Gate, London
SW1W 9BA
*Website:*
www.eatonhouseschools.com
*Type:* Boys Day Only 4–8
*Learning difficulties:* SNU
WI/MLD DYC DYS DYP
*Behavioural and emotional
disorders:* CA TS/BESD
*Physical and medical conditions:*
AT SM WA3/EPI

### EATON HOUSE THE MANOR
### PREPARATORY
58 Clapham Common
Northside, London SW4 9RU
*Website:*
www.eatonhouseschools.com
*Type:* Boys Day Only 3–13
*Learning difficulties:* SNU
WI/DYC DYS DYP
*Behavioural and emotional
disorders:* CA RA/ADD ASP
ASD
*Physical and medical conditions:*
CA

### EATON HOUSE THE VALE
2 Elvaston Place,
London SW7 5QH
*Website:*
www.eatonhouseschools.com
*Type:* Co-educational Day Only
4–11
*Learning difficulties:* CA WI/MLD
*Behavioural and emotional
disorders:* TS
*Physical and medical
conditions:* RA

### THE FALCONS SCHOOL
### FOR BOYS
2 Burnaby Gardens, Chiswick,
London W4 3DT
*Website:* www.falconschool.com
*Type:* Boys Day Only 3–8
*Learning difficulties:* CA WI
*Physical and medical
conditions:* RA/HEA

### FINTON HOUSE SCHOOL
171 Trinity Road, London
SW17 7HL
*Website:* www.fintonhouse.org.uk
*Type:* Co-educational Day Only
4–11
*Learning difficulties:* CA SC
SNU/DOW DYC DYS DYP
*Behavioural and emotional
disorders:* RA/ASP ASD BESD
*Physical and medical conditions:*
CA DS HL RA SM TW WA3/HEA
HI VI

### FRANCIS HOLLAND SCHOOL,
### SLOANE SQUARE SW1
39 Graham Terrace, London
SW1W 8JF
*Website:* www.fhs-sw1.org.uk
*Type:* Girls Day Only 4–18
*Learning difficulties:* RA WI/DYC
DYS DYP
*Behavioural and emotional
disorders:* RA/ADHD
*Physical and medical
conditions:* RA/CP EPI HEA

### GATEHOUSE SCHOOL
Sewardstone Road, Victoria
Park, London E2 9JG
*Website:*
www.gatehouseschool.co.uk
*Type:* Co-educational Day Only
3–11
*Learning difficulties:* CA/DOW
DYS
*Physical and medical conditions:*
TW

### THE HARRODIAN
Lonsdale Road, London
SW13 9QN
*Website:* www.harrodian.com
*Type:* Co-educational Day Only
5–18
*Learning difficulties:* SNU/DYC
DYS DYP

### HEATH HOUSE
### PREPARATORY SCHOOL
37 Wemyss Road, Blackheath,
London SE3 0TG
*Website:*
www.heathhouseprepschool.com
*Type:* Co-educational Day Only
4–11
*Physical and medical conditions:*
W/W

### LANSDOWNE COLLEGE
40–44 Bark Place,
London W2 4AT
*Website:*
www.lansdownecollege.com
*Type:* Co-educational Day Only
14–19 (Lansdowne is an
independent Sixth Form College
with a GCSE Department from
Year 10)
*Learning difficulties:* RA/MLD
DYC DYS DYP
*Behavioural and emotional
disorders:* RA/ADD ADHD ASD
*Physical and medical conditions:*
RA WA3/EPI HEA

### LION HOUSE SCHOOL
The Old Methodist Hall,
Gwendolen Avenue, London
SW15 6EH
*Website:*
www.lionhouseschool.co.uk
*Type:* Co-educational Day Only
3–8
*Learning difficulties:* CA WI/MLD
*Behavioural and emotional
disorders:* RA/ADD ASD
*Physical and medical conditions:*
AT CA IT TW WA2/HEA HI

### MADNI GIRLS SCHOOL
Myrdle Street, London E1 1HL
*Type:* Girls Day Only 12–18
*Learning difficulties:* WI/DYC
*Behavioural and emotional
disorders:* RA
*Physical and medical conditions:*
WA3/HEA VI

### MANDER PORTMAN
### WOODWARD
90–92 Queen's Gate, London
SW7 5AB
*Website:* www.mpw.co.uk
*Type:* Co-educational Day Only
14–19
*Physical and medical conditions:*
W/W

### THE MONTESSORI HOUSE
5 Princes Avenue, Muswell Hill,
London N10 3LS
*Website:*
www.montessori-house.co.uk
*Type:* Co-educational Day Only
1–5
*Learning difficulties:* CA/MLD
*Behavioural and emotional
disorders:* CA/ASD
*Physical and medical conditions:*
CA/HEA

## NORTHCOTE LODGE SCHOOL
26 Bolingbroke Grove, London SW11 6EL
*Website:* www.northcotelodge.co.uk
*Type:* Boys Day Only 8–13
*Learning difficulties:* WI/DYC DYS DYP
*Physical and medical conditions:* RA SM/HEA

## NOTTING HILL AND EALING HIGH SCHOOL GDST
2 Cleveland Road, Ealing, London W13 8AX
*Website:* www.gdst.net/nhehs
*Type:* Girls Day Only 4–18
*Learning difficulties:* WI/DYC DYS DYP
*Behavioural and emotional disorders:* RA/ADD ASP
*Physical and medical conditions:* RA/HEA VI

## PRIMROSE INDEPENDENT SCHOOL
Congregational Church, Highbury Quadrant, Highbury, London N5 2TE
*Type:* Co-educational Day Only 2–11
*Learning difficulties:* WI/MLD DOW DYS DYP
*Behavioural and emotional disorders:* RA/ASP ASD
*Physical and medical conditions:* AT CA/HEA

## QUEEN'S GATE SCHOOL
133 Queen's Gate, Kensington, London SW7 5LE
*Website:* www.queensgate.org.uk
*Type:* Girls Day Only 4–18
*Learning difficulties:* DYC DYS DYP
*Behavioural and emotional disorders:* RA
*Physical and medical conditions:* RA/HEA

## THE ROCHE SCHOOL
11 Frogmore, Wandsworth, London SW18 1HW
*Website:* www.therocheschool.co.uk
*Type:* Co-educational Day Only 2–11
*Learning difficulties:* CA SC WI/MLD DOW DYS DYP
*Behavioural and emotional disorders:* ADD ADHD ASP ASD
*Physical and medical conditions:* RA/IM

## THE ROWANS SCHOOL
19 Drax Avenue, Wimbledon, London SW20 0EG
*Website:* www.kcs.org.uk
*Type:* Co-educational Day Only 3–8
*Learning difficulties:* WI
*Physical and medical conditions:* RA/HEA

## ST DUNSTAN'S COLLEGE
Stanstead Road, London SE6 4TY
*Website:* www.stdunstans.org.uk
*Type:* Co-educational Day Only 3–18
*Learning difficulties:* CA WI/DYC DYS DYP
*Physical and medical conditions:* RA/HI

## ST JAMES JUNIOR SCHOOL
Earsby Street, near Kensington Olympia, London W14 8SH
*Website:* www.stjamesjuniors.co.uk
*Type:* Co-educational Day Only 4–11
*Learning difficulties:* WI/MLD

## ST JOSEPH'S CONVENT SCHOOL
59 Cambridge Park, London E11 2PR
*Type:* Girls Day Only 3–11
*Learning difficulties:* CA SNU/MLD
*Physical and medical conditions:* HEA

## ST MARGARET'S SCHOOL
18 Kidderpore Gardens, London NW3 7SR
*Website:* www.st-margarets.co.uk
*Type:* Girls Day Only 4–16
*Learning difficulties:* RA/MLD DYC DYS DYP
*Behavioural and emotional disorders:* CO
*Physical and medical conditions:* HL SM W WA3

## ST OLAVE'S PREPARATORY SCHOOL
106–110 Southwood Road, New Eltham, London SE9 3QS
*Website:* www.stolaves.org.uk
*Type:* Co-educational Day Only 3–11
*Learning difficulties:* SNU WI/SLD DYS DYP

## ST PAUL'S CATHEDRAL SCHOOL
2 New Change, London EC4M 9AD
*Website:* www.spcs.london.sch.uk
*Type:* Co-educational Boarding and Day 4–13
*Learning difficulties:* WI
*Physical and medical conditions:* RA SM

## STREATHAM & CLAPHAM HIGH SCHOOL
42 Abbotswood Road, London SW16 1AW
*Website:* www.gdst.net/streathamhigh
*Type:* Girls Day Only 3–18 (Boys 3–5)
*Learning difficulties:* CA SNU/DYC DYS DYP
*Behavioural and emotional disorders:* CA CO RA TS ST/ADD ASP ASD BESD CB
*Physical and medical conditions:* AT CA HL IT SM TW WA2/EPI HEA HI IM VI W

### THAMES CHRISTIAN COLLEGE+
Wye Street, Battersea, London SW11 2HB
*Website:* www. thameschristiancollege.org.uk
*Type:* Co-educational Day Only 11–16
*Learning difficulties:* CA WI/DYS DYP

### UNIVERSITY COLLEGE SCHOOL
Frognal, Hampstead, London NW3 6XH
*Website:* www.ucs.org.uk
*Type:* Co-educational Day Only 11–18 (Boys aged 11–18 Girls aged 16–18 (Co-educational Sixth Form only))
*Learning difficulties:* MLD DYS
*Behavioural and emotional disorders:* CO
*Physical and medical conditions:* CA/VI

### UNIVERSITY COLLEGE SCHOOL JUNIOR BRANCH
11 Holly Hill, Hampstead, London NW3 6QN
*Website:* www.ucs.org.uk
*Type:* Boys Day Only 7–11
*Learning difficulties:* DYS DYP
*Behavioural and emotional disorders:* CO/ADD ADHD ASP
*Physical and medical conditions:* RA/HI VI

### WESTMINSTER ABBEY CHOIR SCHOOL
Dean's Yard, London SW1P 3NY
*Website:* www. westminster-abbey.org
*Type:* Boys Boarding Only 8–13
*Learning difficulties:* WI/DYS

### WESTMINSTER CATHEDRAL CHOIR SCHOOL
Ambrosden Avenue, London SW1P 1QH
*Website:* www.choirschool.com
*Type:* Boys Boarding and Day 7–13
*Learning difficulties:* WI/DYS DYP
*Behavioural and emotional disorders:* RA/ADD
*Physical and medical conditions:* RA

### WESTMINSTER TUTORS
86 Old Brompton Road, London SW7 3LQ
*Website:* www.westminstertutors.co.uk
*Type:* Co-educational Day Only 11–25
*Learning difficulties:* SC WI/MLD DYS DYP
*Behavioural and emotional disorders:* RA/ASP
*Physical and medical conditions:* AT RA/HEA

### WETHERBY PREPARATORY SCHOOL
48 Bryanstan Square, London W1H 2EA
*Website:* www.wetherbyprep. co.uk
*Type:* Boys Day Only 8–13
*Learning difficulties:* DYS
*Physical and medical conditions:* RA

# GREATER MANCHESTER

### ABBEY COLLEGE
Cheapside, King Street, Manchester, Greater Manchester M2 4WG
*Website:* www.abbeymanchester.co.uk
*Type:* Co-educational Day Only 14–19
*Behavioural and emotional disorders:* ADHD
*Physical and medical conditions:* TW WA2

### THE MANCHESTER GRAMMAR SCHOOL
Old Hall Lane, Manchester, Greater Manchester M13 0XT
*Website:* www.mgs.org
*Type:* Boys Day Only 9–18
*Learning difficulties:* RA WI/DYC DYS DYP
*Behavioural and emotional disorders:* RA/ADD ADHD ASD
*Physical and medical conditions:* RA/EPI HI VI W

### WITHINGTON GIRLS' SCHOOL
100, Wellington Road, Fallowfield, Manchester, Greater Manchester M14 6BL
*Website:* www.withington. manchester.sch.uk
*Type:* Girls Day Only 7–18
*Learning difficulties:* CA RA WI/DYC DYS DYP
*Behavioural and emotional disorders:* ADD
*Physical and medical conditions:* SM TW W/HEA HI

# MERSEYSIDE

### MERCHANT TAYLORS' BOYS' SCHOOLS
Liverpool Road, Crosby,
Liverpool, Merseyside L23 0QP
*Website:*
www.merchanttaylors.com
*Type:* Boys Day Only 4–18
*Learning difficulties:*
CA SNU/MLD DYC DYS DYP
*Behavioural and emotional disorders:* TS ST/ADD ADHD ASP ASD BESD CB
*Physical and medical conditions:* IT SM/EPI HEA HI VI

### STREATHAM HOUSE SCHOOL
Victoria Road West,
Blundellsands, Liverpool,
Merseyside L23 8UQ
*Website:*
www.streathamhouse.co.uk
*Type:* Co-educational Day Only
2–16 (Boys 2–11)
*Learning difficulties:* CA SC WI/MLD DOW DYC DYS DYP
*Behavioural and emotional disorders:* ADD ADHD ASD
*Physical and medical conditions:* RA/HEA VI

# MIDDLESEX

### BUCKINGHAM COLLEGE SCHOOL
11–17 Hindes Road, Harrow,
Middlesex HA1 1SH
*Website:* www.buckcoll.org
*Type:* Boys Day Only 11–18
(Co-ed Sixth Form, but currently boys only)
*Learning difficulties:*
CA SNU/DYC DYS SP&LD
*Behavioural and emotional disorders:* ADD ADHD ASP BESD
*Physical and medical conditions:* AT RA/HEA

### HAMPTON SCHOOL
Hanworth Road, Hampton,
Middlesex TW12 3HD
*Website:*
www.hamptonschool.org.uk
*Type:* Boys Day Only 11–18
*Learning difficulties:* SNU/DYS DYP
*Behavioural and emotional disorders:* CO TS ST/ADD ADHD ASP ASD TOU
*Physical and medical conditions:* AT CA SM TW W WA2/EPI HEA HI VI

### THE JOHN LYON SCHOOL
Middle Road, Harrow,
Middlesex HA2 0HN
*Website:* www.johnlyon.org
*Type:* Boys Day Only 11–18
*Learning difficulties:* RA/DYC DYS DYP
*Behavioural and emotional disorders:* CO/ASD
*Physical and medical conditions:* SM/EPI VI

### THE LADY ELEANOR HOLLES SCHOOL
102 Hanworth Road, Hampton,
Middlesex TW12 3HF
*Website:* www.lehs.org.uk
*Type:* Girls Day Only 7–18
*Learning difficulties:* WI/DYC DYS DYP
*Behavioural and emotional disorders:* CO/TOU
*Physical and medical conditions:* RA SM TW WA1/EPI HEA VI

### THE MALL SCHOOL
185 Hampton Road, 185
Hampton Road, Twickenham,
Middlesex TW2 5NQ
*Website:*
www.mall.richmond.sch.uk
*Type:* Boys Day Only 4–13
*Learning difficulties:* CA RA WI/DYS DYP
*Behavioural and emotional disorders:* CA
*Physical and medical conditions:* RA SM TW WA2/HEA

### MERCHANT TAYLORS' SCHOOL
Sandy Lodge, Northwood,
Middlesex HA6 2HT
*Website:* www.mtsn.org.uk
*Type:* Boys Day Only 11–18
*Learning difficulties:* RA SNU/DYS DYP
*Behavioural and emotional disorders:* RA/ADD ADHD ASP
*Physical and medical conditions:* RA WA3/CP EPI HEA HI

### NORTHWOOD COLLEGE
Maxwell Road, Northwood,
Middlesex HA6 2YE
*Website:*
www.northwoodcollege.co.uk
*Type:* Girls Day Only 3–18
*Learning difficulties:* WI/DYS
DYP
*Physical and medical conditions:*
CA RA/HEA HI IM VI

### ST HELEN'S SCHOOL
Eastbury Road, Northwood,
Middlesex HA6 3AS
*Website:* www.sthn.co.uk
*Type:* Girls Day Only 3–18
*Learning difficulties:* WI/DYS
*Behavioural and emotional
disorders:* CO
*Physical and medical conditions:*
AT CA SM TW/EPI HEA HI

### ST MARTIN'S SCHOOL
40 Moor Park Road, Northwood,
Middlesex HA6 2DJ
*Website:* www.stmartins.org.uk
*Type:* Boys Day Only 3–13
*Learning difficulties:* SC/DYC
DYS DYP
*Behavioural and emotional
disorders:* ST/ADHD ASP
*Physical and medical conditions:*
RA TW WA3/HEA

# NORFOLK

### BEESTON HALL SCHOOL
West Runton, Cromer, Norfolk
NR27 9NQ
*Website:* www.beestonhall.co.uk
*Type:* Co-educational Boarding
and Day 7–13
*Learning difficulties:*
CA SNU/MLD DYC DYS DYP
*Behavioural and emotional
disorders:* CA TS/ADD ASP
*Physical and medical conditions:*
CA SM TW/CP HEA HI IM

### GLEBE HOUSE SCHOOL
2 Cromer Road, Hunstanton,
Norfolk PE36 6HW
*Website:*
www.glebehouseschool.co.uk
*Type:* Co-educational Boarding
and Day 4–13
*Learning difficulties:* CA WI/DYC
DYS DYP
*Behavioural and emotional
disorders:* RA
*Physical and medical conditions:*
RA

### HETHERSETT OLD HALL SCHOOL
Norwich Road, Hethersett,
Norwich, Norfolk NR9 3DW
*Website:* www.hohs.co.uk
*Type:* Co-educational Day and
Boarding 4–18 (Day boys
admitted aged 4–11.
Day girls admitted aged 4–18.
Boarding girls admitted aged
9–18.
No boys boarding)
*Learning difficulties:* SNU/MLD
DYS
*Behavioural and emotional
disorders:* RA/BESD
*Physical and medical
conditions:* CA SM TW
WA2/HEA IM

### LANGLEY SCHOOL
Langley Park, Loddon, Norwich,
Norfolk NR14 6BJ
*Website:*
www.langleyschool.co.uk
*Type:* Co-educational Boarding
and Day 10–18
*Learning difficulties:* SNU/DYC
DYS DYP
*Behavioural and emotional
disorders:* RA/ADD
*Physical and medical conditions:*
BL CA IT SM TW WA1/CP HEA
IM VI W

### THE NEW ECCLES HALL SCHOOL
Quidenham, Norwich, Norfolk
NR16 2NZ
*Website:*
www.neweccleshall.com
*Type:* Co-educational Day and
Boarding 4–16
*Learning difficulties:*
SC SNU/DYC DYS DYP
*Behavioural and emotional
disorders:* RA ST/ADD ADHD
ASP ASD TOU
*Physical and medical conditions:*
AT CA IT RA SM/HEA HI IM

### RIDDLESWORTH HALL+
Diss, Norfolk IP22 2TA
*Website:*
www.riddlesworthhall.com
*Type:* Co-educational Day and
Boarding 2–13 (Coeducational
boarding)
*Learning difficulties:* SNU/MLD
DYC DYS DYP
*Behavioural and emotional
disorders:* ST/ASD
*Physical and medical
conditions:* IT RA SM WA3/HEA

### ST ANDREWS SCHOOL
Lower Common, East Runton,
Norfolk NR27 9PG
*Type:* Co-educational Day Only
6–12
*Learning difficulties:* MLD DYS
DYP
*Behavioural and emotional
disorders:* ASP ASD
*Physical and medical conditions:*
WA3

**ST NICHOLAS HOUSE KINDERGARTEN & PREP SCHOOL**
Yarmouth Road, North Walsham, Norfolk NR28 9AT
*Website:*
www.stnicholashouse.com
*Type:* Co-educational Day Only 3–11
*Physical and medical conditions:* W/W

**SACRED HEART SCHOOL**
17 Mangate Street, Swaffham, Norfolk PE37 7QW
*Website:*
www.sacredheart.norfolk.sch.uk
*Type:* Co-educational Day and Boarding 3–16
*Learning difficulties:*
CA SC/MLD DYS DYP
*Behavioural and emotional disorders:* ASP
*Physical and medical conditions:* HI

**TAVERHAM HALL PREPARATORY SCHOOL**
Taverham Park, Taverham, Norwich, Norfolk NR8 6HU
*Website:* www.taverhamhall.co.uk
*Type:* Co-educational Boarding and Day 1–13
*Learning difficulties:* CA SNU WI/DYS DYP
*Behavioural and emotional disorders:* ST/ADD
*Physical and medical conditions:* RA SM/EPI HEA

# NORTHAMPTONSHIRE

**GREAT HOUGHTON PREPARATORY SCHOOL**
Great Houghton Hall, Northampton, Northamptonshire NN4 7AG
*Website:* www.ghps.co.uk
*Type:* Co-educational Day Only 1–13
*Learning difficulties:* CA SC SNU WI/DYC DYS DYP
*Behavioural and emotional disorders:* CA CO RA TS ST/ASP ASD
*Physical and medical conditions:* CA TW WA3/HEA VI

**WINCHESTER HOUSE SCHOOL**
High Street, Brackley, Northamptonshire NN13 7AZ
*Website:*
www.winchester-house.org
*Type:* Co-educational Boarding and Day 3–13
*Learning difficulties:* SNU WI

# NORTHUMBERLAND

**ROCK HALL SCHOOL**
Rock, Alnwick, Northumberland NE66 3SB
*Website:*
www.rockhallschool.com
*Type:* Co-educational Day Only 3–13
*Learning difficulties:* DYS
*Behavioural and emotional disorders:* RA ST
*Physical and medical conditions:* RA

# NOTTINGHAMSHIRE

### DAGFA HOUSE SCHOOL
57 Broadgate, Beeston,
Nottingham, Nottinghamshire
NG9 2FU
*Website:*
www.dagfahouse.notts.sch.uk
*Type:* Co-educational Day Only
2–16
*Learning difficulties:* CA WI/MLD
DYC DYS DYP
*Behavioural and emotional
disorders:* ASP ASD
*Physical and medical
conditions:* CA/HI VI

### GREENHOLME SCHOOL
392 Derby Road, Nottingham,
Nottinghamshire NG7 2DX
*Website:*
www.greenholmeschool.co.uk
*Type:* Co-educational Day Only
3–11
*Learning difficulties:* WI

### NOTTINGHAM HIGH SCHOOL
Waverley Mount, Nottingham,
Nottinghamshire NG7 4ED
*Website:*
www.nottinghamhigh.co.uk
*Type:* Boys Day Only 11–18
*Learning difficulties:* WI/DYC
DYS DYP
*Behavioural and emotional
disorders:* ST/ADD ADHD ASP
TOU
*Physical and medical
conditions:* RA/EPI HEA HI IM VI

### PLUMTREE SCHOOL
Church Hill, Plumtree,
Nottingham, Nottinghamshire
NG12 5ND
*Website:*
www.plumtreeschool.co.uk
*Type:* Co-educational Day Only
3–11
*Physical and medical
conditions:* W/W

### RANBY HOUSE SCHOOL
Retford, Nottinghamshire
DN22 8HX
*Website:*
www.ranbyhouseschool.co.uk
*Type:* Co-educational Day and
Boarding 3–13
*Learning difficulties:* CA SC
SNU/MLD DOW DYC DYS DYP
*Behavioural and emotional
disorders:* CA RA ST/ADD ASP
ASD BESD CB
*Physical and medical
conditions:* CA IT SM WA2/HEA

### SALTERFORD HOUSE
### SCHOOL
Salterford Lane, Calverton,
Nottingham, Nottinghamshire
NG14 6NZ
*Website:* www.
salterfordhouseschool.co.uk
*Type:* Co-educational Day Only
2–11
*Learning difficulties:* CA WI/MLD
DYS DYP
*Behavioural and emotional
disorders:* ST/ADHD ASP ASD
*Physical and medical
conditions:* RA WA2/HEA

### WELLOW HOUSE SCHOOL
Wellow, Newark,
Nottinghamshire NG22 0EA
*Website:*
www.wellowhouse.notts.sch.uk
*Type:* Co-educational Day and
Boarding 3–13
*Learning difficulties:* CA WI/DYS
*Physical and medical
conditions:* SM/EPI HEA

# OXFORDSHIRE

### THE CARRDUS SCHOOL
Overthorpe Hall, Banbury,
Oxfordshire OX17 2BS
*Website:*
www.carrdusschool.co.uk
*Type:* Girls Day Only 3–11
(Boys 3–8)
*Learning difficulties:* CA RA
SC WI
*Physical and medical conditions:*
WA3

### CHERWELL COLLEGE
Greyfriars, Paradise Street,
Oxford, Oxfordshire OX1 1LD
*Website:*
www.cherwell-college.co.uk
*Type:* Co-educational Boarding
and Day (Focus on A-levels with
the addition of A-level retake
and final year GCSE, 16–19)
*Learning difficulties:* SC WI/MLD
DYC DYS DYP
*Behavioural and emotional
disorders:* CO/ADD ADHD
*Physical and medical
conditions:* AT RA/HEA IM

### CRANFORD HOUSE SCHOOL
Moulsford, Wallingford,
Oxfordshire OX10 9HT
*Website:*
www.cranford-house.org
*Type:* Co-educational Day Only
3–16 (Boys 3–7)
*Learning difficulties:* WI

## DRAGON SCHOOL
Bardwell Road, Oxford,
Oxfordshire OX2 6SS
*Website:* www.dragonschool.org
*Type:* Co-educational Boarding
and Day 4–13
*Learning difficulties:* WI/DYC
DYS DYP SP&LD
*Behavioural and emotional
disorders:* CO RA/ADD ADHD
ASP
*Physical and medical conditions:*
RA SM TW WA2/HEA

## FERNDALE PREPARATORY
## SCHOOL
5–7 Bromsgrove, Faringdon,
Oxfordshire SN7 7JF
*Website:*
www.ferndaleschool.co.uk
*Type:* Co-educational Day Only
3–11
*Learning difficulties:* CA WI/MLD
DYS
*Behavioural and emotional
disorders:* ADHD
*Physical and medical conditions:*
RA WA3/EPI HEA HI VI

## GREENE'S TUTORIAL
## COLLEGE
45 Pembroke Street, Oxford,
Oxfordshire OX1 1BP
*Website:* www.greenes.org.uk
*Type:* Co-educational Day and
Boarding 6–75 (Boarding (host
families))
*Learning difficulties:* WI/MLD
DYC DYS DYP
*Behavioural and emotional
disorders:* RA/ADD ADHD ASP
BESD
*Physical and medical
conditions:* AT RA SM TW

## THE MANOR PREPARATORY
## SCHOOL
Faringdon Road, Abingdon,
Oxfordshire OX13 6LN
*Website:* www.manorprep.org
*Type:* Co-educational Day Only
2–11
*Learning difficulties:*
CA SNU/DYC DYS DYP
*Physical and medical
conditions:* AT CA HL SM TW W
WA2/HEA HI VI

## THE ORATORY
## PREPARATORY SCHOOL
Goring Heath, Reading,
Oxfordshire RG8 7SF
*Website:*
www.oratoryprep.org.uk
*Type:* Co-educational Day and
Boarding 3–13
*Learning difficulties:* CA WI/DYC
DYS DYP
*Behavioural and emotional
disorders:* RA/ADD
*Physical and medical
conditions:* CA TW WA1/HEA HI

## OXFORD TUTORIAL COLLEGE
12 King Edward Street, Oxford,
Oxfordshire OX1 4HT
*Website:* www.otc.ac.uk
*Type:* Co-educational Day and
Boarding (16+)
*Learning difficulties:* SC WI/MLD
DYS DYP
*Behavioural and emotional
disorders:* RA/ADD ADHD BESD
*Physical and medical
conditions:* AT RA WA3

## ST HELEN & ST KATHARINE
Faringdon Road, Abingdon,
Oxfordshire OX14 1BE
*Website:* www.shsk.org.uk
*Type:* Girls Day Only 9–18
*Learning difficulties:* WI/DYS
*Behavioural and emotional
disorders:* CO/ADD ADHD
*Physical and medical
conditions:* RA SM TW/EPI
HEA HI

## ST HUGH'S SCHOOL
Carswell Manor, Faringdon,
Oxfordshire SN7 8PT
*Website:* www.st-hughs.co.uk
*Type:* Co-educational Boarding
and Day 3–13
*Learning difficulties:* CA WI/MLD
DYS DYP
*Physical and medical
conditions:* HI

## SHIPLAKE COLLEGE
Henley-on-Thames, Oxfordshire
RG9 4BW
*Website:* www.shiplake.org.uk
*Type:* Co-educational Day and
Boarding 11–18 (Day girls
16–18)
*Learning difficulties:* SNU/DYC
DYS DYP
*Behavioural and emotional
disorders:* ST
*Physical and medical
conditions:* SM

## SIBFORD SCHOOL
Sibford Ferris, Banbury,
Oxfordshire OX15 5QL
*Website:*
www.sibford.oxon.sch.uk
*Type:* Co-educational Boarding
and Day 4–18
*Learning difficulties:* CA SNU
WI/DYC DYS DYP
*Behavioural and emotional
disorders:* CO RA/ADD ADHD
ASP ASD
*Physical and medical
conditions:* CA RA SM/CP
HEA IM

## SUMMER FIELDS
Mayfield Road, Oxford,
Oxfordshire OX2 7EN
*Website:*
www.summerfields.oxon.sch.uk
*Type:* Boys Boarding and Day
7–13
*Learning difficulties:* SNU/MLD
DYC DYS DYP
*Behavioural and emotional
disorders:* CO RA/ADD ADHD
ASP BESD
*Physical and medical
conditions:* HL IT RA SM
WA3/HEA HI

## TUDOR HALL SCHOOL
Wykham Park, Banbury,
Oxfordshire OX16 9UR
*Website:*
www.tudorhallschool.com
*Type:* Girls Boarding and Day
11–18
*Learning difficulties:* SNU/DYC
DYS DYP SP&LD
*Behavioural and emotional
disorders:* CO
*Physical and medical
conditions:* CP EPI HEA

# RUTLAND

**BROOKE PRIORY SCHOOL**
Station Approach, Oakham,
Rutland LE15 6QW
*Website:*
www.brooke.rutland.sch.uk
*Type:* Co-educational Day Only
2–11
*Learning difficulties:* CA WI/DYS
DYP
*Physical and medical
conditions:* CA SM TW W WA1
WA2/HEA

# SHROPSHIRE

**ADCOTE SCHOOL FOR GIRLS**
Little Ness, Shrewsbury,
Shropshire SY4 2JY
*Website:*
www.adcoteschool.co.uk
*Type:* Girls Boarding and
Day 4–18
*Learning difficulties:*
CA SNU/MLD DYS DYP
*Behavioural and emotional
disorders:* CA CO TS ST/ADHD
ASP ASD
*Physical and medical
conditions:* RA SM WA3

**CASTLE HOUSE SCHOOL**
Chetwynd End, Newport,
Shropshire TF10 7JE
*Website:*
www.castlehouseschool.co.uk
*Type:* Co-educational Day Only
2–11
*Learning difficulties:* CA SC
SNU WI/MLD DYC DYS DYP
SP&LD
*Behavioural and emotional
disorders:* ST/ADD ASP ASD
*Physical and medical
conditions:* CA RA SM
WA3/HEA HI

**DOWER HOUSE SCHOOL**
Quatt, Bridgnorth, Shropshire
WV15 6QW
*Website:*
www.dowerhouseschool.co.uk
*Type:* Co-educational Day Only
2–11
*Learning difficulties:* WI

**ELLESMERE COLLEGE+**
Ellesmere, Shropshire SY12 9AB
*Website:* www.ellesmere.com
*Type:* Co-educational Boarding
and Day 7–18
*Learning difficulties:* SNU/DYC
DYS DYP
*Behavioural and emotional
disorders:* RA
*Physical and medical
conditions:* RA/HEA

**MOOR PARK SCHOOL**
Moor Park, Ludlow, Shropshire
SY8 4DZ
*Website:* www.moorpark.org.uk
*Type:* Co-educational Boarding
and Day 3–13
*Learning difficulties:* SNU/DYC
DYS DYP
*Behavioural and emotional
disorders:* CO/ADD ADHD ASP
*Physical and medical
conditions:* RA WA3/EPI HEA IM

**MORETON HALL SCHOOL**
Weston Rhyn, Oswestry,
Shropshire SY11 3EW
*Website:* www.moretonhall.org
*Type:* Girls Boarding and Day
3–18 (Boys 3–11)
*Learning difficulties:* SNU
WI/MLD DYC DYS DYP
*Behavioural and emotional
disorders:* CO ST
*Physical and medical
conditions:* IT SM TW WA3/HEA

**THE OLD HALL SCHOOL**
Stanley Road, Wellington,
Telford, Shropshire TF1 3LB
*Website:* www.oldhall.co.uk
*Type:* Co-educational Day Only
4–11
*Learning difficulties:* SNU/DYC
DYS DYP
*Behavioural and emotional
disorders:* RA/ADD ADHD
*Physical and medical
conditions:* SM WA3

## OSWESTRY SCHOOL
## BELLAN HOUSE
Bellan House, Church Street, Oswestry, Shropshire SY11 2ST
*Website:* www.oswestryschool.org.uk
*Type:* Co-educational Day Only 2–9
*Learning difficulties:* SNU/DYS DYP
*Behavioural and emotional disorders:* RA/ADHD ASP
*Physical and medical conditions:* RA/EPI

## PRESTFELDE PREPARATORY
## SCHOOL
London Road, Shrewsbury, Shropshire SY2 6NZ
*Website:* www.prestfelde.co.uk
*Type:* Co-educational Day and Boarding 3–13
*Learning difficulties:* CA SNU/MLD DYS DYP
*Behavioural and emotional disorders:* ADD ASP
*Physical and medical conditions:* SM WA2/EPI HEA

## WREKIN COLLEGE
Wellington, Shropshire TF1 3BH
*Website:* www.wrekincollege.ac.uk
*Type:* Co-educational Boarding and Day 11–19
*Learning difficulties:* RA WI/DYS
*Behavioural and emotional disorders:* ADD ADHD ASP ASD

# SOMERSET

## FARLEIGH FURTHER
## EDUCATION COLLEGE
## (FROME)
North Parade, Frome, Somerset BA11 2AB
*Website:* www.priorygroup.com
*Type:* Co-educational Boarding and Day 16–22
*Behavioural and emotional disorders:* ASD
*Physical and medical conditions:* WA3

## HAZLEGROVE+
Hazlegrove, Sparkford, Yeovil, Somerset BA22 7JA
*Website:* www.hazlegrove.co.uk
*Type:* Co-educational Day and Boarding 2–13
*Learning difficulties:* SNU/DYC DYS DYP
*Physical and medical conditions:* SM TW/HEA HI

## KING'S BRUTON AND
## HAZLEGROVE+
Bruton, Somerset BA10 0ED
*Website:* www.kingsbruton.com and hazlegrove.co.uk
*Type:* Co-educational Boarding and Day 2–18
*Learning difficulties:* SNU WI/DYC DYS DYP
*Behavioural and emotional disorders:* ADD ADHD ASP
*Physical and medical conditions:* RA/CP HEA VI

## KING'S COLLEGE
South Road, Taunton, Somerset TA1 3LA
*Website:* www.kings-taunton.co.uk
*Type:* Co-educational Boarding and Day 13–18
*Learning difficulties:* WI
*Physical and medical conditions:* W

## THE PARK SCHOOL
The Park, Yeovil, Somerset BA20 1DH
*Website:* www.parkschool.com
*Type:* Co-educational Day and Boarding 3–19
*Learning difficulties:* WI/MLD DYS DYP
*Behavioural and emotional disorders:* RA/ASP
*Physical and medical conditions:* AT RA WA3/HEA

## TAUNTON PREPARATORY
## SCHOOL
Staplegrove Road, Taunton, Somerset TA2 6AE
*Website:* www.tauntonschool.co.uk
*Type:* Co-educational Day and Boarding 2–13
*Learning difficulties:* WI/DYC DYS DYP
*Behavioural and emotional disorders:* ST/ADD ADHD
*Physical and medical conditions:* SM WA2

# BATH & NORTH EAST SOMERSET

**KINGSWOOD SCHOOL**
Lansdown, Bath, Bath & North
East Somerset BA1 5RG
*Website:*
www.kingswood.bath.sch.uk
*Type:* Co-educational Boarding
and Day 3–18
*Learning difficulties:* RA WI/DYC
DYS DYP
*Physical and medical
conditions:* RA SM WA3/HEA

# STAFFORDSHIRE

**BROOKLANDS SCHOOL &
LITTLE BROOKLANDS
NURSERY**
167 Eccleshall Road, Stafford,
Staffordshire ST16 1PD
*Website:*
www.brooklandsschool.com
*Type:* Co-educational Day Only
(0–3 year old children in Day
Nursery total 63 in addition to
main School total of 110)
*Learning difficulties:* SNU/MLD
DYS
*Physical and medical
conditions:* VI

**NEWCASTLE-UNDER-LYME
SCHOOL**
Mount Pleasant,
Newcastle-under-Lyme,
Staffordshire ST5 1DB
*Website:* www.nuls.org.uk
*Type:* Co-educational Day Only
3–18
*Learning difficulties:* WI

**SMALLWOOD MANOR
PREPARATORY SCHOOL**
Uttoxeter,
Staffordshire ST14 8NS
*Website:*
www.smallwoodmanor.co.uk
*Type:* Co-educational Day Only
2–11
*Learning difficulties:* CA WI/DYC
DYS DYP
*Physical and medical
conditions:* AT WA3/EPI HEA

# STOCKTON-ON-TEES

**RED HOUSE SCHOOL**
36 The Green, Norton,
Stockton-on-Tees TS20 1DX
*Website:*
www.redhouseschool.co.uk
*Type:* Co-educational Day Only
3–16
*Learning difficulties:* RA WI/DYS
DYP
*Behavioural and emotional
disorders:* RA/ASP TOU
*Physical and medical
conditions:* RA/EPI

**TEESSIDE HIGH SCHOOL**
The Avenue, Eaglescliffe,
Stockton-on-Tees TS16 9AT
*Website:*
www.teessidehigh.co.uk
*Type:* Co-educational Day Only
3–18
*Learning difficulties:* RA WI/DYC
DYS DYP
*Behavioural and emotional
disorders:* RA ST/ADHD ASP
*Physical and medical
conditions:* RA/CP EPI HEA
HI VI

# SUFFOLK

### THE ABBEY
The Prep School for
Woodbridge School, Church
Street, Woodbridge, Suffolk
IP12 1DS
*Website:* www.woodbridge.
suffolk.sch.uk/the_abbey
*Type:* Co-educational Day Only
4–11
*Learning difficulties:* WI/MLD
DYS
*Physical and medical
conditions:* TW WA2

### MORETON HALL
### PREPARATORY SCHOOL
Mount Road, Bury St Edmunds,
Suffolk IP32 7BJ
*Website:* www.moretonhall.net
*Type:* Co-educational Boarding
and Day 2–13
*Learning difficulties:* SC/MLD
DYS
*Behavioural and emotional
disorders:* RA
*Physical and medical
conditions:* CA SM TW WA3

### ORWELL PARK
Nacton, Ipswich,
Suffolk IP10 0ER
*Website:* www.orwellpark.co.uk
*Type:* Co-educational Boarding
and Day 3–13
*Learning difficulties:* SNU/DYC
DYS DYP
*Behavioural and emotional
disorders:* RA/ADHD ASP
*Physical and medical
conditions:* RA WA3/EPI HEA

### THE ROYAL HOSPITAL
### SCHOOL
Holbrook, Ipswich,
Suffolk IP9 2RX
*Website:*
www.royalhospitalschool.org
*Type:* Co-educational Boarding
and Day 11–18
*Learning difficulties:*
SNU WI/MLD DYS DYP
*Behavioural and emotional
disorders:* CO RA
*Physical and medical
conditions:* RA SM WA2/EPI
HEA

### ST JOSEPH'S COLLEGE
Belstead Road, Birkfield,
Ipswich, Suffolk IP2 9DR
*Website:* www.stjos.co.uk
*Type:* Co-educational Day and
Boarding 2–18
*Learning difficulties:* CA WI/DYC
DYS DYP
*Behavioural and emotional
disorders:* RA ST/ADHD
*Physical and medical
conditions:* AT CA RA SL
WA2/CP EPI HEA

# SURREY

### ABERDOUR
Brighton Road, Burgh Heath,
Tadworth, Surrey KT20 6AJ
*Website:*
www.aberdourschool.co.uk
*Type:* Co-educational Day Only
2–13
*Learning difficulties:* CA/DYC
DYS DYP
*Behavioural and emotional
disorders:* RA/ADD ADHD ASP
*Physical and medical
conditions:* RA SM/HEA

### ALDRO SCHOOL
Lombard Street, Shackleford,
Godalming, Surrey GU8 6AS
*Website:* www.aldro.org
*Type:* Boys Boarding and Day
7–13
*Learning difficulties:* CA SNU
WI/MLD DYS DYP
*Behavioural and emotional
disorders:* RA/ADD ASP
*Physical and medical
conditions:* RA TW

### BARFIELD SCHOOL AND
### NURSERY
Guildford Road, Runfold,
Farnham, Surrey GU10 1PB
*Website:*
www.barfieldschool.com
*Type:* Co-educational Day Only
3–13
*Learning difficulties:* WI
*Physical and medical
conditions:* W

### BISHOPSGATE SCHOOL
Englefield Green, Egham,
Surrey TW20 0YJ
*Website:*
www.bishopsgate.surrey.sch.uk
*Type:* Co-educational Day and
Boarding 2–13
*Learning difficulties:* SNU/DYC
DYS DYP
*Behavioural and emotional
disorders:* RA/ADHD
*Physical and medical
conditions:* TW WA2/EPI VI

### BRAMLEY SCHOOL
Chequers Lane, Walton-on-the-
Hill, Tadworth, Surrey KT20 7ST
*Website:*
www.bramleyschool.co.uk
*Type:* Girls Day Only 3–11
*Learning difficulties:* CA WI/MLD
DYC DYS DYP
*Behavioural and emotional
disorders:* ST/ADD TOU
*Physical and medical
conditions:* IT SL SM TW W
WA2/HEA

### CAMBRIDGE TUTORS
### COLLEGE
Water Tower Hill, Croydon,
Surrey CR0 5SX
*Website:* www.ctc.ac.uk
*Type:* Co-educational Boarding
and Day 15–22
*Learning difficulties:* RA WI/MLD
DYS
*Physical and medical
conditions:* IT RA SM

### CROYDON HIGH SCHOOL
### GDST
Old Farleigh Road, Selsdon,
South Croydon, Surrey CR2 8YB
*Website:*
www.croydonhigh.gdst.net
*Type:* Girls Day Only 3–18
*Learning difficulties:* RA/DYS
*Behavioural and emotional
disorders:* RA/ADHD ASD
*Physical and medical
conditions:* RA/HI

### DOWNSEND SCHOOL
1 Leatherhead Road,
Leatherhead, Surrey KT22 8TJ
*Website:* www.downsend.co.uk
*Type:* Co-educational Day Only
2–13 (Children age 2–6 attend
one of our three Nursery & Pre-
Preparatory Departments or
Lodges, based in Ashtead,
Epsom & Leatherhead)
*Learning difficulties:* CA SNU
WI/DYC DYS DYP
*Behavioural and emotional
disorders:* RA/ADD ADHD ASP
*Physical and medical
conditions:* RA W/HEA HI

### DOWNSEND SCHOOL –
### ASHTEAD LODGE
22 Oakfield Road, Ashtead,
Surrey KT21 2RE
*Website:* www.downsend.co.uk
*Type:* Co-educational Day Only
2–6
*Learning difficulties:* RA WI
*Behavioural and emotional
disorders:* RA
*Physical and medical
conditions:* RA TW/HEA

### EWELL CASTLE SCHOOL
Church Street, Ewell, Epsom,
Surrey KT17 2AW
*Website:* www.ewellcastle.co.uk
*Type:* Co-educational Day Only
3–18 (Girls 3–11)
*Learning difficulties:* SC WI/DYC
DYS DYP
*Behavioural and emotional
disorders:* ADD ADHD ASP ASD
*Physical and medical
conditions:* AT RA/EPI HEA

### FELTONFLEET SCHOOL
Cobham, Surrey KT11 1DR
*Website:* www.feltonfleet.co.uk
*Type:* Co-educational Boarding
and Day 3–13
*Learning difficulties:* WI/DYS
DYP
*Behavioural and emotional
disorders:* ADHD
*Physical and medical
conditions:* HEA

### HOE BRIDGE SCHOOL
Hoe Place, Old Woking Road,
Woking, Surrey GU22 8JE
*Website:*
www.hoebridgeschool.co.uk
*Type:* Co-educational Day Only
2–13
*Learning difficulties:* CA WI/DYS
DYP
*Behavioural and emotional
disorders:* CA RA/ADD ADHD
*Physical and medical
conditions:* RA SM TW WA2
WA3/HEA

### KEW GREEN PREPARATORY
### SCHOOL
Layton House, Ferry Lane,
Richmond, Surrey TW9 3AF
*Website:* www.kgps.co.uk
*Type:* Co-educational Day Only
4–11
*Learning difficulties:* CA SNU
WI/MLD DYC DYS DYP
*Behavioural and emotional
disorders:* CA CO TS ST/ADD
CB
*Physical and medical
conditions:* CA IT TW

### THE LARKS
19 Bluehouse Lane, Oxted,
Surrey RH8 0AA
*Website:* www.the-larks.co.uk
*Type:* Co-educational Day Only
(Laverock site now used for The
Larks Day care only – Laverocks
now merked with Hazelwood)
*Learning difficulties:* WI/DYS
DYP
*Behavioural and emotional
disorders:* ADHD
*Physical and medical
conditions:* CA RA/HI

### NEW LIFE CHRISTIAN
### SCHOOL
Cairo New Road, Croydon,
Surrey CR0 1XP
*Website:*
www.newlifecroydon/nlcs.co.uk
*Type:* Co-educational Day Only
4–11
*Learning difficulties:* WI

## OAKFIELD SCHOOL
Coldharbour Road, Pyrford, Woking, Surrey GU22 8SJ
*Website:* www.oakfieldschool.co.uk
*Type:* Co-educational Day Only 3–16
*Learning difficulties:* WI/DYS DYP
*Behavioural and emotional disorders:* RA
*Physical and medical conditions:* RA

## OAKHYRST GRANGE SCHOOL
160 Stanstead Road, Caterham, Surrey CR3 6AF
*Website:* www.oakhyrstgrangeschool.co.uk
*Type:* Co-educational Day Only 4–11
*Learning difficulties:* CA WI/DYS DYP
*Behavioural and emotional disorders:* ST/ASP
*Physical and medical conditions:* RA/HI VI

## OLD VICARAGE SCHOOL
48 Richmond Hill, Richmond, Surrey TW10 6QX
*Type:* Girls Day Only 4–11
*Learning difficulties:* WI

## PRIORY PREPARATORY SCHOOL
Bolters Lane, Banstead, Surrey SM7 2AJ
*Website:* www.prioryprep.co.uk
*Type:* Boys Day Only 2–13
*Learning difficulties:* CA WI/MLD DYC DYS DYP
*Behavioural and emotional disorders:* RA
*Physical and medical conditions:* CA RA SM TW WA3/HEA

## REIGATE GRAMMAR SCHOOL
Reigate Road, Reigate, Surrey RH2 0QS
*Website:* www.reigategrammar.org
*Type:* Co-educational Day Only 11–18
*Learning difficulties:* CA/MLD DYS DYP
*Behavioural and emotional disorders:* ADHD ASP
*Physical and medical conditions:* CA SL SM WA2/EPI HEA HI

## RIPLEY COURT SCHOOL
Rose Lane, Ripley, Woking, Surrey GU23 6NE
*Website:* www.ripleycourt.co.uk
*Type:* Co-educational Day Only 3–13
*Learning difficulties:* WI/DYS DYP
*Behavioural and emotional disorders:* RA
*Physical and medical conditions:* RA SM/EPI HEA HI VI

## ST DAVID'S SCHOOL
23 Woodcote Valley Road, Purley, Surrey CR8 3AL
*Website:* www.st-davidsschool.co.uk
*Type:* Co-educational Day Only 3–11
*Learning difficulties:* CA WI/DYC DYS DYP
*Behavioural and emotional disorders:* RA/ASP
*Physical and medical conditions:* CA RA SM TW/HEA VI

## ST HILARY'S SCHOOL
Holloway Hill, Godalming, Surrey GU7 1RZ
*Website:* www.sthilarysschool.com
*Type:* Co-educational Day Only 1–11
*Learning difficulties:* CA SNU WI/DYS DYP
*Physical and medical conditions:* CA HL IT/HEA HI VI

## ST JOHN'S SCHOOL
Epsom Road, Leatherhead, Surrey KT22 8SP
*Website:* www.stjohnsleatherhead.co.uk
*Type:* Co-educational Boarding and Day 13–18 (Co-ed Sixth Form)
*Learning difficulties:* SNU WI/DYC DYS DYP
*Behavioural and emotional disorders:* CO/ADD ADHD ASP
*Physical and medical conditions:* SM TW WA2 WA3/EPI HEA HI

## SEATON HOUSE SCHOOL
67 Banstead Road South, Sutton, Surrey SM2 5LH
*Website:* www.seatonhouse.sutton.sch.uk
*Type:* Girls Day Only 3–11 (Boys 3–5 Girls 3–11)
*Learning difficulties:* CA RA SC WI/DYS DYP
*Behavioural and emotional disorders:* RA
*Physical and medical conditions:* RA/HEA

## SUTTON HIGH SCHOOL GDST
55 Cheam Road, Sutton, Surrey SM1 2AX
*Website:* www.gdst.net/suttonhigh
*Type:* Girls Day Only 3–18
*Learning difficulties:* SC/MLD DYS DYP
*Behavioural and emotional disorders:* CO ST/BESD
*Physical and medical conditions:* AT SM TW WA3/HEA HI

## TRINITY SCHOOL
Shirley Park, Croydon, Surrey CR9 7AT
*Website:* www.trinity-school.org
*Type:* Boys Day Only 10–18 (Boys 10–18. Girls 16–18)
*Learning difficulties:* WI/DYC DYS DYP
*Behavioural and emotional disorders:* CO/ADD ADHD ASP ASD
*Physical and medical conditions:* SL SM WA1/HEA VI

## WOODCOTE HOUSE SCHOOL
Snow's Ride, Windlesham, Surrey GU20 6PF
*Website:* www.woodcotehouseschool.co.uk
*Type:* Boys Boarding and Day 7–14
*Learning difficulties:* SC SNU/MLD DYC DYS DYP
*Behavioural and emotional disorders:* RA/ADD ASP
*Physical and medical conditions:* RA WA3

# EAST SUSSEX

### BRICKLEHURST MANOR PREPARATORY
Bardown Road, Stonegate,
Wadhurst, East Sussex TN5 7EL
*Website:* www.bricklehurst.co.uk
*Type:* Co-educational Day Only
3–11
*Learning difficulties:*
CA SNU/DYC DYS
*Physical and medical
conditions:* RA/HEA

### EASTBOURNE COLLEGE
Old Wish Road, Eastbourne,
East Sussex BN21 4JY
*Website:*
www.eastbourne-college.co.uk
*Type:* Co-educational Boarding
and Day 13–18 (50% boarding /
50% day
60% boys  / 40% girls)
*Learning difficulties:* MLD
*Physical and medical
conditions:* RA

### LANCING COLLEGE PREPARATORY SCHOOL AT MOWDEN
The Droveway, Hove,
East Sussex BN3 6LU
*Website:*
www.lancingprep.co.uk
*Type:* Co-educational Day Only
3–13
*Learning difficulties:* CA WI/DYS
*Behavioural and emotional
disorders:* RA/ADHD
*Physical and medical conditions:*
SM

### ST ANDREW'S SCHOOL
Meads, Eastbourne,
East Sussex BN20 7RP
*Website:* www.androvian.co.uk
*Type:* Co-educational Boarding
and Day 2–13
*Learning difficulties:* CA SNU
WI/DYC DYS DYP
*Behavioural and emotional
disorders:* RA/ASP
*Physical and medical conditions:*
RA SM/HEA HI IM

### ST CHRISTOPHER'S SCHOOL
33 New Church Road, Hove,
East Sussex BN3 4AD
*Website:*
www.stchristophershove.org.uk
*Type:* Co-educational Day Only
4–13
*Learning difficulties:* CA SNU
WI/MLD DYS
*Behavioural and emotional
disorders:* ST/ADHD ASP
*Physical and medical
conditions:* SM TW W WA2/HEA
VI

# WEST SUSSEX

### BROADWATER MANOR SCHOOL
Broadwater Road, Worthing,
West Sussex BN14 8HU
*Website:*
www.broadwatermanor.com
*Type:* Co-educational Day Only
2–13
*Learning difficulties:* CA WI
*Behavioural and emotional
disorders:* RA
*Physical and medical
conditions:* RA/HEA

### FONTHILL LODGE
Coombe Hill Road,
East Grinstead, West
Sussex RH19 4LY
*Website:*
www.fonthill-lodge.co.uk
*Type:* Co-educational Day Only
2–11 (Single-sex ed 8–11)
*Learning difficulties:* CA WI/DYS
DYP
*Physical and medical
conditions:* CA RA SM TW
W/HEA HI

### HANDCROSS PARK SCHOOL
Handcross, Haywards Heath,
West Sussex RH17 6HF
*Website:*
www.handcrossparkschool.co.uk
*Type:* Co-educational Day and
Boarding 2–13
*Learning difficulties:*
CA SNU/MLD DYC DYS DYP
*Behavioural and emotional
disorders:* CO TS/ADD ADHD
*Physical and medical
conditions:* IT RA SM TW
WA2/EPI HEA IM

# WARWICKSHIRE

### ARNOLD LODGE SCHOOL
Kenilworth Road, Leamington
Spa, Warwickshire CV32 5TW
*Type:* Co-educational Day Only
3–13
*Learning difficulties:* WI/MLD
DYC DYS DYP
*Behavioural and emotional
disorders:* CO ST/ADD ADHD
ASP
*Physical and medical
conditions:* RA/EPI HEA HI VI

### BILTON GRANGE
Rugby Road, Dunchurch,
Rugby, Warwickshire CV22 6QU
*Website:*
www.biltongrange.co.uk
*Type:* Co-educational Boarding
and Day 4–13
*Learning difficulties:*
CA SNU/MLD DYC DYS DYP
*Behavioural and emotional
disorders:* CA CO TS/ADHD
ASP ASD
*Physical and medical
conditions:* CA RA SM/HEA VI

# WEST MIDLANDS

### BABLAKE SCHOOL
Coundon Road, Coventry,
West Midlands CV1 4AU
*Website:* www.bablake.com
*Type:* Co-educational Day Only
11–19
*Learning difficulties:* SNU/DYS
DYP
*Physical and medical conditions:*
TW WA2

### BIRCHFIELD SCHOOL
Albrighton, Wolverhampton,
West Midlands WV7 3AF
*Website:*
www.birchfieldschool.co.uk
*Type:* Co-educational Day and
Boarding 4–13
*Learning difficulties:*
CA SNU/MLD DYC DYS DYP
*Behavioural and emotional
disorders:* RA TS ST/ADD ADHD
ASP
*Physical and medical conditions:*
AT RA SM TW WA3/HEA

### DAVENPORT LODGE SCHOOL
21 Davenport Road, Earlsdon,
Coventry, West Midlands
CV5 6QA
*Website:* www.davenportlodge.
coventry.sch.uk
*Type:* Co-educational Day Only
*Learning difficulties:* CA WI/MLD
DYS
*Behavioural and emotional
disorders:* CA
*Physical and medical conditions:*
TW W WA2

### EDGBASTON HIGH SCHOOL
### FOR GIRLS
Westbourne Road, Edgbaston,
Birmingham, West Midlands
B15 3TS
*Website:*
www.edgbastonhigh.co.uk
*Type:* Girls Day Only 3–18
*Learning difficulties:* RA WI/DYC
DYS DYP
*Behavioural and emotional
disorders:* RA ST
*Physical and medical conditions:*
AT HL IT SM TW WA2/CP EPI
HEA HI IM

### ELMHURST SCHOOL
### FOR DANCE
247–249 Bristol Road,
Edgbaston, Birmingham,
West Midlands B5 7UH
*Website:*
www.elmhurstdance.co.uk
*Type:* Co-educational Boarding
and Day 11–19
*Learning difficulties:* RA WI/DYS
DYP
*Behavioural and emotional
disorders:* RA
*Physical and medical conditions:*
SM TW W WA1 WA2/HI

### HIGHCLARE SCHOOL
10 Sutton Road, Erdington,
Birmingham, West Midlands
B23 6QL
*Website:*
www.highclareschool.co.uk
*Type:* Co-educational Day Only
1–18 (Boys 1–12 & 16–18
(Boys are being accepted into
Senior School from September
2011 from Year 7))
*Learning difficulties:* CA WI/DYS
*Behavioural and emotional
disorders:* RA/ADD ADHD BESD
*Physical and medical conditions:*
AT CA RA SM/HEA HI

## KINGSWOOD SCHOOL
St James Place, Shirley, Solihull,
West Midlands B90 2BA
*Website:*
www.kingswoodschool.co.uk
*Type:* Co-educational Day Only
2–11
*Learning difficulties:* CA SC
SNU/MLD DYC DYS DYP
*Behavioural and emotional
disorders:* ADD ADHD ASP ASD
*Physical and medical
conditions:* SM TW/VI

## NORFOLK HOUSE SCHOOL
4 Norfolk Road, Edgbaston,
Birmingham, West Midlands
B15 3PS
*Type:* Co-educational Day Only
3–11
*Learning difficulties:* RA WI
*Behavioural and emotional
disorders:* RA
*Physical and medical
conditions:* RA

## PRIORY SCHOOL
39 Sir Harry's Road, Edgbaston,
Birmingham, West Midlands
B15 2UR
*Website:* www.prioryschool.net
*Type:* Co-educational Day Only
(Co-ed 1–11)
*Learning difficulties:* SNU/DYC
DYS DYP

## THE ROYAL WOLVERHAMPTON JUNIOR SCHOOL
Penn Road, Wolverhampton,
West Midlands WV3 0EF
*Website:*
www.theroyalschool.co.uk
*Type:* Co-educational Day and
Boarding 2–11
*Learning difficulties:* CA RA
SNU/MLD DYC DYS DYP
*Behavioural and emotional
disorders:* CA CO RA ST/ADHD
CB
*Physical and medical
conditions:* RA SM TW/HEA

## RUCKLEIGH SCHOOL
17 Lode Lane, Solihull,
West Midlands B91 2AB
*Website:* www.ruckleigh.co.uk
*Type:* Co-educational Day Only
3–11
*Learning difficulties:* CA RA
WI/DYS
*Behavioural and emotional
disorders:* RA
*Physical and medical
conditions:* RA/HEA

## SAINT MARTIN'S SCHOOL
Malvern Hall, Brueton Avenue,
Solihull, West Midlands
B91 3EN
*Website:*
www.saintmartins-school.com
*Type:* Girls Day Only 3–18
(Girls may join the school
from 2 years 9 months)
*Learning difficulties:*
CA SNU/DYC DYS
*Physical and medical
conditions:* AT SL TW W WA2/W

## TETTENHALL COLLEGE+
Wood Road, Tettenhall,
Wolverhampton, West Midlands
WV6 8QX
*Website:*
www.tettenhallcollege.co.uk
*Type:* Co-educational Boarding
and Day 2–18
*Learning difficulties:* CA SNU
WI/DYC DYS DYP SP&LD
*Behavioural and emotional
disorders:* ADD ADHD ASD
*Physical and medical
conditions:* RA SM/EPI HEA

## WEST HOUSE SCHOOL
24 St James's Road, Edgbaston,
Birmingham, West Midlands
B15 2NX
*Website:*
www.westhouse.bham.sch.uk
*Type:* Boys Day Only 1–11
(Girls 1–4)
*Learning difficulties:* CA WI/MLD
DYS
*Behavioural and emotional
disorders:* CA ST/ADHD ASD
TOU
*Physical and medical
conditions:* RA TW/HEA

## WOLVERHAMPTON GRAMMAR SCHOOL
Compton Road,
Wolverhampton, West Midlands
WV3 9RB
*Website:* www.wgs.org.uk
*Type:* Co-educational Day Only
10–18
*Learning difficulties:* CA SNU
WI/DYS DYP
*Physical and medical
conditions:* TW WA2/IM

# WILTSHIRE

### FARLEIGH FURTHER EDUCATION COLLEGE SWINDON
Fairview House, 43 Bath Road, Old Town, Swindon, Wiltshire SN1 4AS
*Website:* www.priorygroup.com
*Type:* Co-educational Boarding and Day 16–19
*Behavioural and emotional disorders:* ASP ASD
*Physical and medical conditions:* W

### MEADOWPARK SCHOOL AND NURSERY
Calcutt Street, Cricklade, Wiltshire SN6 6BA
*Website:* www.meadowparkschool.co.uk
*Type:* Co-educational Day Only
*Learning difficulties:* WI
*Physical and medical conditions:* SM TW W

### THE MILL SCHOOL
Whistley Road, Potterne, Devizes, Wiltshire SN10 5TE
*Website:* www.mill.wilts.sch.uk
*Type:* Co-educational Day Only 3–11
*Learning difficulties:* CA WI/DYS
*Physical and medical conditions:* HEA

### PRIOR PARK PREPARATORY SCHOOL+
Calcutt Street, Cricklade, Wiltshire SN6 6BB
*Website:* www.priorparkschools.co.uk
*Type:* Co-educational Boarding and Day 4–13
*Learning difficulties:* CA SNU WI/DYC DYS DYP
*Physical and medical conditions:* RA

### SANDROYD SCHOOL
Rushmore, Tollard Royal, Salisbury, Wiltshire SP5 5QD
*Website:* www.sandroyd.org
*Type:* Co-educational Boarding and Day 7–13 (The Walled Garden pre prep ages 2 1/2–7 years
Sandroyd 7–13 years)
*Learning difficulties:* SNU/MLD DYS DYP
*Behavioural and emotional disorders:* ADD
*Physical and medical conditions:* IT RA SM TW/HEA VI

### STONAR SCHOOL
Cottles Park, Atworth, Wiltshire SN12 8NT
*Website:* www.stonarschool.com
*Type:* Girls Boarding and Day 2–18
*Learning difficulties:* CA SNU/MLD DYC DYS DYP
*Physical and medical conditions:* AT CA RA SM/EPI HEA VI

### SOUTH HILLS SCHOOL
Home Farm Road, Wilton, Salisbury, Wiltshire SP2 8PJ
*Website:* www.southhillsschool.com
*Type:* Co-educational Day Only
*Learning difficulties:* CA WI/MLD DOW
*Behavioural and emotional disorders:* ST
*Physical and medical conditions:* RA

# WORCESTERSHIRE

### BROMSGROVE PRE-PREPARATORY AND NURSERY SCHOOL
Avoncroft House, Hanbury Road, Bromsgrove, Worcestershire B60 4JS
*Website:* www.bromsgrove-school.co.uk
*Type:* Co-educational Day Only 2–7
*Learning difficulties:* CA RA WI/DYS DYP
*Behavioural and emotional disorders:* CA RA ST/ASP
*Physical and medical conditions:* RA/HEA HI VI

### GREEN HILL SCHOOL
Evesham, Worcestershire WR11 4NG
*Website:* www.greenhillschool.co.uk
*Type:* Co-educational Day Only 3–13
*Physical and medical conditions:* W/W

### HOLY TRINITY SCHOOL
Birmingham Road, Kidderminster, Worcestershire DY10 2BY
*Website:* www.holytrinity.co.uk
*Type:* Co-educational Day Only
*Learning difficulties:* CA WI/MLD DYS
*Behavioural and emotional disorders:* ASP
*Physical and medical conditions:* CA/EPI HEA HI IM

### MALVERN ST JAMES
15 Avenue Road, Great Malvern, Worcestershire WR14 3BA
*Website:* www.malvernstjames.co.uk
*Type:* Girls Boarding and Day 4–18
*Learning difficulties:* SNU/MLD DYS DYP
*Physical and medical conditions:* SM TW WA1/W

### RGS THE GRANGE
Grange Lane, Claines, Worcester, Worcestershire WR3 7RR
*Website:* www.rgsao.org
*Type:* Co-educational Day Only 2–11
*Learning difficulties:* CA WI/DYS DYP
*Behavioural and emotional disorders:* RA/ADD ADHD ASP TOU
*Physical and medical conditions:* WA2/EPI HEA HI

### RGS WORCESTER & THE ALICE OTTLEY SCHOOL
Upper Tything, Worcester, Worcestershire WR1 1HP
*Website:* www.rgsao.org
*Type:* Co-educational Day Only 11–18
*Learning difficulties:* WI/DYC DYS DYP
*Behavioural and emotional disorders:* RA/ADD ADHD ASP TOU
*Physical and medical conditions:* RA/EPI HEA HI

### WINTERFOLD HOUSE
Chaddesley Corbett, Kidderminster, Worcestershire DY10 4PW
*Website:* www.winterfoldhouse.co.uk
*Type:* Co-educational Day Only 2–13
*Learning difficulties:* SNU/MLD
*Behavioural and emotional disorders:* RA
*Physical and medical conditions:* RA WA3

# EAST RIDING OF YORKSHIRE

### POCKLINGTON SCHOOL
West Green, Pocklington, East Riding of Yorkshire YO42 2NJ
*Website:* www.pocklingtonschool.com
*Type:* Co-educational Boarding and Day 7–18
*Learning difficulties:* SNU/DYS
*Behavioural and emotional disorders:* RA
*Physical and medical conditions:* RA SM/HEA

# NORTH YORKSHIRE

## AMPLEFORTH COLLEGE
York, North Yorkshire YO62 4ER
*Website:*
www.college.ampleforth.org.uk
*Type:* Co-educational Boarding
and Day 13–18
*Learning difficulties:* WI/DYC
DYS DYP
*Behavioural and emotional
disorders:* CO/ADD ADHD
*Physical and medical
conditions:* RA WA3/CP EPI

## BOOTHAM SCHOOL
Bootham, York, North Yorkshire
YO30 7BU
*Website:*
www.boothamschool.com
*Type:* Co-educational Boarding
and Day 11–18
*Learning difficulties:* CA WI/DYC
DYS DYP
*Behavioural and emotional
disorders:* CO ST/ASP ASD
BESD TOU
*Physical and medical
conditions:* CA SM TW WA2/CP
EPI HEA

## BRAMCOTE SCHOOL
Filey Road, Scarborough,
North Yorkshire YO11 2TT
*Website:*
www.bramcoteschool.com
*Type:* Co-educational Boarding
and Day 3–13
*Learning difficulties:* CA WI/MLD
DYC DYS DYP
*Behavioural and emotional
disorders:* CA/ADD ADHD ASP
*Physical and medical conditions:*
CA RA SM WA3/HEA

## HIGHFIELD PREPARATORY SCHOOL
Clarence Drive, Harrogate,
North Yorkshire HG1 2QG
*Website:*
www.highfieldprep.org.uk
*Type:* Co-educational Day and
Boarding 4–11
*Learning difficulties:* DYS

## LISVANE, SCARBOROUGH COLLEGE JUNIOR SCHOOL
Filey Road, Scarborough,
North Yorkshire YO11 3BA
*Website:*
www.scarboroughcollege.co.uk
*Type:* Co-educational Day and
Boarding 3–11
*Learning difficulties:*
CA SNU/MLD DYS

## MALSIS SCHOOL
Cross Hills, Near Skipton,
North Yorkshire BD20 8DT
*Website:* www.malsis.com
*Type:* Co-educational Boarding
and Day 4–13
*Learning difficulties:* SNU/MLD
DYC DYS DYP
*Behavioural and emotional
disorders:* TS ST
*Physical and medical
conditions:* SM WA3/HEA

## THE MOUNT SCHOOL
Dalton Terrace, York,
North Yorkshire YO24 4DD
*Website:*
www.mountschoolyork.co.uk
*Type:* Co-educational Day and
Boarding 3–18
*Learning difficulties:* CA WI/DYS
*Behavioural and emotional
disorders:* CO
*Physical and medical conditions:*
AT SM TW WA2/CP HEA IM

## QUEEN MARY'S SCHOOL
Baldersby Park, Topcliffe,
Thirsk, North Yorkshire YO7 3BZ
*Website:* www.queenmarys.org
*Type:* Girls Boarding and Day
2–16 (Boys 3–7)
*Learning difficulties:* SNU/MLD
DYS DYP
*Behavioural and emotional
disorders:* TS
*Physical and medical
conditions:* AT SM WA3/EPI

# SOUTH YORKSHIRE

## BIRKDALE SCHOOL
Oakholme Road, Sheffield,
South Yorkshire S10 3DH
*Website:*
www.birkdaleschool.org.uk
*Type:* Boys Day Only 4–18
(Co-ed VIth Form)
*Learning difficulties:* WI/DYS
DYP
*Behavioural and emotional
disorders:* ADD
*Physical and medical
conditions:* HEA HI

## WESTBOURNE SCHOOL
60 Westbourne Road, Sheffield,
South Yorkshire S10 2QT
*Website:*
www.westbourneschool.co.uk
*Type:* Co-educational Day Only
4–16
*Learning difficulties:* CA SC
SNU/MLD DYS
*Physical and medical
conditions:* EPI

# WEST YORKSHIRE

### THE FROEBELIAN SCHOOL
Clarence Road, Horsforth,
Leeds, West Yorkshire LS18 4LB
*Website:* www.froebelian.co.uk
*Type:* Co-educational Day Only
3–11
*Learning difficulties:* CA RA
WI/DYS DYP
*Behavioural and emotional
disorders:* RA/ADD ASD
*Physical and medical
conditions:* RA/HEA

### FULNECK SCHOOL+
Fulneck, Leeds, West Yorkshire
LS28 8DS
*Website:*
www.fulneckschool.co.uk
*Type:* Co-educational Day and
Boarding 3–18
*Learning difficulties:* CA SNU
WI/DYC DYS DYP
*Behavioural and emotional
disorders:* ADD ASP
*Physical and medical
conditions:* VI

### MOORFIELD SCHOOL
Wharfedale Lodge, Ben
Rhydding Road, Ilkley,
West Yorkshire LS29 8RL
*Website:*
www.moorfieldschool.co.uk
*Type:* Co-educational Day Only
2–11
*Learning difficulties:* CA RA
WI/DYS
*Behavioural and emotional
disorders:* RA
*Physical and medical
conditions:* RA TW WA3/HEA

### MOORLANDS SCHOOL
Foxhill Drive, Weetwood Lane,
Leeds, West Yorkshire LS16 5PF
*Website:*
www.moorlands-school.co.uk
*Type:* Co-educational Day Only
2–13
*Learning difficulties:* CA SNU/
MLD PMLD DOW DYS DYP
*Physical and medical
conditions:* IT TW WA3/HEA

### THE RASTRICK INDEPENDENT SCHOOL
Ogden Lane, Rastrick,
Brighouse, West Yorkshire
HD6 3HF
*Website:*
www.rastrickschool.co.uk
*Type:* Co-educational Day Only
(Day Pupils from Birth to
Sixteen years of age)
*Learning difficulties:*
SNU WI/MLD DYS DYP
*Behavioural and emotional
disorders:* TS ST/ASP
*Physical and medical
conditions:* AT IT RA WA3/EPI
HEA HI

### RICHMOND HOUSE SCHOOL
170 Otley Road, Leeds,
West Yorkshire LS16 5LG
*Website:* www.rhschool.org
*Type:* Co-educational Day
Only 3–11
*Learning difficulties:* CA SC
WI/DYS DYP
*Behavioural and emotional
disorders:* RA ST
*Physical and medical
conditions:* CA RA TW WA3/IM

### SUNNY HILL HOUSE SCHOOL
Wrenthorpe Lane, Wrenthorpe,
Wakefield, West Yorkshire
WF2 0QB
*Website:*
www.silcoates.wakefield.sch.uk/
sunnyhillhouse.html
*Type:* Co-educational Day Only
2–7
*Learning difficulties:* CA WI

### WOODHOUSE GROVE SCHOOL
Apperley Bridge, West Yorkshire
BD10 0NR
*Website:*
www.woodhousegrove.co.uk
*Type:* Co-educational Boarding
and Day 11–18
*Learning difficulties:*
SNU WI/DYS DYP
*Behavioural and emotional
disorders:* ST/ADD ADHD ASP
*Physical and medical
conditions:* SM/CP EPI HEA HI

# Northern Ireland

## COUNTY DOWN

**ROCKPORT SCHOOL**
15 Rockport Road, Craigavad,
Holywood, County Down
BT18 0DD
*Website:*
www.rockportschool.com
*Type:* Co-educational Boarding
and Day 3–16 (Boarding 7–13)
*Learning difficulties:*
SNU WI/DOW DYS
*Physical and medical conditions:*
HEA

## COUNTY TYRONE

**THE ROYAL SCHOOL
DUNGANNON**
1 Ranfurly Road, Dungannon,
County Tyrone BT71 6EG
*Website:*
www.royaldungannon.com
*Type:* Co-educational Day and
Boarding 11–19
*Learning difficulties:* RA WI/DYC
DYS DYP
*Behavioural and emotional
disorders:* CO RA/ADD
*Physical and medical
conditions:* CA SL SM TW
WA2/EPI HEA HI VI W

# Scotland

## ABERDEENSHIRE

### ST MARGARET'S SCHOOL FOR GIRLS
17 Albyn Place, Aberdeen,
Aberdeenshire AB10 1RU
*Website:* www.stmargaret.
aberdeen.sch.uk
*Type:* Girls Day Only 3–18
(Boys 3–5)
*Learning difficulties:* RA WI/DYS
DYP
*Behavioural and emotional
disorders:* RA/ADD ADHD ASP
*Physical and medical
conditions:* RA/EPI

## ANGUS

### HIGH SCHOOL OF DUNDEE
Euclid Crescent, Dundee,
Angus DD1 1HU
*Website:*
www.highschoolofdundee.org.uk
*Type:* Co-educational Day Only
5–18
*Learning difficulties:*
CA SNU/DYC DYS DYP
*Behavioural and emotional
disorders:* RA/ADD ADHD ASP
*Physical and medical
conditions:* RA/HEA HI VI

## FIFE

### ST LEONARDS SCHOOL
South Street, St Andrews, Fife
KY16 9QJ
*Website:* www.stleonards-fife.org
*Type:* Co-educational Boarding
and Day 4–19
*Learning difficulties:* SNU
WI/MLD DYC DYS DYP
*Behavioural and emotional
disorders:* ADD ADHD ASP

# GLASGOW

### CRAIGHOLME SCHOOL
72 St. Andrew's Drive,
Pollokshields, Glasgow
G41 4HS
*Website:* www.craigholme.co.uk
*Type:* Girls Day Only 3–18
(Boys 3–5 in Nursery only)
*Learning difficulties:* RA WI/DYC
DYS DYP
*Behavioural and emotional
disorders:* RA/ASP ASD
*Physical and medical
conditions:* AT HL IT RA SM TW
W WA3/EPI HEA HI VI

### HUTCHESONS' GRAMMAR SCHOOL
21 Beaton Road, Glasgow
G41 4NW
*Website:* www.hutchesons.org
*Type:* Co-educational Day Only
5–18
*Learning difficulties:* WI/DYC
DYS DYP
*Behavioural and emotional
disorders:* RA/ADD ADHD ASP
ASD
*Physical and medical
conditions:* SM TW W WA2/EPI
HEA HI IM VI

# LOTHIAN

### BELHAVEN HILL
Dunbar, Lothian EH42 1NN
*Website:* www.belhavenhill.com
*Type:* Co-educational Boarding
and Day 7–13
*Learning difficulties:* WI/DYS
DYP
*Physical and medical
conditions:* TW WA2/HEA

### DUNEDIN SCHOOL
Liberton Bank House, 5 Nether
Liberton Lane, Edinburgh,
Lothian EH16 5TY
*Website:*
www.dunedin.edin.sch.uk
*Type:* Co-educational Day Only
10–17
*Learning difficulties:* CA SC
SNU/MLD DYC DYS DYP
*Behavioural and emotional
disorders:* CA CO TS ST/ASP
BESD
*Physical and medical conditions:*
CA IT TW W WA1 WA2/VI

### GEORGE WATSON'S COLLEGE
67–71 Colinton Road,
Edinburgh, Lothian EH10 5EG
*Website:* www.gwc.org.uk
*Type:* Co-educational Day Only
3–18
*Learning difficulties:* SNU
WI/DYC DYS DYP
*Behavioural and emotional
disorders:* ADD ADHD ASP ASD
*Physical and medical
conditions:* CA SM TW WA2/CP
EPI HEA HI IM VI W

### ST GEORGE'S SCHOOL FOR GIRLS
Garscube Terrace, Edinburgh,
Lothian EH12 6BG
*Website:*
www.st-georges.edin.sch.uk
*Type:* Girls Day and Boarding
1–18 (Boys 2–4)
*Learning difficulties:* CA RA SC
WI/MLD DYC DYS DYP
*Behavioural and emotional
disorders:* CO RA/ADD ASP
BESD
*Physical and medical
conditions:* AT BL CA HL IT SM
TW WA2 WA3/EPI HEA HI IM VI

# PERTH AND KINROSS

### KILGRASTON+
Bridge of Earn, Perth, Perth and Kinross PH2 9BQ
*Website:* www.kilgraston.com
*Type:* Girls Boarding and Day 2–18 (Boys day 2–9)
*Learning difficulties:* CA SNU/DYC DYS DYP
*Behavioural and emotional disorders:* CO TS ST
*Physical and medical conditions:* IT SM WA2/EPI

### MORRISON'S ACADEMY
Ferntower Road, Crieff, Perth and Kinross PH7 3AN
*Website:* www.morrisonsacademy.org
*Type:* Co-educational Day Only 3–18
*Learning difficulties:* SNU/DYS DYP
*Behavioural and emotional disorders:* CO/ASP
*Physical and medical conditions:* RA

### STRATHALLAN SCHOOL
Forgandenny, Perth, Perth and Kinross PH2 9EG
*Website:* www.strathallan.co.uk
*Type:* Co-educational Boarding and Day 9–18 (Junior House for Boys and Girls aged 9 to 13 Senior School for Boys and Girls aged 13 to 18)
*Learning difficulties:* SNU/DYS DYP SP&LD
*Behavioural and emotional disorders:* RA/ADD ADHD ASP
*Physical and medical conditions:* SM TW WA3/EPI HEA

# RENFREWSHIRE

### BELMONT HOUSE
Sandringham Avenue, Newton Mearns, Renfrewshire G77 5DU
*Website:* www.belmontschool.co.uk
*Type:* Co-educational Day Only 3–18
*Learning difficulties:* MLD DYS DYP
*Behavioural and emotional disorders:* ASP
*Physical and medical conditions:* WA1

# Wales

## BRIDGEND

### ST CLARE'S SCHOOL
Newton, Porthcawl, Bridgend
CF36 5NR
*Website:*
www.stclares-school.co.uk
*Type:* Co-educational Day
Only 3–18
*Physical and medical
conditions:* W

### ST JOHN'S SCHOOL
Church Street, Newton,
Porthcawl, Bridgend CF36 5NP
*Website:* www.stjohnsschool-porthcawl.com
*Type:* Co-educational Day
Only 3–16
*Learning difficulties:* CA RA
WI/MLD DYS
*Behavioural and emotional
disorders:* RA TS

## CARDIFF

### HOWELL'S SCHOOL, LLANDAFF GDST
Cardiff Road, Llandaff, Cardiff
CF5 2YD
*Website:*
www.howells-cardiff.gdst.net
*Type:* Co-educational Day
Only 3–18
*Learning difficulties:* RA WI/DYS
DYP
*Physical and medical
conditions:* RA WA3/HEA

## CONWY

### ST DAVID'S COLLEGE+
Llandudno, Conwy LL30 1RD
*Website:*
www.stdavidscollege.co.uk
*Type:* Co-educational Boarding
and Day 11–18
*Learning difficulties:* SNU/MLD
DYC DYS DYP
*Behavioural and emotional
disorders:* TS/ADD ADHD ASP

# DENBIGHSHIRE

**HOWELL'S SCHOOL**
Park Street, Denbigh,
Denbighshire LL16 3EN
*Website:* www.howells.org
*Type:* Girls Boarding and Day
2–18
*Learning difficulties:* CA WI/MLD
DYS DYP
*Behavioural and emotional
disorders:* RA
*Physical and medical
conditions:* SM WA3/EPI HEA

# MONMOUTHSHIRE

**ST JOHN'S-ON-THE-HILL**
Castleford Hill, Tutshill,
Chepstow, Monmouthshire
NP16 7LE
*Website:*
www.stjohnsonthehill.co.uk
*Type:* Co-educational Boarding
and Day (Nursery from
3 months)
*Learning difficulties:*
CA SNU/MLD DYS DYP
*Behavioural and emotional
disorders:* RA/ASP
*Physical and medical
conditions:* RA SM/HEA

# POWYS

**CHRIST COLLEGE**
Brecon, Powys LD3 8AF
*Website:*
www.christcollegebrecon.com
*Type:* Co-educational Boarding
and Day 11–18
*Learning difficulties:* WI/DYS
*Behavioural and emotional
disorders:* RA

# SWANSEA

**CRAIG-Y-NOS SCHOOL**
Clyne Common, Bishoptston,
Swansea SA3 3JB
*Website:* www.craigynos.com
*Type:* Co-educational Day Only
2–11
*Learning difficulties:* CA WI/DYS
DYP
*Behavioural and emotional
disorders:* RA/ASP ASD
*Physical and medical conditions:*
CA RA/HEA IM

## 4.4

# Profiles of Independent Mainstream Schools with Specialist Provision

## SYMBOL KEY

### Gender
● Girls
● Boys
● Coed

### CReSTeD
◆ Crested Registered

### Accommodation
🏠 Boarding only
🏠 Boarding and Day
🏠 Day and Boarding
🏠 Day only

### Has 6th Form
▲ Has 6th Form

# Egerton Rothesay School ● 🏠

Durrants Lane, Berkhamsted, Hertfordshire HP4 3UJ
**T:** 01442 865275
**F:** 01442 864977
**E:** admin.dl@eger-roth.co.uk
**W:** www.eger-roth.co.uk

**Headteacher** Mrs Nicola Boddam-Whetham
**School Status** Co-ed Independent Day only
**Religious denomination** Christian
**Membership** ISA
**Special needs provision ADD**, **ASD**, **ASP**,
**CP**, **DYC**, **DYP**, **DYS**, **EPI**, HEA, HI, **IM**, **MLD**,

SP&LD, VI, WA1
**Age range** 5–16
**No of Pupils** 197; *Girls* 67; *Boys* 130
**Average class size** 9

A Very Different Education, ERS is a school especially for the child who can benefit from additional support. This means delivering the best possible education for each child whilst providing a genuinely supportive framework that will help them to achieve their full potential. We are an inclusive school; welcoming children with a wide range of abilities, from all faiths – or none – and from all cultures. We believe that learning should be enjoyable and rounded, being about preparing each child for life after school, as well as exams. ERS focuses on students who have found; or would find it difficult to progress and succeed within another school. We have a range of specialist support; teachers and therapists who provide for an array of children whose additional needs may include Dyslexia, Dyspraxia, Speech, Language and Communication needs, Asperger's and High Functioning Autism. Classes are grouped for individual requirements. The school has an accepting atmosphere in which children feel understood and in which they do not feel 'different'. This boosts self confidence and aids the enrichment of learning. Every child at Egerton Rothesay is seen as a unique person and an individual student. We aim to make an excellent contribution to the life of each student ensuring that they can be supported in the way that they personally need to maximize their individual learning potential. ERS provides a broad education whilst offering pupils a range of individually tailored strategies enabling each to access the curriculum. Our aim is always to identify what we can do for your child, and then to work with our resources, and your support, so that we can help them to be successful. Our input can be for the child's whole school career, through to GCSE or simply on an interim basis to help refocus their progress, depending on their needs. All learning and social activities take place within an environment offering exceptional pastoral care and whole person development that is driven and informed by the school's Christian foundation. ERS is also more than just a local school. Students travel to the school from all locations, many using the comprehensive minibus service that the school runs over a 35 mile radius. You are most welcome to come to the school to see if you think our approach would be right for your child. To arrange a visit please contact Liz Martin (01442 877060 or liz.martin@eger-roth.co.uk) or see our website: www.eger-roth.co.uk for more information.

## 4·5

# Index of Independent Mainstream Schools

## Learning difficulties
*Support provided/Currently have pupils*
*diagnosed with learning difficulties*

| | |
|---|---|
| The Abbey, Woodbridge | WI/MLD DYS |
| Abbey Gate School, Chester | CA WI/MLD DYS DYP |
| The Abbey School, Reading | WI/DYS DYP |
| Abbot's Hill School, Hemel Hempstead | CA SNU WI/DYC DYS DYP |
| Aberdour, Tadworth | CA/DYC DYS DYP |
| Adcote School for Girls, Shrewsbury | CA SNU/MLD DYS DYP |
| Airthrie School, Cheltenham | CA SNU/DYS DYP |
| Akeley Wood School, Buckingham | SNU/MLD DYS DYP |
| Aldro School, Godalming | CA SNU WI/MLD DYS DYP |
| Alleyn's School, London | WI/DYC DYS DYP |
| Ampleforth College, York | WI/DYC DYS DYP |
| Arnold Lodge School, Leamington Spa | WI/MLD DYC DYS DYP |
| Arnold School, Blackpool | SNU WI/MLD DYC DYS DYP |
| Ashford School, Ashford | CA SNU/MLD DYS DYP |
| Ashgrove School, Bromley | WI/DYS DYP |
| Aston House School, London | SNU/DYS DYP |
| Avenue House School, London | RA WI/MLD DYS |
| Babington House School, Chislehurst | CA WI/DYS DYP |
| Bablake School, Coventry | SNU/DYS DYP |
| Barfield School and Nursery, Farnham | WI |
| Beeston Hall School, Cromer | CA SNU/MLD DYC DYS DYP |
| Belhaven Hill, Dunbar | WI/DYS DYP |

| | |
|---|---|
| Davenport Lodge School, Coventry | CA WI/MLD DYS |
| Derby High School, Derby | CA RA WI/DYC DYS DYP |
| Dolphin School, Reading | WI/DYS |
| The Dominie, London | DYC DYS DYP |
| Dorchester Preparatory and Independent Schools, Dorchester | CA WI/DYC DYS DYP |
| Dover College, Dover | WI/DYS DYP |
| Dower House School, Bridgnorth | WI |
| Downe House, Thatcham | SNU/DYS DYP |
| Downsend School, Leatherhead | CA SNU WI/DYC DYS DYP |
| Downsend School – Ashtead Lodge, Ashtead | RA WI |
| Dragon School, Oxford | WI/DYC DYS DYP SP&LD |
| Duff Miller, London | WI/MLD DYS DYP |
| Dulwich Preparatory School, Cranbrook, Cranbrook | CA SNU WI/DYS DYP |
| Dunedin School, Edinburgh | CA SC SNU/MLD DYC DYS DYP |
| Durlston Court, New Milton | CA SNU/MLD DYC DYS DYP |
| Eastbourne College, Eastbourne | MLD |
| Eaton House Belgravia, London | SNU WI/MLD DYC DYS DYP |
| Eaton House The Manor Preparatory, London | SNU WI/DYC DYS DYP |
| Eaton House The Vale, London | CA WI/MLD |
| Edgbaston High School for Girls, Birmingham | RA WI/DYC DYS DYP |
| Egerton Rothesay School, Berkhamsted | CA SC SNU/MLD DYC DYS DYP SP&LD |
| Ellesmere College, Ellesmere | SNU/DYC DYS DYP |
| Elmhurst School for Dance, Birmingham | RA WI/DYS DYP |
| Emmanuel School, Derby | CA WI |
| Ewell Castle School, Epsom | SC WI/DYC DYS DYP |
| Fairfield Preparatory School, Loughborough | WI/DYS DYP |
| The Falcons School for Boys | CA WI |
| Farringtons School, Chislehurst | WI/MLD DYS DYP |
| Felsted School, Felsted | CA WI/DYS |
| Feltonfleet School, Cobham | WI/DYS DYP |
| Ferndale Preparatory School, Faringdon | CA WI/MLD DYS |
| Finton House School, London | CA SC SNU/DOW DYC DYS DYP |
| Fonthill Lodge, East Grinstead | CA WI/DYS DYP |
| Francis Holland School, Sloane Square SW1, London | RA WI/DYC DYS DYP |
| The Froebelian School, Leeds | CA RA WI/DYS DYP |
| Fulneck School, Leeds | CA SNU WI/DYC DYS DYP |
| Gatehouse School, London | CA/DOW DYS |
| Gateway Christian School, Ilkeston | RA WI |
| Gems Bolitho School, Penzance | CA SNU/MLD DYC DYS DYP |
| George Watson's College, Edinburgh | SNU WI/DYC DYS DYP |
| Glebe House School, Hunstanton | CA WI/DYC DYS DYP |
| Godstowe Preparatory School, High Wycombe | CA SC SNU/MLD DOW DYC DYS DYP |
| Gracefield Preparatory School, Fishponds | WI/MLD |
| Great Houghton Preparatory School, Northampton | CA SC SNU WI/DYC DYS DYP |
| Greenbank Preparatory School, Cheadle | CA SC SNU/MLD DYC DYS DYP |

| | |
|---|---|
| Greene's Tutorial College, Oxford | WI/MLD DYC DYS DYP |
| Greenholme School, Nottingham | WI |
| Haberdashers' Aske's Boys' School, Elstree | RA/DYS DYP |
| Hampton School, Hampton | SNU/DYS DYP |
| Handcross Park School, Haywards Heath | CA SNU/MLD DYC DYS DYP |
| Haresfoot Preparatory School, Berkhamsted | CA WI/DYS |
| The Harrodian, London | SNU/DYC DYS DYP |
| Hatherop Castle School, Cirencester | SNU WI/MLD |
| Hazlegrove, Yeovil | SNU/DYC DYS DYP |
| Herries School, Maidenhead | WI |
| Hethersett Old Hall School, Norwich | SNU/MLD DYS |
| High Elms Manor School, Watford | CA WI/MLD DYC DYS DYP |
| Highfield Preparatory School, Harrogate | DYS |
| High March School, Beaconsfield | CA WI/DYC DYS DYP |
| High School of Dundee, Dundee | CA SNU/DYC DYS DYP |
| Highclare School, Birmingham | CA WI/DYS |
| Hilden Oaks School, Tonbridge | WI |
| Hoe Bridge School, Woking | CA WI/DYS DYP |
| Holy Trinity School, Kidderminster | CA WI/MLD DYS |
| Horris Hill School, Newbury | SNU/MLD DYS DYP |
| Howell's School, Denbigh | CA WI/MLD DYS DYP |
| Howell's School, Llandaff GDST, Cardiff | RA WI/DYS DYP |
| Hurst Lodge School, Ascot | CA SC WI/MLD DYC DYS DYP |
| Hutchesons' Grammar School, Glasgow | WI/DYC DYS DYP |
| Ilford Ursuline Preparatory School, Ilford | SNU/MLD DYS DYP |
| The John Lyon School, Harrow | RA/DYC DYS DYP |
| Kelly College Preparatory School, Tavistock | CA WI/DYS DYP |
| Kent College Infant & Junior School, Canterbury | SC SNU/MLD DYC DYS DYP |
| Kent College Pembury, Tunbridge Wells | WI/DYC DYS DYP |
| Kew Green Preparatory School, Richmond | CA SNU WI/MLD DYC DYS DYP |
| Kilgraston, Perth | CA SNU/DYC DYS DYP |
| King Edward VII and Queen Mary School, Lytham St Annes | CA WI/DYC DYS DYP |
| King's Bruton and Hazlegrove, Bruton | SNU WI/DYC DYS DYP |
| King's College, Taunton | WI |
| King's Preparatory School, Rochester | WI/DYS DYP |
| Kingshott School, Hitchin | DYS DYP |
| Kingsley School, Bideford | SC SNU/DYS DYP |
| Kingswood School, Solihull | CA SC SNU/MLD DYC DYS DYP |
| Kingswood School, Bath | RA WI/DYC DYS DYP |
| Kirkham Grammar School, Preston | SNU/DYC DYS |
| Kirkstone House School, Bourne | CA SNU WI/MLD DYS DYP |
| The Lady Eleanor Holles School, Hampton | WI/DYC DYS DYP |
| Lancing College Preparatory School at Mowden, Hove | CA WI/DYS |
| Langley School, Norwich | SNU/DYC DYS DYP |
| Lansdowne College, London | RA/MLD DYC DYS DYP |

| | |
|---|---|
| The Larks, Oxted | WI/DYS DYP |
| Lime House School, Carlisle | CA SC SNU WI/MLD DYS DYP |
| Lion House School, London | CA WI/MLD |
| Lisvane, Scarborough College Junior School, Scarborough | CA SNU/MLD DYS |
| Littlegarth School, Colchester | CA SNU WI/MLD DYC DYS DYP |
| Lord Wandsworth College, Hook | RA WI/DYS |
| Loreto Preparatory School, Altrincham | CA WI/MLD DYS |
| Loughborough High School, Loughborough | RA WI/DYC DYS DYP |
| Madni Girls School, London | WI/DYC |
| The Mall School, Twickenham | CA RA WI/DYS DYP |
| Malsis School, Near Skipton | SNU/MLD DYC DYS DYP |
| Maltman's Green School, Gerrards Cross | CA WI/MLD DYS DYP |
| Malvern St James, Great Malvern | SNU/MLD DYS DYP |
| The Manchester Grammar School, Manchester | RA WI/DYC DYS DYP |
| Manor House School, Ashby-de-la-Zouch | CA SC WI/DYC DYS DYP |
| The Manor Preparatory School, Abingdon | CA SNU/DYC DYS DYP |
| The Maynard School, Exeter | WI/DYS DYP |
| Mayville High School, Southsea | SNU/DYS DYP |
| Meadowbrook Montessori School, Bracknell | CA RA SNU/MLD DYS |
| Meadowpark School and Nursery, Cricklade | WI |
| Merchant Taylors' Boys' Schools, Liverpool | CA SNU/MLD DYC DYS DYP |
| Merchant Taylors' School, Northwood | RA SNU/DYS DYP |
| The Mill School, Devizes | CA WI/DYS |
| Milton Abbey School, Blandford Forum | SNU/DYC DYS DYP SP&LD |
| The Montessori House, London | CA/MLD |
| Moorfield School, Ilkley | CA RA WI/DYS |
| Moorlands School, Leeds | CA SNU/MLD PMLD DOW DYS DYP |
| Moorlands School, Luton | DYS DYP |
| Moor Park School, Ludlow | SNU/DYC DYS DYP |
| Moreton Hall Preparatory School, Bury St Edmunds | SC/MLD DYS |
| Moreton Hall School, Oswestry | SNU WI/MLD DYC DYS DYP |
| Morrison's Academy, Crieff | SNU/DYS DYP |
| The Mount School, York | CA WI/DYS |
| The New Eccles Hall School, Norwich | SC SNU/DYC DYS DYP |
| New Life Christian School, Croydon | WI |
| Newcastle-under-Lyme School, Newcastle-under-Lyme | WI |
| Norfolk House School, Birmingham | RA WI |
| Norfolk Lodge Montessori Nursery, Barnet | RA |
| North Cestrian Grammar School, Altrincham | CA WI/MLD DYC DYS DYP |
| Northbourne Park School, Deal | CA SNU/DYC DYS DYP |
| Northcote Lodge School, London | WI/DYC DYS DYP |
| Northwood College, Northwood | WI/DYS DYP |
| Notting Hill and Ealing High School GDST, London | WI/DYC DYS DYP |
| Nottingham High School, Nottingham | WI/DYC DYS DYP |
| Oakfield School, Woking | WI/DYS DYP |

| | |
|---|---|
| Oakhyrst Grange School, Caterham | CA WI/DYS DYP |
| The Old Hall School, Telford | SNU/DYC DYS DYP |
| Old Vicarage School, Richmond | WI |
| The Oratory Preparatory School, Reading | CA WI/DYC DYS DYP |
| The Oratory School, Reading | SNU/MLD DYS DYP |
| Orwell Park, Ipswich | SNU/DYC DYS DYP |
| Oswestry School Bellan House, Oswestry | SNU/DYS DYP |
| Overndale School, Old Sodbury | CA |
| Oxford Tutorial College, Oxford | SC WI/MLD DYS DYP |
| Papplewick School, Ascot | WI/MLD DYS |
| The Park School, Yeovil | WI/MLD DYS DYP |
| The Perse School, Cambridge | CA SNU/MLD DYC DYS DYP |
| Pocklington School, Pocklington | SNU/DYS |
| Polam Hall, Darlington | CA SC SNU/MLD DYS DYP |
| Port Regis Preparatory School, Shaftesbury | SNU WI/DYC DYS DYP |
| The Portsmouth Grammar School, Portsmouth | WI |
| Portsmouth High School GDST, Southsea | WI/DYS DYP |
| Prestfelde Preparatory School, Shrewsbury | CA SNU/MLD DYS DYP |
| Primrose Independent School, London | WI/MLD DOW DYS DYP |
| Prior Park Preparatory School, Cricklade | CA SNU WI/DYC DYS DYP |
| Priory Preparatory School, Banstead | CA WI/MLD DYC DYS DYP |
| Priory School, Birmingham | SNU/DYC DYS DYP |
| Queen Elizabeth's Hospital, Bristol | SNU/DYS DYP |
| Queen Mary's School, Thirsk | SNU/MLD DYS DYP |
| Queen's Gate School, London | DYC DYS DYP |
| Ramillies Hall School, Cheadle | CA SNU/DYC DYS DYP |
| Ranby House School, Retford | CA SC SNU/MLD DOW DYC DYS DYP |
| Raphael Independent School, Hornchurch | WI/DYS |
| The Rastrick Independent School, Brighouse | SNU WI/MLD DYS DYP |
| Red House School, Norton | RA WI/DYS DYP |
| The Red Maids' School, Bristol | CA SNU/DYS |
| Reigate Grammar School, Reigate | CA/MLD DYS DYP |
| RGS The Grange, Worcester | CA WI/DYS DYP |
| RGS Worcester & The Alice Ottley School, Worcester | WI/DYC DYS DYP |
| The Richard Pate School, Cheltenham | CA SNU WI/MLD DYS |
| Richmond House School, Leeds | CA SC WI/DYS DYP |
| Rickmansworth PNEU School, Rickmansworth | CA SNU/DYS DYP |
| Riddlesworth Hall, Diss | SNU/MLD DYC DYS DYP |
| Ripley Court School, Woking | WI/DYS DYP |
| The Roche School, London | CA SC WI/MLD DOW DYS DYP |
| Rock Hall School, Alnwick | DYS |
| Rockport School, Holywood | SNU WI/DOW DYS |
| Roselyon, Par | CA WI/MLD DYS DYP |
| The Rowans School, London | WI |
| Rowden House School, Bromyard | MLD SLD PMLD DOW DYC DYP SP&LD |

| | |
|---|---|
| The Royal Hospital School, Ipswich | SNU WI/MLD DYS DYP |
| The Royal School Dungannon, Dungannon | RA WI/DYC DYS DYP |
| The Royal Wolverhampton Junior School, Wolverhampton | CA RA SNU/MLD DYC DYS DYP |
| Ruckleigh School, Solihull | CA RA WI/DYS |
| Russell House School, Sevenoaks | WI/DYS DYP |
| Ryde School, Ryde | SNU/DYC DYS DYP |
| St Andrew's School, Eastbourne | CA SNU WI/DYC DYS DYP |
| St Andrew's School, East Runton | MLD DYS DYP |
| St Andrew's School, Reading | WI/DYS |
| St Bees School, St Bees | SNU WI/DYC DYS DYP |
| St Bernard's Preparatory School, Slough | CA WI/DYS |
| St Christopher School, Letchworth Garden City | SNU/DYS DYP |
| St Christopher's School, Hove | CA SNU WI/MLD DYS |
| St Christopher's School, Totnes | CA/MLD DYS DYP |
| St Crispin's School, Leicester | CA RA SC SNU WI/MLD DYC DYS DYP |
| St David's College, Llandudno | SNU/MLD DYC DYS DYP |
| St David's School, Purley | CA WI/DYC DYS DYP |
| St Dunstan's College, London | CA WI/DYC DYS DYP |
| St Faith's at Ash School, Canterbury | CA RA WI/DYS DYP |
| St Gabriel's, Berkshire | CA SNU/MLD DYC DYS DYP |
| St George's School for Girls, Edinburgh | CA RA SC WI/MLD DYC DYS DYP |
| St Helen & St Katharine, Abingdon | WI/DYS |
| St Helen's School, Northwood | WI/DYS |
| St Hilary's School, Godalming | CA SNU WI/DYS DYP |
| St Hilda's School, Harpenden | SC WI/DYC DYS DYP |
| St Hugh's School, Woodhall Spa | CA SNU WI/MLD DYC DYS |
| St Hugh's School, Faringdon | CA WI/MLD DYS DYP |
| St Ia School, St Ives | RA WI |
| St James Junior School, London | WI/MLD |
| St John's School, Leatherhead | SNU WI/DYC DYS DYP |
| St John's School, Porthcawl | CA RA WI/MLD DYS |
| St John's-on-the-Hill, Chepstow | CA SNU/MLD DYS DYP |
| St Joseph's College, Ipswich | CA WI/DYC DYS DYP |
| St Joseph's Convent School, London | CA SNU/MLD |
| St Joseph's In The Park, Hertford | CA SC SNU/DYC DYS DYP |
| St Joseph's School, Launceston | SNU/MLD DYS DYP |
| St Lawrence College Junior School, Ramsgate | CA WI/MLD DYS DYP |
| St Leonards School, St Andrews | SNU WI/MLD DYC DYS DYP |
| St Margaret's School, London | RA/MLD DYC DYS DYP |
| St Margaret's School for Girls, Aberdeen | RA WI/DYS DYP |
| St Martin's School, Northwood | SC/DYC DYS DYP |
| St Mary's Junior School, Cambridge | CA/DYC DYS |
| St Mary's Preparatory School, Lincoln | CA SNU/MLD DYS DYP |
| St Mary's School, Ascot, Ascot | WI/DYS DYP |

| | |
|---|---|
| Tudor Hall School, Banbury | SNU/DYC DYS DYP SP&LD |
| Twyford School, Winchester | SNU/DYS |
| University College School, London | MLD DYS |
| University College School Junior Branch, London | DYS DYP |
| Walhampton School, Lymington | CA SNU/MLD DYS DYP |
| Walthamstow Hall, Sevenoaks | WI/DYC DYS DYP |
| Wellow House School, Newark | CA WI/DYS |
| West Buckland Preparatory School, Barnstaple | CA RA/MLD DYC DYS DYP |
| West Buckland School, Barnstaple | CA SNU WI/DOW DYC DYS DYP |
| West House School, Birmingham | CA WI/MLD DYS |
| Westbourne School, Sheffield | CA SC SNU/MLD DYS |
| Westminster Abbey Choir School, London | WI/DYS |
| Westminster Cathedral Choir School, London | WI/DYS DYP |
| Westminster Tutors, London | SC WI/MLD DYS DYP |
| Westonbirt School, Tetbury | SNU/DYC DYS DYP |
| Wetherby Preparatory School London | DYS |
| Winchester College, Winchester | SNU/DYC DYS DYP |
| Winchester House School, Brackley | SNU WI |
| Windermere School, Windermere | WI |
| Winterfold House, Kidderminster | SNU/MLD |
| Withington Girls' School, Manchester | CA RA WI/DYC DYS DYP |
| Wolverhampton Grammar School, Wolverhampton | CA SNU WI/DYS DYP |
| Woodcote House School, Windlesham | SC SNU/MLD DYC DYS DYP |
| Woodhouse Grove School, Apperley Bridge | SNU WI/DYS DYP |
| Wrekin College, Shropshire | RA WI/DYS |
| Wycliffe College, Stonehouse | SNU WI/DYC DYS DYP |
| Wycliffe Preparatory School, Stonehouse | CA SNU WI/DYC DYS DYP |
| Wycombe Abbey School, High Wycombe | SNU WI/DYC DYS DYP |

## Behavioural and emotional disorders

*Support provided/Currently have pupils
diagnosed with disorders*

| | |
|---|---|
| Abbey College, Manchester | ADHD |
| Abbey Gate School, Chester | CA TS ST/ADD ASD |
| The Abbey School, Reading | TS ST/ADD |
| Abbot's Hill School, Hemel Hempstead | CO/ASP BESD |
| Aberdour, Tadworth | RA/ADD ADHD ASP |
| Adcote School for Girls, Shrewsbury | CA CO TS ST/ADHD ASP ASD |
| Akeley Wood School, Buckingham | ADD ASP |
| Aldro School, Godalming | RA/ADD ASP |
| Alleyn's School, London | CO/ADD ASP TOU |
| Ampleforth College, York | CO/ADD ADHD |

| | |
|---|---|
| Arnold Lodge School, Leamington Spa | CO ST/ADD ADHD ASP |
| Arnold School, Blackpool | CA CO ST/ADD ADHD BESD |
| Ashford School, Ashford | CO RA/ADHD ASP ASD |
| Aston House School, London | ST |
| Beeston Hall School, Cromer | CA TS/ADD ASP |
| Belmont House, Newton Mearns | ASP |
| Benenden School, Cranbrook | RA |
| Bilton Grange, Rugby | CA CO TS/ADHD ASP ASD |
| Birchfield School, Wolverhampton | RA TS ST/ADD ADHD ASP |
| Birkdale School, Sheffield | ADD |
| Bishopsgate School, Egham | RA/ADHD |
| Bootham School, York | CO ST/ASP ASD BESD TOU |
| Brabyns School, Stockport | ASP |
| Bramcote School, Scarborough | CA/ADD ADHD ASP |
| Bramley School, Tadworth | ST/ADD TOU |
| Bredon School, Tewkesbury | CO TS/ADD |
| Bristol Cathedral School, Bristol | RA/ADD ADHD ASP TOU |
| Broadwater Manor School, Worthing | RA |
| Bromsgrove Pre-preparatory and Nursery School, Bromsgrove | CA RA ST/ASP |
| Bronte School, Gravesend | CA/ADD ADHD ASP |
| Broomwood Hall School, London | CA/ADD ASP |
| Buckingham College School, Harlow | ADD ADHD ASP BESD |
| Bury Grammar School Boys, Bury | RA |
| Cambridge Centre for Sixth-form Studies, Cambridge | CA CO RA |
| Castle House School, Newport | ST/ADD ASP ASD |
| Channing School, London | ADHD |
| Cheltenham College Junior School, Cheltenham | CA CO/ADD ADHD ASP |
| Cheltenham Ladies' College, Cheltenham | CO RA ST/ADD ADHD |
| Cherwell College, Oxford | CO/ADD ADHD |
| Christ College, Brecon | RA |
| Clifton College, Bristol | CO RA/ADD ASP |
| Clifton College Preparatory School, Bristol | ST/ADD ASP BESD |
| Clifton High School, Bristol | CO |
| Craig-y-Nos School, Bishoptston | RA/ASP ASD |
| Craigholme School, Glasgow | RA/ASP ASD |
| Croydon High School GDST, South Croydon | RA/ADHD ASD |
| Dagfa House School, Nottingham | ASP ASD |
| Dallington School, London | ST/ADD |
| Dame Bradbury's School, Saffron Walden | RA/ASD |
| Davenport Lodge School, Coventry | CA |
| Derby High School, Derby | RA/ASD |
| Dolphin School, Reading | RA/ASP ASD |
| The Dominie, London | ADHD |
| Dorchester Preparatory and Independent Schools, Dorchester | RA/ADD ADHD ASP ASD |

| | |
|---|---|
| Downe House, Thatcham | RA |
| Downsend School, Leatherhead | RA/ADD ADHD ASP |
| Downsend School – Ashtead Lodge, Ashtead | RA |
| Dragon School, Oxford | CO RA/ADD ADHD ASP |
| Dulwich Preparatory School, Granbrook | ADHD ASP |
| Dunedin School, Edinburgh | CA CO TS ST/ASP BESD |
| Duff Miller, London | ADD ADHD |
| Durlston Court, New Milton | ADHD |
| Eaton House Belgravia, London | CA TS/BESD |
| Eaton House The Manor Preparatory, London | CA RA/ADD ASP ASD |
| Eaton House The Vale, London | TS |
| Edgbaston High School for Girls, Birmingham | RA ST |
| Egerton Rothesay School, Berkhamsted | ST/ADD ASP ASD |
| Ellesmere College, Ellesmere | RA |
| Elmhurst School for Dance, Birmingham | RA |
| Emmanuel School, Derby | RA/ASP |
| Ewell Castle School, Epsom | ADD ADHD ASP ASD |
| Fairfield Preparatory School, Loughborough | ASP |
| Farieigh Further Education College (Ecome), Frome | ASD |
| Farieigh Further Education College, Swindon, Swindon | ASP ASD |
| Farringtons School, Chislehurst | RA |
| Felsted School, Felsted | RA |
| Feltonfleet School, Cobham | ADHD |
| Femdale Preparatory School, Faringdon | ADHD |
| Finton House School, London | RA/ASP ASD BESD |
| Francis Holland School, Sloane Square SW1, London | RA/ADHD |
| The Froebelian School, Leeds | RA/ADD ASD |
| Fulneck School, Leeds | ADD ASP |
| Gateway Christian School, Ilkeston | RA |
| Gems Bolitho School, Penzance | CA/ADD ADHD ASP |
| George Watson's College, Edinburgh | ADD ADHD ASP ASD |
| Glebe House School, Hunstanton | RA |
| Godstowe Preparatory School, High Wycombe | CA CO/ADD ADHD ASP ASD |
| Gracefield Preparatory School, Fishponds | TS |
| Great Houghton Preparatory School, Northampton | CA CO RA TS ST/ASP ASD |
| Greenbank Preparatory School, Cheadle | RA TS |
| Greene's Tutorial College, Oxford | RA/ADD ADHD ASP BESD |
| Haberdashers' Aske's Boys' School, Elstree | ADHD |
| Hampton School, Hampton | CO TS ST/ADD ADHD ASP ASD TOU |
| Handcross Park School, Haywards Heath | CO TS/ADD ADHD |
| Hatherop Castle School, Cirencester | ST |
| Hethersett Old Hall School, Norwich | RA/BESD |
| High Elms Manor School, Watford | RA/ADD ASP ASD |
| High March School, Beaconsfield | RA |
| High School of Dundee, Dundee | RA/ADD ADHD ASP |

| | |
|---|---|
| Highclare School, Birmingham | RA/ADD ADHD BESD |
| Hoe Bridge School, Woking | CA RA/ADD ADHD |
| Holy Trinity School, Kidderminster | ASP |
| Horris Hill School, Newbury | ADD |
| Howell's School, Denbigh | RA |
| Hurst Lodge School, Ascot | RA/ADD ADHD ASP |
| Hutchesons' Grammar School, Glasgow | RA/ADD ADHD ASP ASD |
| Ilford Ursuline Preparatory School, Ilford | TS/ADHD |
| The John Lyon School, Harrow | CO/ASD |
| Kelly College Preparatory School, Tavistock | ASD |
| Kent College Infant & Junior School, Canterbury | CA CO |
| Kent College Pembury, Tunbridge Wells | CO/ADD BESD |
| Kew Green Preparatory School, Richmond | CA CO TS ST/ADD CB |
| Kilgraston, Perth | CO TS ST |
| King Edward VII and Queen Mary School, Lytham St Annes | RA/ADD ADHD |
| King's Bruton and Hazlegrove, Bruton | ADD ADHD ASP |
| Kingswood School, Solihull | ADD ADHD ASP ASD |
| Kirkstone House School, Peterborough | ADHD ASP ASD |
| The Lady Eleanor Holles School, Hampton | CO/TOU |
| Lancing College Preparatory School at Mowden, Hove | RA/ADHD |
| Langley School, Norwich | RA/ADD |
| Lansdowne College, London | RA/ADD ADHD ASD |
| The Larks, Oxted | ADHD |
| Lime House School, Carlisle | ADD ADHD ASP |
| Lion House School, London | RA/ADD ASD |
| Littlegarth School, Colchester | CA ST/ADD ADHD |
| Lord Wandsworth College, Hook | RA/ADD ASP |
| Loreto Preparatory School, Altrincham | CA ST |
| Madni Girls School, London | RA |
| The Mall School, Twickenham | CA |
| Malsis School, Near Skipton | TS ST |
| Maltman's Green School, Gerrards Cross | CO |
| The Manchester Grammar School, Manchester | RA/ADD ADHD ASD |
| Manor House School, Ashby-de-la-Zouch | RA/ADD ASP |
| The Maynard School, Exeter | CO |
| Mayville High School, Southsea | ST/ADD ADHD ASP ASD |
| Meadowbrook Montessori School, Bracknell | RA TS/ADHD ASP ASD CB |
| Merchant Taylors' Boys' Schools, Liverpool | TS ST/ADD ADHD ASP ASD BESD CB |
| Merchant Taylors' School, Northwood | RA/ADD ADHD ASP |
| Milton Abbey School, Blandford Forum | CO TS ST/ADD ADHD |
| The Montessori House, London | CA/ASD |
| Moorfield School, Ilkley | RA |
| Moorlands School, Luton | CA TS ST/ASD |
| Moor Park School, Ludlow | CO/ADD ADHD ASP |
| Moreton Hall Preparatory School, Bury St Edmunds | RA |

| | |
|---|---|
| Rowden House School, Bromyard | ADD ADHD ASP ASD BESD CB TOU |
| The Royal Hospital School, Ipswich | CO RA |
| The Royal School Dungannon, Dungannon | CO RA/ADD |
| The Royal Wolverhampton Junior School, Wolverhampton | CA CO RA ST/ADHD CB |
| Ruckleigh School, Solihull | RA |
| St Andrew's School, Eastbourne | RA/ASP |
| St Andrew's School, East Runton | ASP ASD |
| St Bees School, St Bees | RA/ADD ADHD BESD |
| St Christopher's School, Hove | ST/ADHD ASP |
| St Christopher School, Letchworth Garden City | ASP |
| St Christopher's School, Totnes | RA/ADHD ASD BESD |
| St Crispin's School, Leicester | CA TS ST/ADD ADHD ASP BESD |
| St David's College, Llandudno | TS/ADD ADHD ASP |
| St David's School, Purley | RA/ASP |
| St Faith's at Ash School, Canterbury | CA RA ST/BESD |
| St Gabriel's, Berkshire | CA CO/ADD ASP BESD |
| St George's School for Girls, Edinburgh | CO RA/ADD ASP BESD |
| St Helen & St Katharine, Abingdon | CO/ADD ADHD |
| St Helen's School, Northwood | CO |
| St Hugh's School, Woodhall Spa | CA/ADD ADHD ASP ASD CB |
| St Ia School, St Ives | RA |
| St John's School, Leatherhead | CO/ADD ADHD ASP |
| St John's School, Porthcawl | RA TS |
| St John's-on-the-Hill, Chepstow | RA/ASP |
| St Joseph's College, Ipswich | RA ST/ADHD |
| St Joseph's in the Park, Hertford | ADD ADHD |
| St Joseph's School, Launceston | RA |
| St Lawrence College Junior School, Ramsgate | CA RA TS ST/ASP ASD |
| St Leonards School, St Andrews | ADD ADHD ASP |
| St Margaret's School, London | CO |
| St Margaret's School for Girls, Aberdeen | RA/ADD ADHD ASP |
| St Martin's School, Northwood | ST/ADHD ASP |
| St Mary's Junior School, Cambridge | CA RA |
| St Mary's Preparatory School, Lincoln | RA/ASD |
| St Piran's School, Hayle | ST |
| St Teresa's Catholic Independent & Nursery School, Princes Risborough | ADD ADHD ASP ASD |
| St Ursula's Convent School, Wigton | ASP ASD |
| St Ursula's High School, Westbury-on-Trym | RA/ADD ADHD ASP |
| Sacred Heart School, Swaffham | ST/ADD |
| Salterford House School, Nottingham | ST/ADHD ASP ASD |
| Sancton Wood School, Cambridge | ASP TOU |
| Sandroyd School, Salisbury | ADD |
| Seaton House School, Sutton | RA |
| Sedbergh Junior School, Sedbergh | TS/ASP ASD |
| Sedbergh School, Sedbergh | TS/ADD |

| | |
|---|---|
| Shiplake College, Henley-on-Thames | ST |
| Sibford School, Banbury | CO RA/ADD ADHD ASP ASD |
| South Hills School, Salisbury | ST |
| Steephill Independent School, Longfield | RA ST |
| Stonyhurst College, Clitheroe | CO ST/ADD ADHD ASP |
| Strathallan School, Perth | RA/ADD ADHD ASP |
| Streatham & Clapham High School, London | CA CO RA TS ST/ADD ASP ASD BESD CB |
| Streatham House School, Liverpool | ADD ADHD ASD |
| Summer Fields, Oxford | CO RA/ADD ADHD ASP BESD |
| Sutton High School GDST, Sutton | CO ST/BESD |
| Taunton Preparatory School, Taunton | ST/ADD ADHD |
| Taverham Hall Preparatory School, Norwich | ST/ADD |
| Teesside High School, Eaglescliffe | RA ST/ADHD ASP |
| Terra Nova School, Holmes Chapel | RA/ADHD ASP |
| Tettenhall College, Wolverhampton | ADD ADHD ASD |
| Thorngrove School, Newbury | RA |
| Thorpe Hall School, Southend-on-Sea | CA TS ST/ADD ADHD ASP ASD |
| Trinity School, Croydon | CO/ADD ADHD ASP ASD |
| Trinity School, Teignmouth | CA CO TS ST/ADD ADHD ASP |
| Tudor Hall School, Banbury | CO |
| University College School, London | CO |
| University College School Junior Branch, London | CO/ADD ADHD ASP |
| Walhampton School, Lymington | ST/ASP |
| Walthamstow Hall, Sevenoaks | CO ST/ASP |
| West Buckland Preparatory School, Barnstaple | RA/ADD ADHD |
| West Buckland School, Barnstaple | CA CO RA TS ST/ADD ADHD ASP BESD |
| West House School, Birmingham | CA ST/ADHD ASD TOU |
| Westminster Cathedral Choir School, London | RA/ADD |
| Westminster Tutors, London | RA/ASP |
| Withington Girls' School | ADD |
| Winchester College, Winchester | RA/ADD ADHD ASP |
| Winterfold House, Kidderminster | RA |
| Woodcote House School, Windlesham | RA/ADD ASP |
| Woodhouse Grove School, Apperley Bridge | ST/ADD ADHD ASP |
| Wrekin College, Wellington | ADD ADHD ASP ASD |
| Wycliffe Preparatory School, Stonehouse | RA/ADD |
| Wycombe Abbey School, High Wycombe | CO/ADHD |

# Physical and medical conditions

## Support provided/Currently have pupils with impairments or medical conditions

| | |
|---|---|
| The Abbey, Woodbridge | TW WA2 |
| Abbey College, Manchester | TW WA2 |

| | |
|---|---|
| Abbey Gate School, Chester | CA SM TW WA1 WA2/HEA HI VI |
| The Abbey School, Reading | SL SM TW WA2/HEA |
| Abbot's Hill School, Hemel Hempstead | IT SM/EPI HEA HI VI |
| Aberdour, Tadworth | RA SM/HEA |
| Adcote School for Girls, Shrewsbury | RA SM WA3 |
| Airthrie School, Cheltenham | HEA HI |
| Akeley Wood School, Buckingham | RA/HEA HI |
| Aldro School, Godalming | RA TW |
| Alleyn's School, London | RA SM TW/EPI HEA HI VI |
| Ampleforth College, York | RA WA3/CP EPI |
| Arnold Lodge School, Leamington Spa | RA/EPI HEA HI VI |
| Arnold School, Blackpool | SL SM WA2/HEA HI |
| Ashford School, Ashford | RA SM W WA3/HEA |
| Aston House School, London | CA SM TW WA3/HEA VI |
| Avenue House School, London | RA SM WA3/HEA |
| Babington House School, Chislehurst | RA/HI |
| Bablake School, Coventry | TW WA2 |
| Barfield School and Nursery, Farnham | W |
| Beeston Hall School, Cromer | CA SM TW/CP HEA HI IM |
| Belhaven Hill, Dunbar | TW WA2/HEA |
| Belmont House, Newton Mearns | WA1 |
| Benenden School, Cranbrook | RA SM WA2/HEA HI VI |
| Bilton Grange, Rugby | CA RA SM/HEA VI |
| Birchfield School, Wolverhampton | AT RA SM TW WA3/HEA |
| Birkdale School, Sheffield | HEA HI |
| Bishopsgate School, Egham | TW WA2/EPI VI |
| Bootham School, York | CA SM TW WA2/CP EPI HEA |
| Bournemouth Collegiate Prep School, Poole | W |
| Bournemouth Collegiate School, Bournemouth | AT RA WA3/HEA |
| Brabyns School | EPI |
| Bramcote School, Scarborough | CA RA SM WA3/HEA |
| Bramley School, Tadworth | IT SL SM TW W WA2/HEA |
| Bredon School, Tewkesbury | IT SL SM TW W WA2/HEA |
| Bricklehurst Manor Preparatory, Wadhurst | RA/HEA |
| Bristol Cathedral School, Bristol | RA/HEA VI |
| Broadwater Manor School, Worthing | RA/HEA |
| Bromsgrove Pre-preparatory and Nursery School, Bromsgrove | RA/HEA HI VI |
| Bronte School, Gravesend | CA RA SM WA3/HEA |
| Brooke Priory School, Oakham | CA SM TW W WA1 WA2/HEA |
| Brooklands School & Little Brooklands Nursery, Stafford | VI |
| Broomwood Hall School, London | IT RA SM TW/HEA HI VI |
| Buckingham College School, Harrow | AT RA/HEA |
| Bury Grammar School Boys, Bury | RA/EPI HEA HI |
| Cambridge Centre for Sixth-form Studies, Cambridge | RA SM/HEA |
| Cambridge Tutors College, Croydon | IT RA SM |

| | |
|---|---|
| Farringtons School, Chislehurst | RA SM WA3/EPI HEA HI VI |
| Felsted School, Felsted | AT CA IT RA SM TW WA2 WA3/EPI |
| Feltonfleet School, Cobham | HEA |
| Ferndale Preparatory School, Faringdon | RA WA3/EPI HEA HI VI |
| Finton House School, London | CA DS HL RA SM TW WA3/HEA HI VI |
| Fonthill Lodge, East Grinstead | CA RA SM TW W/HEA HI |
| Francis Holland School, Sloane Square SW1, London | RA/CP EPI HEA |
| The Froebelian School, Leeds | RA/HEA |
| Fulneck School, Leeds | VI |
| Gatehouse School, London | TW |
| Gateway Christian School, Ilkeston | RA/HEA |
| Gems Bolitho School, Penzance | IT SM TW/HI |
| George Watson's College, Edinburgh | CA SM TW WA2/CP EPI HEA HI IM VI W |
| Glebe House School, Hunstanton | RA |
| Godstowe Preparatory School, High Wycombe | CA RA SM/CP EPI HEA HI |
| Gracefield Preparatory School, Fishponds | WA3 |
| Great Houghton Preparatory School, Northampton | CA TW WA3/HEA VI |
| Green Hill School, Evesham | W/W |
| Greenbank Preparatory School, Cheadle | AT RA SM TW WA1 WA2/HEA |
| Greene's Tutorial College, Oxford | AT RA SM TW |
| Hampton School, Hampton | AT CA SM TW W WA2/EPI HEA HI VI |
| Handcross Park School, Haywards Heath | IT RA SM TW WA2/EPI HEA IM |
| Haresfoot Preparatory School, Berkhamsted | CA RA/HEA HI IM |
| Hazlegrove, Yeovil | SM TW/HEA HI |
| Heath House Preparatory School, London | W/W |
| Hethersett Old Hall School, Norwich | CA SM TW WA2/HEA IM |
| High Elms Manor School, Watford | AT CA TW WA1 WA2/HEA HI W |
| High March School, Beaconsfield | AT CA RA TW WA2/EPI HEA |
| High School of Dundee, Dundee | RA/HEA HI VI |
| Highclare School, Birmingham | AT CA RA SM/HEA HI |
| Hoe Bridge School, Woking | RA SM TW WA2 WA3/HEA |
| Holy Trinity School, Kidderminster | CA/EPI HEA HI IM |
| Horris Hill School, Newbury | SM/HI |
| Howell's School, Denbigh | SM WA3/EPI HEA |
| Howell's School, Llandaff GDST, Cardiff | RA WA3/HEA |
| Hurst Lodge School, Ascot | AT RA/EPI HEA HI IM VI |
| Hutchesons' Grammar School, Glasgow | SM TW W WA2/EPI HEA HI IM VI |
| Ilford Ursuline Preparatory School, Ilford | TW WA2 |
| The John Lyon School, Harrow | SM/EPI VI |
| Kent College Infant & Junior School, Canterbury | TW WA3/HEA |
| Kent College Pembury, Tunbridge Wells | SM WA3/HEA |
| Kew Green Preparatory School, Richmond | CA IT TW |
| Kilgraston, Perth | IT SM WA2/EPI |
| King Edward VII and Queen Mary School, Lytham St Annes | SM WA2/HEA VI |
| King's Bruton and Hazlegrove, Bruton | RA/CP HEA VI |

| | |
|---|---|
| North Cestrian Grammar School, Altrincham | CA SL SM TW W WA2/EPI HI W |
| Northbourne Park School, Deal | CA RA/HEA HI VI |
| Northcote Lodge School, London | RA SM/HEA |
| Northwood College, Northwood | CA RA/HEA HI IM VI |
| Notting Hill and Ealing High School GDST, London | RA/HEA VI |
| Nottingham High School, Nottingham | RA/EPI HEA HI IM VI |
| Oakfield School, Woking | RA |
| Oakhyrst Grange School, Caterham | RA/HI VI |
| The Old Hall School, Telford | SM WA3 |
| The Oratory Preparatory School, Reading | CA TW WA1/HEA HI |
| Ormer House Preparatory School, Alderney | W/W |
| Orwell Park, Ipswich | RA WA3/EPI HEA |
| Oswestry School Bellan House, Oswestry | RA/EPI |
| Oxford Tutorial College, Oxford | AT RA WA3 |
| Papplewick School, Ascot | RA |
| The Park School, Yeovil | AT RA WA3/HEA |
| The Perse School, Cambridge | AT CA HL RA SM TW WA2 WA3/EPI HEA VI |
| Plumtree School, Nottingham | W/W |
| Pocklington School, Pocklington | RA SM/HEA |
| Polam Hall, Darlington | AT CA RA SM WA3/HEA HI |
| Port Regis Preparatory School, Shaftesbury | DS HL RA SM TW/HEA HI |
| Portsmouth High School GDST, Southsea | RA/HEA |
| Prestfelde Preparatory School, Shrewsbury | SM WA2/EPI HEA |
| Primrose Independent School, London | AT CA/HEA |
| Prior Park Preparatory School, Cricklade | RA |
| Priory Preparatory School, Banstead | CA RA SM TW WA3/HEA |
| Priory School, Shanklin | W/W |
| The Purcell School, Bushey | RA/VI |
| Queen Elizabeth's Hospital, Bristol | RA SM W/CP EPI HEA HI |
| Queen Mary's School, Thirsk | AT SM WA3/EPI |
| Queen's Gate School, London | RA/HEA |
| Ramillies Hall School, Cheadle | CA RA/HI VI |
| Ranby House School, Retford | CA IT SM WA2/HEA |
| Raphael Independent School, Hornchurch | RA |
| The Rastrick Independent School, Brighouse | AT IT RA WA3/EPI HEA HI |
| Red House School, Norton | RA/EPI |
| The Red Maids' School, Bristol | CA SM TW/HEA VI |
| Reigate Grammar School, Reigate | CA SL SM WA2/EPI HEA HI |
| RGS The Grange, Worcester | WA2/EPI HEA HI |
| RGS Worcester & The Alice Ottley School, Worcester | RA/EPI HEA HI |
| The Richard Pate School, Cheltenham | CA TW WA2/CP EPI HEA VI |
| Richmond House School, Leeds | CA RA TW WA3/IM |
| Rickmansworth PNEU School, Rickmansworth | HEA |
| Riddlesworth Hall, Diss | IT RA SM WA3/HEA |
| Ripley Court School, Woking | RA SM/EPI HEA HI VI |

| School | Provision |
|---|---|
| St Hugh's School, Woodhall Spa | CA IT SM TW WA2/HEA HI IM VI |
| St Ia School, St Ives | RA/HEA |
| St John's School, Leatherhead | SM TW WA2 WA3/EPI HEA HI |
| St John's-on-the-Hill, Chepstow | RA SM/HEA |
| St Joseph's College, Ipswich | AT CA RA SL WA2/CP EPI HEA |
| St Joseph's Convent School, London | HEA |
| St Joseph's In The Park, Hertford | CA/HEA HI |
| St Joseph's School, Launceston | RA/HEA |
| St Lawrence College Junior School, Ramsgate | RA SM WA3/HEA HI |
| St Margaret's School, London | HL SM W WA3 |
| St Margaret's School for Girls, Aberdeen | RA/EPI |
| St Martin's School, Northwood | RA TW WA3/HEA |
| St Mary's Junior School, Cambridge | HEA HI |
| St Mary's Preparatory School, Lincoln | AT IT RA SM TW/CP HEA HI IM VI |
| St Mary's School, Ascot, Ascot | RA SM WA2/EPI HEA HI W |
| St Michael's, Barnstaple | TW/HI VI |
| St Nicholas House Kindergarten & Prep School, North Walsham | W/W |
| St Nicholas' School, Fleet | RA/HEA |
| St Paul's Cathedral School, London | RA SM |
| St Piran's School, Hayle | RA SM WA3/CP |
| St Teresa's Catholic Independent & Nursery School, Princes Risborough | CA TW WA2/HI |
| St Ursula's Convent School, Wigton | HEA |
| St Ursula's High School, Westbury-on-Trym | CP HEA |
| Steephill Independent School, Longfield | RA TW WA2 |
| Stonar School, Melksham | AT CA RA SM/EPI HEA VI |
| Stonyhurst College, Clitheroe | SM WA3/EPI HEA HI |
| Strathallan School, Perth | SM TW WA3/EPI HEA |
| Streatham & Clapham High School, London | AT CA HL IT SM TW WA2/EPI HEA HI IM VI W |
| Streatham House School, Liverpool | RA/HEA VI |
| The Stroud School, Romsey | RA |
| Summer Fields, Oxford | HL IT RA SM WA3/HEA HI |
| Sutton High School GDST, Sutton | AT SM TW WA3/HEA HI |
| Taunton Preparatory School, Taunton | SM WA2 |
| Taverham Hall Preparatory School, Norwich | RA SM/EPI HEA |
| Teesside High School, Eaglescliffe | RA/CP EPI HEA HI VI |
| Terra Nova School, Holmes Chapel | RA SM W/HEA |
| Tettenhall College, Wolverhampton | RA SM/EPI HEA |
| Thorngrove School, Newbury | RA/CP HEA |
| Thorpe Hall School, Southend-on-Sea | CA HL SL SM TW WA2/EPI HEA |
| Trinity School, Croydon | SL SM WA1/HEA VI |
| Trinity School, Teignmouth | CA IT SM TW WA2/HEA |
| Tudor Hall School, Banbury | CP EPI HEA |
| Twyford School, Winchester | RA SM/HEA |

| | |
|---|---|
| University College School, London | CA/VI |
| University College School Junior Branch, London | RA/HI VI |
| Walhampton School, Lymington | CA RA SM TW WA3/HEA HI |
| Walthamstow Hall, Sevenoaks | AT SL SM TW/HEA |
| Wellow House School, Newark | SM/EPI HEA |
| Westbourne School, Sheffield | EPI |
| West Buckland Preparatory School, Barnstaple | CA SM TW W WA2/HEA VI |
| West Buckland School, Barnstaple | CA/EPI HEA HI VI |
| West House School, Birmingham | RA TW/HEA |
| Westminster Cathedral Choir School, London | RA |
| Westminster Tutors, London | AT RA/HEA |
| Westonbirt School, Tetbury | EPI HEA HI |
| Wetherby Preparatory School, London | RA |
| Winchester College, Winchester | VI |
| Winterfold House, Kidderminster | RA WA3 |
| Withington Girls' School, Manchester | SM TW W/HEA HI |
| Wolverhampton Grammar School, Wolverhampton | TW WA2/IM |
| Woodcote House School, Windlesham | RA WA3 |
| Woodhouse Grove School, Apperley Bridge | SM/CP EPI HEA HI |
| Wycliffe College, Stonehouse | RA |
| Wycliffe Preparatory School, Stonehouse | CA RA SM/EPI HEA |
| Wycombe Abbey School, High Wycombe | RA SM TW WA3/EPI HEA |

## PART FIVE

# REFERENCE SECTION

# Council for the Registration of Schools Teaching Dyslexic Pupils (CReSTeD)

Registered charity number 1052103

CReSTeD (The Council for the Registration of Schools Teaching Dyslexic Pupils) produces an annual register of schools that provide for children with specific learning difficulties (dyslexia). CReSTeD is still concerned mainly with dyslexia provision, but dyslexia rarely exists in isolation and so we now also include dyspraxia, dyscalculia, Attention Deficit Disorder and pragmatic and semantic language difficulties.

The aim is to help parents and those who advise them to choose a school that has been approved to published criteria. CReSTeD was established in 1989 and works alongside the British Dyslexia Association and Dyslexia Action. Schools wishing to be included in the Register are visited by a CReSTeD consultant, whose report is considered by the CReSTeD Council before registration can be finalized.

Consulting the Register should enable parents to decide which schools they wish to approach for further information. Students with SpLD have a variety of difficulties and so have a wide range of special needs. An equally wide range of teaching approaches is necessary. CReSTeD has therefore grouped schools together under six broad categories, which are designed to help parents match their child's needs to an appropriate philosophy and provision. The six categories of schools are:

1 *Dyslexia Specialist Provision (DSP) Schools.* The school is established primarily to teach pupils with dyslexia. The curriculum and timetable are designed to meet specific needs in a holistic, coordinated manner, with a significant number of teaching staff holding nationally recognized qualifications in teaching dyslexic pupils.

2 *Specialist Provision Schools (SPS).* The school is established primarily to teach pupils with SpLD. The curriculum and timetable are designed to meet specific needs in a holistic, coordinated manner with a significant number of staff qualified in teaching dyslexic pupils.

3 *Dyslexia Unit (DU)*. The school has a designated unit or centre that provides specialist tuition on a small group or individual basis, according to need. The unit or centre is an adequately resourced teaching area under the management of a senior specialist teacher, who coordinates the work of other specialist teachers and ensures ongoing liaison with all mainstream teachers. This senior specialist teacher will probably have head of department status, and will certainly have significant input into the curriculum design and delivery.

4 *Specialist Classes (SC)*. Schools where SpLD pupils are taught in separate classes within the school for some lessons, most probably English and mathematics. These are taught by teachers with qualifications in teaching SpLD pupils. These teachers are deemed responsible for communicating with the pupils' other subject teachers.

5 *Withdrawal System (WS)*. Schools where SpLD pupils are withdrawn from appropriately selected lessons for specialist tuition from a teacher qualified in teaching SpLD pupils. There is ongoing communication between mainstream and specialist teachers.

6 *Maintained Sector (MS)*. Maintained schools where the school supports dyslexic pupils to access the curriculum, where there is a system of identifying dyslexic pupils, and where there is a withdrawal system for individualized literacy support. There is a positive ongoing communication between mainstream and SEN staff, and the Senior Management Team (SMT).

NB: listings below contain details of DSP, DU, SC and WS schools only.

A school in one category may also offer the sort of care found in a different, less intensive category. For example, a Dyslexia Unit category school may offer a Withdrawal System. If a school seems appropriate in other ways, parents should check directly with the school.

CReSTeD examines the adequacy of the school's provision for SpLD pupils. The school is likely to have been inspected by Ofsted (or its equivalent) for both the education and boarding provision. Such reports, which may be obtainable from the school, deal with many statutory matters including Criminal Record Bureau checks. Information obtained from these statutory reports assist with the production of the CReSTeD consultant's report on a school.

Schools listed have chosen to be visited and registered. They are normally revisited at three-yearly intervals.

A copy of the Register, together with further information about CReSTeD, may be obtained by contacting CReSTeD on 01242 604852, by e-mail at admin@crested.org.uk, or by writing to The Administrator, Greygarth, Litttleworth, Winchcombe, Cheltenham GL54 5BT. Alternatively, visit the website at www.crested.org.uk.

# Dyslexia Specialist Provision Schools – DSP

**Appleford School**
Shrewton, Salisbury, Wiltshire SP3 4HL
Tel: (01980) 621020
Fax: (01980) 621366
E-mail: secretary@appleford.wilts.sch.uk
Independent; rural; boarding, weekly boarding and day
83 boys and girls 7–14

**Blossom House School**
8A The Drive, Wimbledon, London SW20 8TG
Tel: 0208 946 7348
Fax: 0208 944 5848
Village; independent; day
160 boys and girls 3–19

**Brown's School**
Cannock House, Hawstead Lane, Chelsfield, Orpington, Kent BR6 7PH
Tel: (01689) 876816
Fax: (01689) 827118
E-mail: info@brownsschool.co.uk
Independent; rural; day
40 boys and girls 6–13

**Centre Academy**
92 St John's Hill Battersea London SW11 1SH
Tel: 020 7738 2344
Fax: 020 7738 9862
E-mail: info@centreacademy.net
City; Independent; Day
46 Boys and 9 Girls 10–19

**More House School**
Moons Hill, Frensham, Farnham,
Surrey GU10 3AP
Tel: (01252) 792303
Fax: (01252) 797601
E-mail: schooloffice@morehouseschool.co.uk
Independent; rural; boarding, weekly boarding and day
396 boys 8–18

**Northease Manor School**
Rodmell, Lewes, East Sussex BN7 3EY
Tel: (01273) 472915
Fax: (01273) 472202
E-mail: office@northease.co.uk
Independent; rural; weekly boarding and day
85 boys and girls 10–17

**St David's College**
Llandudno Conwy LL30 1RD
Tel: (01492) 875974
Fax: (01492) 870383
E-mail: hmsec@stdavidscollege.co.uk
Independent; rural; boarding; weekly boarding and day
250 boys and girls 11–18

**Stanbridge Earls School**
Stanbridge Lane, Romsey, Hampshire SO51 0ZS
Tel: (01794) 529400
Fax: (01794) 511201
E-mail: admin@stanbridgeearls.co.uk
Independent; rural; boarding and day
190 boys and girls 10–19

**Sunnydown School**
Portley House, 152 Whyteleafe Road, Caterham,
Surrey CR3 5ED
Tel: (01883) 342281
Fax: (01883) 341342
E-mail: head@sunnydown.surrey.sch.uk
Local authority; edge of town; weekly boarding and day
70 boys 11–16

**Trinity School**
11-13 New Road, Rochester, Kent ME1 1BG
Tel: (01634) 812233
Fax: (01634) 812233
E-mail: trinityschoolrochester@btconnect.com
Independent; town; day
70 boys and girls 6–18+

# Dyslexia Unit – DU

**Avon House School**
490 High Road, Woodford Green, Essex IG8 0PN
Tel: (020) 8504 1749
Fax: (020) 8505 5337
E-mail: avonhousedyslexiacentre@msn.com
Independent; edge of town; day
100 boys and 87 girls 3–11

**Barnardiston Hall Preparatory School**
Hall Road, Barnardiston, Haverhill,
Suffolk CB9 7TG
Tel: (01440) 786316
Fax: (01440) 786355
E-mail: lesley@barnardiston-hall.co.uk
Independent; rural; boarding, weekly boarding and day
111 boys and 100 girls 2–13

**Bethany School**
Curtisden Green, Goudhurst, Cranbrook, Kent
TN17 1LB
Tel: (01580) 211273
Fax: (01580) 211151
E-mail: registrar@bethanyschool.org.uk
Independent; rural; weekly boarding and day
400 boys and girls 11–18

**Bloxham School**
Bloxham, near Banbury, Oxfordshire OX15 4PE
Tel: (01295) 720222
Fax: (01295) 721897
E-mail: registrar@bloxhamschool.com
Independent; rural; boarding, weekly boarding
and day
430 boys and girls 11–18

**Bredon School**
Pull Court, Bushley, Tewkesbury, Gloucestershire
GL20 6AH
Tel: (01684) 293156
Fax: (01684) 298008
E-mail: enquiries@bredonschool.co.uk
Independent; rural; boarding, weekly boarding
and day
240 boys and girls 4–18

**Clayesmore Preparatory School**
Iwerne Minster, Blandford Forum,
Dorset DT11 8PH
Tel: (01747) 811707
Fax: (01747) 811692
E-mail: prepsec@clayesmore.com
Independent; village; boarding and day
177 boys and 10 girls 3–13

**Clayesmore School**
Iwerne Minster, Blandford Forum,
Dorset DT11 8LL
Tel: (01747) 812122/81311
Fax: (01747) 813187
E-mail: hmsec@clayesmore.com
Independent; rural; boarding and day
425 boys and girls 13–18

**Clifton College Preparatory School**
The Avenue, Clifton, Bristol BS8 3HE
Tel: (0117) 315 7502
Fax: (0117) 315 7504
E-mail: admissions@clifton-college.avon.sch.uk
Independent; edge of town; boarding, weekly
boarding and day
400 boys and girls 8–13

**Cobham Hall**
Cobham, Gravesend, Kent DA12 3BL
Tel: (01474) 823371
Fax: (01474) 825902
E-mail: enquiries@cobhamhall.com
Independent; rural; boarding; weekly and day
180 girls 11–18

**Danes Hill School**
Leatherhead Road, Oxshott, Surrey KT22 0JG
Tel: (01372) 842509
Fax: (01372) 844452
E-mail: lel@daneshill.surrey.sch.uk
Independent; rural; day
880 boys and girls 3–13

**DLD College**
100 Marylebone Lane, London W1U 2Q
Tel: 020 7935 8411
Fax: 020 7935 0755
E-mail: dld@dld.org
Urban city; independent; day, boarding
142 boys; 127 girls; 14–19

**Ellesmere College**
Ellesmere, Shropshire SY12 9AB
Tel: (01691) 622321
Fax: (01691) 623286
E-mail: hmsecretary@ellesmere.com
Independent; rural; boarding and day
610 boys and girls 7–18

**Finborough School**
The Hall, Great Finborough, Stowmarket, Suffolk
IP14 3EF
Tel: (01449) 773600
Fax: (01449) 773601
E-mail: admin@finborough.suffolk.sch.uk
Independent; village; boarding, weekly boarding
and day
275 boys and girls 2½–18

**Fulneck School**
Fulneck, Pudsey, Leeds, West Yorkshire LS28
8DS
Tel: (0113) 257 0235
Fax: (0113) 255 7316
E-mail: general@fulneckschool.co.uk
Independent; semi-rural; boarding, weekly
boarding and day
220 boys and 192 girls 3–18

**Hazlegrove School, King's Bruton Preparatory
School**
Sparkford, Yeovil, Somerset BA22 7JH
Tel: (01963) 440314
Fax: (01963) 440569
E-mail: office@hazlegrove.co.uk
Independent; rural; boarding and day
388 boys and girls 2–13

## Holmwood House School
Chitts Hill, Lexden, Colchester, Essex CO3 9ST
Tel: (01206) 574305
Fax: (01206) 768269
E-mail: headmaster@holmwood.essex.sch.uk
Independent; edge of town; weekly boarding
and day
211 boys and 117 girls 4–13

## Kingham Hill School
Kingham, Chipping Norton, Oxfordshire OX7 6TH
Tel: 01608 658999
Fax: 01608 658658
E-mail: admissions@kingham-hill.oxon.sch.uk
Rural; independent; boarding; day
285 boys and girls; 11–18

## King's School
Bruton, Somerset BA10 0ED
Tel: (01749) 814200
Fax: (01749) 813426
E-mail: office@kingsbruton.com
Independent; rural; boarding and day
315 boys and girls 13–18

## Kingsley School Bideford
(previously Grenville College) Northdown Road,
Bideford, Devon EX39 3LY
Tel: (01237) 426200
E-mail: admissions@kingsleyschoolbideford.co.uk
Independent; rural town; boarding and day
157 boys and 101 girls 11–18

## Kingswood House School
56 West Hill, Epsom, Surrey KT19 8LG
Tel: (01372) 723590
Fax: (01372) 749081
E-mail: office@kingswoodhouse.org
Independent; rural; day
190 boys 3–13, girls 3–7

## Lime House School
Holm Hill, Dalston, Carlisle, Cumbria CA5 7BX
Tel: (01228) 710225
Fax: (01228) 710508
E-mail: lhsoffice@aol.com
Independent; rural; boarding and day
230 boys and girls 4–18

## Mayville High School
35 St Simon's Road, Southsea,
Hampshire PO5 2PE
Tel: (02392) 734847
Fax: (02392) 293649
E-mail: enquiries@mayvillehighschool.com
Independent; city; day
242 boys and 216 girls 2–16

## Millfield Preparatory School
Edgarley Hall, Glastonbury, Somerset BA6 8LD
Tel: 01458 832446
Fax: 01458 833679
E-mail: office@millfieldprep.com
Rural; independent; boarding and day
212 boys and 174 girls 7–13

## Moyles Court School
Moyles Court, Ringwood, Hampshire BH24 3NR
Tel: (01425) 472856
Fax: (01425) 474715
E-mail: info@moylescourt.co.uk
Independent; rural; boarding and day
94 boys and 71 girls 4–16

## Newlands School
Eastbourne Road, Seaford, Sussex BN25 4NP
Tel: (01323) 490000
Fax: (01323) 898420
E-mail: enquiries@newlands-school.com
Independent; edge of town; boarding and day
120 boys and girls 5–18

## Ramillies Hall School
Ramillies Avenue, Cheadle Hulme,
Cheshire SK8 7AJ
Tel: (0161) 485 3804
Fax: (0161) 486 6021
E-mail: study@ramillieshall.co.uk
Independent; rural; boarding, weekly boarding
and day
120 boys and girls 7–13

## St Bees School
St Bees, Cumbria CA27 0DS
Tel: 01946 828000
Fax: 01946 828011
E-mail: mailbox@st-bees-school.co.uk
Village; independent; boarding week; boarding;
day
300 boys and girls 4–18

## Sidcot School
Winscombe, North Somerset BS25 1PD
Tel: (01934) 843102
Fax: (01934) 844181
E-mail: info@sidcot.org.uk
Independent; rural; boarding and day
520 boys and girls 3–18

## Slindon College
Slindon House, Arundel, West Sussex BN18 0RH
Tel: (01243) 814320
Fax: (01243) 814702
E-mail: registrar@slindoncollege.co.uk
Independent; village; boarding, weekly boarding
and day
100 boys 9–16

**Tettenhall College**
Wood Road, Tettenhall, Wolverhampton,
West Midlands WV6 8QX
Tel: (01902) 751119
Fax: (01902) 741940
E-mail: head@tettcoll.co.uk
Independent; urban; boarding, weekly boarding
and day
495 boys and girls 2–18

**Walhampton School**
Lymington, Hampshire SO41 5ZG
Tel: (01590) 672013
Fax: (01590) 678498
E-mail: office@walhampton.com
Independent; rural; boarding, weekly boarding
and day
197 boys and girls 7–13

**Wycliffe College**
Bath Road, Stonehouse, Gloucestershire
GL10 2JQ
Tel: (01453) 822432
Fax: (01453) 827634
E-mail: Deborah.mccarthy@wycliffe.co.uk
Independent; rural; boarding and day
259 boys and 153 girls 13–18

**Wycliffe College Preparatory School**
Ryeford Hall, Stonehouse, Gloucestershire
GL10 2LD
Tel: 01453 820470
Fax: 01453 827634
E-mail: prep@wycliffe.co.uk
Rural; independent; boarding; day
216 boys and 171 girls 2½–13
Specialist Classes – SC

# Specialist Classes – SC

**Bruern Abbey School**
Chesterton House, Chesterton, Oxfordshire
OX26 1UY
Tel: (01869) 242448
Fax: (01869) 243949
E-mail: secretary@bruernabbey.org
Independent; rural; weekly boarding and day
87 boys 4–11

**Mount Carmel Preparatory School**
1 Aughton Park Drive, Aughton, Ormskirk,
Lancashire L39 5BU
Tel: (01695) 473254
E-mail: head@mountcarmel.me.uk
Independent; city; day
130 boys and girls 2–16

**St Crispin's School**
6 St Mary's Road, Leicester LE2 1XA
Tel: (0116) 270 7648
Fax: (0116) 270 9647
E-mail: enquiries@stcrispins.co.uk
Independent; city; day
130 boys and girls 2–16
Withdrawal System – WS

# Withdrawal System – WS

**Kilgraston School**
Bridge of Earn, Perthshire PH2 9BQ
Tel: (01738) 812257
Fax: (01738) 813410
E-mail: headoffice@kilgraston.com
Independent; rural; weekly boarding and day
255 pupils, girls 5–18, boys 5–13

**Manor House School**
Manor House Lane, Little Bookham,
Surrey KT23 4EN
Tel: 01372 458538
Fax: 01372 450514
E-mail: admin@manorhouseschool.org
Rural urban; independent; day
354 girls 2–16

**Milton Abbey School**
Blandford Forum, Dorset DT11 0BZ
Tel: (01258) 880484
Fax: (01258) 881910
E-mail: info@miltonabbey.co.uk
Independent; rural; boarding and day
197 boys 13–18, girls 16–18

**Our Lady's Convent School**
Burton Street, Loughborough, Leicestershire
LE11 2DT
T/Fax: (01509) 263901
E-mail: office@olcs.leics.sch.uk
Independent; town; boarding and day
5 boys 3–18 and 420 girls 3–13

**Prior Park Preparatory School**
Calcutt Street, Cricklade, Wiltshire SN6 6BB
Tel: (01793) 750275
Fax: (01793) 750910
E-mail: prepoffice@priorpark.co.uk
Independent; edge of town; boarding, weekly
boarding and day
230 boys and girls 3–13

**St John's School**
Newton, Porthcawl CF36 5NP
Tel: 01656 783404
Fax: 01656 783535
E-mail: head@stjohnsschool-porthcawl.com
Coastal, rural; independent; day
85 boys and 50 girls 3–16

**St Lawrence College**
Ramsgate, Kent CT11 7AE
Tel: 01843 587666
Fax: 01843 572915
E-mail: info@slcuk.com
Coastal, rural; independent; day, boarding
213 boys and 129 girls 11–18

**Thames Christian College**
Wye Street, Battersea, London SW11 2HB
Tel: (020) 7228 3933
Fax: (020) 7924 1112
E-mail: info@thameschristiancollege.org.uk
Independent; city; day
100 boys and girls 11–16

**Ysgol Rhydygors**
Llanstephan Road, Johnstown, Carmarthen
SA31 3NQ
Tel: (01267) 231171
Fax: (01267) 220336
E-mail: head.rhydygors@ysgolccc.org.uk
Local Authority Special School; semi-rural;
weekly boarding
45 boys and girls 7–16

# Useful Addresses and Associations

**Action for Blind People**
14–16 Verney Road, London SE16 3DZ
Tel: (020) 7635 4800
Freephone Helpline: (0800) 915 4666
Fax: (020) 7635 4900

Action for Blind People provides free and confidential support for blind and partially sighted people in all aspects of their lives. One call to Action ensures that visually impaired people receive help with anything from finding a job, applying for benefit, housing issues, aids and adaptations, holiday breaks or information on local services. We also offer advice to people who have a visually impaired friend or family member. Whatever the need, Action can help.

**Action for Sick Children**
32b Buxton Road, High Lane, Stockport
SK6 8BH
Helpline: (0800) 074 4519
Website: www.actionforsickchildren.org
Contact: Pamela Barnes, Chairman

Offers support and advice for the parents of sick children. Aims to join parents and professionals in promoting high-quality health care for children in hospital and at home. Services include publications, research and a branch network which offers advice and support.

**ADDISS**
PO Box 340, Edgware, Middlesex
HA8 9HL
Tel: (020) 8952 2800
Fax: (020) 8952 2909
E-mail: info@addiss.co.uk

The National Attention Deficit Disorder Information and Support Service provides people-friendly information and resources to anyone who needs assistance – parents, sufferers, teachers or health professionals.

**Advice Service Capability Scotland (ASCS)**
11 Ellersly Road, Edinburgh EH12 6HY
Tel: (0131) 313 5510
Textphone: (0131) 346 2529
Fax: (0131) 346 1681
E-mail: ascs@capability-scotland.org.uk
Website: www.capability-scotland.org.uk

Capability Scotland will be a major ally in supporting disabled people to achieve full equality and to have choice and control of their lives by 2020. Capability Scotland provides flexible services to children, young people and adults with a range of disabilities and their families and carers. These include community living, day and residential services, employment services, respite/short breaks, education and learning, family support and activities, and disability equality training. ASCS (Advice Service Capability Scotland) is a national disability advice and information service. ASCS has a small lending library, which can be used by anyone living in Scotland.

**Advisory Centre for Education (ACE) Ltd**
1C Aberdeen Studios, 22 Highbury Grove, London N5 2DQ
**General Advice:** (0808) 800 5793
Mon–Thurs 10 am–1 pm
**E-mail:** enquiries@ace-ed.org.uk
**Website:** www.ace-ed.org.uk

The Advisory Centre for Education is an independent national education advice centre that offers free and confidential telephone advice to parents from 10 am to 1 pm on the above numbers. ACE helps explain the state school system, formal procedures, and aspects of education law, particularly in the areas of admission and exclusion appeals, and special educational needs issues. ACE has a full range of publications described in a free publication leaflet and offers training to parents' groups, governors, LEA officers and teachers. Contact the business line 020 7697 1140 for these services, e-mail ACE at enquiries@ace-ed.org.uk or write to ACE at the above address. Information on all these issues is also available on the ACE website www.ace-ed.org.uk, which is currently being updated.

**Afasic**
Olive House, 1st Floor, 20 Bowling Green Lane, London EC1R 0BD

Admin: (020) 7490 9410
Helpline: (0845) 355 5577/
(020) 7490 9420
E-mail: info@afasic.org.uk
Website: www.afasic.org.uk

Afasic represents children and young adults with speech, language and communication difficulties and supports and provides information to parents/carers and professionals.

## Association of Educational Psychologists

26 The Avenue, Durham DH1 4ED
Tel: (0191) 384 9512
Fax: (0191) 386 5287
E-mail: aep@aep.org.uk
Website: www.aep.org.uk
Secretary: Charles Ward

The AEP is the independently certificated trade union and professional association for educational psychologists. It represents the professional and employment interests of 93 per cent of qualified educational psychologists working in the UK, most of whom work for local government. It is the only professional association or trade union in the UK organized exclusively by and for educational psychologists. The AEP is unequivocally the voice of the educational psychology profession and has just over 3,000 members.

## Association of National Specialist Colleges (NATSPEC)

39 Sanders Road, Quorn, Loughborough, Leicestershire LE12 8JN
Tel/Fax: (01509) 554357
E-mail: kevin.obrien43@ntlworld.com
Website: www.natspec.org.uk
Chief Executive: Kevin O'Brien

NATSPEC member colleges seek to offer the widest choice of innovative, high-quality, cost-effective and appropriate further education and training, in residential or day settings, for young people and adults with learning difficulties and/or disabilities.

## Association for Spina Bifida and Hydrocephalus (ASBAH)

ASBAH House, 42 Park Road, Peterborough PE1 2UQ
Helpline: (0845) 450 7755
Fax: (01733) 555985
E-mail: helpline@asbah.org
Website: www.asbah.org
Executive Director: Ms Jackie Bland, MA

ASBAH provides information, advice and support for people with spina bifida and/or hydrocephalus, and their families, carers and professionals.

## Autism Independent UK

(formerly The Society for the Autistically Handicapped – SFTAH)
199–203 Blandford Avenue, Kettering, Northants NN16 9AT
Tel: (01536) 523274
Fax: (01536) 523274
E-mail: autism@autismuk.com
Website: www.autismuk.com

Training, group homes, information, free membership via the website. Forum, educational videos and animation video.

## Beat: beating eating disorders

Wensum House, 103 Prince of Wales Road, Norwich, Norfolk NR1 1DW
Admin: (0300) 123 3355
Helpline: (0845) 634 1414
Mon–Fri 10.30 am–8.30 pm, Sat 1–4.30 pm
Youth Helpline: (0845) 634 7650
Mon–Fri 4–8.30 pm, Sat 1–4.30 pm
(18 years and under)

Fax: (01603) 664915
E-mail: info@b-eat.co.uk
Website: www.b-eat.co.uk

Beat is the leading UK-wide charity providing information, help and support for people affected by eating disorders – anorexia, bulimia nervosa and binge eating disorder. Details of local contacts are freely available to the caller ringing our helpline. Beat's vision is that eating disorders will be beaten. Beat services and support include:

*Helplines*: national telephone, e-mail and text helplines.

*Self Help*: UK-wide network of groups run by volunteers.

*Information*: a website at www.b-eat.co.uk, leaflets and literature for individuals and organizations, details and contacts for treatment services in the UK.

*Training*: courses and conferences for health, education and social care staff.

*Media*: information and resources for journalists and broadcasters.

*Research*: support for academic and clinical studies, and research trials.

**bibic**
Knowle Hall, Bridgwater,
Somerset TA7 8PJ
**Tel**: (01278) 684060
**E-mail**: info@bibic.org.uk
**Website**: www.bibic.org.uk
**Director of Family Services**:
Vivienne Streeter

bibic exists to maximize the potential of children with learning difficulties affecting their sensory communication, social, motor and learning abilities. Working with parents and carers, bibic has a valuable support system that offers time to talk, expert advice and practical help. Individual programmes are produced to improve the quality of life for the whole family unit. Therapists teach the child's parents or carers how to help their child's development with carefully tailored holistic programmes and a comprehensive nutrition programme. Progress is carefully monitored and programmes are adjusted as and when necessary.

## The Bobath Centre for Children with Cerebral Palsy

250 East End Road, London N2 8AU
Tel: (020) 8444 3355
Fax: (020) 8444 3399

The Bobath treatment concept was developed by Dr and Mrs Bobath in the 1940s and is a holistic interdisciplinary approach involving occupational physio- and speech and language therapists. Treatment is provided on an individual basis (outpatient only), and therapists teach parents and carers how to continue therapy at home/or in school. A letter of referral is required from the child's consultant paediatrician or general practitioner giving full medical history and birth details. Letters should be addressed to the Appointments and Funding Manager. On the basis of this information an application for funding may be made to the NHS. When the Centre has been notified in writing that its fees will be met, a consultation or course of treatment will be offered. If you would like further information, this may be obtained from the Appointments and Funding Manager. The Centre organizes postgraduate training courses in the Bobath treatment approach for physio-,

occupational and speech and language therapists who are working with children who have cerebral palsy. Details may be obtained from the Training Coordinator. Further information is available on the website (www.bobath.org.uk).

## Breakthrough Deaf/Hearing Integration

Alangale House, The Close, West Hill Campus, Bristol Road, Birmingham B29 6LN
Tel: (0121) 472 6447
Fax: (0121) 471 4368

## British Association of Teachers of the Deaf (BATOD)

Tel: (0845) 643 5181
E-mail: exec@batod.org.uk
Website: www.batod.org.uk
National Executive Officer:
Mr Paul Simpson

The British Association of Teachers of the Deaf (BATOD) is the only Association representing the interests of Teachers of the Deaf in the UK. BATOD promotes excellence in the education of all deaf children, young people and adults and safeguards the interests of Teachers of the Deaf. Nationally, conferences are organized to develop the professional expertise of Association members and to promote issues connected with the education of deaf children. There are eight regions/nations, which organize workshops and activities locally. Courses and conferences are open to non-members. Associate membership is open to those who are not qualified Teachers of the Deaf.

## British Deaf Association

10th Floor, Coventry Point, Market Way,
Coventry CV1 1EA
**Tel (voice):** (02476) 550 936
**Textphone:** (02476) 550 393
**Videophone:** 841 297 143
**Fax:** (02476) 221 541
**E-mail:** helpline@bda.org.uk
**Website:** www.bda.org.uk

## British Dyslexia Association

Unit 8, Bracknell Beeches, Old Bracknell
Lane, Bracknell RG12 7BW
**Tel:** (0845) 251 9003
**Helpline:** (0845) 251 9002
**Fax:** (0845) 251 9005
**E-mail:** admin@bdadyslexia.org.uk
**Helpline e-mail:** helpline@bdadyslexia.
org.uk
**Website:** www.bdadyslexia.org.uk
**Helpline/Information Service:**
10 am–4.00 pm Mon, Thurs and Fri;
5.00 pm–7.00 pm Tues and Weds

The British Dyslexia Association is the
voice of dyslexic people, working to
establish a dyslexia-friendly society
where barriers to dyslexic people do not
exist. We run many services to reach this
aim. Our services include training events,
Inset days and conferences to inform
people about dyslexia, ie courses for
teachers on how to identify dyslexia and
provide the required adjustments. We
also run a national helpline (accredited
by the Telephone Helpliners Association)
manned by specialist teachers and
knowledgeable volunteers to give advice
and information about dyslexia. All our
calls are treated confidentially and the
information, advice and signposting
given are always impartial, empowering
people to make choices.

## British Institute of Learning Disabilities (BILD)

Campion House, Green Street,
Kidderminster, Worcestershire DY10 1JL
**Tel:** (01562) 723010
**Fax:** (01562) 723029
**E-mail:** enquiries@bild.org.uk
**Website:** www.bild.org.uk

BILD works towards improving the quality
of life of people with learning disabilities.

## The British Kidney Patient Association (BKPA)

3 The Windmills, St Mary's Close Turk
Street, Alton GU34 1EF
**Tel:** (01420) 541424
**Fax:** (01420) 89438
**E-mail:** info@britishkidney-pa.co.uk
**Website:** www.britishkidney-pa.co.uk
**Contact:** Ms Rosemary Macri

The BKPA was founded in 1975 by
Elizabeth Ward, whose son was
diagnosed with kidney failure at the age
of 13 years. At that time there was no
national association concerned with the
plight of Britain's kidney patients. Now
kidney patients can turn to the BKPA for
support, advice and, perhaps more
importantly, financial help and a much
needed break with their families.
The work of the BKPA falls roughly into
two halves engendered by two quite
separate needs: on the one hand the
material and physical needs of the
patients and their relatives, and on the
other the necessity to lobby for more
and improved facilities and increased
governmental funding, so that all parents
may benefit from improvements in
technology and pharmaceutical
achievements.

## British Psychological Society

48 Princess Road East,
Leicester LE1 7DR
Tel: (0116) 254 9568

The British Psychological Society is the professional body incorporated by Royal Charter to maintain standards for the profession of psychology in the UK. The Directory of Chartered Psychologists, published by the Society, contains the names and addresses of Chartered Educational Psychologists who can provide services for parents and children with Special Educational Needs.

## British Retinitis Pigmentosa Society

PO Box 350, Buckingham MK18 1GZ
Tel: (01280) 821334
Helpline: (0845) 123 2354
Fax: (01280) 815900
E-mail: info@brps.org.uk
Website: www.brps.org.uk

## The British Stammering Association

15 Old Ford Road, London E2 9PJ
Tel: (020) 8983 1003 (3 lines)
Helpline: (0845) 603 2001
Fax: (020) 8983 3591
E-mail: ch@stammering.org
Website: www.stammering.org
Tel/Fax: (01606) 77374 (Visits and training arranged without charge)

The BSA is the largest charity in Europe helping children who stammer. It provides free information for parents, teenagers and teachers, and a helpline is available to discuss specific problems. It also offers a mail-order service on specialist publications and a video pack for teachers. Training courses for teachers are held across the country, giving advice on how to help and support pupils who stammer. The BSA has produced three CDs to support pupils who stammer in school. Details of its services can be found on its website at www.stammering.org.

## Brittle Bone Society

Great Paterson House, 30 Guthrie Street, Dundee DD1 5BS
Tel: (01382) 204446
Helpline: (0800) 0282459
Fax: (01382) 206771
E-mail: bbs@brittlebone.org
Website: www.brittlebone.org

The Society provides advice, encouragement and practical help for anyone affected by osteogenesis imperfecta (brittle bones).

## Cambian Group

4th Floor, Waterfront Building, Chancellors Road, Hammersmith Embankment, London W6 9RU
Tel: +44 (0)20 8735 6174
Fax: +44 (0)20 8735 6151
Website: www.cambiangroup.com
SEN Helpline: 0800 288 9779;
www.sen.cambiangroup.com

'Outstanding' specialist residential schools for children and young adults with autism, Asperger's syndrome and complex needs.

For over 30 years Cambian has been challenging the limitations of ASD, helping children and young people with autism, Asperger's syndrome and complex needs achieve exceptional outcomes. Our specialist residential schools are continuously rated

'Outstanding' by Ofsted. We are trusted by over 5,000 parents and work in partnership with 70 local authorities.

### Centre for Studies on Inclusive Education (CSIE)

The Park, Daventry Road, Knowle, Bristol BS4 1DQ
Tel: (0117) 353 3150
Fax: (0117) 353 3150
E-mail: admin@csie.org.uk
Website: www.csie.org.uk

The Centre for Studies on Inclusive Education (CSIE), set up in 1982, is a registered charity working to promote equality and eliminate discrimination in education. At the heart of CSIE's work is the belief that everyone is equal. Every child and young person, therefore, should feel welcome, visible and respected, regardless of attainment, gender, gender identity, ethnic/cultural background, impairment, or any other perceived or actual difference. The Centre works towards raising public awareness and transforming education so that everyone can benefit from, and contribute to, life in local schools.

### Cerebra – For Brain Injured Children and Young People

Lyric Building, King Street, Carmarthen SA31 1BD
Tel: (0800) 323 1159
Helpline: (0800) 328 1159
Fax: (01267) 244213
E-mail: info@cerebra.org.uk
Website: www.cerebra.org.uk

Our Parent Support team provides free information, contact services and legal advice. Cerebra also funds research into causes, prevention, evidence-based treatments and therapies. A grant scheme provides respite holidays, equipment and necessities not available elsewhere. The postal lending library stocks books, sensory toys, CD-ROMS and videos. A bulletin is published quarterly.

### The Child Psychotherapy Trust

Star House, 104–108 Grafton Road, London NW5 4BD
Tel: (020) 7284 1355
Fax: (020) 7284 2755
E-mail: info@psychotherapy.org.uk
Website: www.childpsychotherapytrust.org.uk

Launched in 1987, the Child Psychotherapy Trust is a national charity dedicated to increasing the number of child psychotherapists available throughout the UK to treat emotionally damaged children, adolescents and their families. It is convinced of the benefits of treating emotional difficulties early, before they become entrenched. The Trust publishes a range of material including a series of Understanding Childhood leaflets, written by child psychotherapists, for parents, carers and people working with children and families, which aim to promote understanding of children's emotional health, development and behaviour. It also publishes a newsletter available for £10 per year. The Trust supports and manages various outreach projects, but does not itself offer psychotherapy or referral services.

### Children's Legal Centre

University of Essex, Wivenhoe Park, Colchester, Essex CO4 3SQ

Tel: (01206) 877910 (General enquiries)
Fax: (01206) 877963
E-mail: clc@essex.ac.uk
Website: www.childrenslegalcentre.com

The Children's Legal Centre is a unique, independent national charity concerned with law and policy affecting children and young people. It opened in 1981 as the major UK project for the International Year of the Child and is staffed by lawyers and professionals with expertise in child law. For general information regarding legislation affecting children, young people and their families, please look up our website or ring the Child Law Advice Line Freephone (0808) 802 0008 between 9.00 am and 5.00 pm. The Centre's Education Law and Advocacy Unit holds a national education law contract to provide free legal advice and assistance from the Community Legal Service Direct. Opening hours are Monday to Friday, 9.30 am to 5 pm. We can provide advice on all aspects of education law, including: exclusions; special educational needs; admissions to school; school transport; bullying; home education; education negligence; human rights claims; Secretary of State complaints; Local Government Ombudsman complaints; and judicial reviews. Education Law Advice Line: 0845 345 4345. The Children's Legal Centre produces a number of user-friendly legal guides and a monthly journal called childRIGHT. For more information, contact our publications office on 01206 877920.

## CLAPA (Cleft Lip and Palate Association)

1st Floor, Green Man Tower, 332b Goswell Road, London EC1V 7LQ

Tel: (020) 7833 4883
Fax: (020) 7833 5999
E-mail: info@clapa.com
Website: www.clapa.com
Chief Executive: Gareth Davies

CLAPA was set up in 1979 as a partnership between parents and professionals involved with the treatment of cleft lip and/or palate to provide specialist support for parents, the growing child, the adolescent and the adult. As well as practical parent-to-parent support services, CLAPA runs a helpline, dispatches feeding equipment, publishes a range of information leaflets, organizes workshops for health professionals and, through its 50 branches, raises money towards facilities for local hospital treatment.

## Colostomy Association

2 London Road, East Street, Reading, Berkshire RG1 4QL
Tel: (0118) 939 1537
Helpline: (0800) 328 4257
E-mail: cass@colostomyassociation.org.uk
Website: www.colostomyassociation.org.uk

## Community Link MacMillan Cancer Support

89 Albert Embankment, London SE1 7UQ
Cancerline: (0808) 808 2020
Fax: (020) 7840 7841
Website: www.macmillan.org.uk

Community Link provides free confidential support services for people affected by cancer, and is part of national cancer charity Macmillan Cancer Support. Community Link works with UK cancer self-help and support groups, to help people with cancer, their families and carers, offering emotional and practical support close to home.

### Contact a Family

209–211 City Road, London EC1V 1JN
Tel: (020) 7608 8700
Helpline: (0808) 808 3555 (Mon–Fri,
10 am–4 pm; Mon 5.30–7.30 pm)
Textphone: (0808) 808 3556
Fax: (020) 7608 8701
E-mail: info@cafamily.org.uk
Website: www.cafamily.org.uk

Contact a Family is the only UK-wide charity providing advice, information and support to parents of all disabled children – no matter what their health condition. We enable parents to get in contact with other families through a family linking service, both on a local and national basis. Our freephone helpline provides a one-stop shop for families of children with disabilities, offering advice on welfare rights, community care issues, education needs and a listening ear with access to interpreters. We have a number of local, regional and national offices plus volunteer family workers around the UK. Part of our service is to provide information to professionals and development advice to support groups. We also work to influence services and have campaigns that aim to improve the quality of life for families with disabled children.

Our wide range of publications for parents and professionals includes *The Contact a Family Directory – Specific Conditions, Rare Disorders and UK Family Support Groups*, price £35 (new edition every year). Most of our information materials can be found on our website; others will need to be ordered.

### Cornelia de Lange Syndrome Foundation UK

The Gate House, 104 Lodge Lane, Grays, Essex RM16 2UL
Tel: (01375) 376439
E-mail: info@cdls.org.uk
Website: www.cdls.org.uk
General Manager: Jacquie Griffin

The CdLS Foundation exists to ensure early and accurate diagnosis of CdLS nationwide. It promotes research into the causes and manifestations of the syndrome and helps people with a diagnosis of CdLS to make informed decisions throughout their lifetimes. The foundation has a helpline and also produces booklets and other information packs about the condition, which are sent to carers and professionals to spread awareness and provide basic information about CdLS. There is a quarterly newsletter, which covers new stories about research developments and family news.

### The Council for the Advancement of Communication with Deaf People

Durham University Science Park, Block 4, Stockton Road, Durham DH1 3UZ
Tel: (0191) 383 1155
Textphone: (0191) 383 7915
Fax: (0191) 383 7914
E-mail: durham@cacdp.org.uk
Website: www.cacdp.org.uk
Chief Executive: Miranda Pickersgill

CACDP aims to improve communication between deaf and hearing people by the development of curricula and examinations in communication skills. CACDP offers certification in British Sign Language, Lipspeaking, Communication with Deafblind People and Deaf

Awareness, and carries out the selection, training, monitoring and registration of examiners.

**CReSTeD (Council for the Registration of Schools Teaching Dyslexic Pupils)**
Greygarth, Littleworth, Winchcombe, Cheltenham GL54 5BT
Tel/Fax: (01242) 604852
Administrator: Ms Christine Hancock

The CReSTeD Register provides information to parents and those who advise them on choosing schools for children with SpLD (dyslexia). Working alongside the British Dyslexia Association and Dyslexia Action, CReSTeD was established in 1989 to produce a list of suitable schools, both maintained and independent. All schools listed have been through an establishment registration procedure, including a visit by a CReSTeD-selected consultant. For a list of schools see pages 475–81.

**Cystic Fibrosis Trust**
11 London Road, Bromley,
Kent BR1 1BY
Tel: (020) 8464 7211
Helpline: (0300) 373 1000
Fax: (020) 8313 0472
E-mail: enquiries@cftrust.org.uk
Website: www.cftrust.org.uk

The Cystic Fibrosis Trust is the UK's only national charity dedicated to all aspects of Cystic Fibrosis (CF). The CF Trust funds research aimed at treating the symptoms of, and finding an effective treatment for, Cystic Fibrosis. It also aims to ensure appropriate health care for those with CF and provides information, advice and practical support for people with Cystic Fibrosis and their families across the UK.

**deafPLUS**
BVSC, The Centre for Voluntary Action, 138 Digbeth, Birmingham B5 6DR

Tel: (0121) 643 4343
Textphone: (0121) 525 3092
Fax: (0121) 643 4541
E-mail: julia.pitt@deafPLUS.org
Website: www.deafPLUS.org
Advocacy Officer: Julia Pitt

**The Disability Law Service**
39–45 Cavell Street,
London E1 2BP
Tel: (020) 7791 9800
Minicom: (020) 7791 9801
Fax: (020) 7790 9802
E-mail: advice@dls.org.uk

Provides a broad range of free legal
advice and assistance on Post-16
education and other areas for disabled
people, their families and carers,
including community care, employment
welfare, benefits and disability
discrimination.

**Disability Rights UK**
12 City Forum, 250 City Road, London
EC1V 8AF
Tel: (020) 7250 3222
Fax: (020) 7247 8765

Disability Rights UK works to create
a society where everyone with lived
experience of disability or health
conditions can participate equally as
full citizens.

We strengthen the voice of disabled
people to make our rights real, as an
effective national organization led by
people with a wide range of impairments
or health conditions.

## Disability Sports Events

Belle Vue Centre, Longsight,
Manchester M12 5GL
**Tel:** (0161) 953 2499
**Fax:** (0161) 953 2420
**E-mail:** info@dse.org.uk
**Website:** www.disabilitysport.org.uk

DSE is the Events arm of the English
Federation of Disability Sport (EFDS).
DSE develops sporting opportunities for
disabled people to compete in a range of
sports. DSE coordinate regional and
national championships for disabled
people to compete in a range of sports,
including Mini Games for children aged
6–12 through to National Junior
Swimming and Athletics.

## Disabled Living Foundation

380–384 Harrow Road, London W9 2HU
**Helpline:** (0845) 130 9177
**Tel:** (020) 7432 8009
**Fax:** (020) 7266 2922
**E-mail:** advice@dlf.org.uk
**Website:** www.dlf.org.uk
**Head of Services:** Sue Clements

The Disabled Living Foundation is a
national charity, which provides free and
impartial advice and information on
equipment to enable disabled and older
people to manage daily living activities.
Its services are open to all: disabled
people, carers, relatives, students and
professionals. The organization runs a
telephone, letter and e-mail enquiry

---

### Disability Rights Handbook
### (38th Edition, Published May 2013) – April 2013–2014

The biggest changes to benefits since the introduction of the welfare state explained in the
*Disability Rights Handbook*, 38th Edition (April 2013–2014)

The new edition of the *Disability Rights Handbook* (April 2013–2014) is a must buy if you
need advice or provide it.

April 2013 sees the biggest changes to the benefit system since the introduction of the welfare
state and will affect over 2 million disabled people. The 'handbook' will focus on the new
personal Independent Payment (PIP) informing you how it works and how to claim it.

- disability living allowance will be replaced by a new benefit for people of working age,
  the Personal Independence Payment (PIP)

- council tax benefit will go, as will much of the social fund, to be replaced by local schemes
  run by local authorities

The *Disability Rights Handbook* is written by benefits specialists and provides information and
guidance on benefits and services to advisors, disability organizations and disabled people.

**RRP: £29.99**
**www.disabilityrightsuk.org**

service and an equipment demonstration centre. It also publishes a range of fact sheets.

### Dogs for the Disabled
The Frances Hay Centre, Blacklocks Hill, Banbury, Oxon OX17 2BS
Tel: (01295) 252600
Fax: (01295) 252668
E-mail: info@dogsforthedisabled.org

Specially selected dogs are trained as assistance dogs to perform tasks that adults and children with disabilities find difficult or impossible. We also provide services for families with a child with autism. Practical tasks include retrieving articles (eg TV remote), opening and closing doors, activating light switches, helping people to get undressed, help with rising from a chair or walking

independently of other aids. Dogs are trained to suit individual needs, and provide independence, security and companionship.

### Down's Syndrome Association
Langdon Down Centre, 2a Langdon Park, Teddington TW11 9PS
Tel: (0845) 230 0372
Fax: (0845) 230 0373
E-mail: info@downs-syndrome.org.uk
Website: www.downs-syndrome.org.uk

The Down's Syndrome Association is the only charity in the country which works exclusively with people with Down's syndrome. It exists to provide support, information and advice to people with Down's syndrome, their parents/carers, families and those professionals who work with them. The Association has

---

## Down's Syndrome Association
### Education Support Packs for Mainstream and Special Schools

The *Education Support Packs* are a comprehensive and practical resource, with versions for mainstream schools and also for special schools that include, or are thinking about including, children with Down's syndrome.

Unlike existing resources, the *Education Support Packs* are unique in being designed to meet the needs of hard-pressed teaching professionals with little time or specialist knowledge of Down's syndrome. Drawing on the huge professional experience of their creators, they include information on a range of topics such as dealing with challenging behaviour, methods for improving literacy, numeracy and communication, plus a wide range of curriculum-based differentiated teaching materials.

The *Education Support Packs* are available to download free from the Down's Syndrome Association website **www.downs-syndrome.org.uk** or can be ordered from our national office at £10 per copy for the mainstream pack and £10 or £25 for the special schools one, including P&P.

a network of affiliated parent-led support groups, a national office and resource centres in Teddington and offices in Belfast and Cardiff. It is a national charity covering England, Wales and Northern Ireland.

## Down's Syndrome Scotland

158–160 Balgreen Road, Edinburgh
EH11 3AU
Tel: (0131) 313 4225
Fax: (0131) 313 4285
E-mail: info@dsscotland.org.uk
Website: www.dsscotland.org.uk

Down's Syndrome Scotland provides information and support to people with Down's syndrome, parents, carers and professionals. We also produce a wide range of publications and deliver first class training.

## Dyslexia Action

Park House, Wick Road, Egham, Surrey
TW20 0HH

Tel: (01784) 222300
Fax: (01784) 222333
E-mail: info@dyslexiaaction.org.uk
Website: www.dyslexiaaction.org.uk
Chief Executive: Shirley Cramer

Dyslexia Action is a national charity and the UK's leading provider of services and support for people with dyslexia and literary difficulties. We specialize in assessment, teaching and training. We also develop and distribute teaching materials and undertake research. Dyslexia Action is the largest supplier of specialist training in this field and is committed to improving public policy and practice. We partner with schools, LEAs, colleges, universities, employers, voluntary sector organizations and Government to improve the quality and quantity of help for people with dyslexia and specific learning difficulties. Our services are available through 26 centres and 160 teaching locations around the UK. Over half a million people benefit from our work each year.

Assessment · Education · Training

**Dyslexia Action** is a national charity and the UK's leading provider of services and support for people with dyslexia and literacy difficulties.

We specialise in assessment, teaching and training. We develop and distribute teaching materials and undertake research.

Our services are available through our 26 centres and 160 teaching locations - many in schools - around the UK. Over half a million people benefit from our work each year.

**We offer a one-stop shop of services including:**

• Free surgeries and advice
• Assessments by chartered psychologists and trained teachers
• Specialist literacy, study skills and maths tuition
• First-class teacher training to develop careers helping dyslexic people
• Online shopping for our own and other specialist resources

**Contact Dyslexia Action**
**T** 01784 222300 **F** 01784 222333 **E** info@dyslexiaaction.org.uk
**www.dyslexiaaction.org.uk**
Dyslexia Action is the working name for Dyslexia Institute Limited. Reg. Charity No. 268502

**Dyspraxia Foundation**

8 West Alley, Hitchin, Herts SG5 1EG

Tel: (01462) 455016

Helpline: (01462) 454986

Fax: (01462) 455052

E-mail:
dyspraxia@dyspraxiafoundation.org.uk

Website: www.dyspraxiafoundation.org.uk

The objectives of the Dyspraxia Foundation are: to support individuals and families affected by dyspraxia; to promote better diagnostic and treatment facilities for those who have dyspraxia; to help professionals in health and education to assist those with dyspraxia; to promote awareness and understanding of dyspraxia. Services provided: publishes leaflets, booklets, books and guides for parents, those who have dyspraxia and professionals; organizes conferences and talks about dyspraxia and related topics for parents, carers and professionals. Local support groups: for details of Parent Volunteer Local Support Groups, if available, please contact the National Office. Membership: various subscription categories. Details available from the National Office.

**Electronic Aids for the Blind**

Suite 14, 71–75 High Street, Chislehurst, Kent BR7 5AG

Tel: (020) 8295 3636

Fax: (020) 8295 3737

A national charity helping blind and partially sighted people of all ages to achieve their fullest potential by awarding partial grants and arranging fund-raising appeals to third parties to purchase

---

# Maths Learning Difficulties/Dyscalculia

## INSET- CPD - Assessments - Publications

# Dr Steve Chinn

www.stevechinn.co.uk          steve.chinn@btinternet.com

Steve was founder and Principal of the only UK school for dyslexics to be awarded Beacon Status and the ISA Award for Excellence. He has lectured in over 25 countries on maths LD and dyscalculia as well as across the UK. He is Chair of the British Dyslexia Association's dyscalculia committee.

### Books by Steve Chinn

'The Trouble with Maths. A Practical Guide to Helping learners with Numeracy Difficulties' 2nd edn (2012) (Routledge) *1st edn received the nasen/TES 'Book for Teaching and Learning Award' 2004*
'More Trouble with Maths: A Complete Guide to Identifying and Diagnosing Mathematical Difficulties' (2012) *This book includes standardised tests.* nasen/Routledge
'Mathematics for Dyslexics, Including Dyscalculia' (Wiley) 3rd edition. 2007 (with Richard Ashcroft)
'The Fear of Maths: Sum Hope[3]' Souvenir Press. 2011
The 'What to do when you can't ....' series of maths books .Egon. 2010 from SEN Marketing
'Addressing the Unproductive Classroom Behaviours of Students with Special Needs' JKP. 2010

specialist or suitably adapted equipment for personal use where no statutory obligations exist and where there is financial hardship.

## emPOWER

c/o Limbless Association Rehabilitation Centre, Queen Mary's Hospital, Roehampton Lane, London SW15 5PR
Tel: (020) 8788 1777
Fax: (020) 8788 3444
E-mail: enquiries@empowernet.org
Website: www.empowernet.org

A consortium of users of prosthetics, orthotics, wheelchairs and electronic assistive technology which campaigns for a 'natural look' based on individual needs.

## ENABLE Scotland

2nd Floor, 146 Argyle Street, Glasgow G2 8BL

Tel: (0141) 226 4541
Fax: (0141) 204 4398
E-mail: info@enable.org.uk
Website: www.enable.org.uk

ENABLE Scotland can provide information about issues affecting children with learning disabilities in Scotland. It has a network of local branches across Scotland offering mutual support to parents and runs a range of services, including supported living, employment training and support, flexible support service and family-based respite care.

## Epilepsy Action

New Anstey House, Gate Way Drive, Yeadon, Leeds LS19 7XY
Tel: (0113) 210 8800
Helpline: (0808) 800 5050
Fax: (0113) 391 0300
E-mail: epilepsy@epilepsy.org.uk
Website: www.epilepsy.org.uk

www.epilepsy.org.uk
Epilepsy Helpline: 0808 800 5050
text: 0753 741 0044
email: helpline@epilepsy.org.uk

Epilepsy Action is the leading epilepsy organisation in the UK. We support people with epilepsy in education, by working with individuals, families, carers and professionals to increase awareness and understanding of the condition.

**Our services include:**
- A free telephone and email helpline service.
- Online resources for professionals and families.
- Free information packs for schools and educational settings.
- A range of information resources including DVDs, books, magazines, booklets and factsheets.
- A professional membership scheme to assist education, health and social care staff.
- Epilepsy awareness sessions for schools and education settings.
- Regional and national events.

**Epilepsy Action**
New Anstey House, Gate Way Drive, Yeadon, Leeds LS19 7XY
**tel.** 0113 210 8800 **fax** 0113 391 0300 **Epilepsy Helpline freephone** 0808 800 5050 **email** epilepsy@epilepsy.org.uk
Epilepsy Action is a working name of British Epilepsy Association. A company limited by guarantee (registered in England No. 797997). Registered charity in England (No. 234343)

Epilepsy Action is the leading epilepsy organization, acting as the voice for the UK's estimated 600,000 people with epilepsy, as well as their friends, families, carers, health professionals and the many other people on whose lives the condition has an impact. As well as campaigning to improve epilepsy services and raise awareness of the condition, we offer assistance to people in a number of ways including a national network of branches, Accredited Volunteers, regular regional events and freephone, text and e-mail helplines.

## Epilepsy Scotland

48 Govan Road, Glasgow G51 1JL
Tel: (0141) 427 4911
Helpline: (0808) 800 2200
Fax: (0141) 419 1709
E-mail: enquiries@epilepsyscotland.org.uk
Website: www.epilepsyscotland.org.uk

Epilepsy Scotland lobbies policymakers for better policies and services to meet local needs, and campaigns against the stigma of epilepsy by raising public awareness. Services include relevant literature and information on epilepsy, a video library, an interactive website, and a freephone helpline for people with epilepsy, their families, carers and professionals. Epilepsy Scotland provides training courses in epilepsy management and offers a community support service for adults with epilepsy and additional community care needs. We support a network of groups throughout Scotland.

## Equality and Human Rights Commission

FREEPOST PRLL – GHUX – CTRX,
Arndale House, Arndale Centre,
Manchester M4 3EQ

Tel: (0845) 604 6610
Fax: (0845) 604 6630
E-mail: englandhelpline@ equalityhumanrights.com
Website: www.drc-gb.org

## European Agency for Development in Special Needs Education

Østre Stationsvej 33, DK-5000 Odense C, Denmark
Tel: +45 64 41 00 20
Fax: +45 64 41 23 03
E-mail: secretariat@european-agency.org
Website: www.european-agency.org

## Family Fund

Unit 4, Alpha Court, Monks Cross Drive, Huntington, York YO32 9WN
Tel: (01904) 621115
Textphone: (01904) 658085
Low-cost line: (0845) 130 4542
Fax: (01904) 652625
E-mail: info@familyfund.org.uk
Website: www.familyfund.org.uk

The purpose of the Family Fund is to ease the stress on families who care for severely disabled children aged 17 and under, by providing grants and information related to the care of the child.

## The Foundation for Conductive Education

The National Institute of Conductive Education, Cannon Hill House, Russell Road, Moseley, Birmingham B13 8RD
Tel: (0121) 449 1569
Monday–Friday, 9 am–5 pm
Fax: (0121) 449 1611
E-mail: foundation@conductiveeducation.org.uk
Website: www.conductive-education.org.uk

Director of Fundraising and Marketing: Treena Jones

A national charity formed in 1986 'to establish and develop the science and skill of Conductive Education in the UK'. The National Institute of Conductive Education provides direct services to children and adults with motor disorders, such as cerebral palsy and dyspraxia in children and Parkinson's disease, multiple sclerosis, stroke or head injury in adults. Through a system of positive teaching and learning support, Conductive Education maximizes participants' control over bodily movement in ways that are relevant to daily living. The National Institute also undertakes research and offers a comprehensive range of professionally oriented, skills-based training courses at all levels, including the BA (Hons) Conductive Education degree in conjunction with the University of Wolverhampton. Covers UK and overseas.

**Fragile X Society**
53 Winchelsea Lane, Hastings TN35 4LG
Tel: (01424) 813147
Contact: Mrs Lesley Walker

**Friends of Landau-Kleffner Syndrome**
3 Stone Buildings, Lincoln's Inn, London WC2A 3XL
E-mail: info@friendsoflks.com
Website: www.friendsoflks.com

**The Guide Dogs for the Blind Association**
Hillfields, Burghfield Common, Reading RG7 3YG

Tel: (01189) 835555
E-mail: guidedogs@guidedogs.org.uk
Website: www.guidedogs.org.uk
Contact: Chris Dyson

**Hearing Aided Young Adults**
7–11 Armstrong Road, London W3 7JL
Tel: (020) 8743 1110
Fax: (020) 8742 9043

**Hearing Concern**
95 Gray's Inn Road, London WC1X 8TX
Tel: (020) 7740 9871
SMS: (07624) 809978
Fax: (020) 7740 9872
Helpline: (0845) 074 4600
E-mail: info@hearingconcern.org.uk
Website: www.hearingconcern.org.uk

Hearing Concern is a people-centred charity offering one-to-one support, advice, access and inclusion to all deaf and hard of hearing people whose main mode of communication is speech.

**Hearing Impairment Service**
The Education Centre, Church Street, Pensnett, Dudley, West Midlands DY5 4HB
Tel: (01384 818009)
Fax: (01384 814241)
E-mail: pss.cs@dudley.gov.uk
Website: www.dudley.gov.uk

The Hearing Impairment Service provides a range of services to children, parents and educational establishments. A team of specialist teachers and teaching assistants provide support, advice and, where appropriate, specialist resource materials to children who have a hearing impairment.

## Helen Arkell Dyslexia Centre

Frensham, Farnham, Surrey GU10 3BW
Tel: (01252) 792400
Fax: (01252) 795669
E-mail: enquiries@arkellcentre.org.uk
Website: www.arkellcentre.org.uk
Principal: Mrs Bernadette McLean

A registered charity providing comprehensive help and care for children and adults with specific learning difficulties, including assessment, tuition, speech and language therapy, and short courses, as well as teacher training and schools support. Financial help is available. Specialist books on dyslexia for parents and teachers are available by mail order.

## Henshaw's Society for Blind People

Atherton House, 89–92 Talbot Road,
Old Trafford, Manchester M16 0GS
Tel: (0161) 872 1234
Fax: (0161) 848 9889
E-mail:
childrenfamiliesmcr@henshaws.org.uk
Website: www.henshaws.org.uk

Henshaw's give expert care, advice and support to children and families affected by sight loss – right where it's needed most. We run this service across the North West, offering a wide range of support services for children and parents who are blind and visually impaired. Working together, we enable and encourage children and parents to live to the full – building the skill they need, to get the future they want.

## Hyperactive Children's Support Group (HACSG)

71 Whyke Lane, Chichester, West Sussex
PO19 7PD
Tel: (01243) 539966
E-mail: hyperactive@hacsg.org.uk
Website: www.hacsg.org.uk
Contact: Mrs Sally Bunday

The HACSG provides ideas and information to parents, carers and professionals seeking help for ADHD/Hyperactive children and young people. Non-drug therapies are our main interest. Free introductory pack available on request.

## I CAN

8 Wakely Street, London EC1V 7QE
Tel: (0845) 225 4071
Fax: (0845) 225 4072
E-mail: info@ican.org.uk
Website: www.talkingpoint.org.uk and www.ican.org.uk

I CAN is the children's communication charity. It works to develop speech, language and communication skills for all children, with a particular focus on children who find communication hard. I CAN works to ensure all people who have a responsibility to children, either directly or indirectly, from parent to teachers to policymakers, understand the importance of good communication skills. It does this through:

Information, training, support and online resources for children, families and professionals.

Direct service provision through two schools for children with severe and complex disabilities, and a network of early years provisions.

Consultancy and outreach services through I CAN's Early Talk and Primary Talk programmes and Communications Skills Centres.

Raising awareness through campaigns such as Make Chatter Matter and through initiatives such as the Chatterbox Challenge.

Campaigning to place communication skills at the heart of children's policy.

## Independent Panel for Special Education Advice

6 Carlow Mews, Woodbridge, Suffolk IP12 1EA
Advice Line: (0800) 018 4016
Admin: (01394) 384711
Chief Executive: Angie Lee-Foster

IPSEA offers free and independent advice and support to parents of children with special educational needs, including free advice on LEAs' legal duties towards children with SEN, home visits where necessary, free support and possible representation for those parents appealing to the Special Educational Needs Tribunal, and free second opinions on a child's needs and the provision required to meet those needs.

## The Institute for Neuro-Physiological Psychology

1 Stanley Street, Chester, Cheshire CH1 2LR
Tel: (01244) 311414
E-mail: mail@inpp.org.uk
Founder: Peter Blythe
Director: Sally Goddard-Blythe

Established in 1975 to carry out research into the effects of central nervous system dysfunctions on children with learning difficulties, and to develop appropriate CNS remedial and rehabilitation programmes. INPP can diagnose what underlies dyslexia, dyspraxia and other specific learning difficulties, and then devise an appropriate physical correction programme to be done each day at home or school. The children are regularly monitored, and as the basic causes are corrected they begin to benefit from teaching and the educational process. INPP also runs several courses for other professionals in the identification, assessment and remediation of neuro-developmental difficulties.

## LDA

Abbeygate House, East Road, Cambridge CB1 1DB
Tel: (0845) 120 4776
Fax: (0800) 783 8648

LDA offers an extensive selection of innovative, high-quality resources to make teaching easier and learning a lot more fun. LDA aims to help every child achieve their best in a fun and inclusive learning environment. Working hard to find and develop new and exciting products to help children with special needs or additional support requirements to reach their full potential, LDA's range encompasses everything from language, literacy and inclusion to maths, motor skills and PSHE.

## Learning and Teaching Scotland

The Optima, 58 Robertson Street, Glasgow G2 8DU
Tel: (0141) 282 5000
Fax: (0141) 282 5050
E-mail: enquiries@LTScotland.org.uk
Website: www.LTScotland.org.uk

Learning and Teaching Scotland is a national public body sponsored by the

Scottish Government. LT Scotland's remit is to provide advice, support, resources and staff development that enhance the quality of educational experiences in Scotland, with a view to improving attainment and achievement for all and promoting lifelong learning. It combines expertise on the school and pre-school curriculum and on the use of information and communications technology (ICT) in education and lifelong learning. LT Scotland is actively involved in software and internet development and multimedia production of educational resources.

### Leber's Optic Neuropathy Trust
13 Palmar Road, Maidstone,
Kent ME16 0DL
Tel: (01622) 751025
Contact: Mrs T Handscombe

### Lennox-Gastaut Support Group
9 South View, Burrough on the Hill,
Melton Mowbray LE14 2JJ
Tel: (01664) 454305
E-mail:
andrew.gibson15@btopenworld.com
Contact: Andrew Gibson

### Leukaemia CARE
One Birch Court, Blackpole East,
Worcester WR3 8SG
Tel: (01905) 755977
Fax: (01905) 755166
CARE Line: (0800) 169 6680
E-mail: info@leukaemiacare.org.uk
Website: www.leukaemiacare.org.uk
Fundraising Website:
www.raise4leukaemia.org.uk
Administration: Stephanie Whitehouse

Leukaemia CARE is a national charity that provides care and support to patients, their families and carers during the difficult journey through the diagnosis and treatment of blood and lymphatic cancers. Leukaemia CARE provides the only dedicated freephone care line for patients and their families that enables people to discuss their feelings, concerns and emotions at such a difficult period of time.

### Limbless Association
Queen Mary's Hospital, Roehampton
Lane, London SW15 5PR
Tel: (020) 8788 1777
Fax: (020) 8788 3444
E-mail:
enquiries@limbless-association.org
Website: www.limbless-association.org

Information on a disabled football team, run in cooperation with Chelsea Football Club, also available.

### The London Centre for Children with Cerebral Palsy
54 Muswell Hill, London N10 3ST
Tel: (020) 8444 7242

Provides Conductive Education for children with cerebral palsy, and courses for professionals working with children in mainstream education who have cerebral palsy.

### LOOK – National Federation of Families with Visually Impaired Children
c/o Queen Alexandra College,
49 Court Oak Road, Harborne,
Birmingham B17 9TG

Tel: (0121) 428 5038
Fax: (0121) 427 9800
E-mail: steve@look-uk.org
Website: www.look-uk.org

LOOK provides information, support and advice to families of visually impaired children.

## Lowe's Syndrome Association

29 Gleneagles Drive, Penwortham, Preston, Lancashire PR1 0JT
Tel: (01772) 745070
E-mail: info@lowesyndrome.org
Contact: David and Julie Oliver

## The Makaton Charity

Manor House, 46 London Road, Blackwater, Surrey GU17 0AA
Tel: (01276) 606760
Fax: (01276) 36725
E-mail: info@makaton.org
Website: www.makaton.org

Makaton is a language programme using signs and symbols to help people to communicate. It is designed to support spoken language and the signs and symbols are used with speech, in spoken word order. With Makaton, children and adults can communicate straight away using signs and symbols. Many people then drop the signs or symbols naturally at their own pace, as they develop speech.

The Makaton Charity exists to ensure that all people living with learning and communication disabilities have the tools and resources they need to communicate. We work towards this through providing training, resources, information and family support.

## Marfan Association UK

Rochester House, 5 Aldershot Road, Fleet, Hampshire GU51 3NG
Tel: (01252) 810472
Fax: (01252) 810473
Chairman/Support Coordinator: Mrs Diane L Rust

Marfan syndrome is an inherited disorder of connective tissue, which may affect the eyes, skeleton, lungs, heart and blood vessels and may be life-threatening. The Marfan Association UK exists to support those with the condition, providing educational material about Marfan syndrome for both medical and lay sectors and encouraging research projects.

## MIND (The Mental Health Charity)

15–19 Broadway, London E15 4BQ
Tel: (020) 8519 2122
Information Line: (0300) 123 33931
E-mail: info@mind.org.uk
Website: www.mind.org.uk
Chief Executive: Paul Farmer

We're Mind, the mental health charity. We're here to make sure anyone with a mental health problem has somewhere to turn for advice and support.

## Muscular Dystrophy Campaign

4th Floor, 61 Southwark Street, London SE1 0HL
Tel: (020) 7803 4800
Fax: (020) 7401 3495
Freephone: (0800) 652 6352
E-mail: info@muscular-dystrophy.org
Website: www.muscular-dystrophy.org

The Muscular Dystrophy Campaign is the national charity funding research into treatments and cures for the muscular dystrophies and allied muscle wasting conditions. The Campaign also supports adults and children affected by these conditions with expert clinical care and grants towards equipment. The charity relies on voluntary donations to fund its work.

### National Association for Gifted Children

Suite 1.2, Challenge House, Sherwood Drive, Bletchley, Milton Keynes
MK3 6DP
Tel: (01908) 646433
Helpline: (01908) 646433
Fax: (0870) 770 3219
E-mail: amazingchildren@nagcbritain.org.uk
Website: www.nagcbritain.org.uk

NAGC is a not-for-profit organization that supports the social, emotional and learning needs of children and young people with high learning potential. It works with parents/carers and professionals through its Information and Advice Service, face-to-face workshops, local club activities and fully resourced website. Our aim is to enable every child with high learning potential to grow in confidence, thrive and achieve fulfillment.

### National Association of Independent and Non-Maintained Special Schools (NAIMS)

Action for Children, Penhurst School, New Street, Chipping Norton, Oxfordshire OX7 5LN
Tel: (01608) 642559
Fax: (01608) 647029
E-mail: stephen-bb@nch.org.uk
Principal: Mr S Bajdala-Brown

## Muscular Dystrophy *Campaign*

**nasen**

nasen House, 4/5 Amber Business Village, Amber Close, Amington, Tamworth B77 4RP
**Tel:** (01827) 311500
**Fax:** (01827) 313005
**E-mail:** welcome@nasen.org.uk
**Contact:** Ms Beverley Walters

nasen is the leading UK professional association embracing all special and additional educational needs and disabilities, promoting the education, training, development and support of all those working within this field. Membership of nasen is an invaluable source of advice, support and practical solutions, offering an exclusive and vital range of benefits that support teachers, governors, teaching assistants and the entire education support network to deliver high quality inclusive practice. Benefits include fresh and creative education resources, dynamic conferences and seminars with world-class speakers, an inspirational professional development programme, plus print and online journals and magazines, exhibitions and access to recently completed research. nasen also contributes greatly and has a strong influence on policy and practice in the area of special educational needs through consultation and joint projects with other professional bodies.

**The National Autistic Society**

393 City Road, London EC1V 1NG
**Tel:** (020) 7833 2299
**Helpline:** (0808) 800 4104
Mon–Fri, 10 am–4 pm
**Fax:** (020) 7833 9666
**E-mail:** nas@nas.org.uk
**Website:** www.autism.org.uk

The National Autistic Society is the UK's leading charity for people affected by autism. For 50 years we have worked to help children and young people across the autism spectrum enjoy their lives and reach their goals. A well-rounded education, tailored to the needs of the individual, can make all the difference. It gives them the best start and paves the way for a full and meaningful adult life. In working with families and carers, no other specialist provider offers more education services across the autism spectrum. Our provision varies from day through to weekly, termly and full 52-week boarding.

**National Deaf Children's Society**
15 Dufferin Street, London EC1Y 8UR
**Tel:** (020) 7490 8656 (voice & text)
**Freephone Helpline:**
(0808) 800 8880 (voice & text) open

Mon–Thurs, 9.30 am–5 pm,
Fri 9.30 am–12 noon
**Fax:** (020) 7251 5020
**E-mail:** helpline@ndcs.org.uk
**Website:** www.ndcs.org.uk

The National Deaf Children's Society (NDCS) is the national charity dedicated to creating a world without barriers for deaf children and young people. NDCS is an organization of families, parents and carers, and provides emotional and practical support through our Freephone Helpline, network of trained support workers, wide range of other support services including an audiologist and technology team, and our publications and website. We have free membership for parents and carers, and for the professionals who support deaf children. NDCS can also help with welfare rights, benefit claims and making education choices. Events and activities are free to members.

## The National Eczema Society

Hill House, Highgate Hill,
London N19 5NA
Helpline: (0870) 241 3604
Fax: (020) 7281 6395
E-mail: helpline@eczema.org
Website: www.eczema.org

## National Reye's Syndrome Foundation of the UK

15 Nicholas Gardens, Pyrford, Woking,
Surrey GU22 8SD
Tel: (01932) 346843
E-mail: Gordon.Denney@ukgateway.net
Website: www.reyessyndrome.co.uk
Contact: Mr Gordon Denney

Reye's syndrome is a children's disease that affects the liver and brain. It is an acute disorder that affects children when they seem to be recovering from a viral illness. The latest advice from the Medicines and Healthcare Products Regulatory Agency requires all aspirin products to carry a warning that children under 16 should not take aspirin because of a possible link with Reye's syndrome. The National Reye's Syndrome Foundation of the UK was formed to provide funds for research into the cause, treatment, cure and prevention of Reye's syndrome and Reye-like illnesses, to inform both the public and medical communities, and to provide support for parents whose children have suffered from the disease.

## The National Society for Epilepsy

Chesham Lane, Chalfont St Peter,
Buckinghamshire SL9 0RJ
Tel: (01494) 601300
Helpline: (01494) 601 400 Mon–Fri
(national rate) 10 am–4 pm
Fax: (01494) 871927
Website: www.epilepsynse.org.uk

The National Society for Epilepsy (NSE) is the UK's leading epilepsy charity. We provide:

specialist medical and residential services for adults with epilepsy;

information resources including leaflets, books and DVDs on the medical, psychological and social aspects of living with epilepsy;

The National Deaf Children's Society (NDCS) is the national charity dedicated to creating a world without barriers for deaf children and young people. There are over 35,000 deaf children in the UK and three more babies are born deaf every day. NDCS represents the interests and campaigns for the rights of all deaf children and young people from birth until they reach independence.

NDCS provides vital support to deaf children and their families in all aspects of their lives. The charity offers clear balanced information to support parents in helping their deaf child reach their full potential. This support is provided through a Freephone Helpline, a network of family officers and a range of family events. NDCS also holds activity events for deaf children and young people to help them develop confidence.

Contact the NDCS:
The National Deaf Children's Society
15 Dufferin Street, London EC1Y 8UR
Freephone Helpline: 0808 800 8880 (voice/ text)
    open Mon–Fri, 10am–5pm
Fax: 020 7251 5020
E-mail: helpline@ndcs.org.uk
Visit our website: www.ndcs.org.uk

every deaf child

information about epilepsy from our website (www.epilepsy.org.uk);

a confidential helpline for anyone wanting to know more about epilepsy, with information, written resources and emotional support (01494 604 400, Mon–Fri, 10 am–4 pm);

trained volunteers who provide information about epilepsy in health-care settings, and deliver a Schools Awareness Programme;

customized training including epilepsy awareness courses and epilepsy awareness and rectal diazepam training;

fundraising events and opportunities;

an Associate Membership scheme giving people the opportunity to keep up to date with information about epilepsy and support our work.

## Network 81

1–7 Woodfield Terrace, Chapel Hill, Stansted, Essex CM24 8AJ
Tel: (0845) 077 4055
Fax: (0845) 077 4057
E-mail: network81@btconnect.com
Website: www.network81.org
Administrator: Val Rosier

Network 81 offers practical help and support to parents throughout all stages of assessment and statementing as outlined in the Education Act 1996 and Code of Practice 2001. Our national helpline offers an individual service linked to a national network of local contacts. We can also offer advice and information on the organization of assessment in schools and give guidelines on how to choose a school. Network 81 produces a range of literature aimed at familiarizing

parents with the assessment and statementing procedures. Many parents found our Network 81's Parents' Guide particularly useful. We also run extensive training programmes for parents and those working with parents.

## The Neuro Foundation

(formerly known as The Neurofibromatosis Association) Quayside House, 38 High Street, Kingston upon Thames KT1 1HL
Tel: (020) 8439 1234
Monday–Thursday 9 am–4 pm
Fax: (020) 8439 1200
E-mail: info@nfauk.org
Website: www.nfauk.org

The vision of The Neuro Foundation is to improve the lives of those affected by Neurofibromatosis (NF). Every day a baby is born in the UK with NF, one of the world's most common neuro-genetic conditions. Categorized into NF1 and NF2, the severity of the condition will vary from person to person and whilst some may live a normal life, many of those with NF could have a multitude of medical, physical and psychological complications.

## Newlife Foundation for Disabled Children

Newlife Centre, Hemlock Way, Cannock, Staffordshire WS11 7GF
Tel: (01543) 468888
Fax: (01543) 468999
E-mail: info@newlifecharity.co.uk
Website: www.newlifecharity.co.uk

## Ohdo Syndrome Family Network

36 Borrowdale Avenue, Gatley, Cheadle SK8 4QF
Tel: (0161) 428 8583
E-mail: patseville@btinternet.com

## Paget Gorman Society

2 Dowlands Bungalows, Dowlands Lane,
Smallfield, Surrey RH6 9SD
Tel: (01342) 842308
E-mail: pru.phillips@googlemail.com
Website: www.pgss.org

Advice and information for parents and
professionals concerned with speech
and language-impaired children. The
Society runs courses in Paget Gorman
Signed Speech (PGSS). Publications and
a video are available.

## Parents for Inclusion

336 Brixton Road, London SW9 7AA
Tel (business line): (020) 7738 3888
Helpline: (0800) 652 3145
Minicom: (020) 7582 5333
Fax: (020) 7735 3828
E-mail: info@parentsforinclusion.org
Website: www.parentsforinclusion.org

Parents helping parents so that disabled
children can learn, make friends and
have a voice in ordinary school and
throughout life. We are a national charity
based in London.

## The Partially Sighted Society

7/9 Bennetthorpe, Doncaster DN2 6AA
Tel: (0844) 477 4966
Fax: (0844) 477 4969
E-mail: info@partsight.org.uk
Website: www.partsight.org.uk

Mail order for heavy lined paper, books
and advisory service.

## Perthes Association

PO Box 773, Guildford,
Surrey GU1 1XN
Tel (Admin): (01483) 534431
Helpline: (01483) 306637
E-mail: admin@perthes.org.uk
Website: www.perthes.co.uk

The Association advises families of
children suffering from Perthes' disease
and associated conditions in all parts
of the British Isles and abroad. Perthes'
disease (a potentially crippling disease
of the hip) is a form of osteochondritis,
which affects 5.5 per 100,000 children
(mainly boys) between the ages of 2 and
15 years. Perthes Association volunteers
are at the end of the telephone line for
any worried or distressed parents, and
will visit them if possible or put them in
touch with a family living locally.

## Physical Impairment and Medical Inclusion Service

(formerly known as The Physical and
Sensory Service)
The Education Centre,
Church Street, Pensnett, Dudley,
West Midlands DY5 4HB
Tel: (01384 818004)
Fax: (01384 814241)
E-mail: pss.cs@dudley.gov.uk
Website: www.dudley.gov.uk

The Physical Impairment and Medical
Inclusion Service provides a range of
services to children, parents and
educational establishments. A team of
specialist teachers and teaching
assistants provide support, advice and,
where appropriate, specialist resource
materials to children who have a physical
impairment.

## Prader-Willi Syndrome Association (UK)

125a London Road, Derby DE1 2QQ
Tel: (01332) 365676
Monday–Friday 9.30 am–3.30 pm,
answerphone at other times

Fax: (01332) 360401
E-mail: admin@pwsa.co.uk
Website: www.pwsa.co.uk

## Rathbone

Head Office, Churchgate House, 56
Oxford Street, Manchester M1 6EU
Special Education Advice Line:
(0800) 085 4528
Fax: (0161) 238 6356

A national charity supporting parents of
children with special educational needs
to help them reach their potential and get
the best education throughout their time
at school. The service is available to
parents for whom English is a second
language and we provide information
and advice in the following languages:
Urdu, Hindi, Punjabi, Guajarati and
Bengali. Outreach service is also
available throughout the North-West.

## REACH Charity Ltd – Association for Children with Upper Limb Deficiency

PO Box 54, Helston,
Cornwall TR13 8WD
Tel: (0845) 130 6225
Fax: (0845) 130 0262
E-mail: reach@reach.org
Website: www.reach.org.uk

Each year, there are babies born in the
UK missing part of one or both arms and
hands. 'Reach' aims to provide affected
families with the opportunity to get
together, share experiences and
information on what to do (or not to do)
and where to go for advice regarding
treatment. The Management Committee
comprises 'Reach' parents who give their
time voluntarily with one full-time paid
administrator. 'Reach' organizes family

meetings, confidence building events,
provides one-handed recorders, helps
with grants for computer equipment for
children with no hands, adaptations to
sports equipment, bicycles, cars, or
musical instruments. Please, pause
and consider the effect on a child with
one or no hands in a two-handed
society.

## RNID, for Deaf and Hard of Hearing People

19–23 Featherstone Street,
London EC1Y 8SL
Tel: (0808) 808 0123 – Helpline
Textphone: (0808) 808 9000 – Helpline
Fax: (020) 7296 8199
E-mail: informationline@rnid.org.uk
Website: www.rnid.org.uk
Chief Executive: Dr John Low

RNID is the largest charity representing
the nine million deaf and hard of hearing
people in the UK. As a membership
charity, we aim to achieve a radically
better quality of life for deaf and hard
of hearing people. We do this by
campaigning and lobbying vigorously,
by raising awareness of deafness and
hearing loss, and by providing services
and through social, medical and
technical research.

## Royal Association for Disability and Rehabilitation (RADAR)

12 City Forum, 250 City Road, London
EC1V 8AF
Tel: (020) 7250 3222
Minicom: (020) 7250 4119
E-mail: radar@radar.org.uk
Website: www.radar.org.uk

Information on all aspects of disability.

## Royal College of Speech and Language Therapists

2 White Hart Yard, London SE1 1NX
Tel: (020) 7378 1200
Fax: (020) 7403 7254

## Royal Mencap Society

Caron Lane, Head of Advice &
Information Service, 4 Swan Courtyard,
Coventry Road, Charles Edward Road,
Birmingham B26 1BU
Tel: (0121) 707 7877
Helpline: (0808) 808 1111
E-mail: help@mencap.org.uk
Website: www.mencap.org.uk
Chairman: Brian Baldock CBE
Chief Executive: Jo Williams CBE

Royal MENCAP Society is a registered
charity that offers services to adults and
children with learning disabilities. We
offer help and advice on benefits,
housing and employment via the Helpline
Tel: 0808 808 1111. Helplines are open
from Monday to Friday, 9.30 am–4.30
pm; Wednesday, subject to change
(open am, closed pm). Language Line is

also used. Office is open from Monday
to Friday (9 am–5 pm) 0121 707 7877.
This Helpline covers England only.
Wales Helpline: 0808 8000 300. Northern
Ireland Helpline: 08457 636 227. We offer
help and advice to anyone or we can
signpost them in the right direction.
We can also provide information and
support for leisure, recreational services
(Getaway Clubs), residential services
and holidays.

## The Royal National Institute of Blind People (RNIB)

105 Judd Street, London WC1H 9NE
Helpline: (0845) 766 9999
(Open 9 am–5 pm Monday–Friday;
on Wednesdays the Helpline is open
9 am–4 pm. Messages can be left on our
answer phone outside these hours.)
E-mail: e&einformation@rnib.org.uk
Website: www.rnib.org.uk
Chief Executive: Lesley-Anne Alexander

RNIB offers support to all children with
sight problems, including those who have
other special needs too. It also supports

families because of the crucial role they play in the education and development of their child. In addition, RNIB provides information, resources and training for the many professionals from education, health and social services who work with them.

## Rubinstein Taybi Syndrome Support Group

162 Buckfield Road, Leominster, Herefordshire HR6 8HF
Tel: (01568) 616149
Contact: Mrs Rosemary Robertson

To offer support to families and carers and provide information about the condition.

## SCOPE

Scope Response, PO Box 833, Milton Keynes MK12 5NY
Tel: (0808) 800 3333
Text: SCOPE plus your message to 80039. Texts are free to sender.
E-mail: response@scope.org.uk
Website: www.scope.org.uk

## Scottish Centre for Children with Motor Impairments

Craighalbert Centre, 1 Craighalbert Way, Cumbernauld, Glasgow G68 0LS
Tel: (01236) 456100
Fax: (01236) 736889
E-mail: sccmi@craighalbert.org.uk
Website: www.craighalbert.org.uk

Grant-aided school for children aged 0–8 with motor impairments, combining principles of Conductive Education with the Scottish curriculum.

## The Scottish Society for Autism

New Struan School, Bradbury Campus, 100 Smithfield Loan, Alloa, Clackmannanshire FK10 1NP
Tel: (01259) 222000
Fax: (01259) 724239
E-mail: newstruan@autism-in-scotland.org.uk
Website: www.autism-in-scotland.org.uk

SSA is the leading provider of services for autism in Scotland. It runs New Struan School, the only accredited school for

About cerebral palsy.
For disabled people achieving equality.

Scope's mission is to drive the change to make our society the first in which disabled people achieve full equality.

Scope's services include schools and other provision for children and young adults. For more information visit our website or contact Scope Response.

Scope and DIAL UK have merged to provide an expanded national advice and information network for disabled people, their families and those that support them.

**Scope Response**
Freephone Helpline: 0808 800 3333
response@scope.org.uk
www.scope.org.uk
Registered Charity

**DIAL UK**
Tel: 01302 310123
Dialuk@scope.org.uk
www.dialuk.scope.org.uk

autism in Scotland (both residential and day pupils); residential and specialist day services for adults; the only respite care centre for autism in the UK; nationwide family support services; training for carers and professionals; support self-help groups and local societies; and produces information and a members' magazine. SSA undertakes community care assessments and gives guidance on diagnosis, assessment and care management. Advice on all aspects of autism is available from SSA's professional staff.

### Scottish Spina Bifida Association
The Dan Young Building,
6 Craighalbert Way, Cumbernauld,
Glasgow G68 0LS
Tel: (01236) 794500
Fax: (01236) 736435
Chief Executive: Andrew H D Wynd
PA to CEO: Julie Snaddon
Services and Development Manager:
Diane Waugh

The Scottish Spina Bifida Association seeks to increase public awareness and understanding of individuals with spina bifida/hydrocephalus and allied disorders. It aims to support all those affected to identify their needs and to empower them to make informed choices and decisions.

### Scottish Support for Learning Association
11 Mayshand Road,
Loanhead EH20 9HJ
Tel: (0141) 883 6134
E-mail: info@ssla.org.uk
Website: www.ssla.org.uk
Contact: Sheena Richardson

### SENNAC: Special Educational Needs – National Advisory Council
Pett Archive & Study Centre,
Toddington, Cheltenham,
Gloucestershire GL54 5DP
Hon General Secretary: Mr John Cross

### Sense, The National Deafblind & Rubella Association
101 Pentonville Road, London N1 9LG
Tel: (0845) 127 0060
Fax: (0845) 127 006
Minicom: (0845) 127 0062
E-mail: enquiries@sense.org.uk
Website: www.sense.org.uk

Sense is the national voluntary organization supporting and campaigning for people who are deafblind, their families, their carers, and professionals who work with them. People of all ages and with widely varying conditions use Sense's specialist services. Founded as a parents' self-help group in 1955, Sense is now the leading national organization working with deafblind people. Sense offers advice, help and information to deafblind people and their families; supports families through a national network and local branches; runs a holiday programme for deafblind children and adults; provides education, residential, respite and day services; and offers training and consultancy.

### Sense Scotland
TouchBase, 43 Middlesex Street,
Glasgow G41 1EF
Tel: (0141) 429 0294
Fax: (0141) 429 0295
E-mail: info@sensescotland.org.uk
Website: www.sensescotland.org.uk

Sense Scotland works with children and adults who have communication support needs because of deafblindness, sensory impairment, learning or physical disability. They lead in communication and innovative support services for people who are marginalized because of challenging behaviour, health care and continuity across age groups. Sense Scotland works closely with families and colleagues from health, education and social work.

Services include: family advisory services; community living and support for adults; support services for adults and for children; residential short breaks for adults and children; art development and outdoor education work for children and adults; practice training for professionals; assessments; representations, consultation and policy development; and health and general information enquiry services.

### Sense West

9a Birkdale Avenue, Off Heeley Road, Selly Oak, Birmingham B29 6UB
**Tel:** (0121) 415 2723 (voice and text)
**Fax:** (0121) 472 2723

Sense West provides a regional advisory service to families, deafblind people and professionals working with them, an adult service department offering a range of residential provision and learning opportunities based on individual need for deafblind and multiple disabled sensory-impaired adults, and a Training and Consultancy Service offering advice, assessment and training to people involved with the education and care of deafblind children and adults. They also provide day services based in Birmingham and Exeter, an Outreach

service, both Communicator-Guide service and Intervenor Service (in the Midlands and South West) and an information service.

### The Sequal Trust

(Special Equipment and Aids for Living)
3 Ploughmans Corner, Wharf Road, Ellesmere, Shropshire SY12 0EJ
**Tel/Fax:** (01691) 624222

A national charity which fundraises to supply communication aids to those people with speech, movement or learning difficulties, on a lifelong loan basis. Registration fee is £20 for life membership. There is no age limit for application, but an assessment of need is required from a health care professional and applicants need to be on a low income or solely in receipt of benefits.

### The SIGNALONG Group

Stratford House, Waterside Court, Neptune Way, Rochester, Kent ME2 4NZ
**Tel:** (0845) 450 8422
**Website:** www.signalong.org.uk

SIGNALONG is a sign-supporting system based on British Sign Language intended to promote communication in learning disabilities and autism. The charity has devised a uniform method of presenting signs with drawings and descriptions, and has published the widest range of illustrated signs in Britain, catering for all ages and abilities. Resources are available in paper and electronic format. Manuals contain full signing instructions, but training and advice are also provided, both by SIGNALONG staff and by independent accredited tutors. SIGNALONG works with other organizations to develop symbol resources and to promote total communication to enable understanding and expression of choice.

## Skill – National Bureau for Students with Disabilities

Unit 3, Floor 3, Radisson Court, 219 Long Lane, London SE1 4PR
Tel: (020) 7450 0620
Fax: (020) 7450 0650
Information Service: (0800) 328 5050 (voice), (0800) 068 2422 (text)
Info Service Textphone:
Tuesdays 11.30 am–1.30 pm,
Thursdays 1.30 pm–3.30 pm
E-mail: info@skill.org.uk
Website: www.skill.org.uk
Director: Barbara Waters

Skill is a national voluntary organization that promotes opportunities for young people and adults with any kind of impairment or learning difficulty – in further, higher and adult education,

work-based learning, entry to employment and volunteering.

## Social Emotional and Behavioural Difficulties Association

Room 211, The Triangle, Exchange Square, Manchester M4 3TR
Tel: (0161) 240 2418
Fax: (0161) 838 5601
E-mail: admin@sebda.org
Website: www.sebda.org
Executive Director: Dr Ted Cole

SEBDA provides accredited training and supports professionals working with children with behavioural difficulties.

## Special Needs Advisory Project Cymru (SNAP)

10 Cooper's Yard, Curran Road, Cardiff CF10 5NB
Tel: (029) 2038 4868
Fax: (029) 2038 8776
E-mail: snapcym@aol.com.uk

SNAP Cymru offers information and support to families of children and young people who have, or may have, special educational needs/disability.

### Tourette Syndrome (UK) Association

(trading as Tourettes Action)
Kings Court, 91–93 High Street, Camberley, Surrey GU15 3RN
**Tel:** (01276) 482 900
**Helpline:** (0300) 777 8427
**E-mail:** help@tourettes-action.org.uk
**Website:** www.tourettes-action.org.uk

A Registered Charity dedicated to providing support, educating, informing and campaigning; and promoting medical research on behalf of all those affected by TS.

### Tuberous Sclerosis Association

PO Box 12979, Barnt Green, Birmingham B45 5AN
**Tel/Fax:** (0121) 445 6970
**E-mail:** diane.sanson@tuberous-sclerosis.com
**Website:** www.tuberous-sclerosis.org
**Contact:** Mrs Diane Sanson

Offers support to people with tuberous sclerosis and their families or carers. Promotes education, publicity and information to increase awareness and understanding. There are Specialist Advisers to advise on any problems relating to TS. The TSA also organizes regional and national meetings and conferences and operates a Benevolent Fund. There are a number of specialist clinics around the country.

**Vision Aid**
PO Box 2211, Deane, Bolton BL6 9FW
Tel: (01204) 64265
E-mail: visionaiduk@aol.com

**Visual Impairment Service**
The Education Centre, Church Street,
Pensnett, Dudley, West Midlands
DY5 4HB
Tel: (01384 818005)
Fax: (01384 814241)
E-mail: pss.cs@dudley.gov.uk
Website: www.dudley.gov.uk

The Visual Impairment Service provides a
range of services to children, parents and
educational establishments. A team of
specialist teachers and teaching
assistants provide support, advice and,
where appropriate, specialist resource
materials to children who have a visual
impairment.

**Williams Syndrome Foundation Ltd**
161 High Street, Tonbridge TN9 1BX
Tel: (01732) 365152
Fax: (01732) 360178
E-mail:
John.Nelsonwsfoundation@btinternet.com
Website: www.williams-syndrome.org.uk

**YoungMinds**
48–50 St John Street,
London EC1M 4DG
Tel: (020) 7336 8445 (Parents Information
Service: (0808) 802 5544)
Fax (office): (020) 7336 8446
E-mail: enquiries@youngminds.org.uk
Website: www.youngminds.org.uk

YoungMinds is the UK's leading charity
committed to improving the emotional
well-being and mental health of children
and young people, and empowering their
parents and carers. We also offer a range
of intensive training and consultancy
solutions for professionals who work with
children, aimed at increasing knowledge
and understanding of CAMHS.

# 5.3

# Bibliography

The following list has been compiled with the kind assistance of editorial contributors and offers suggested further reading on many aspects of special educational needs.

## General

'The Code of Practice for the Identification and Assessment of SEN'

'Special Educational Needs: A guide for parents'

'Meeting Special Educational Needs – A programme of action'

'Meeting Special Educational Needs – A programme of action' – a summary, also available in Braille, on audio-cassette and in British Sign Language

*(All the above publications are available from the Department for Education (DFE) Tel: 0845 602 2260)*

'Young Adults with Special Needs: Assessment, Law and Practice – Caught in the Acts', John Friel, Jessica Kingsley Publishers, ISBN: 9781853022319

'Network 81 Parents' Guide' Network 81, 1–7 Woodfield Terrace, Chapel Hill, Stansted, Essex CM24 8AJ, Tel: 0870 770 3306, £8.50

'How and Why Children Fail', edited by Ved Varma, Foreword by James Hemming, Jessica Kingsley Publishers, ISBN: 9781853021862, £17.95

'Special Education Handbook', Advisory Centre for Education (ACE), Tel: 020 7704 3370, ISBN: 187 067231 3, £17.99

'Supporting Support Assistants – A practical handbook for SENCOs in mainstream primary and secondary schools', Stephanie Lorenz, 1996

'Supporting Special Educational Needs in Secondary School Classrooms', Jane Lovey, David Fulton Publishers, 2002, ISBN: 1853468320, £19.99

'Tribunal Toolkit', Advisory Centre for Education, Tel: 020 7704 3370

'Taking Action: Your Child's Right to Special Education – The definitive guide for parents, teachers, advocates and advice workers', J White and I Rubain, 2000, Questions Publishing, ISBN: 184 190010 9

'Disability Rights Handbook' (38th Edition, Published May 2013) – April 2013–2014. www.disabilityrightsuk.org

'Children First', Royal Association for Disability and Rehabilitation (RADAR) Publications Department, 12 City Forum, 250 City Road, London EC1V 8AF

'Children in Difficulty: A guide to understanding and helping', J Elliot and M Place, RoutledgeFalmer, 2004, ISBN: 0415 325 447, £19.99

'Hope for the Journey – Helping children through good times and bad. Story building for parents, teacher and therapist', C R Snyder, D McDermott, W Cook and M A Rapoff, Percheron Press, 2002, ISBN: 0971242704 £17.21

'Spelling: Remedial strategies', Diane Montgomery, Cassell, 1997, ISBN: 0304329746

'Understanding and Supporting Children with Emotional or Behavioural Difficulties', edited by P Cooper, Jessica Kingsley, 1999, ISBN: 9781853026669

## For students aged 16+ with disabilities

'After Age 16 – What next?' Please log on to: www.after16.org.uk, Family Fund, Unit 4, Alpha Court, Monks Cross Drive, Huntingdon YO32 9WN, Tel: 01904 621115

'COPE: Directory of Post-16 Residential Education and Training for Young People', Helen Evans, Tessa Doe, Debbie Stec and Hilary Jones, Lifetime Publishing, 2006, ISBN: 0904979114, £36.99

'The Association of National Specialist Colleges Directory', A directory of colleges with specialist provision for disabled students: please log on to www.natspec.org.uk, Chief Executive: Kevin O'Brien, 39 Sanders Road, Quorn, Loughborough, Leicestershire LE12 8JN, Tel: 01509 5543573

'Youthaid Guide to Training and Benefits for Young People', Published by Youthaid, 322 St John Street, London EC1V 4NT, Tel: 020 7833 8499, E-mail: youthaid@gn.apc.org, ISBN: 1907658202, £6.00

'Your Future Needs Assessment' (Scotland Only), Published by the Special Needs Forum of Children in Scotland, Contact: Children in Scotland, 5 Shandwick Place, Edinburgh EH2 4RG, Tel: 0131 228 8484, Fax: 0131 228 8585 £2.95

A range of publications covering all aspects of education for disabled students is available from Skill, The National Bureau for Students with Disabilities, Chapter House, 18–20 Crucifix Lane London SE1 3JW Tel: 0800 328 5050 (voice) or 0800 068 2422 (text)

## Higher education

'UCAS Handbook', Available from UCAS or careers offices. UCAS Helpline, Tel: 01242 227788, Minicom: 01242 225857, Website: www.ucas.ac.uk

'The Big Official UCAS Guide to University and College Entrance', UCAS.Sheedon and Ward

'Into HE: A guide to higher education for people with disabilities', Skill, The National Bureau for Students with Disabilities, Chapter House, 18–20 Crucifix Lane, London SE1 3JW, Tel: 0800 328 5050 (voice) or 0800 068 2422 (text)

## ADD/ADHD

'The Difficult Child', Stanley Turecki, Bantam Books, 2000, ISBN: 0553380362, £8.66

'Is Your Child Hyperactive, Inattentive, Impulsive, Distractible? Helping the ADD/hyperactive child', Stephen Garber, Marianne Daniels Garber and Robyn Spizman, Villard Books, Random House, 1995, ISBN: 067975945X, £9.72

'Power Parenting for Children with ADD', Grad L Flick, Prentice-Hall International, 1996, ISBN: 0876288778, £12.99

'Beyond Ritalin', Stephen Garber, Marianne Daniels Garber and Robyn Spizman, Harper Perennial, 1997, ISBN: 006977256, £7.10

'Taking Charge of ADHD', Russell Barkley, Guildford Press, 2000, ISBN: 1572306009, £14.50

## Autism/Asperger's Syndrome

'The Autistic Spectrum: A guide for parents and professionals', Lorna Wing Constable and Robinson, 2002, ISBN: 1841196746

'The Complete Guide to Asperger's Syndrome', Tony Attwood, Jessica Kingsley Publishers, 2006, ISBN: 9781843104957

'Autism and Asperger's Syndrome', Simon Baron-Cohen, Oxford University Press, 2008, ISBN: 9786198504900

'Parenting a child with Asperger syndrome: 200 tips and strategies', Brenda Boyd, Jessica Kingsley Publishers, 2003, ISBN: 9781843101376

'Teaching young children with autism spectrum disorders to learn: a practical guide for parents and staff in mainstream schools and nurseries', Liz Hannah, The National Autistic Society, 2001, ISBN: 9781899280322

'How to help your autistic spectrum child: practical ways to make life run smoothly', J Brealy and B Davies, White Ladder Press, 2006, ISBN: 9781905410057

A wide selection of resources for people affected by autism and for professionals are available from The National Autistic Society. See our online shop www.autism.org.uk/shop 393 City Road, London EC1V 1NG, Tel: 020 7833 2299, E-mail: nas@nas.org.uk, Website: www.autism.org.uk, Helpline: 0845 070 4004 (Mon–Fri, 10 am–4 pm)

## Cerebral palsy

A range of publications on cerebral palsy is available from SCOPE. SCOPE Response, PO Box 833, Milton Keynes MK12 5NY, Tel: 0808 800 3333, Fax: 01908 321051, E-mail: response@scope.org.uk

'The Cerebral Palsy Handbook', Marion Stanton, Vermilion Publishing, 2002, ISBN: 0091876761

'My Perfect Son has Cerebral Palsy: A mother's guide of helpful hints', Marie A Kennedy, 1st Books Library, 2001, ISBN: 0759609543

## Cystic fibrosis

A range of publications on cystic fibrosis is available from the Cystic Fibrosis Trust, either by post or from the Trust's website, 11 London Road, Bromley Kent BR1 1BY, Tel: 020 8464 7211, Fax: 020 8313 0472, E-mail enquiries@cftrust.org.uk, Website: www.cfrust.org.uk

## Deafness and hearing impairment

A range of publications on childhood deafness is available from the National Deaf Children's Society, 15 Dufferin Street, London EC1Y 8PD, Tel: 020 7251 5020

'Issues in Deaf Education', S Gregory *et al*, David Fulton Publishers, 1998, ISBN: 1853465127

## Down's syndrome

'Down's Syndrome – The facts', Mark Selikowitz, Oxford University Press, 2004, ISBN: 0192626620, £13.00

'A Parent's Guide to Down's Syndrome', Siegfried M Pueschel, Brookes Publishing Co, 2000, ISBN: 1557664528

'The Down's Syndrome Handbook: A practical guide for parents and carers', Dr Richard Newton, Vermilion Publishing, 2004, ISBN: 0091884306

'Down's Syndrome – An Introduction for Parents and Carers', Cliff Cunningham Souvenir Press, 3rd edition, 2006, ISBN: 0285636979

## *Dyscalculia*

'The Trouble with Maths', Steve Chinn, Routledge, ISBN: 978-0-415-67010-4, £25.00

'More Trouble with Maths', Steve Chinn, Routledge, ISBN: 978-0-415-67013-5, £39.99

'The Fear of Maths', Steve Chinn, Souvenir Press, ISBN: 978-0285640511, £10.00

'Working with Dyscalculia', Ann Henderson, Fil Came and Mel Brough, Learning Works, 2003, ISBN: 0953105520

'Dyscalculia Guidance', B Butterworth and D Yeo, NFER-Nelson, 2004, ISBN: 0708711529

## *Dyslexia*

### For parents

'Dyslexia: A parent's survival guide', C Ostler, Ammonite Books, 1999, ISBN: 1869866134

'Overcoming Dyslexia (A straightforward guide for families and teachers)', B Hornsby, Macdonald & Co, ISBN: 0091813204

'The Scars of Dyslexia (Eight case studies in emotional reactions)', J Edwards, Cassell, 1995, ISBN: 0304329444

'Susan's Story (An autobiographical account of my struggle with words)', Susan Hampshire, Corgi, 1990, ISBN: 0552135860

'This Book Does not Make Sens, Cens, Sns, Scens, Sense', J Auger, Better Books

'Reversals', E Simpson, Gollancz

### General

'Dyslexia: 100 years on', T & E Miles, Open University Press, 1999, ISBN: 0335200346

'Dyslexia in Children', Fawcett & Nicholson, Harvester Wheatsheaf

'The Pattern of Difficulties', T R Miles, Whurr

'Developmental Dyslexia', M E Thompson, Whurr

'Dyslexia', 2nd edition, M J Snowling, Blackwell

'Dyslexia: Speech and Language: A practitioner's handbook', 2nd edition, Snowling & Stackhouse, Whurr

'Psychological Assessment of Dyslexia', M Turner, Whurr

'Specific Learning Difficulties (Dyslexia): Challenges & responses', Pumfrey & Reason, Routledge

'Dyslexia: A practitioner's handbook', Gavin Reid, Wiley, ISBN: 0471973912

'The Routledge Companion to Dyslexia', Gavin Reid (ed), Routledge, 2009, ISBN: 9780415430791

## Teaching

'Dyslexia in Practice – A guide for teachers', edited by Janet Townsend and Martin Turner, Kluwer, 2000, ISBN: 0306462516 (0306462524, pbk)

'Dyslexia: A teaching handbook', Thompson & Watkins, Whurr, ISBN: 1861560397

'Learning Difficulties in Reading & Writing', NFER-Nelson

'Specific Learning Difficulties (Dyslexia): A teacher's guide', M Crombie, Jordanhill College of Education

'Dealing with Dyslexia', Heaton & Winterson, Better Books, 1996, ISBN: 1897635575

'Children with Special Learning Difficulties', Tansley & Pankhurst, NFER-Nelson

'Reading Writing & Dyslexia: A cognitive analysis', A Ellis, Lawrence Erlbaum, 1993, ISBN: 0863773079

'Instrumental Music for Dyslexics: A teaching handbook', S Ogelthorpe, Whurr

'Overcoming Dyslexia: A practical handbook for the classroom', Broomfield & Combley, Whurr

## Resources

'Learning to Learn', S Malone, Nasen, ISBN: 1874784434

'Alpha to Omega', Hornsby & Shear, Heinemann, 1999, ISBN: 0435103881

'Spotlight on Words', G Aitken, Robinswood Press, 1970, ISBN: 1869981510

'Easy Type', R Kinloch, Egon Publishers, 1994, ISBN: 0905858905

'New Phonic Blending Kit', Learning Materials Ltd

## For the older student

'Help for the Dyslexic Adolescent', E G Stirling, St David's College, Llandudno

'Use Your Head', T Buzan, BBC, 1999, ISBN: 056337103X

'Study Skills: A pupil's survival guide', C Ostler, Ammonite Books

'Adult Dyslexia: Assessment, counselling and training', McLoughlin, Fitzgibbon & Young, Whurr, 1993, ISBN: 1897635354

'Dyslexia at College', D Gilroy & T Miles, Routledge, 1995, ISBN: 0415127785

A range of teaching and learning resources for parents, adults, teachers and psychologists is available from Dyslexia Action, Park House, Wick Road, Egham, Surrey TW20 0HH, Tel: 01784 222300, Fax: 01784 222333, E-mail: info@dyslexiaaction.org.uk, Website: www.dyslexiaaction.org.uk

'How to Detect and Manage Dyslexia', P Ott, Heinemann, 1997, ISBN: 0435104195

'Living with Dyslexia', B Riddick, Routledge, 1997, ISBN: 0415125014

'The Dyslexia Handbook', A series of articles on different aspects of dyslexia, British Dyslexia Association, ISBN: 1872653316

## Dyspraxia

'Developmental Dyspraxia', 2nd edition, 1999, Madeleine Portwood, ISBN: 1853465739 £21.50 + p&p

'Take Time', Mary Nash-Wortham and Jean Hunt, £13.95 + p&p

'Dyspraxia – Developmental Co-ordination Disorder', Amanda Kirby, Souvenir Press Ltd, 1994, ISBN: 0285635123, £13.50 + p&p

*All the above are available from The Dyspraxia Foundation, 8 West Alley, Hitchin, Hertfordshire SG5 1EG, Tel: 01462 455016, Fax: 01462 455052, Website: www.dyspraxiafoundation.org.uk*

## Epilepsy

'Epilepsy', Jill Parkinson and Mike Johnson, Continuum, ISBN: 0826487483

'Epilepsy, Learning and Behaviour in Children', F M Besal, in *Epilepsia*, 1995, 36 (1), 58–63, Raven Press, New York

'Established antiepileptic drugs', M Brodie *et al* in *Seizure*, 1997, 6, 159–74

'Behaviour problems in children with new-onset epilepsy', D W Dunn *et al* in *Seizure*, 1997, 4, 283–87

'Educational Attainment in Children and Young People with Epilepsy', P Thomson, in *Epilepsy and Education – A medical symposium on changing attitudes to epilepsy in education*, edited by Jolyon Oxley and Gregory Stores, Labaz Sanofi UK, London, 1986

## Gifted children

'Challenge of the Able Child', David George, David Fulton Publishers, ISBN: 1853463469, £12.99

'Supporting the Child of Exceptional Ability at Home and at School', S Leyden, David Fulton, 2002, ISBN: 1853468789

The National Association for Gifted Children (NAGC) publishes a range of resources, publications and newsletters for its members. Contact the NAGC, Suite 14, Challenge House, Sherwood Drive, Bletchley, Milton Keynes MK3 6DP, Helpline: 0845 450 0221 Monday–Friday 9.15 am–4 pm, General Enquiries: 0845 450 0295, Fax: 0870 7703219, E-mail: amazingchildren@nagcbritain.org.uk, Website: www.nagcbritain.org.uk

'Able, Gifted and Talented', Janet Bates and Sarah Munday, £7.99

'Gifted Children: A guide for parents and professionals', Kate Distin (ed), Jessica Kingsley, available from NAGC at £15 inc p&p

'Discovering and Developing Talent in Schools: An Inclusive Approach', Bette Gray-Fow, NACE/David Fulton, 2005, £17.00

'Exceptionally Gifted Children' 2nd edition, Miraca Gross, RoutledgeFalmer, 2004, £23.99

'Learning without Limits', Susan Hart, Open University Press, 2004, £20.99

'Gifted Young Children: A guide for teachers and parents', 2nd edition, Louise Porter, Open University Press, 2005, £21.99

'Gifted and Talented in the Early Years', Margaret Sutherland, Paul Chapman, 2005, £16.99

'Too Clever by Half: A fair deal for gifted children', C Winstanley, Trentham Books, 2004, £18.99

## Leukaemia

'Living with Leukaemia', Patsy Westcott, Hodder Wayland, 2002, ISBN: 0750241616

'Childhood Leukaemia: The facts' (The Facts Series), John S Lilleyman, Oxford University Press, 2000, ISBN: 019263142X

## Muscular dystrophy

'Muscular Dystrophy: The facts', Alan E H Emery, Oxford University Press, 2000, ISBN: 0192632175

'Childhealth Care Nursing: Concepts, theories and practice', edited by B Carter and A K Dearmun, Blackwell Scientific, 1995, ISBN: 0632036893, £19.99

'Inclusive Education for Children with Muscular Dystrophy and other Neuromuscular Conditions, Guidance for primary and secondary schools', 2nd edition, is available from the Muscular Dystrophy Campaign, 61 Southwark Street, London SE1 0HL, Tel: 020 7803 4800, website: www.muscular-dystrophy.org

'Wheelchair Provisions for Children and Adults with Muscular Dystrophy and other Neuromuscular Conditions'. A comprehensive guidance aimed at helping staff plan appropriate wheelchair and seating provision for both children and adults with a neuromuscular condition. Although primarily aimed at Wheelchair Service staff, it can also be a useful resource of best practice for users, parents, carers and other health professionals. Muscular Dystrophy Campaign, 61 Southwark Street, London SE1 0HL, Tel: 020 7803 4800, website: www.muscular-dystrophy.org. *Free:* A guide for families with a newly diagnosed child. A guide for families with a child aged 5–12. Materials for children, including siblings and classmates.

## Speech and language difficulties

### AFASIC Publications

'Supporting Your Child's Speech and Language', 12 booklets, price from £1 to £2 each, full set £15.00, plus p&p

'Glossary Sheets on Speech and Language Impairments', 28 individual sheets that explain terms used to describe children with speech and language impairments, 50 p each, £10.00 for the full set, plus p&p

'Accessing Speech and Language Therapy for your Child – A guide to the law', £3.00, plus p&p

'Children and Young People with Speech and Language Impairments in Mainstream Secondary Schools' £3.00, plus p&p

'Choosing a School – An AFASIC guide to educational options for children with speech and language impairments', £3.00, plus p&p

### AFASIC Resources

'How to Identify and Support Children with Speech and Language Difficulties', £9.99, plus p&p

'Understanding Children with Dyspraxia/DCD in the Early Years', £10.00, plus p&p

'Language & Literacy: Joining together' (special price) £4.00, plus £9.00 p&p

*All the above publications are available from AFASIC, 1st Floor, 120 Bowling Green Lane, London EC1R 0BD, Tel: 020 7490 9410, Fax: 020 7251 2834, website: www.afasic.org.uk*

## Spina bifida and hydrocephalus

'Teaching the Student with Spina Bifida', Fern L Rowley-Kelly & Donald H Reigel, Paul Brookes Publishing, ISBN: 10557660646

'Living with Spina Bifida', Adrian Sandler MP, University of North Carolina Press, 2004, Obtainable from Trevor Brown Associates, Tel: 020 7388 8500 ISBN: 1080782352X, £14.95

'Spinabilities: A young person's guide to spina bifida', edited by Marlene Lutkenhoff and Sonya Oppenheimer, Woodbine House Inc, 1997, ISBN: 0933139867, £12.99

'Hydrocephalus – Its implications for teaching and learning', ASBAH, Peterborough, 2008, ISBN: 090 6687128

'Current Concepts in Spina Bifida and Hydrocephalus', Carys Bannister and Brian Tew, MacKeith Press, distributed by Blackwell Scientific Publishers, ISBN: 0901260916

'LINK', quarterly magazine of ASBAH, obtainable from ASBAH, 42 Park Road, Peterborough PE1 2UQ, Tel: 0845 450 7755, Fax: 01733 555985, E-mail: helpline@asbah.org. To view the full range of publications produced by ASBAH visit www.asbah.org

## Gilles de la Tourette syndrome

'Tourette Syndrome: The facts', Mary Robertson and Simon Baron-Cohen, Oxford University Press, 1998, ISBN: 019852398X, £9.99

'Teaching the Tiger: A handbook for individuals involved in the education of students with attention deficit disorders, Tourette syndrome or obsessive-compulsive disorder', Marilyn P Dornbush and Sheryl K Pruitt, Hope Press, 1995, ISBN: 1878267345, £18.37

'Tourette Syndrome', Amber Carroll and Mary Robertson, David Fulton Publishers, 2000, ISBN: 1853466565

## Visual impairment

*Visibility* focuses primarily on the education of visually impaired children and young people who attend mainstream schools or colleges. *Eye contact* focuses on the education of visually impaired children with additional disabilities. Both journals are published three times a year by RNIB (Royal National Institute for the Blind). Annual Subscription: £10.50 (UK), £15.00 (overseas) for each journal. To subscribe, contact: RNIB Customer Services, PO Box 173, Peterborough PE2 6WS, Tel: 0845 702 3153, E-mail: cservices@rnib.org.uk

*Curriculum Close-Up* is a free termly newsletter for anyone involved in the education of blind and partially sighted children. Each issue focuses on a different subject. For your free subscription contact: Suzy McDonald, Curriculum Information Officer, RNIB 58–72 John Bright Street, Birmingham B1 1BN, Tel: 0121 665 4223, E-mail: suzy.mcdonald@rnib.org.uk

The book sales catalogue contains a wide range of publications about education and employment in the field of sight problems. More than 350 different titles are available through mail order, including books, videos and other materials. For your copy contact: RNIB Customer Services, PO Box 173, Peterborough PE2 6WS, Tel: 0845 702 3153, E-mail: cservices@rnib.org.uk

*Insight* magazine: Essential reading for parents, teachers, teaching assistants and health and social care professionals working with children and young people with sight problems, including those with complex needs. Includes free photocopiable supplements full of practical tips on making lessons accessible for all learners with sight problems. Published by RNIB six times a year. Visit: rnib.org.uk/insightmagazine for up-to-date subscription details.

*Products and publications:* RNIB supplies a range of adapted games and learning materials specially designed for children with sight loss including those with additional disabilities. We publish a range of books, magazines, leaflets, videos and DVDs for parents and professionals. Visit: rnib.org.uk/shop.

Parents and professionals can keep up to date with publications about sight loss and complex needs from RNIB and publishers around the world by subscribing to RNIB's free eNewsletter at: rnib.org.uk/booksforprofessionals.

*Useful publications:* Visit RNIB Online Shop to browse and purchase the following publications, and more, at rnib.org.uk/shop or contact RNIB Customer Services, Tel: 0303 123 9999, e-mail: cservices@rnib.org.uk:

'Count Me In' A DVD promoting the inclusion, achievement and involvement of blind and partially sighted children including those with complex needs in a range of early years, mainstream and special school settings, RNIB, 2009

'Learning Together' (second edition) A creative approach to learning for children with multiple disabilities and a visual impairment, Mary Lee and Linda MacWilliam, RNIB, 2003

'Focus on Foundation' (second edition) Packed with practical ideas for the successful inclusion of children with sight loss in early year's settings including reception classes, RNIB, 2008, ISBN: 9781858789170

'Which Way' An early years guide for parents of children with sight problems who have additional complex communication, learning or physical needs, RNIB, 2002, ISBN: 1 85878 527 8

'Exploring Quality' How to audit, review and profile your school's provision for pupils who have multiple disabilities and visual impairment, Judy Bell and Lucy Naish, RNIB, 2005, ISBN: 1 85878 653 3

'Exploring Access in Mainstream' How to audit your mainstream school environment, focusing on the needs of children who have multiple disabilities and visual impairment, Judy Bell, Louise Clunies-Ross and Lucy Naish, RNIB, 2004, ISBN: 1 85878 630 4

# Glossary of Abbreviations

## Special needs support provided (independent mainstream schools)

### Learning difficulties

| | |
|---|---|
| CA | Some children with special needs receive help from classroom assistants |
| RA | There are currently very limited facilities for pupils with learning difficulties but reasonable adjustments can be made if necessary |
| SC | Some children with special needs are taught in separate classes for specific subjects |
| SNU | School has a dedicated Special Needs Unit, which provides specialist tuition on a one-to-one or small group basis by appropriately qualified teachers |
| WI | There is no dedicated Special Needs Unit but some children with special needs are withdrawn individually from certain lessons for one-to-one tuition |

### Behavioural disorders/emotional and behavioural difficulties/challenging behaviour

| | |
|---|---|
| CA | Some children with behavioural problems receive help from classroom assistants |
| CO | Trained counsellors available for pupils |
| RA | There are currently very limited facilities for pupils with behavioural disorders but reasonable adjustments can be made if necessary |
| ST | Behaviour management strategies identified in school's behaviour management policy |
| TS | Staff trained in behaviour management available |

### Physical impairments/medical conditions

| | |
|---|---|
| AT | Adapted timetable for children with health problems |
| BL | Materials can be provided in Braille |
| CA | Some children with behavioural problems receive help from classroom assistants |
| DS | Signing by staff and pupils |
| HL | Hearing loops available |
| IT | Specialist IT provision available |
| RA | There are currently very limited facilities for pupils with physical impairments or medical conditions but reasonable adjustments can be made if necessary |
| SL | Stairlifts |
| SM | Staff with medical training available |
| TW | Accessible toilet and washing facilities |
| W | School has wheelchair access (unspecified) |
| WA1 | School is fully wheelchair accessible |
| WA2 | Main teaching areas are wheelchair accessible |
| WA3 | No permanent access for available wheelchairs; temporary ramps available |

## Special needs

| | |
|---|---|
| ADD | Attention Deficit Disorder |
| ADHD | Attention Deficit Hyperactivity Disorder |
| ASD | Autistic Spectrum Disorder |
| ASP | Asperger's Syndrome |
| BESD | Behavioural, Emotional and Social Disorders |
| CB | Challenging Behaviour |
| CP | Cerebral Palsy |
| DOW | Down's Syndrome |
| DYC | Dyscalculia |
| DYP | Dyspraxia |
| DYS | Dyslexia |
| EPI | Epilepsy |
| HEA | Health Problems (eg heart defect, asthma) |
| HI | Hearing Impairment |
| IM | Impaired Mobility |
| MLD | Moderate Learning Difficulties |
| PMLD | Profound and Multiple Learning Difficulties |
| SLD | Severe Learning Difficulties |
| SP&LD | Speech and Language Difficulties |
| TOU | Tourette's Syndrome |
| VI | Visual Impairment |
| W | Wheelchair User |

## Associations and accrediting bodies

| | |
|---|---|
| ALI | Action Learning Institute |
| AOC | Association of Colleges |
| ARC | Association for Residential Care |
| AWCEBD | The Association of Workers for Children with Emotional and Behavioural Difficulties |
| BDA | The British Dyslexia Association |
| BILD | British Institute of Learning Disabilities |
| BSA | Boarding Schools Association |
| CES | Catholic Education Service |
| CReSTeD | Council for the Registration of Schools Teaching Dyslexic Pupils |
| ECIS | European Council of International Schools |
| EQUALS | Entitlement and Quality Education for Pupils with Severe Learning Difficulties |
| FEFC | Further Education Funding Council |
| GBA | Governing Bodies Association |
| HMC | The Headmasters' and Headmistresses' Conference |
| IAPS | The Independent Association of Prep Schools |
| ISA | The Independent Schools Association |
| ISC | The Independent Schools Council |
| ISI | The Independent Schools Inspectorate |
| JEC | Joint Epilepsy Council |
| LSC | Learning & Skills Council |
| NAES | National Association of EBD Schools |
| NAIMS | The National Association for Independent and Non-maintained Schools |
| NAS | National Autistic Society |
| NASEN | The National Association for Special Educational Needs |
| NASS | The National Association for Voluntary and Non-maintained Special Schools |
| NATSPEC | The National Association of Specialist Colleges |
| NCSE | National Council for Special Education |
| NCVO | National Council of Voluntary Organisations |
| NFAC | National Federation of Access Centres |
| OCR | Oxford, Cambridge and RSA Examinations |
| OPSIS | National Association for the Education, Training and Support of Blind and Partially Sighted People |
| SHMIS | The Society of Headmasters and Headmistresses of Independent Schools |
| SRCON | Surrey Regional Colleges Network |
| TSC | Training Standards Council |
| WJEC | Welsh Joint Education Committee |

# *Tailor-made services for parents*

- Bespoke advice on day and boarding school choices

- Sixth form and tutorial college options: A Level, IB, Cambridge Pre-U

- Full guardianship service

- Assessment and guidance on schools with special needs provision

- Practice interviews and exam technique for prep and senior school entry

✆ +44 (0)20 7734 0161

✉ schools@gabbitas.co.uk   🌐 www.gabbitas.co.uk

Gabbitas Education
CONSULTANTS SINCE 1873

# Main Index

## C

## M

# O

## S

# Y